Modern Statistical Methods:
Descriptive and Inductive

Modern Statistical Methods:

Descriptive and Inductive

BY

Palmer O. Johnson

Professor of Education and Chairman, Department of Statistics
University of Minnesota

AND

Robert W. B. Jackson

Professor of Educational Research
University of Toronto

Rand McNally & Company

CHICAGO

RAND McNALLY EDUCATION SERIES

B. Othanel Smith, *Consulting Editor*

LIBRARY OF CONGRESS CATALOG CARD NUMBER: 59-6024

To Karin, Gisela, Michael, and Peter

Preface

This book is designed to lead students in education, psychology, and the other social sciences from the beginnings of statistical methodology to an advanced level of instruction. It is addressed particularly to graduate students and to senior undergraduates, some of whom may have had an introductory course in statistical methods. However, the text is self-contained: in each case a number of the simpler descriptive statistical methods are used either as an introduction to more complex descriptive methods or as tools for testing statistical hypotheses and for estimation. But we have included only those we believe to be useful and essential, and we have not given all the possible variations of formulae for techniques such as, for instance, correlation analysis. At best, these variants of the standard procedures are often approximations only, based on assumptions of doubtful validity, and made necessary by peculiar experimental conditions that should have been avoided through proper selection of an experimental design.

Students at this particular stage of their university program need to go beyond the purely descriptive techniques and become acquainted with and develop an understanding of the statistical methods used in interpreting data and drawing inferences from the results. Such skills are needed, for example, to enable them to comprehend the current literature in their chosen field, since much of this will contain statistical analyses of the results secured from surveys and experiments. Moreover, in nearly all subject fields, students at this level are required to design and conduct relatively simple experiments or surveys and to analyze and interpret the results of them. Therefore we have included all the basic tests of hypotheses, the theory of estimation, and multivariate analysis, leading to complex descriptive methods. While we could not cover every topic exhaustively, we believe that we have incorporated sufficient from each major area to form a compact and relatively comprehensive set of techniques and skills.*

Our guiding purpose has been to present each concept and technique as concisely and rigorously as possible, avoiding lengthy verbal descriptions while retaining completeness of presentation of the basic concepts, assumptions, and skills. But we have not made exclusive use of the mathematical

* Those students who may later wish to specialize in statistical methods should find this text an adequate and valuable introduction to advanced concepts and techniques.

form of expression; our stress throughout has been on an arithmetical approach. The little mathematics used has been largely algebra, requiring no more on the part of the student than a mastery of secondary school mathematics. We have also used numerous real examples, as explanatory material in the text and as exercises, to illustrate the concepts and the arithmetical processes involved in the calculation of the required statistics.

We wish to acknowledge our indebtedness to the authors and publishers, as noted, for permission to quote copyrighted materials properly attributed to them in the text. We are particularly grateful to the following authors and publishers for their kind permission to reproduce certain tables given in the Appendixes:

1. Professor George W. Snedecor and The Iowa State College Press for permission to reproduce Table 10. 5. 3, "5% and 1% Points for the Distribution of F," from *Statistical Methods* (Fifth Edition), 1956.

2. Professor Sir Ronald A. Fisher, Cambridge, Dr. Frank Yates, Rothamsted, and Messrs. Oliver and Boyd Ltd., Edinburgh, for permission to reprint Table No. III, "Distribution of *t*," and Table No. IV, "Distribution of χ^2," from their book, *Statistical Tables for Biological, Medical, and Agricultural Research.*

PALMER O. JOHNSON
ROBERT W. B. JACKSON

February 28, 1959

Table of Contents

CHAPTER I

Development of Modern Statistical Methods

The Origins

Save in the very beginning and again during possibly the past decade, the history of statistics has been very largely the story of the labors of a small number of eminent mathematicians and statisticians.* Each in turn dominated the statistical world of his day and bequeathed to posterity, through his publications and his students, the precious record of his invaluable contributions to statistical methodology. An intriguing avenue of speculation is opened by recognition of the fact that not all of these were mathematicians, the honors being perhaps even between the mathematicians and the practical men. Interestingly enough, completely new fields of development have more often than not been opened by the practical statisticians and then more deeply tilled by the mathematicians. Statistics always has been, and probably always will be, essentially practical in nature. It derives its vitality from, and has its justification in, the imperative needs of practical problems for solution.

It is a sobering thought that the word *statist* originally (1584) meant a "politician" or a "statesman." The root word is from the Latin *status* or state, and even as late as the first part of the nineteenth century, statistics was deemed to be only that branch of political science concerned with the facts related to the condition of the state. This limitation on the nature of the data has been removed long since, and modern statistical methods are applicable to the description, analysis, and interpretation of data relating to any natural phenomenon. But many of the terms used in statistical methods are a legacy from the time when statistics was concerned only with the facts of human affairs. The term *population,* for instance, originally meant, and in common usage still does mean, the total number of inhabitants of the state, but it has been generalized in statistics to mean an aggregate of members, not necessarily human, living, or even material, but perhaps of possibilities only. The observations we make in a specific experiment or other study normally constitute only a small part of all possible observations of that kind—a *sample* of the *population,* to use a term to be defined more exactly later. And it seems only fair, in view of

---

* For a detailed history of statistical methods, see Helen M. Walker, *Studies in the History of Statistical Method* (Baltimore: The Williams and Wilkins Company, 1929).

the origin of the science of statistics, that much of the theory of sampling of populations has been developed in recent years by officials in government departments and in similar organizations. Not all the sampling has been of human affairs, but enough of it has been concerned with affairs of state to indicate a return today to something of the original connotation of the term "statist." We must recognize, however, that statistical methods had developed and matured during the interval, gaining much from other sciences and from mathematics in particular.

Gambling and Probability

The association of statistics with mathematics began early and under conditions which indicate that at least one of the progenitors of statistical methods must have been something of a disreputable but otherwise delightful character. The ancient kings and other governors, like their counterparts of today, counted and classified their subjects for the very practical purposes of military service and taxation, to mention only two of the multitude of government activities. Most, but not all, of the descriptive statistical methods, classical as well as modern, were devised to serve these purposes. Modern statistical methods, however, lean very heavily on the *theory of probability*, originally developed by mathematicians in connection with the equally practical, albeit somewhat less respectable, problems that arise in games of chance. The whole body of analytical statistical methods, whereby we draw inferences concerning the population from the set of observations that constitute our sample, is founded on probability. The positions of the gambler and of the modern statistician are strikingly similar, as will be evident from the discussion in subsequent chapters of the theory of estimation and tests of hypotheses. Both calculate and are governed by the risk associated with a possible decision or course of action: whether to wager on the turn of a card in the case of the former, for example, and, for the latter, whether to conclude that a set of experimental results is "significant." The actual result that will occur in any single event is of course unknown, but the theory of probability does tell us what will happen in a very large number of such events, i.e. in the long run. From this theory we can determine the chance (the probability) of a particular one of all possible results occurring in a single event, and on this basis decide what to do. Small wonder, perhaps, that practical researchers in the early days viewed with awe, and came perilously close to deifying, the so-called *laws* derived by the mathematicians from the theory of probability.

Astronomy and the Law of Errors

In brief, the foundations of the theory of probability were laid by the mathematicians Pascal and Fermat about the middle of the seventeenth century; the theory was systematized, more fully developed, and placed on a sound mathematical basis by Bernoulli in the early years of the eighteenth century. Shortly after, about 1721, De Moivre discovered the formula for what we now call the *normal curve* or *law of errors*, deriving it from the binomial theorem of the theory of probability as a by-product of his work on games of chance. Little more was done for more than half a century, except that the scene shifted from games of chance to errors of observation, in astronomy in particular, and attempts were made to establish a theory of errors of observation. Laplace restated De Moivre's law of error in a memoir in 1778, in which he evaluated the integral from zero to infinity. Tables of the normal probability integral were published by Kramp in 1799. The first quarter of the nineteenth century, however, witnessed a rapid development, based largely on the work of Laplace, Gauss, and Legendre in mathematical astronomy. The German astronomers Gauss, Encke, and Bessel (the latter two apparently using material originating with Gauss) developed the concepts and formulae for the standard deviation, standard errors of the mean and standard deviation, and the probable error. These, together with the development of the principle of least squares, form the basis of modern analytical statistical methods, but the writers of that time apparently felt that they applied only to the field of astronomy. The extension of the work, begun in connection with games of chance and developed in relation to the errors of observation in astronomy, to the social sciences was largely due in the first instance to the influence of Quetelet and Galton.

The Spread to Social Sciences

What occurred in the nineteenth century in statistical methodology as related to the social sciences was really a fusion of two streams of development. The collection of official statistics dates back to the dawn of recorded history, and the need for such information steadily increased as civilizations became more complex. Descriptive statistics as such, however, originated more directly with the work of Graunt in 1662 on deaths in London (England), leading to the activities of various statistical agencies concerned not so much with the mere collection of statistics as with their interpretation and publication. In 1693, for instance, the astronomer Halley published the first mortality tables, and Petty and many others around 1700 endeavored to interpret the scanty data available in order to aid the processes of government. Little progress in this direction could be made until official and related statistics became more accurate and complete. Possibly because of the general interest of the day in matters scientific, and in observation and measurement in particular, these statistics were in a fair state (though woefully inadequate by our standards) shortly after the mathematical astronomers had completed their work on the theory of errors of observations. The stage was set, therefore, for the incorporation of the results derived from the theory of probability into the process of interpreting the masses of social data collected by governments and private organizations.

While the lives of Quetelet (1796–1874) and Galton (1822–1911) overlap, there can be little doubt that Galton was more greatly influenced by Quetelet than the reverse. The difference in ages, and the unusual combination of positions held by Quetelet, meant that he had achieved a fusion of the two streams of development of statistical methods and exerted great influence in many fields before Galton appeared on the statistical scene. Quetelet was interested in mathematics, astronomy, anthropology, physics, census and vital statistics, and statistics of mental and moral traits. He realized that statistical methods, in particular the theory of probability, could be applied to the data from each of these fields, and so applied them, thus establishing that statistical methodology was general and could be used in many fields. In study after study of problems in diverse fields, for example, he showed that the sets of observations followed more or less closely the normal curve of error, and that the properties of this distribution could be used, not only to describe what was found, but to predict what would occur (e.g. in number and type of crimes committed).

Galton, inspired by the work of Quetelet, applied the normal curve in his numerous studies of social phenomena, believing it to be a general law "applicable to thousands of instances." But the importance of his work lies, not in his use of the normal distribution, but in his development of new statistical methods. He was an insatiable collector of facts, and his constant endeavor was to devise ways and means of reducing the masses of data to a few simple expressions that might be used in description and comparison. Galton devised, among other things, the system of percentiles (centile points) and percentile ranks, including the median and the quartile deviation. He is best known, however, for his work on regression and correlation, which had its origin in his interest in natural inheritance and in his desire to express or measure the influence of heredity. All he had done on the subject was summarized and published, in 1889, in *Natural Inheritance*.

It was this book of Galton's that stimulated a whole series of studies and reports by the famous Karl Pearson—his early series was in four parts and entitled "Mathematical Contributions to the Theory of Evolution," indicative of the connection with Galton's work. He extended and generalized the theory of regression and correlation, including multiple and partial correlation coefficients and methods for dealing with non-quantitative data. Of those associated with him, mention should be made of Yule, Filon, Elderton, and Sheppard. Many of the papers by Spearman (on correlation of ranks, correction for attenuation, and the Spearman-Brown prophecy formula) reflect the interest aroused in various fields by this fundamental work of Pearson and his associates. Important as this was, Pearson's greatest contribution was probably his derivation of the chi-square distribution (in 1900) for use in testing the significance of differences between observed values and those expected on the basis of some hypothesis. This was the first of the series of such distributions now used in statistical estimation and statistical tests of significance of experimental results. But the major credit for initiating the study of the distribution of various measures, such as the mean, standard deviation, and correlation coefficient, in repeated random sampling belongs to another—to William S. Gosset, who published under the pseudonym "Student."

Knowledge of Exact Sampling Distributions

Earlier writers had stopped at the derivation of the formulae for the standard or probable error of various statistical measures. Student, who was an experimentalist rather than a mathematician, first saw and enunciated the basic problem that has dominated statistical theory ever since his first paper in 1908, namely, to discover the exact sampling distributions of statistical measures. The importance of this problem had probably escaped earlier writers because they were mainly interested in the *description* of a set of observations and, even in the study of errors of observation in astronomy, the statistical methods of the time served the purpose. Student, on the other hand, was a brewer employed by Messrs.Guinness of Dublin, and part of his job was the interpretation of the relatively few observations secured from experiments. To his everlasting credit, he saw clearly the practical problem involved and its theoretical consequences. In the years 1908 and 1909, in papers published in *Biometrika*, he gave the sampling distributions for the square of the standard deviation (variance), for the quotient of the mean by its standard error, for the correlation coefficient between independent variates, and introduced the now famous *t*-distribution. The significance of Student's contribution was not immediately understood, and the development of statistical methods based on it would have been slow had it not been that R. A. Fisher appreciated the implications of Student's researches, extended them, and demonstrated beyond a shadow of a doubt their immense practical value in the interpretation of experimental results.

R. A. Fisher's Influence

Fisher has acknowledged his debt to Student in no uncertain terms and, indeed, in the introductory chapter of his *Statistical Methods for Research Workers* speaks in this way of Student's work: ". . . from the first edition it has been one of the chief purposes of this book to make better known the effect of his researches, . . ."† But the contribution by, and in-

† Seventh Edition; Edinburgh: Oliver and Boyd, 1938, p. 25.

fluence of, the disciple far surpassed that of the man purported to be the master. The period from the early 1920's to date may well be thought of as the "Fisherian Era" in the statistical world: his name is known and his work revered by men and women of all nationalities.

Fisher's early papers were concerned with the sampling distribution of correlation coefficients, but he soon turned to the work of Student on the *t*-distribution, giving a rigorous proof of his results in 1923, later extending them and generalizing to the well known *z*-distribution used in the analysis of variance and covariance. It was undoubtedly the practical work in his Statistical Laboratory at the Rothamsted Agricultural Station that stimulated and directed Fisher's genius. He combined into one powerful tool the proper design of experiments, exact tests of significance, theory of estimation, and simple but adequate arithmetical processes required in the interpretation of experimental data. Part of the value of his work, and that which makes it unique, is a happy blend of the rigor and exactness of the mathematician with the common-sense approach of the practical man: the Fisherian solution to a problem is exact, practical, and understandable.

Fisher's influence has been greatest in agriculture, biology, and genetics, in which fields he has advanced the theory of statistics so rapidly that very few researchers have managed to keep pace with him. Other fields, such as education and psychology, have witnessed a belated acknowledgment of the importance and usefulness of his results—even to the extent, in some instances, of an uncritical application of them in situations where there is some doubt that they can serve without adaptation.

What was needed, in these and in other fields, was a consolidation of all that had been done and a careful examination of the logic and general principles underlying statistical estimation and tests of significance. Credit for seeing the need, and for meeting it in large part, must be given to J. Neyman and E. S. Pearson who, in a series of papers in the 1930's, set forth the logical and mathematical foundations for the theory of estimation and tests of hypotheses. Their studies provided the basis and the impetus for the development of a number of new statistical methods, but were probably even more important for another reason, namely, that they permitted an assessment of the worth of existing methods. Abraham Wald in his recent book, *Statistical Decision Functions* (1950), extended the work of Neyman and Pearson. This contribution is destined to exert much influence on the foundations of statistical theory and practice.

Recent years have witnessed a radical departure from the classical statistical methods which were based on the assumption that the variables concerned were normally distributed. Much of the development today is directed towards statistical methods applicable to situations where the distributions are non-normal in form and towards statistical tests of significance that are altogether independent of restrictions imposed by the form of the population from which the samples may have been drawn (e.g. the *sign* test). Mention must be made, also, of the new procedure for testing statistical hypotheses devised by Wald, called the sequential analysis of statistical data, whereby the data may be analyzed continuously as they become available. In the classical procedure, which is still the most frequently used, the data are analyzed only *in toto* and at the end of the experiment or survey, not while it was in process.

Sampling Theory

The history of the development of sampling theories and practice‡ warrants separate treatment, partly because it is different but mainly because it illustrates so well within a narrow field the general mode of development of statistical methods. Little had been done, and that largely in a haphazard manner in conjunction with censuses, before the beginning of the present century. A. A. Kiaer, Director of the Norwegian Bureau of Statistics, was the man originally responsible for the use of sampling investigations to collect official and other statistics independently of the census. It was through his reports to the International Institute of Statistics (in 1895, 1899, and 1901) that the method was brought to the attention of statisticians in other parts of the world and in other fields. The need for the method arose in the very practical requirement for specific and detailed information, and in particular for up-to-date information, that could not be obtained through the usual census. The first such investigation, conducted by Kiaer in 1894, was in connection with a proposed retirement pension and sickness insurance scheme for Norway. The survey included only a small percentage of the population, but those persons investigated were carefully selected, according to a predetermined sampling design, to be "representative" of the country as a whole (fundamentally, his sampling design was that of stratification with proportional selection within each stratum). Note that Kiaer was a practical statistician and that he developed the method because it was part of his job to supply the required information. By sheer insight and common sense he devised a method that was sound, although the theory of sampling designs of that type (stratified) was not known until forty years later (Neyman, 1934).

Kiaer's reports to the International Institute of Statistics received rough treatment and aroused a storm of criticism: in the main, from those who felt that the hallowed census method was being attacked. The opponents of sampling investigations insisted (and very strongly, since they based their arguments on logical grounds rather than on facts) that a complete inquiry could never be replaced by a partial, although representative, investigation. How wrong they were has been demonstrated conclusively

‡ Based on You Poh Seng, "Historical Survey of Sampling Theories and Practice," *Journal of the Royal Statistical Society*, Series A (General), CXIV, Part II (1951), 214–31.

by Mahalanobis, for example, who showed by his results in a practical problem that a sampling survey may be, under certain conditions, not only cheaper but considerably more accurate than a complete count.§

In the discussion at the meeting of the Institute in 1901, Bortkiewicz suggested that the scientific basis for the theory of sampling lay in the calculus of probability, although he did not propose a solution. It was Professor Bowley who devised, in 1906, a systematic solution to the problem of determining the magnitude of the errors associated with the estimates obtained from sampling surveys. He proposed an adaptation of the methods developed by Karl Pearson and Edgeworth to test the truth (or significance) of practical deductions from experimental and other data. The advantage of this new approach to the problems posed by Kiaer was that Bowley could prove mathematically that the process of securing information by sampling was sound and that estimates of the errors involved could be calculated. The following twenty years were noteworthy for the number of sampling investigations conducted, many of them by Bowley and his colleagues, with results of immense practical importance in the social and economic fields. In 1934, in a paper to the Royal Statistical Society, Neyman presented the theoretical basis of many types of sampling designs, in particular group sampling and stratified sampling, and propounded the theory of interval estimation (suggested earlier by Fisher). About the same time, however, the United States became the main center for theoretical and applied studies of sampling, both public and private. Federal, state, and private agencies on this continent have made extensive and regular use of sampling surveys, including theoretical studies and a check on the results thereby deduced through an application in practical situations of the various types of sampling designs proposed. Much the same sort of development has been fathered in India by the Indian Statistical Institute, under its brilliant director, P. C. Mahalanobis. The result has been that today practically every social and economic survey makes use of some type of sampling design, only too often incorrectly, unfortunately, since the full theory of sampling theory and design is not generally understood or taught. The lack of any systematic treatment of the subject has been largely remedied, however, by the publication recently of four books devoted to the theory of sampling—by Yates, 1949, by Deming, 1950, by Cochran, 1953, and by Hanson, Hurwitz, and Madow, 1953.

Mention must be made of the very important advances made by Fisher and his co-workers in a particular phase of the general problem of sampling, more generally thought of as the design of experiments. Unlike Kiaer and Bowley, who were concerned with surveys that in many respects resembled censuses, Fisher and his associates were engaged in agricultural field experiments and laboratory and other experiments in biology. Basically, Fisher was concerned with the design of experiments and the sampling problems

§ P. C. Mahalanobis, "Why Statistics?" *Sankhya*, X (Sept. 1950), 195–220.

associated with experimental work, in particular with the problem of obtaining a valid estimate of sampling error to use in tests of significance of experimental results. The statistical methods he devised and the principles of sampling he enunciated have proved useful in the general theory of sampling, but the specific experimental designs developed by him have not as yet been used to any great extent in studies of social and economic problems—probably because they do not seem to be directly applicable to census and survey sampling.

The Role of Statistical Methods Today

The early statisticians and mathematicians who calculated the probabilities associated with games of chance and developed the theory of errors of observation in astronomy realized only dimly, if at all, the immense possibilities of the tools they were instrumental in devising. Of them all, perhaps only Quetelet and Galton had interests sufficiently catholic that they could see beyond the narrow confines of one field. But, since statistical methodology was in their day still in an embryonic stage, even these men could not visualize the extent to which statistical methods would pervade nearly all aspects of life in the second half of the twentieth century. Two significant, and well publicized, examples of the use of statistical principles and methods in medicine in recent years come readily to mind: the careful design of the experiments, including the use of control groups, and the detailed statistical analysis of the results obtained, in the large-scale use of fluorine in public water supplies (dentistry) and in the use of the Salk polio vaccine (preventive medicine).‖

The widespread use of statistical methods is, by and large, a product of the past quarter-century. When Fisher published the first edition of *Statistical Methods for Research Workers* in 1925, for instance, not only the author but also the methods he expounded were relatively unknown. Today, no matter where you turn, the ubiquitous statistics wends his quiet useful way. It is not that statistical methods constitute a science that has forcefully and dramatically forged to the fore, but rather that they constitute a powerful technique for extracting relevant items of information from large and small masses of data. Statistics is closely akin to mathematics in this respect, particularly in its universality, but it is something more than a mere branch of applied mathematics. In essence, it is a particularized branch of the general scientific method, whereby we add slowly but surely to our scanty store of trustworthy knowledge about ourselves and the things around us.

Viewed in this light, then, the phenomenal development and widespread

‖ The design of the experiments for testing poliomyelitis vaccine was not in keeping with rigorous principles in 59 per cent of the trials. See K. A. Brownlee's review article on *Evaluation of 1954 Field Trial of Poliomyelitis Vaccine: Summary Report.* See "Statistics of the 1954 Polio Vaccine Trials," *Journal of the American Statistical Association*, L (1955), 1005–13.

application of statistical methods during the present century is quite understandable. As the scientific method grew and expanded, so did statistical methodology. Like the Elephant Child of Kipling's story, man has always had an insatiable bump of curiosity, a desire to *know* and to *understand*. His flounderings in the sea of half-truths and superstitions promised to end through the use of the scientific method: he learned to count, to observe, to measure, and to conduct experiments in the proper (scientific) manner. But he rapidly found himself in a sea of a different sort—a sea of undigested (and, at first, indigestible) facts and bits of information. Observations differed, measurements varied, results of experiments seemed to be contradictory, and the large masses of data collected proved unmanageable because of their very size.# How could an earnest seeker after truth reduce the mass to something understandable, reconcile apparent disagreement, make due allowance for variation, and extract the relevant from the irrelevant? Statistical methods supplied the answers, and were, in fact, devised for just such purposes.

Reduction of masses of data is, as we indicated earlier, only one of the many uses of statistical methods. We may wish not only to describe and compare, but to draw inferences from the data. Basic to the latter process is the logic of induction; from what we observe in a *sample* we infer what is, or should be, in the *population* from which it was taken. Included in this general process are problems of estimating the values of measures of characteristics of distributions for the population from those calculated for the sample and, also, problems of testing hypotheses related to the population or its characteristics. Most readers will be somewhat familiar with estimation, but they will not be as familiar with the process of testing hypotheses unless they are engaged in research or are consumers of research reports. The process of testing hypotheses comprises an interesting combination of deductive and inductive reasoning, generally similar to the procedure common to all sciences. The starting point is normally some general hypothesis; if it is true, then certain results must occur (deductive reasoning). Then we observe what does occur, in an experiment or otherwise, and on the basis of our observations, as compared with those expected, reach certain conclusions regarding the truth or falsity (more correctly, the acceptability or non-acceptability) of the original hypothesis.

Once it is realized that the vast majority of researches are concerned with inferences about populations, in the statistical sense of that term, the function and use of modern statistical methods become apparent. Practically all arguments concerning the properties of populations are statistical arguments, and in the social sciences in particular statistical methods are the only means whereby proper and valid conclusions may be reached.

Early workers, such as Darwin, must have been frustrated and exasperated by such problems.

[handwritten margin note: N.B. estimating the values of measures of characteristics of distributions for the pop. from those calculated for the sample]

In fact, it is not unfair to state that only to the extent that statistical methods are used in the design and analysis of studies in social sciences, such as psychology and education, may these be considered to have attained the level of "scientific" studies.   Statistical methods are, then, part and parcel of the general scientific method: they are essential whenever the population under study is subject to variation of one kind or another.   And in the social sciences variation is the one thing that is common in all studies.

Univariate: a series of numerical
    values (variate) of one object (uni)
data: comprise a set of observations of some
    phenomenon.

CHAPTER II

Classification and Reduction of Univariate Data and Bases for Statistical Reasoning

The fundamental purpose of statistical methods is to help us comprehend and interpret the results of research studies and surveys. Whether the data relate to the population of the country, to the sexual behavior of humans (the Kinsey reports*), to the effectiveness of advertising and propaganda, or to the value of a new vaccine (the Salk polio vaccine experiment), they must be reduced in some fashion if we are to understand and interpret them properly. Statistical methodology enables us to do this. The results of the summary may be used, not only to describe what has been observed, but through use in subsequent appropriate statistical analyses to help us to draw valid inferences and conclusions from our data. In this introductory chapter we will present, first, some of the more important methods of summarizing univariate data and, second, the bases of statistical reasoning as related to the use of these methods. The extension to the reduction and interpretation of bivariate and multivariate data will be discussed at appropriate points in subsequent chapters as the sequence of topics unfolds.

REDUCTION OF UNIVARIATE DATA

reduction by:
1. classification (ordered groups.)
2. summary values (measures of charact.)

When the data are large in number and modern mechanical aids are not available, the reduction is accomplished in two stages. The first of these consists in the *classification* of the original data into a relatively small number of ordered groups, each group extending over a specified range of the original values. This procedure imposes an arbitrary arrangement on the data, reduces the mass of figures to a size (perhaps a small table of 25 groups) that permits of a ready comprehension of its characteristics, and puts it into a form that simplifies subsequent calculations. The second stage consists of a further reduction through the calculation of a limited number of *summary values* that are valid measures of the characteristics of the large body of original data.

* For a constructive criticism of the sampling and statistical methods of the Kinsey reports, see W. G. Cochran, F. Mosteller, and J. W. Tukey, "Principles of Sampling," *Journal of the American Statistical Association*, XL (1954), 13–35.

Summarizing univariate data: by ordered groups (classification) and measures
of characteristics (mean, st.dev, skewness, kurtosis, etc.)

Basis of statistical reasoning: Populations + samples, repeated
random sampling + stat. reasoning; several pop. dist. to explain
+ illustrate the process of repeated sampling

Where the number of cases is small, or for any number of cases if adequate mechanical aids such as IBM machines are available, the few summary values desired may be calculated directly from the original data. But it behooves the statistician to investigate the original data carefully in any event, before he plans his statistical analysis as well as when he is interpreting his results. In many cases the selection of an appropriate statistical method and a valid interpretation of the results depend upon an adequate understanding and comprehension of the nature of the original data, especially of any peculiarities of arrangement or character that they may possess.

Types of Data — *categorical + quantitative*

There are several types of data, and there are often several statistical methods to choose from. The problem is to select that particular method which can be validly (and most efficiently) applied to the kind of data we may encounter. Readers will remember that, in the past, specific statistical methods have been developed to describe and interpret the data collected in various fields, notably in experimental work in agriculture and biology. Strictly speaking, a particular statistical method is probably appropriate only for the specific type of data for which it was originally devised. Accordingly, a researcher must first learn how to recognize the major types of data, and then learn how to apply the methods appropriate for each type.

Essentially, data comprise a set of observations of some phenomenon, and have the fundamental characteristic that they vary, not all being of the same kind or amount. For instance, in studying the characteristics of *N. B.* a group of humans, we will undoubtedly find that they vary in height, weight, and age: it would be strange if they did not also vary in number of dental cavities, in number of siblings, in sex, and in eye-color, race, personality, and so on. Clearly, the type of data is almost wholly determined by the type of variation operating.

For convenience, we may classify variation as either *categorical* or *quantitative*. In the former, all possible observations fall into one or other of a set of distinct and generally non-ordered categories. The two possible categories for the variable sex, for example, are male and female. Note that the categories are mutually exclusive, there is no inherent order, and the data are the frequency of occurrence in each category. In quantitative variation, on the other hand, the observations have numerical values and possess an inherent order. Thus age and height, or number of siblings, for instance, are quantitative variables in this sense, and the observations may be ordered according to magnitude from smallest to largest, or vice versa.

Quantitative variation may itself be subdivided into two types, *discontinuous* and *continuous*. In the first-named, the observations may take only specified values, and generally only integer values. Number of

categorical variation — mutually exclusive (male + female), no inherent order, the data are the frequency of occurrence in each category
quantitative variation — observations have numerical value and possess an inherent order.

children in a family is a variable of this kind: the only possible values that may occur are 0, 1, 2, 3, and so on. In continuous variation, in contrast, the observations may take all possible values (at least in theory). Chronological age is an example of data that exhibit continuous variation; since any of the possible values (in terms of years, months, days, hours, minutes, seconds, or fractions thereof) may occur, do exist, and have a meaning.† In terms of a *scale* imposed on the variation, possible because of the inherent order, for discontinuous variation the observations may occur only at *particular* points on the scale, whereas for continuous variation the observations may occur (in theory) at *any* of the infinite number of points on the scale.

For most data the variation either is continuous or may be assumed to be continuous without doing any violence either to the data or to the results of statistical analyses. But this is not always true, and the nature of the variation underlying the data must always be determined *before* selecting and applying a specific statistical method. Categorical data and discontinuous data, for instance, are often confused, sometimes with disastrous results so far as the statistical analysis is concerned. The distinction between them, by the way, must often be made largely on the basis of whether or not there is an inherent order in the observations.

Units

Attention must also be paid to the exact nature of the units in which the data are expressed. In *categorical variation* the data are the frequencies or number of cases for each category and the unit is that of our numbering system. For this reason, the analysis of categorical data is often called a *frequency* analysis. A difficulty may arise, however, where repeated observations are made of the same attribute of a group of persons or things, e.g. if each member of a group of persons is rated on some attribute of personality by several observers. In analyzing such data, the researcher must first decide whether the unit of frequency is a "person" or a "rating."

In the case of *discontinuous variation*, the data may be expressed in terms of specific numerical values and a definition and an interpretation are determined by the situation. The units involved in number of children in a family, or in number of dental cavities observed, for instance, need no explanation.

Where the variation is *continuous*, interpretation of a unit is different but normally simple enough. If the unit is a *year* of chronological age, for example, it is a *range* covering a number of possible values of the variable or, in terms of an imposed scale, a section of the scale with a specified width. In most cases of continuous variation the values reported have been rounded off to the nearest unit—the desired unit having been de-

† Operationally, owing to the limitations on the degree of accuracy with which we may measure, or which is practicable, all quantitative variation is discontinuous in fact.

termined and specified beforehand. Because of the arbitrary mathematical rule governing the rounding-off process, any reported value could actually have been any one of the series of possible values falling in the range extending from half a unit below up to half a unit above that value. Thus a weight of 165 pounds, if one pound were the unit adopted, would be reported for any one of the ten possible values, 164.5, 164.6, . . ., 165.3, and 165.4. This definition of a unit is called a *mathematical* definition and is the one commonly accepted and used. Unless otherwise stated, it is the definition used throughout this text for examples in which the variation is or may be assumed to be continuous.

Exceptions to this general rule are rare, but they do exist and are important. One of the commonest examples occurs in connection with data relating to chronological age. The conventional practice is to report age as "age last birthday," not age to the nearest birthday.‡ Accordingly, a reported age of 11 years, say, means any one of the possible values in the range extending from 11 years, 0 days, to 11 years, 364 days—plus an extra day in every leap year. In cases when no other meaning is clearly indicated, however, we apply the mathematical definition even though the variation is operationally discontinuous, e.g. in the case of scores on objective mental tests.

Tabular Presentation of Data§ *(one of the simplest methods of reducing a mass of figures)*

One of the simplest methods of reducing a mass of figures is to organize them into a table. This may be the end of the statistical process, e.g. in

TABLE II.1

EXAMPLE OF CATEGORICAL DATA: SIMPLE CLASSIFICATION

Ratings of 1,486 Sixteen-year-old Seamen

CATEGORY	FREQUENCY *(no. of occurrences)*
Messmen	685
Deck	255
Engine	250
Coal Burning Firemen	222
Cooks and Bakers	74
Total	1,486

Source, Lt. William G. Torpey, "A Saga of Sixteen-year-old Seamen," *The Harvard Educational Review,* XVI, No. 1 (Winter, 1946), 51.

‡ The exception to this exception arises in life insurance statistics, where chronological age is calculated to the nearest birthday—at least to determine premium payments. In this case, of course, we have returned to the mathematical definition of the unit.

§ For the role of graphical methods in the analysis and interpretation of statistical data, the student should read Chapter III in Johnson and Jackson, *Introduction to Statistical Methods* (Englewood Cliffs, N.J.: Prentice-Hall, Inc., 1953).

government departments concerned only with the collection and publication of information; in most cases it represents but the first step in the process of statistical analysis.

For *categorical data* the table will comprise a list of the categories and the frequency of occurrence of the observations for each, an example of which is given in Table II.1. We may, of course, have quite complex tables of categorical data, with divisions and subdivisions of the categories. The example given in Table II.2 illustrates the $2 \times k$ type frequently encountered. In this case the classification is categorical for both factors, but it is not unusual to find a combination of non-ordered classes and ordered numerical values for discontinuous or continuous data, as illustrated in Tables II.3 and II.4.

TABLE II.2

EXAMPLE OF CATEGORICAL DATA: MULTIPLE CLASSIFICATION

Cases of Gastric Disorder Dismissed
from Hospitals in Oxford Area
during 1945

GASTRIC DISORDER	SEX OF PATIENT	
	Male	*Female*
Gastric ulcer	22	9
Duodenal ulcer	52	5
Other gastric disorders	535	415
Total	609	429

Source, H. Cotton, "The Collection of Morbidity Data from Hospitals," *Journal of the Royal Statistical Society*, Series A (General), CXI, Part I (1948), 17.

TABLE II.3

EXAMPLE OF COMBINATION OF DISCONTINUOUS AND CATEGORICAL DATA

Number of Aliens Crossing the Land Borders of
the U.S.A. Periodically

YEAR	ALIEN BORDER CROSSERS		
	Active	*Intermittent*	*Total*
1941	77,751	202,636	280,387
1942	90,541	275,013	365,554
1943	109,975	281,535	391,510
1944	114,321	324,974	439,295
1945	116,798	262,557	379,355

Source, E. P. Hutchinson and Ernest Rubin, "Estimating the Resident Alien Population of the United States," *Journal of the American Statistical Association*, XLII, No. 239 (September, 1947), 392.

TABLE II.4

EXAMPLE OF COMBINATION OF CONTINUOUS AND CATEGORICAL DATA

Information on and Attitude Toward Taft-Hartley Law,
for 1,088 Industrial Production Workers

INFORMATION TEST SCORE	ATTITUDE TOWARD TAFT-HARTLEY LAW		
	Favor	*Oppose*	*No Opinion*
13	1	4	1
12	10	14	4
11	37	51	17
10	45	68	31
9	62	75	40
8	55	62	49
7	38	61	37
6	34	49	45
5	23	35	48
4	14	19	27
3	4	13	11
2	0	2	2

Source, John G. Gleason, "Attitude vs. Information on the Taft-Hartley Law," *Personnel Psychology*, II, No. 3 (Autumn, 1949), 295.

For *discontinuous data*, the tables may resemble those for categorical data, except that the classes are ordered, but it is more common to find numerical values used as the basis for classifying. An example of ordered classes, for both factors, is shown in Table II.5.

TABLE II.5

EXAMPLE OF DISCONTINUOUS DATA: ORDERED CLASSES

Skill and Adjustment of 180 West Indian Technicians

SKILL	ADJUSTMENT					TOTAL
	Excellent	*Good*	*Average*	*Poor*	*Very Bad*	
Very skilled	24	7	3	2		36
Good	17	43	27	6		93
Average		9	13	13	2	37
Poor			2	6		8
Very bad				3	3	6
Total	41	59	45	30	5	180

Source, A. H. Richmond, "Relation Between Skill and Adjustment of a Group of West Indian Negro Workers in England," *Occupational Psychology*, XXV, No. 3 (July, 1951), 161.

An illustration of the more usual form for discontinuous data is given in Table II.6.

TABLE II.6

EXAMPLE OF DISCONTINUOUS DATA: QUANTITATIVE DATA

Classification of Families by Number of Children,
Based on Family Allowances Paid in June, 1952

NUMBER OF CHILDREN IN FAMILY	NUMBER OF FAMILIES	
	Ontario	Quebec
1	273,305	181,874
2	213,069	141,045
3	98,203	88,034
4	40,991	54,584
5	17,257	33,838
6	7,782	21,135
7	3,892	12,830
8	1,784	7,954
9	809	4,205
10	341	2,018
11	109	847
12	30	259
13	11	67
14	1	11
15	0	1
Total	657,584	548,702

Taken from the monthly statistics published in mimeographed form by the Treasury Office, Department of National Health and Welfare, Ottawa, Canada. The number of families with no children is not, of course, reported since they will not be in receipt of family allowances.

The small number of cases of Table II.5 could be classified and tabulated by hand, but for a very large number of cases, or for a complex table, for either discontinuous or continuous data it is practically essential to employ some form of a mechanical sorter and counter, such as an IBM machine. Tabulating by hand may be done by sorting cards on which the data have been recorded or by tallying the observations directly from the original data sheets. An example of the use of tallies is given in Table II.7. In a completed table prepared for subsequent use or publication, the tallies will not, of course, be shown.

For *continuous data*, in most situations there are far too many possible values to show each separately in a table, and we *group* adjoining values in some fashion. The data reported in the resulting table are called *grouped data*, in contrast with *ungrouped data* where the actual observations are reported. Generally we do not group the data if the number of observations is small, if the number of possible values is small, or if modern calculating machines are available for use in the analysis of the data. As is the case for other types of data, the process of counting the number of

TABLE II.7

ILLUSTRATION OF USE OF TALLIES IN CONSTRUCTING A TABLE

Professional Qualifications and Marital Status of Women Teachers in
Elementary Schools in Ontario, November, 1951

TEACHING CERTIFICATE	MARITAL STATUS		TOTAL
	Single	*Married*	
First Class (I)	卌 卌 (10)	卌 II (7)	(17)
Second Class (II)	II (2)	卌 II (7)	(9)
Total	(12)	(14)	(26)

Taken from *Schools and Teachers in the Province of Ontario*, Part I, Public and Separate Schools, November, 1951 (Toronto, Ontario: King's Printer).

cases falling in each group, or *class interval*, as it is generally denoted, may be done manually or by machine.

The selection of appropriate groups or class intervals is governed by a number of factors, of which the most important are (1) the nature of the distribution of the original values, and (2) the amount of information it may be expedient to sacrifice in order to secure a better understanding of the data and to save labor in subsequent calculations. A rule of wide applicability is that we should use 20 to 25 class intervals or groups. This is based on the knowledge that for a normal distribution the resulting loss of information is somewhat less than 1 per cent.‖ Whether all the class intervals should be of the same width or whether class intervals of unequal width should be used is determined largely by the nature of the distribution of the original values. It is not at all unusual to find situations where the use of intervals of equal width is equivalent to the use of very coarse grouping for the majority of the original values, which might be quite misleading. For instance, it is clear from Table II.6 that any grouping together of the small families would quite effectively destroy considerable information and very drastically affect any values derived from subsequent calculations. However, the general rule is to use intervals of equal width unless the nature of the distribution of the original values is such that the use of class intervals of unequal width is indicated as preferable.

A number of minor points may also be mentioned briefly. The class intervals are expressed in multiples of the unit used in reporting the data, and it is convenient to arrange the intervals so that their mid-points lie at possible values, not fractions thereof. Peculiarities in the occurrence of

‖ For a discussion of this point, see R. A. Fisher, *Statistical Methods for Research Workers*, pp. 52, 53.

the original values, such as unusual concentrations, should also be taken into account: e.g. it is advisable to select intervals such that the concentration of cases occurs at the mid-points of the intervals, not at the end-points. Further, if class intervals of unequal width are employed, subsequent calculations are greatly simplified if the widths selected are multiples of the width of the narrowest interval. Also, wherever possible one should avoid the use of open-ended intervals, since the calculations necessary for certain analyses cannot be performed without a knowledge of the exact upper and lower limits of the class intervals.

The data of Table II.8 illustrate the values encountered when ungrouped data are used.# Since we assume continuous variation, each of the possible scores is interpreted as an interval: the score of 82, for example, extends from 81.5 to 82.5 with a mid-point of 82.0. We may wish, however, to group the scores into broader intervals, as illustrated in Table II.9. The exact upper and lower limits of the corresponding class intervals will be determined on the same basis as for the ungrouped values, e.g. "81–82" is interpreted as "80.5–82.5," and "78–82" as "77.5–82.5." An example of published tables with class intervals of unequal width and with one open-ended interval is shown in Table II.10.

TABLE II.8

Illustration of Ungrouped Continuous Data:
Scores on an Intelligence Test

SCORE	FREQUENCY	SCORE	FREQUENCY	SCORE	FREQUENCY	SCORE	FREQUENCY
82	1	69	25	56	11	43	2
81	1	68	21	55	13	42	5
80	5	67	35	54	16	41	3
79	5	66	24	53	17	40	2
78	8	65	37	52	10	39	1
77	12	64	31	51	14	38	1
76	12	63	22	50	12	37	2
75	21	62	40	49	11	36	1
74	20	61	25	48	7	35	1
73	20	60	18	47	9	34	–
72	20	59	23	46	6	33	2
71	19	58	20	45	7		
70	24	57	19	44	3	Total	664

In some studies, the tables show another kind of frequency—not the frequency for each value or class interval, but the total number of cases *below*, or *above*, the value or class interval. The resulting frequency is known as *cumulative frequency*, since the subtotals of the original frequencies are calculated and presented. An example of frequencies of this kind, and

The first step in the reduction process, which has been omitted for convenience, was to determine the number of pupils having each of the possible scores.

TABLE II.9

ILLUSTRATION OF GROUPED CONTINUOUS DATA:
SCORES ON AN INTELLIGENCE TEST

From the data of Table II.8

A: NARROW INTERVALS		B: BROAD INTERVALS	
Class Interval	Frequency	Class Interval	Frequency
81–82	2	78–82	20
79–80	10	73–77	85
77–78	20		
75–76	33	68–72	109
73–74	40		
71–72	39	63–67	149
69–70	49	58–62	126
67–68	56		
65–66	61	53–57	76
63–64	53		
61–62	65	48–52	54
59–60	41	43–47	27
57–58	39		
55–56	24	38–42	12
53–54	33		
51–52	24	33–37	6
49–50	23	Total	664
47–48	16		
45–46	13		
43–44	5		
41–42	8		
39–40	3		
37–38	3		
35–36	2		
33–34	2		
Total	664		

incidentally of the type of situation in which they may be employed, is given in Table II.11 where a comparison is made between intelligence test scores of honors and ordinary university graduates.** The cumulative frequencies and cumulative percentages show the number and per cent, respectively, with scores *below* the upper limit of each class interval.††

** The student should construct the Cumulative Frequency Polygon and the Cumulative Percentage Frequency Polygon for the data in Table II.11. See Johnson and Jackson, *op. cit.*, pp. 84–85.

†† The other kind of subtotals or cumulative values could have been used, showing the number or per cent *above* the lower limit of each class interval, by cumulating down from the top. Students should, as an exercise, calculate this set of cumulative frequencies and cumulative percentages.

TABLE II.10

ILLUSTRATION OF CLASS INTERVALS OF
UNEQUAL WIDTH: CONTINUOUS DATA

Distribution of Estimated Civilian Population, 1949,
by Age and Sex

AGE GROUP	POPULATION (IN THOUSANDS)	
	Males	*Females*
Under 14 years	19,365	18,600
14 to 19 years	6,110	6,385
20 to 24 years	5,591	5,952
25 to 44 years	21,299	22,480
45 to 64 years	15,127	15,307
65 years and over	5,321	5,879
Total	72,813	74,603

Source, U.S. Bureau of the Census, *Statistical Ab-
stract of the United States: 1951* (72nd ed.; Washington,
D.C., 1951), Table No. 11, p. 11.

Interpretation of Categorical Data

Preparation of a simple or complex table is about as far as one can go
in the process of reduction of purely categorical data. The impossibility
of assigning numerical equivalents to the unordered classes precludes the
calculation of any summary values for such data.‡‡ The interpretation of
categorical data may be facilitated, however, in a number of ways. One
obvious means, whenever a large number of classes has been used, is to
combine like classes in order to obtain a simpler table. The use of percentage rather than actual frequencies for categorical data is another means
that could well be considered the standard method, especially in publications designed for popular consumption. Reference need only be made to
the form in which the results of public opinion polls are almost invariably
presented to demonstrate the widespread use of percentages in such
situations. A third way is to use ratios and rates, which is an almost
universal practice in medical and population statistics.

No general rule can be given as to which method should be used in
different situations. The researcher must in each case determine what his
data do show and what particular point or points should be drawn to the
attention of the reader. Then he must select the method that does what
he wants done, possibly trying several before a final selection is made.
To illustrate this point, the age distributions of the population of Ontario
in 1941 and 1951 are shown in Table II.12. Although the average age was

‡‡ With the exception of a measure of the degree of relationship between factors and
the related statistical test of significance, which will be discussed in subsequent chapters.

TABLE II.11

ILLUSTRATION OF USE OF CUMULATIVE FREQUENCIES: COMPARATIVE STUDIES

Distribution of Intelligence Among University and College Students

TEST SCORES	HONORS GRADUATES			ORDINARY GRADUATES		
		Cumulative			Cumulative	
	Frequency	Frequency	Percentage	Frequency	Frequency	Percentage
95–100	2	40	100.0	3	222	100.0
90–94	7	38	95.0	12	219	98.6
85–89	3	31	77.5	29	207	93.2
80–84	8	28	70.0	24	178	80.2
75–79	3	20	50.0	31	154	69.4
70–74	6	17	42.5	29	123	55.4
65–69	2	11	27.5	26	94	42.3
60–64	6	9	22.5	25	68	30.6
55–59	1	3	7.5	13	43	19.4
50–54	1	2	5.0	17	30	13.5
45–49		1	2.5	6	13	5.9
40–44	1	1	2.5	2	7	3.2
35–39				2	5	2.3
30–34				2	3	1.4
25–29					1	0.5
20–24					1	0.5
15–19				1	1	0.5
Total	40			222		

Source, Godfrey H. Thomson, "The Distribution of Intelligence Among University and College Students," *The British Journal of Educational Psychology*, XV (1945), 76–77.

practically the same in the two years, the age distributions differed greatly. The differences are shown most clearly, not by the average, but by the percentage increase for each age group (see the last column of Table II.12). Reporting averages alone would in such cases be equivalent to throwing away the most significant information revealed by the data. A calculating machine, animate or inanimate, will not study the data and use common sense in the selection of a statistical method and in the interpretation of the results: the researcher must do so if he is to be worthy of his hire.§§

Reduction and Interpretation of Discontinuous and Continuous Data

For non-categorical data, either the original or the grouped values can be neatly summarized by calculating statistics that are measures of the *characteristics* of the distributions. These summary values may then be used in describing the distributions and in interpreting the data. The characteristics of frequency distributions for which measures are required are

§§ Our own experience indicates that practical decisions in industry and government are generally based on simple statistics, such as percentages and ratios. Perhaps no more is needed, and the practical man may be justified in his distrust of the results derived from the application of abstruse mathematical formulae in ordinary situations.

TABLE II.12

CHANGES IN THE AGE DISTRIBUTION
OF THE POPULATION OF ONTARIO
1941–1951

AGE GROUP	CENSUS YEAR		INCREASE	
	1941	*1951*	*Actual*	%
0–4	297,924	514,722	216,798	72.77
5–9	301,515	399,292	97,777	32.43
10–14	324,804	325,300	496	0.15
15–19	339,116	315,685	−23,431	−6.91
20–24	323,989	352,360	28,371	8.76
25–29	315,706	387,239	71,533	22.66
30–34	286,504	351,043	64,539	22.53
35–39	268,380	340,797	72,417	26.98
40–44	250,321	302,342	52,021	20.78
45–49	232,617	268,129	35,512	15.27
50–54	214,094	247,478	33,384	15.59
55–59	181,734	210,308	28,574	15.72
60–64	149,626	182,484	32,858	21.96
65–69	116,342	155,097	38,755	33.31
70–74	85,888	115,919	30,031	34.97
75–79	55,233	70,419	15,186	27.49
80–84	29,619	38,027	8,408	28.39
85–89	11,039	15,799	4,760	43.12
90–94	2,679	4,262	1,583	59.09
95+	525	840	315	60.00
Total	3,787,655	4,597,542	809,887	21.38%

central position, variability, skewness, and *kurtosis.* These characteristics are not of equal importance; the last two named are, in fact, of little importance in most situations. They will be discussed here, however, for two reasons: first, because the measures of them are useful in describing distributions and, second, because such measures will be needed in subsequent chapters when the validity of certain assumptions regarding the type of distribution occurring is to be tested.

The definition of these characteristics can be illustrated by reference to Table II.9, which is typical of the vast majority of frequency distributions encountered in the social sciences. By *central position* we mean the score about which the original values seem to be concentrated or clustered: e.g. by inspection we see that the central position of Table II.9 will be a score value near, perhaps a little above, 60. By variability we mean the extent to which the original values are *scattered* or *dispersed* about the central position: observe that, while the intelligence test scores are concentrated or clustered about the central position of the distribution, some of the values vary widely from it—from a low of 33 to a high of 82 (Table II.8). Skewness and kurtosis refer more directly to the actual *shape* of the distribution: skewness to *symmetry*, or lack of it, of the distribution, and kurtosis to the *flatness* or *peakedness* of the distribution. The distribution of intelligence scores is obviously not perfectly symmetrical, because the frequencies drop rather abruptly toward the upper end, and much more slowly toward the lower end, of the score scale. The distribution is, therefore, somewhat *asymmetrical* or *skewed*. The distribution appears also to be peaked, at least in comparison with that of Table II.10 which is relatively flat.‖‖

The various statistics discussed and illustrated in subsequent sections have been carefully selected from a much larger number of possible measures and are, in our opinion, adequate and sufficient for the vast majority of purposes. The criteria used as a guide in the selection are as follows, not all of which, unfortunately, are satisfied equally well by all the measures. A statistic should:

(a) provide a valid measure of the characteristic;

(b) be useful in a wide variety of actual situations;

(c) be readily understandable, either directly or through its properties;

(d) be relatively easy to calculate;

(e) be rigorously defined, so that no subjective element enters into its determination;

(f) be based on all the observations, i.e. truly represent the whole distribution, not just a part of it;

(g) vary as little as possible in repeated experimentation under like conditions; and

(h) be used in analyzing and drawing inferences from the data as well as in describing them.

Measures of Central Position

The two most commonly used measures of central position are the *median* and the *mean*.## Only in the case of a perfectly symmetrical distribution are the two measures identically equal in value.

The *median* is defined as the "middle" value of the distribution: if the values are arranged in order of magnitude, the median is the value such that an equal number of larger and smaller values lie above and below it, respectively. It satisfies all the criteria except (e), (g), and possibly (h), but the mean is a more desirable measure because it satisfies these three also and the others almost as well as the median. The most severe re-

‖‖ The student should construct the Frequency Polygon for the Scores on the Intelligence Test from Table II.9, and the Histogram for the Ages of Civilian Males, 1949, from Table II.10. For method see Johnson and Jackson, *op. cit.*, Chapter III.

Other measures that have been advocated for use in special situations are used so infrequently that they warrant no more than a passing reference. The *mode* is defined as the value that occurs most frequently, the *geometric mean* as the Nth root of the product of N values (or the antilog of the mean of the logarithms of the values), and the *harmonic mean* as the reciprocal of the mean of the reciprocals of the values.

striction on the value and use of the median arises because it is not rigorously defined: under certain conditions its value is not determinate, save through the use of supplementary assumptions that are not implicit in its definition.

The *mean* is defined as the quotient of the sum of the values by their number.*** If we denote the mean by the symbol M, any one of the original values by X, the number of such values by N, and the process of summation by Σ, then this definition may be written $M = \Sigma X/N$. The interpretation of the mean is not quite as obvious as that of the median. One may think of it as the point on the base of a graph (which has been drawn on stiff paper or cardboard and cut out) about which it may be balanced—i.e. as a center of gravity. But a more useful concept is probably that of a common amount which might have been distributed to each of the N cases. Obviously, the mean need not necessarily be equal to the median in value, nor need the mean equal in value any one of the original observations—only very rarely, in fact, will this happen.

In illustrating the calculation of the values of the median and mean, it is convenient to distinguish between the procedures to be followed with *ungrouped* and with *grouped* data. The definitions of the two measures remain unaltered, however, since only the calculation process is changed to correspond with the circumstances.

Calculation of Median and Mean for Ungrouped Data

Consider, first, the calculation of the median in a situation where the number of cases is small and the data are ungrouped. For example, the average daily attendances reported for eight school sections in one rural municipality in Ontario for the school year 1950–51 were as follows (arranged in order of magnitude): 16, 18, 19, 21, 21, 22, 24, and 39 pupils. Strictly speaking, the value of the median is not determinate from the definition. Since the number of cases is even, there is no "middle" value, and the fourth and fifth values (21) happen to be equal so there is no value between them that would serve. The same difficulty may occur even if the number of cases is odd, as is evident from the above set of ordered values if the first (16) is omitted—we now have two less than, one equal to, and three greater than, the "middle" value. Difficulties of this kind occur in the calculation of the median whether the variation be continuous or discontinuous, although they are generally aggravated in the case of the latter type since only certain specific values can appear. The difficulties generally become greater, not less, when the number of cases is large and the data are ungrouped.

*** It is the *arithmetic* mean, so called to distinguish it from the others of the family of means and to indicate the process used in the calculation of its value.

Obviously, the lack of a rigorous definition, which leads to indeterminateness in value, makes the median an unsatisfactory measure of central position for ungrouped data. This can be overcome through the use of a convention and assumption that supplement the definition (it is probably better not to use the median as a measure of central position for ungrouped data, especially if the number of observations is small). In general, we assume that the underlying variation is continuous and that the frequency for a particular value is spread evenly over the corresponding interval. The convention adopted is that the median is the point on the assumed continuous scale such that exactly half the cases fall below it and the other half above it. For the eight average daily attendance values, for instance, we assume that the two cases for the value 21 are spread evenly over the interval 20.5 to 21.5, and accordingly, by the convention, the median will be 21.0—exactly four observations will fall below that point on the scale and four above it.††† If we had omitted the value 16 in order to secure an odd number of cases, as suggested earlier, the median will be the point on the continuous scale such that exactly 3.5 cases fall below and above it, namely 21.25. Similarly, using the data of Table II.6, the median number of children in a family in Ontario‡‡‡ is found to be 1.76 (assuming that the interval for 2 children, for instance, extends from 1.5 to 2.5), and, using the data of Table II.8, the median intelligence test score is 63.79.

No such difficulties arise in the calculation of the value of the mean for ungrouped continuous or discontinuous data: dividing the sum of the values by their number will always yield a determinate value for the mean. For the average daily attendance figures in the eight school sections, we have $\Sigma X = 180; N = 8$; and $M = 180/8 = 22.5$. Calculation of the mean number of children in a family from the data of Table II.6 is similar, but to obtain the total number of children (ΣX) we must, of course, for each row multiply the number of children in the family by the corresponding number of families. This process gives the following values: Ontario, $M = 1,344,916/657,584 = 2.045$; Quebec, $M = 1,467,334/548,702 = 2.674$. Likewise, for the intelligence test scores of Table II.8 each score must be multiplied by the corresponding frequency in order to obtain the proper total ($M = 41,682/664 = 62.774$).

Students should note that in the last two examples we have actually used a variant of the fundamental formula for the mean, namely $M = \Sigma fX$

††† Unfortunately, if a "gap" occurs at the middle of the distribution (e.g. if the values had been 16, 18, 19, 20, 22, 22, 24, 39) the value of the median remains indeterminate. In such cases, one can either use the mid-point of the gap as the median value or group the values in such a manner that no gap occurs—or, the wiser course, make no attempt to calculate the value of the median.

‡‡‡ Note that any such values for the data of this table must be interpreted in terms of "families in receipt of family allowances," not of *all* families.

$/N$, where X denotes any one of the several possible values (number of children in family and score, respectively), f denotes the corresponding frequency (number of families of that size and number of pupils having that score, respectively), and the other symbols—M, Σ, and N—have the meaning earlier ascribed to them.

Since the calculation of the median is based essentially on an ordering and counting process, its value is affected only by the position of an observation, not by its magnitude. The mean, on the other hand, being based on the sum of the actual values, is affected by the magnitude of an observation. It follows, therefore, that the median will not be affected by extreme values, whereas the mean will. In each of the above three examples, as it happens, one or more "extreme" values occurs and consequently the mean is pulled away, in that direction, from the value of the median. In any given situation the researcher must select the measure that he deems best represents his data, or at least justify his choice of a particular measure.§§§

Calculation of the Median and Mean for Grouped Data

When the data are grouped to form a frequency distribution, all information concerning the actual values of the observations falling within a particular class interval is lost. In one sense, therefore, the values of both the median and of the mean are indeterminate for grouped data, at least in terms of the original definitions. This indeterminateness is overcome through the use of supplementary assumptions. In the calculation of the median, it is assumed that the values within a class interval are spread evenly over that interval; in the calculation of the mean, on the other hand, it is assumed that all the values within an interval fall at the midpoint of that interval. Other assumptions regarding the distribution of cases within an interval could be made, but these two have the advantage that the calculation of the values of the median and mean is made as simple as possible.

Naturally, because we have introduced what is termed an *error of grouping*, the values of the median and mean calculated for grouped data will differ somewhat from those obtained for the same set of original data without grouping. In general, the broader the group the greater the grouping error, but much depends on the selection of the class intervals and the nature of the original distribution.

To illustrate the process of calculation and the nature of the errors of grouping, we will determine the values of the median and the mean for several groupings of the data of Tables II.6 and II.8, and, in the case of the former, show that the use of class intervals of unequal width may re-

§§§ If the situation warrants it, the researcher may report the value of the mean and of the median—perhaps even show the entire distribution if it is an unusual one.

duce the grouping error of the median and mean when a distribution is very skewed. Consider, first, the data of Table II.6, regrouped into class intervals of equal widths of 2, 3, and 5 of the original units (children) and into one set of class intervals of unequal width, as shown in Tables II.13A and II.13B, respectively, for the first case and the last. The calculation of the values of the median and mean is in each case shown in the section following the table proper, and the procedure may be illustrated by reference to the data of Table II.13A. To find the median, we note that it must lie within the first class interval (see cumulative frequencies), which we assume extends from 0.5 to 2.5, and at a distance from the beginning of the interval proportional to $\frac{328,792}{486,374}$. Accordingly, Median = 0.5 + (2) $\left(\frac{328,792}{486,374}\right)$ = 1.85 since the lower limit of the interval is 0.5 and its width is 2.

In the last five columns of Table II.13A, two methods whereby the value of the mean may be obtained are shown—in order, the direct or long method using the actual mid-points of the intervals, and an indirect or "short" method (since the calculations are simpler) using what is termed a *computation variable*. For the first method, the mid-point value (X) of each interval is multiplied by the corresponding frequency (f) to obtain the set of products (fX) shown in the sixth column of the table. Substituting the sum of these products ($= \Sigma fX$) in the formula, we have

$$M = \frac{\Sigma fX}{N} = \frac{1,409,710}{657,584} = 2.144$$

The computation variable is introduced to reduce the labor of calculation, by substituting for the mid-point values other values that are smaller and easier to use. Where the class intervals are of *equal* width,||||| the computation variable, x, is defined as $x = \frac{X - X_o}{h}$ where X denotes the mid-point of an interval, X_o the mid-point value selected as a new origin, and h the common width of the class intervals. It does not matter, theoretically, which mid-point value is selected for X_o, but the labor is greatly reduced if the new origin is so selected that the smaller values of x occur opposite the larger frequencies. Using x as a new variable, the products fx are calculated and summed, and the mean value of the computation variable, denoted by C, calculated as follows:

$$C = \frac{\Sigma fx}{N} = -\frac{1,103,501}{657,584} = -1.678$$

||||| If the class intervals are unequal in width, this formula does not apply. Although for some sets of class intervals of unequal width it is possible to adapt the formula appropriately, for others it is not and a computation variable cannot be used.

TABLE II.13

ILLUSTRATION OF CALCULATION OF MEDIAN AND MEAN:
GROUPED DISCONTINUOUS DATA

Classification of Families by Number of Children, Ontario, June, 1952:
from data of Table II.6

A: Class Intervals Two Original Units in Width

NO. OF CHILDREN IN FAMILY	CALCULATION OF MEDIAN		CALCULATION OF MEAN			COMPUTATION VARIABLE x	fx
	Frequency f	Cumulative Frequency F	Frequency f	Midpoint of Interval X	fX		
1,2	486,374	486,374	486,374	1.5	729,561.0	−2	−972,748
3,4	139,194	625,568	139,194	3.5	487,179.0	−1	−139,194
5,6	25,039	650,607	25,039	5.5	137,714.5	0	0
7,8	5,676	656,283	5,676	7.5	42,570.0	1	5,676
9,10	1,150	657,433	1,150	9.5	10,925.0	2	2,300
11,12	139	657,572	139	11.5	1,598.5	3	417
13,14	12	657,584	12	13.5	162.0	4	48
Total	657,584	—	657,584	—	1,409,710.0	—	−1,103,501

$$\text{Median} = 0.5 + (2)\left(\frac{328,792}{486,374}\right) = 0.5 + (2)(.676) = 1.85$$

$$\text{Mean} = M = \frac{\Sigma fX}{N} = \frac{1,409,710}{657,584} = 2.144$$

Using Computation Variable

$$M = X_o + hC = 5.5 + (2)\left(\frac{-1,103,501}{657,584}\right)$$
$$= 5.5 - 2(1.678) = 2.144$$

B: Class Intervals of Unequal Width

NO. OF CHILDREN IN FAMILY	CALCULATION OF MEDIAN		CALCULATION OF MEAN		
	Frequency f	Cumulative Frequency F	Frequency f	Midpoint of Interval X	fX
1	273,305	273,305	273,305	1.0	273,305.0
2	213,069	486,374	213,069	2.0	426,138.0
3	98,203	584,577	98,203	3.0	294,609.0
4,5	58,248	642,825	58,248	4.5	262,116.0
6,7	11,674	654,499	11,674	6.5	75,881.0
8–11	3,043	657,542	3,043	9.5	28,908.5
12–15	42	657,584	42	13.5	567.0
Total	657,584	—	657,584	—	1,361,524.5

$$\text{Median} = 1.5 + (1)\left(\frac{55,487}{213,069}\right) = 1.5 + 0.26 = 1.76$$

$$\text{Mean} = \frac{\Sigma fX}{N} = \frac{1,361,524.5}{657,584} = 2.070$$

To get back to the original units of X, the value of C must be multiplied by the width of the class interval and the product, with due regard to sign, added to the value of X selected as the new origin, i.e. X_o. Expressed as a formula, $M = X_o + hC$. For this particular example, $C = -1.678$, $h = 2$, and $X_o = 5.5$, so that $M = 5.5 + (2)(-1.678) = 2.144$.

The values of the median and mean for the class intervals of three and five original units in width, calculated in a similar manner, are 2.19 and 2.367, and 3.06 and 3.113, respectively. Note that as the intervals become broader these values depart more and more from those calculated from the ungrouped data. The discrepancies are particularly great in this example because the original distribution was markedly skewed—actually quite J-shaped. If class intervals of unequal width are used, and widths selected as shown in Table II.13B so that the lower end of the distribution with the large frequencies is not affected, the value of the median is unchanged and that of the mean affected but little. The effect of grouping is not as great in the example about to be considered, but the changes noted above should be sufficient warning of the need for the statistician to examine his data carefully before he undertakes even the relatively simple and seemingly unimportant step of selecting class intervals.

The effect of grouping on the values of the median and mean for continuous data may be illustrated, using class intervals of equal width varying from two points to ten, for the intelligence test data of Table II.8. For the ungrouped data, the median was 63.79 and the mean 62.774. For the various groupings, the value of the median varies from 63.21 to 63.70 and the value of the mean from 62.620 to 62.795. (The class intervals used, giving the top one only in each case, were 81–82, 78–82, 73–82, and 78–87, respectively.) Students should note that the differences in the values for the final two sets of width ten (median, 63.70 versus 63.21; mean, 62.786 versus 62.620) are as great as when the width of the interval is altered. It is obvious that the *placing* of the class intervals may be even more important than the *width* of the interval as far as the grouping error is concerned.

Measures of Variability

The *range* is probably the simplest measure of variability, being defined as the difference between the largest and the smallest values in the distribution, and is the appropriate measure to use if it is the extremes in which we are interested. But other than the advantages of ease of calculation and simplicity of interpretation, the range has little to commend it. It is obviously a very unstable value, and for grouped data its value is indeterminate unless, by supplementary convention, some particular point is specified within the lowest and the highest intervals. Also, strange as it may seem at first sight, the range is not independent of the size of the group; it increases, on the average, with the number of observations. In the routine work of statistical quality control in industry, nevertheless, the range (being so easy to calculate) may be used more than any other measure of variability, although it is often transformed to another measure, the standard deviation, through use of a factor obtained from a set of tables prepared for the purpose (*Biometrika*, XVII (1925), 386).

Several variations of the range, designed to overcome its major weaknesses, have been proposed. Of these, the best known is the *semi-interquartile range* (often called the *quartile deviation*), which is based, not on the two extreme observations, but on two other points on the scale well removed from them—known as the *upper* and *lower quartiles*. The quartiles are similar in definition to the median: the lower quartile is the point such that exactly one-quarter of the cases lie below it, and the upper quartile is the point such that exactly one-quarter of the cases lie above it. The quartile deviation is defined as half the difference (or range) between the two quartile points—whence comes the term "semi-interquartile range."###

None of these *range* statistics, however, measures directly the dispersion or variation about the central point of the distribution. They are, therefore, completely inappropriate if the information we seek is how much, on the average, the several values in the distribution deviate from the central point. In fact, the ranges of several distributions of a variable may be equal, although the distributions may be greatly different in dispersion about their central points. The dispersions about the central points of the two distributions in Table II.6, as a case in point, are obviously different, but the ranges are practically identical.

The *mean* is the measure of central position from which the deviations are almost invariably taken.* But, by definition of the mean, the sum of the deviations from it must be identically equal to zero, for *any* distribution. To overcome this difficulty, the deviations are squared in order to secure a set of positive values. The mean of this set of squared deviations, the *mean squared deviation*, is calculated, and the square root of it, called the *standard deviation*, is used as the measure of variability. If we denote the standard deviation by *Sd*, then

$$Sd = \sqrt{\frac{\Sigma(X - M)^2}{N}}$$

where M denotes the mean, X any one of the original observations, and N the number of cases.

Students should, as an exercise, calculate the values of the quartiles and of the quartile deviation for the distribution of intelligence test scores of Table II.8.

* The *median* should be used in the calculation of the *mean deviation* (or *average deviation*), which is defined as the mean of the absolute values of the deviations of the observations from the median (very often taken from the *mean*, despite the definition).

The standard deviation satisfies, in large part, the several criteria for a statistic set forth earlier. In most statistical work it is used as *the* measure of variability, and the mean is used as *the* measure of central position— partly because they are used almost exclusively in mathematical statistics. Neither is particularly easy to interpret: the standard deviation, for instance, does not possess any simple or obvious properties that would aid in its interpretation. For distributions that are approximately *normal* in form (a term that will be defined later in this chapter), they are the best measures that may be employed: for very asymmetrical distributions, on the other hand, they may be quite inappropriate, as Fisher points out.[†] Moreover, for statistical work concerned with sampling and tests of hypotheses, a better measure of variability is secured by using the square root of the *variance*, where the variance, v, equals $\dfrac{\Sigma\,(X-M)^2}{N-1}$. These points will be given due consideration in subsequent chapters as the occasion arises.

Calculation of Standard Deviation for Ungrouped Data

To simplify the calculations, we may write the formula for the standard deviation in the following form:

$$Sd = \sqrt{\frac{\Sigma X^2}{N} - M^2} \quad \text{or} \quad Sd = \sqrt{\frac{1}{N}\left\{\Sigma X^2 - \frac{(\Sigma X)^2}{N}\right\}}$$

For the average daily attendance figures used to illustrate the calculation of the median and mean for ungrouped data, for example, we calculate X^2 and the other values as indicated:[‡]

School Section	Average Daily Attendance X	X^2	
1	19	361	$N = 8$
2	18	324	
3	24	576	$\Sigma X = 180$
4	39	1,521	
5	22	484	$\Sigma X^2 = 4404$
6	16	256	
7	21	441	$Sd = \sqrt{550.5 - 506.25} = 6.65$
8	21	441	
Total	180	4,404	or $Sd = \sqrt{\frac{1}{8}(4404 - 4050)} = 6.65$

For ungrouped data like those of Tables II.6 and II.8 we use, for convenience, a variant of the fundamental formula for the standard deviation

[†] R. A. Fisher, *op. cit.*, pp. 47–48.

[‡] Students should note, in these and in subsequent calculations, that additional figures are carried throughout the process and only the final result is rounded off to the number of figures desired. Premature rounding off of values may lead to a serious discrepancy in the results (e.g. if M is taken as 23 in the above calculations).

in order to make proper allowance for the number of cases for each size of family or score. Using f to denote the frequency for any value of X, we may write

$$Sd = \sqrt{\frac{\Sigma fX^2}{N} - M^2} \quad \text{or} \quad Sd = \sqrt{\frac{1}{N}\left\{\Sigma fX^2 - \frac{(\Sigma fX)^2}{N}\right\}}$$

For the data of Table II.6, we have:

Ontario: $N = 657{,}584$; $\Sigma fX = 1{,}344{,}916$; $\Sigma fX^2 = 3{,}800{,}918$; whence $Sd = 1.264$

Quebec: $N = 548{,}702$; $\Sigma fX = 1{,}467{,}334$; $\Sigma fX^2 = 5{,}852{,}132$; whence $Sd = 1.875$

Accordingly, not only are families in Quebec somewhat larger on the average than those in Ontario, but they vary considerably more in size (in terms of deviations from the family of average size).§ Similarly, for the data of Table II.8, we find:

$N = 664$; $\Sigma fX = 41{,}682$; $\Sigma fX^2 = 2{,}673{,}918$; whence $Sd = 9.295$

Calculation of Standard Deviation for Grouped Data

In calculating the value of the standard deviation for grouped data we make the assumption (as we did in the case of the mean) that all cases within an interval are concentrated at the mid-point of the interval. Consequently, the formulae for the standard deviation will be the same as those considered immediately above, but X now denotes the mid-point of a class interval and f the corresponding frequency. Where the class intervals are of equal width, a computation variable, x, may be used and the formulae become:

$$Sd = h\sqrt{\frac{\Sigma fx^2}{N} - C^2} \quad \text{or} \quad Sd = h\sqrt{\frac{1}{N}\left\{\Sigma fx^2 - \frac{(\Sigma fx)^2}{N}\right\}}$$

where h is the common width of the class intervals.‖ For the data of Table II.13A, for example, we find the following values: $N = 657{,}584$; $\Sigma fX = 1{,}409{,}710$; $\Sigma fX^2 = 4{,}000{,}530$; and $Sd = 1.220$.

Using the computation variable as indicated in that table, we have: $N = 657{,}584$; $\Sigma fx = -1{,}103{,}501$; $\Sigma fx^2 = 2{,}096{,}409$; whence $Sd = (2)(.6099) = 1.220$.

The value of the standard deviation for this case is somewhat less than that for the ungrouped data: for the very broad groups of five units we

§ Such a difference in the two distributions is also revealed by the set of ratios, by family size, obtained by dividing the number of families in Quebec by the number in Ontario.

‖ As noted previously, if the class intervals are unequal in width a computation variable can be used only if the widths have a common factor, which would be substituted for h in the above formulae.

have $N = 657{,}584$; $\Sigma fx = 14{,}910$; $\Sigma fx^2 = 15{,}212$; $h = 5$; and $Sd = (5)$ $(.1504) = 0.752$. Thus, for this peculiar form of distribution, the broader the grouping the smaller the value of the standard deviation obtained. The effect here is directly the opposite of that observed for distributions like those of Table II.9, to which we will presently turn. Note that for the class intervals of unequal width of Table II.13B the effect is different. We have $N = 657{,}584$; $\Sigma fX = 1{,}361{,}524.5$; $\Sigma fX^2 = 3{,}964{,}441.75$; and Sd $= 1.320$. Thus in a distribution of this form and with grouping only at the upper part of the scale where fewer cases occur, the value of the standard deviation calculated for class intervals of unequal width may be greater than that found for the original ungrouped data.

Most textbooks in statistical method state that where grouped data are used a correction should be made to the calculated value of the standard deviation.# This correction consists of subtracting from Sd^2 one-twelfth of the square of the width of the class interval, which naturally reduces the calculated value of the standard deviation. What is not generally emphasized, however, is that the correction should be made if, and only if,

(a) the total number of cases is large (N is at least 500, preferably at least 1,000);

(b) fewer than 20 class intervals have been used;

(c) the variation is continuous, or may be assumed to be continuous;

(d) the frequency distribution is roughly symmetrical with frequencies tapering off to zero in both directions.

Condition (d) is most important: under no circumstances should the correction be applied if the distribution is J-shaped, U-shaped, or even moderately asymmetrical. For the J-shaped distribution considered above, for example, the standard deviations calculated for the grouped distributions are too small to begin with: to reduce them still more by applying the correction for grouping would be sheer folly.

The frequency distribution of Table II.8 more nearly satisfies the above conditions, although it is slightly skewed. The corresponding values of the standard deviations, uncorrected and corrected, for the various widths of the class intervals are given in Table II.14. When relatively fine grouping is used, Sheppard's adjustment tends to over-correct and should not be used. For broader class intervals, the adjustment does yield better values, but note that a change in position of the class intervals may have an effect almost as great as the grouping error itself. It is quite clear from this and the previous example that some discretion must be exercised in applying this correction for broad grouping: its use yields better results under some circumstances, but poorer results under others.

Known as Sheppard's correction for grouping (from the formulae derived by W. F. Sheppard).

TABLE II.14

ILLUSTRATION OF EFFECT OF CORRECTION FOR GROUPING
ON THE VALUE OF THE STANDARD DEVIATION
Data of Table II.8

WIDTH OF CLASS INTERVAL	STANDARD DEVIATION	
	Uncorrected	*Corrected*
Ungrouped	9.295	—
2	9.296	9.278
5	9.412	9.301
10	9.859	9.427
10	9.615	9.172

Measures of Skewness and Kurtosis

Taking into account both practical and theoretical considerations, the best measures of these characteristics are probably those obtained through use of what Fisher has called the series of k-statistics, which are derived from the sums of powers of the original observations, as explained below.**

If we define

$$s_1 = \Sigma X \qquad\qquad s_3 = \Sigma X^3$$
$$s_2 = \Sigma X^2 \qquad\qquad s_4 = \Sigma X^4$$

and, in terms of deviations from the mean, *(the method of moments)*

$$S_2 = s_2 - \frac{s_1^2}{N} \qquad\qquad S_3 = s_3 - \frac{3}{N} s_2 s_1 + \frac{2}{N^2} s_1^3$$

$$S_4 = s_4 - \frac{4}{N} s_3 s_1 + \frac{6}{N^2} s_2 s_1^2 - \frac{3}{N^3} s_1^4$$

then

$$k_1 = \frac{s_1}{N} \qquad\qquad k_2 = \frac{S_2}{N-1}$$

$$k_3 = \frac{N}{(N-1)(N-2)} S_3$$

$$k_4 = \frac{N}{(N-1)(N-2)(N-3)} \left[(N+1) S_4 - 3 \frac{N-1}{N} S_2^2 \right]$$

To measure skewness†† we use the statistic g_1, where

$$g_1 = \frac{k_3}{k_2^{3/2}}$$

and to measure kurtosis†† we use the statistic g_2, where

$$g_2 = \frac{k_4}{k_2^2}$$

** Students interested in a discussion of the theoretical advantages of these statistics should read the special appendix on them in R. A. Fisher, *op. cit.*, pp. 74–79. One practical advantage is that the formulae are particularly well adapted for calculations by modern machines.

†† For an example showing the complete solution in testing normality, see P. O. Johnson, *Statistical Methods in Research* (Englewood Cliffs, N.J.: Prentice-Hall, Inc., 1949), pp. 153–57.

Where broad grouping intervals are used, subject to the conditions set forth earlier for Sheppard's correction for grouping, the values of k_2 and k_4 for the computation variable are adjusted as follows, where the primes denote the corrected values:

$$k_2' = k_2 - \frac{1}{12} \qquad\qquad k_4' = k_4 + \frac{1}{120}$$

As pointed out earlier, however, such corrections for grouping are to be applied only where their use is clearly indicated.

For the model normal distribution, discussed in the next part, which is perfectly symmetrical and mesokurtic (neither flattened nor peaked) the expected values of g_1 and g_2 are exactly zero. When g_1 is positive, the distribution is said to be *positively skewed* (the observations are concentrated at the lower end of the distribution, with the long tail of the distribution extending to the right); when g_1 is negative, the distribution is said to be *negatively skewed* (the observations are concentrated at the upper end of the distribution, with the long tail of the distribution extending to the left). As for kurtosis, the distribution is said to be *leptokurtic* (relatively peaked) when g_2 is positive, and is said to be *platykurtic* (relatively flat) when g_2 is negative.

The figures given in Table II.15 illustrate the procedure to be followed in calculating the k-statistics. The same process applies to grouped data where a computation variable is used, and the k's adjusted as may be necessary to get back to the original units. Note that for g_1 and g_2, which are pure numbers, no such adjustment for units need be made, although a correction for grouping, if such be needed, can be applied to k_2 and k_4 as determined for the computation variable. The values of the various statistics, respectively for Ontario and Quebec, are given in Table II.16. The two distributions considered in this example are obviously very skewed and leptokurtic: they differ greatly in these characteristics, for instance, from the distribution of intelligence test scores of Table II.9. But even the distributions of families by size in the two provinces differ considerably in their characteristics—in central position, variability, skewness and kurtosis; these differences are revealed clearly by a comparison of the corresponding measures shown in Table II.16 (k_1, k_2, g_1, and g_2). One may conclude that, as compared with families in Ontario, those in Quebec are somewhat larger on the average and that their distribution is more variable but less skewed and less leptokurtic.

Admittedly the calculation of the values of g_1 and g_2 is rather laborious, particularly when N is large. Nevertheless these are the best measures of skewness and kurtosis that have been devised and should be used whenever these characteristics are to be described. Students may be relieved to learn that measures of these characteristics are needed, or at least used, rather infrequently and that in most practical problems the measures of central position and variability suffice. Possibly the commonest use of the

MODERN STATISTICAL METHODS

TABLE II.15

ILLUSTRATION OF CALCULATION OF THE k-STATISTICS
From data of Table II.6

NUMBER OF CHILDREN IN FAMILY X	SQUARE X^2	CUBE X^3	FOURTH POWER X^4	NUMBER OF FAMILIES Ontario	NUMBER OF FAMILIES Quebec
1	1	1	1	273,305	181,874
2	4	8	16	213,069	141,045
3	9	27	81	98,203	88,034
4	16	64	256	40,991	54,584
5	25	125	625	17,257	33,838
6	36	216	1,296	7,782	21,135
7	49	343	2,401	3,892	12,830
8	64	512	4,096	1,784	7,954
9	81	729	6,561	809	4,205
10	100	1,000	10,000	341	2,018
11	121	1,331	14,641	109	847
12	144	1,728	20,736	30	259
13	169	2,197	28,561	11	67
14	196	2,744	38,416	1	11
15	225	3,375	50,625	0	1
Total	—	—	—	657,584	548,702

measures of skewness and kurtosis is to determine whether an observed distribution differs in these characteristics from the model distributions (the normal distribution, in particular).

TABLE II.16

VALUES OF STATISTICS DERIVED FROM TABLE II.15

STATISTIC	ONTARIO DISTRIBUTION	QUEBEC DISTRIBUTION
N	657,584	548,702
$s_1 = \Sigma X$	1,344,916	1,467,334
$s_2 = \Sigma X^2$	3,800,918	5,852,132
$s_3 = \Sigma X^3$	14,493,754	31,287,688
$s_4 = \Sigma X^4$	70,941,986	203,394,320
S_2	1,050,244	1,928,200
S_3	2,423,973	5,325,215
S_4	13,246,491	35,635,735
k_1	2.0452	2.6742
k_2	1.5971	3.5141
k_3	3.6862	9.7052
k_4	20.1444	27.8990
g_1	1.83	1.47
g_2	7.90	2.26

Centile Points and Percentile Ranks

Quite a different method of describing a distribution is used frequently in psychology and education, employing the measures—centile points and percentile ranks—devised by Galton more than half a century ago.‡‡ In brief, a *centile point* is the point on the scale of a distribution below which a specified percentage of the observations are found. A *percentile rank*, on the other hand, is the percentage of cases in a distribution that lie below a specified point on the scale. Naturally, the two sets of values are related, since they are both derived from the same distribution in terms of percentage of cases, but their interpretations are quite different. The first is a point on the scale; the second is a percentage value. Of the two sets, the percentile ranks are probably more useful than centile points to the average teacher, in that they give directly the percentage of the norm group that had scores below specified score values.§§

EXERCISES

1. The data on page 40 have been taken from record sheets of a survey of motor cars and indicate the form in which data are frequently encountered in practice. Set up appropriate tables for each variable, following the suggestions given in the chapter, and indicate the type of data used in each case.
2. Set up what seem to you to be two important double classification tables from the data of Question 1.
3. Construct a table of triple classification for a set of three variables that seem to give a meaningful pattern in the data of Question 1.
4. Interpret the data of each of the tables in questions 1 to 3, inclusive, following the suggestions given in the text.
5. Answer the following questions, using the methods described in the chapter, for the data of Question 1:
   (a) What appears to be the most popular make of car?
   (b) What proportion of the drivers of each make of car carry car insurance?
   (c) Is there a tendency to insure only late-model cars?
   (d) Do those in a specified occupation seem to favor one make of car?
   (e) For which occupation are the drivers the oldest? the youngest?
   (f) Does income seem to be affected by occupation?
   (g) Do those of higher income seem to own later-model cars?
6. Using Age of Driver from the table in Question 1, calculate the values of the mean and median for (a) the ungrouped data, and for grouped data using class

‡‡ For a discussion of the origin of this method, and for illustrations of the calculations involved, students should read Chapter IV of Johnson and Jackson, *op. cit.*

§§ Although percentile ranks resemble the usual percentage marks assigned to examination papers, they are quite different. Percentile ranks should be interpreted as measures of *relative* merit; percentage marks are, at least in theory, a measure of *absolute* merit.

OBSERVATION NUMBER	MAKE OF CAR	YEAR OF MODEL	CAR INSURED	AGE OF DRIVER	OCCUPATION OF DRIVER	ANNUAL INCOME OF DRIVER
1	D	1954	Yes	23	Salesman	$ 3,400
2	F	1949	Yes	48	Executive	8,600
3	D	1954	Yes	49	Housewife	—
4	P	1951	Yes	31	Clerk	2,800
5	F	1954	Yes	26	Lawyer	4,300
6	F	1954	Yes	31	Doctor	8,300
7	F	1954	No	57	Minister	4,600
8	F	1954	No	20	Teacher	2,600
9	C	1946	No	31	Laborer	1,600
10	F	1953	No	39	Professor	5,200
11	B	1950	Yes	19	Housewife	—
12	P	1954	Yes	33	Executive	6,500
13	F	1948	Yes	30	Laborer	2,100
14	F	1953	Yes	29	Clerk	2,600
15	P	1947	Yes	63	Executive	4,500
16	F	1953	Yes	30	Clerk	2,900
17	F	1949	Yes	31	Minister	3,700
18	C	1954	Yes	21	Clerk	2,300
19	P	1954	Yes	49	Clerk	3,400
20	C	1952	Yes	31	Salesman	2,200
21	P	1954	Yes	29	Clerk	3,000
22	P	1953	Yes	18	Teacher	2,300
23	D	1946	Yes	23	Teacher	2,700
24	B	1953	Yes	28	Salesman	4,300
25	F	1949	Yes	30	Laborer	1,800
26	F	1953	No	60	Clerk	3,600
27	F	1952	Yes	25	Housewife	—
28	C	1954	Yes	39	Priest	—
29	P	1952	Yes	36	Executive	9,400
30	F	1954	No	29	Doctor	6,800
31	F	1954	Yes	67	Dentist	9,700
32	P	1953	Yes	52	Teacher	6,900
33	C	1954	Yes	28	Clerk	2,900
34	B	1952	Yes	57	Lawyer	7,800
35	D	1954	Yes	46	Laborer	2,800
36	F	1951	No	31	Executive	6,200
37	B	1953	Yes	25	Housewife	—
38	P	1954	Yes	58	Clerk	3,100
39	F	1951	No	26	Bus Driver	3,400
40	D	1951	Yes	25	Laborer	1,800
41	B	1951	No	28	Teacher	4,200
42	P	1953	Yes	28	Barber	1,900
43	D	1954	Yes	21	Student	—
44	C	1952	Yes	19	Clerk	2,100
45	B	1954	Yes	59	Executive	12,400
46	F	1953	No	34	Housewife	—
47	P	1953	Yes	32	Salesman	6,300
48	F	1954	Yes	26	Optician	3,900
49	P	1954	No	24	Bookkeeper	2,500
50	F	1953	Yes	33	Clerk	4,000

intervals (b) 18–19, 20–21, 22–23, . . ., (c) 18–22, 23–27, 28–32, . . ., and (d) 18–27, 28–37, 38–47, ... What effect did grouping have on these values of the measures of central position? Is the use of intervals of unequal width indicated?

7. For the set of 300 arithmetic scores given below, set up frequency distributions where the class intervals are in width (a) 1 score unit, (b) 2 score units, (c) 3 score units, (d) 5 score units, and (e) 10 score units.

Table of Achievement Test Scores (Arithmetic)

48	39	57	90	73	44	103	64	127	44	73	98
81	74	63	45	107	52	108	65	43	60	93	85
14	34	65	56	78	64	75	57	82	64	64	72
40	43	60	49	83	57	102	42	84	55	57	90
53	31	66	59	76	38	95	22	62	79	116	89
45	31	51	73	53	30	100	16	86	60	84	78
69	67	50	37	76	68	86	24	102	73	64	64
51	58	43	47	85	57	82	58	41	78	115	67
52	53	42	62	78	64	91	38	102	52	88	76
38	17	70	77	88	44	84	87	64	55	81	58
81	29	79	95	82	77	61	44	119	58	96	78
74	62	52	67	115	75	82	64	53	93	74	70
79	54	67	69	82	77	60	47	105	51	59	110
67	75	52	84	24	51	61	70	95	76	101	65
35	86	19	68	64	30	69	64	121	43	86	79
46	77	68	50	51	24	59	33	58	91	101	67
66	100	56	31	78	93	54	70	118	74	77	60
61	70	33	79	103	110	84	72	115	105	76	81
49	79	52	54	121	75	78	47	66	84	69	79
56	97	82	68	68	90	44	53	68	69	68	77
81	89	57	37	70	39	73	118	137	64	82	107
49	70	40	64	85	91	52	97	59	88	45	90
71	65	78	72	68	93	44	67	77	71	95	99
68	77	61	56	59	87	87	116	98	70	80	86
61	81	55	37	35	117	65	96	78	61	76	84

8. For the data of Question 7, calculate the values of the mean and median for (a) the ungrouped data, and for grouped data using class intervals (b) 10–14, 15–19, 20–24, . . ., (c) 10–19, 20–29, 30–39, . . ., and (d) 10–29, 30–49, 50–69, ... What effect did grouping have on these values? Would the use of class intervals of unequal width have shown less effect?

9. Calculate the values of the standard deviations for the ungrouped and grouped distributions of questions 6 and 8. What effect did grouping have on these values? Does the "correction for grouping" compensate properly and adequately? Select class intervals of unequal width for the data referred to in Question 8 and see what effect this has on the value of the standard deviation calculated therefrom.

10. Calculate the set of Fisher's k-statistics and the values of g_1 and g_2 for the ungrouped data of Question 7.

11. Test the normality of the grouped scores on the intelligence test given in Table II.9B.

Bases of Statistical Reasoning

This second part of our introductory chapter attempts to lay the bases of statistical reasoning in relation to the statistical measures we have just defined and illustrated. A number of the results presented herein will in themselves prove interesting and useful to the reader, but the chief purpose of this part is to introduce the highest level of statistical methodology, viz. statistical inference. Here, inquiry goes well beyond the mere fact-gathering or descriptive stage and aims at the drawing of valid conclusions from empirical investigations of scientific problems.

Populations and Samples

The facts upon which inductive synthesis is based are certain regularities which are noted in the proportionate frequency with which certain simple events occur, or do not occur, when the conditions under which they may happen are reconstructed again and again in repeated trials. As we saw in the previous chapter, the origin of the theory of probability lies in the regularities that occur in games of chance (e.g. coin-tossing), and which were observed by gamblers and referred to mathematicians for study and explanation. Various models that can be set up in this way provide the scientist or statistician with the means by which he can conceptualize mathematically some real problem, whether he is a worker in physics, in biology, or in the social sciences. That is, the researcher starts simplifying the problem by recourse to some sort of a model representing those features of reality most fundamental for the problem under consideration. The models to be described in this and subsequent chapters serve as standards against which the research worker can compare and interpret his experimental or other observational results.

As we intimated earlier, the theory of probability is basic in statistical inference. While there is no single definition of probability acceptable to all, for most practical purposes, i.e. our primary interest in application, we may regard it simply as a *proportionate frequency*. But before we can proceed with this interpretation, it is necessary to introduce the concepts of *population* and *sample*.

We observe, whether we are tossing coins or collecting other observations, that as the body of data (the aggregate) increases, its distribution becomes more regular. It is easy to imagine, therefore, that the frequency distribution (or proportionate frequency distribution) may be described by a limiting smooth curve that might be superimposed on a graph, a histogram, for example, constructed from grouped continuous data. This concept of the limiting aggregate corresponds to that of the infinite population of the statistician, in the sense of the aggregate formed, or that would be formed, by a complete enumeration of the objects or of the characteristics being studied.

There are situations where complete enumeration is impossible or where the size of the population is unlimited. There is no such thing, for instance, as a finite population formed by the results of tossing a penny. This is true, also, of most scientific experiments. It is always *possible* to toss another penny, or in most cases to carry out another experiment, no matter how many previous tosses have been made or previous experiments have been carried out. We speak of such populations as being *infinite*, in contrast to those that can in fact be counted. Strictly speaking, only in our imagination does the infinite population exist, although finite populations very large in number (for most practical purposes indistinguishable from infinite populations) do exist in reality. Thus any particular population may be hypothetical or real, and finite or infinite in number.

The concept of a limiting distribution is of special value in the case of infinite populations, or of finite populations that are too large to be enumerated. The ideal smooth curve of the distribution function is rarely if ever reached in empirical studies: we speak of it as representing the distribution of the population. However, we can define the *probability* of an event, such as the appearance of a head in the toss of a coin, as the frequency with which the event occurs in the population, and the probability that an observation will lie between any two values can be specified by the appropriate proportionate area under the ideal curve. A *theoretical* distribution function, therefore, gives the frequency with which the values of the variable occur in the population in the same way that an *empirical* distribution gives the frequency with which the values of the variable occur in the sample.

In practice, of course, we rarely have populations at our command: in fact, the data we do have may be, even at their best, fragmentary. In a typical statistical investigation, such as one using the method of the experiment or of the sample survey (see Chapter XIV), the researcher specifies that the observations gathered by some sampling procedure are taken from a particular population that he either knows to be, or is willing to assume is, suitable or appropriate. He then computes certain functions of his observations as estimates of the parameters of that population, as we noted in the earlier part of this chapter. To test statistical hypotheses concerning these population parameters (see Chapter III), and to set up confidence or fiducial limits for them (see Chapter X), knowledge of the probability distributions of the statistics, or of certain functions of them, is required. Since these distributions may be derived mathematically from the specified parent population distributions, they are often termed *derived sampling distributions*. In this chapter, however, we will be concerned, not with the mathematical derivations, but mainly with empirical sampling studies leading to the illustration and determination of the sampling distributions of certain frequently used statistics.

The statistical methods treated herein not only provide the appropriate basis for drawing valid inferences from sample results but set the conditions governing the selection of the sample from the population that must be met if valid inferences are to be drawn. These conditions must also be satisfied in the design of our experiments and surveys, as we shall see in subsequent chapters. That this must be so, is evident upon reflection of the fact that sampling theory provides the models against which we compare our observed results. It is on the basis of this comparison that we draw inferences, which will be valid only if these conditions are met, concerning the phenomena we may be observing.

In order for statistical theory to have general application, the concepts of *randomness* and the *random sample* have been introduced. If the sample is to be representative of the population from which it is drawn, the elements of the sample must have been chosen at random. Perhaps the definition of a random sample of n elements (parts, units, individuals, or observations, whatever they may be called) is most easily understood by considering all possible different samples of n elements that could be drawn without replacement from any given finite population of N elements. From the theory of combinations we know that we can select $_NC_n$ different samples of size n from that population. We define a random sample of n elements as a sample selected from among the $_NC_n$ different possible samples in such manner that every sample has the same probability (prob. $= 1/_NC_n$) of being chosen.

Frankly, it is rather difficult to define in simple terms exactly what *is* meant by randomness. However, if we say that in choosing elements from the population no one element must be favored over any other element, we do express fairly closely what is meant. To illustrate the process, it is convenient to establish populations of various kinds and actually draw samples from them. In practice, we draw a simple random sample element by element. A very common method (used in lotteries, for instance) is, first, to number the elements in the population from 1 to N and, second, to take a series of random numbers between 1 and N. For this purpose, mechanical means are often employed, such as a revolving drum from which a card is picked from time to time (the numbers not being visible to the person drawing the card) or one of the tables of random numbers may be used.‖‖

As an example, let us assume that we wish to secure a random sample of 15 school boards from the population of 307 school boards in towns and villages in Ontario. One method is to utilize some property that is independent of the one under investigation: here, in an alphabetical list of towns

‖‖ L. H. C. Tippett, *Tracts for Computers, XV, Random Sampling Numbers* (Cambridge, Eng.: Cambridge University Press, 1927).

R. A. Fisher and F. Yates, *Statistical Tables for Biological Agricultural, and Medical Research* (Edinburgh: Oliver and Boyd, 1938), Table XXXIII, pp. 82–87.

Rand Corporation, *A Million Random Digits with 100,000 Normal Deviates* (Glencoe, Ill.: The Free Press, 1955).

and villages the *position* will be independent of any possible connection with the "properties" of school boards. We could take every twentieth place in the list, beginning with a position in the first 20 names selected at random, but this could either yield 16 places or leave the final 7 unrepresented. Dividing the list into 15 blocks of 8 groups of 20 and 7 groups of 21 places, sampling at random from each block, would yield the desired 15 places but set up a varying probability of being selected. To follow the lottery procedure, which involves writing the names on identical cards and using some mechanical means to mix and select, would probably be too time-consuming and expensive. The simplest and most efficient means would seem to be the use of a table of random numbers; the school boards can be numbered, and then a random sample of the numbers from 1 to 307 selected. One way, here, would be to take three adjacent rows or columns of the tables, assign three consecutive numbers to each school board number, as follows:

Place Number	1	2	. . .	306	307
Corresponding Random Numbers	(002;003;004)	(005;006;007)	. . .	(917;918;919)	(920;921;922)

and ignore any duplications occurring and any numbers that lie below 002 or above 922. Using the first three adjacent columns of the first page of Fisher and Yates' table, for instance, the towns and villages selected would have the following numbers:

Random No.	034	167	125	555	162	844	630	332	576	181	266	234	523	378	702
Place No.	11	56	42	185	54	281	210	111	192	60	89	78	174	126	234

Observe that the place number is found by dividing the random number by 3: the first table of assigned numbers was designed so that this might be done.

In the sections that follow, however, we will use the more easily understood lottery system, or at least an adaptation of it. This involves, save for the coin-tossing demonstration to be given first, setting up real finite populations (of numbers on cards, in our case) and actually drawing numbers from the population, replacing the card drawn (after recording the number typed on it) in each case before mixing and drawing the next. This procedure, known as *sampling with replacement*, does come reasonably close to satisfying the conditions of sampling from an infinite population.

Repeated Random Sampling and Statistical Reasoning

Much of the lack of understanding of the nature and purpose of statistical reasoning, and many of the abuses and misuses thereof, stem from a lack of knowledge of its limitations. Sampling theory is based on the process of repeated sampling—the drawing of a number of random samples from a specified population. From actual or theoretical results, i.e. by actually drawing a large number of samples or by deriving the expected results mathematically, we learn how the estimates of the parameters of the population that are derived from the samples distribute themselves in repeated sampling. Many of these estimates will prove to be reasonably close to the population value, of course, while others will depart from it by varying amounts, and we can determine the relative frequency of occurrence of estimates that depart from the population value by any specified amount. This gives us a model distribution, showing what results may be expected in repeated sampling from such a population where the only factor operating is the selection at random of members to constitute the sample. But this is all we do know, much as we may wish to know more, and it is all that we can use in drawing inferences about the population from sample results.

We use the knowledge so gained in this way. In a practical problem, we secure results for a sample and on the basis of such sample results wish to draw inferences concerning the population in which we are interested. Our procedure consists essentially in comparing what we found for our sample with the model distribution, i.e. with what we would expect to obtain in repeated random sampling from that population. If our sample result is one that could occur rather frequently in repeated random sampling, it seems reasonable to conclude that it is in fact a sample drawn at random from that population. However, if our sample result is one that could occur only very infrequently in repeated random sampling, what we have observed is a rather unlikely event if the only factor operating is the random selection process, and consequently it seems reasonable to conclude that our sample is not one drawn at random from that population but one drawn either not at random or from some other population.

In either case, of course, we may be wrong in our conclusion, but at least we have a valid and objective basis for reaching such conclusions. In addition, we can indicate, by reference to the relative frequency of occurrence of the event we observed in the distribution of the values in repeated sampling, something of the degree of confidence that can be placed in our conclusions. In many respects the statistician is like a gambler who, knowing the risks, places his wager in a fashion that is most likely to yield profitable results.

Before discussing this aspect of statistical reasoning in more detail, we wish to introduce a number of population distributions, to explain and illustrate the process of repeated sampling, and to show some examples of actual and theoretical distributions of certain of the sample estimates so obtained. We have limited our discussion to the more important and commonly used distributions, treating only the positive binomial, Poisson, negative binomial, normal, and rectangular population distributions, and in that order. Our empirical sampling results refer only to the positive binomial, Poisson, normal, and rectangular population distributions, since these are typical of the forms most frequently encountered in practice by the researcher.

The Positive Binomial Distribution

Probably the simplest and easiest way of introducing the concepts of sampling and repeated sampling is to consider their application in one of the problems originally propounded by the gamblers, namely, tosses of one or more coins. In this as in many other applications of the theory of sampling, the population from which the samples are supposed to be drawn is hypothetical and infinite. It consists in this case of all possible tosses of all possible coins. Also, the results derived from theory for the distribution of sample estimates in repeated sampling are those for an infinite number of samples drawn at random under like conditions from that population. These are the ideal curves to which reference was made in an earlier section.

In the toss of a coin either a head or a tail will appear uppermost: we can overlook the possibility of the coin balancing on edge, since this event will occur so infrequently that it may safely be ignored. The result, the appearance of a head or a tail, constitutes a single sample from the hypothetical and infinite population of all possible tosses of single coins. A second toss yields another sample, and so on. If for each toss we record whether a head or a tail appears uppermost, this set of observations will indicate, on the basis of experimental evidence, the form of the distribution in repeated sampling. Although for any single toss the result is altogether unpredictable, we know that in the long run heads and tails will appear with equal frequency—assuming the coin is unbiased and the proper conditions of tossing are observed. We say that the probability of a head appearing uppermost is $\frac{1}{2}$.

Let us, for simplicity of discussion, denote the probability of an event, E, by the letter p, and the probability of the other event, or all other events, i.e. not-E, by the letter q. Then we can state that $0 \leqslant p \leqslant 1$, $0 \leqslant q \leqslant 1$, and $p + q = 1$ where, for example, $0 \leqslant p \leqslant 1$ is read as "p is greater than or equal to 0 and less than or equal to 1." Now for a toss of a coin, $p = q = \frac{1}{2}$, and we can think of the event, E, as the appearance of a head (denoted by H) and the other possible event, not-E, as the appearance of a tail (denoted by T). If we denote the number of tosses by N, then the *expected* number of heads appearing will be $Np = \frac{N}{2}$ and the *expected* number of tails appearing will be $Nq = \frac{N}{2}$. The whole set of expected values can be simply expressed by the formula $N(p + q)$ which, when expanded, becomes $Np + Nq$ and shows the *expected* number of E's and not-E's.

We are now in a position to extend the argument to tosses of two coins simultaneously, and later to tosses of k coins simultaneously.## In tossing two coins, the number of *combinations* that can occur is three: two heads (HH), a head and a tail (HT), and two tails (TT). But there are two possible orders or *permutations* for the head-and-tail combination, HT and TH, if we think of the two coins being numbered or otherwise distinguished (one might be a nickel and the other a dime, for example). Therefore, we have *four* possible arrangements or permutations of the two coins—HH, HT, TH, and TT—each of which is equally likely to occur (with a probability of $\frac{1}{4}$) in a single toss of two coins because the two coins operate independently, or will if the proper conditions of tossing are observed. Consequently, we can say that the *probability* of an HH combination is $\frac{1}{4}$, of an HT combination (i.e. HT or TH) is $\frac{1}{2}$, and of a TT combination is $\frac{1}{4}$. In four tosses of two coins, for example, the expected number of appearances of these combinations would be $1HH$, $2HT$, and $1TT$. But again we may express all this in a simple formula, viz. $N(p + q)^2$, which, when expanded to reveal the combinations, becomes $Np^2 + 2Npq + Nq^2$. Since $p = q = \frac{1}{2}$, as before, this may be written $N(\frac{1}{4} + \frac{1}{2} + \frac{1}{4})$ and the probabilities of the several combinations are seen to be equal to those derived earlier.

Before proceeding to the general case of tossing k coins simultaneously, we should explain that we used above, and will use later, two theorems in probability that apply to mutually independent events, such as the tossing of two or more coins or rolls of two or more dice. The first theorem, generally known as the *product theorem*, may be expressed as follows:

> *If, in a given toss or trial, the two or more events are mutually independent,**** *then the probability that both or all such events will occur in that trial is the product of their several probabilities.*

Thus, the probability of HH is $(\frac{1}{2})(\frac{1}{2}) = \frac{1}{4}$, and of TT is $(\frac{1}{2})(\frac{1}{2}) = \frac{1}{4}$, in a single toss of two coins. Similarly, if we tossed three coins, the probability of HHH is $(\frac{1}{2})(\frac{1}{2})(\frac{1}{2}) = \frac{1}{8}$, and so on. The second theorem, known as the *addition theorem*, is expressed in this way:

> *If, in a given toss or trial, the two or more events are mutually exclusive,*††† *the probability that exactly one of them will occur in that trial is the sum of their separate probabilities.*

In the case of the toss of two coins, for instance, the arrangements HT and

In so doing, we are following in the footsteps of the mathematicians who originally developed the theory for the edification of their gambler friends.

*** That is, all the events can occur in that single trial, but the occurrence of any one does not affect the probability of occurrence of any other.

††† That is, only one of the events can occur in the single trial.

TH are mutually exclusive, and the probability of the *combination HT*, i.e. the arrangement *HT or* the arrangement *TH*, is ¼ + ¼ = ½ .‡‡‡

The extension to the general case of *N* tosses of *k* coins simultaneously is given by the formula $N(p + q)^k$ which applies, of course, to any values of *p* and *q* (the general case is not restricted to the coin-tossing situation). The general formula for the expansion of $(p + q)^k$, known as the binomial expansion and yielding the probabilities of the several combinations, is as follows:

$$p^k + \frac{k}{1}p^{k-1}q + \frac{(k)(k-1)}{(1)(2)}p^{k-2}q^2 + \frac{(k)(k-1)(k-2)}{(1)(2)(3)}p^{k-3}q^3$$
$$+ \ldots + \frac{k}{1}pq^{k-1} + q^k$$

Multiplying these probabilities by *N*, the number of tosses or trials, yields the expected frequencies, e.g. in *N* tosses of *k* coins, the expected frequency of exactly *k* heads would be Np^k, and so on, the exponents of *p* and *q* indicating the corresponding combination. The resulting distribution is known as the *positive binomial distribution*.

Tables have been prepared which enable the user to read directly from them the values of these several probabilities of the binomial expansion for a wide range of values of *p* and *k*. One such table has been prepared and published by the United States Department of Commerce.§§§ But for small values of *k* (less than 20, say), it is not too difficult a matter to calculate the several terms by use of appropriate factors. Note that the ratio of the $(s + 1)$-th term to the *s*th term is $\frac{k-s}{s+1} \cdot \frac{q}{p}$, where *s* takes values from *o* to *k*. Similarly, the ratio of the $(s - 1)$-th term to the *s*th term is $\frac{s}{k-s+1} \cdot \frac{p}{q}$. The procedure followed in calculating terms is illustrated in Table II.17. Students should note that if decimal fractions are used, as would normally be the case, a sufficient number of significant figures must be used in the calculation of the first term or later terms may be sadly in error—a sort of compounding of errors may occur through such a process of successive multiplication. Probably the most satisfactory procedure is to begin with a term near the middle of the distribution and calculate the values of the terms above and below it by using the two multiplying factors.

The measure of the characteristics of the positive binomial distribution are simple in form, being functions of *k*, *p*, and *q*, only. Using corresponding Greek symbols to denote the values of Fisher's *k*-statistics for this theoretical population distribution, we find

‡‡‡ Students should, as an exercise, derive the results for tossing three coins simultaneously, and also those for rolls of two dice.

§§§ *Tables of the Binomial Probability Distribution*, Applied Mathematics Series, AMS6.

(mean) → $K_1 = kp$ $K_3 = kpq(q - p)$

(variance) → $K_2 = kpq$ $K_4 = kpq(1 - 6pq)$

whence $\gamma_1 = \dfrac{q - p}{\sqrt{kpq}}$ and $\gamma_2 = \dfrac{1 - 6pq}{kpq}$

Note that the mean, K_1, increases as either k or p, or both, is increased; the variance, K_2, increases as k is increased, but decreases steadily as p departs from the value $\frac{1}{2}$, being a maximum at $\dfrac{k}{4}$ for $p = q = \frac{1}{2}$; the skewness approaches zero as p approximates to q in value, or as k becomes large, since γ_1 is of the order $\dfrac{1}{\sqrt{k}}$; and the kurtosis approaches zero as the product pq approaches the value $\frac{1}{6}$, or as k becomes large since γ_2 is of the order $\dfrac{1}{k}$. ||||| For the case illustrated in Table II.17, for which $k = 10$ and $p = q = \frac{1}{2}$, we have $K_1 = 5$; $K_2 = 2.5$; $\gamma_1 = 0$; $\gamma_2 = -0.2$. The distribution is symmetrical, although platykurtic, the values being distributed about a mean of 5 with standard deviation equal to 1.58.###

TABLE II.17

ILLUSTRATION OF CALCULATION OF PROBABILITIES OF VARIOUS COMBINATIONS FOR A TOSS OF 10 COINS SIMULTANEOUSLY

COMBINATION	S	MULTIPLYING FACTOR	PROBABILITY OF OCCURRENCE
10 heads, 0 tails	0	—	1/1024
9 heads, 1 tail	1	10	10/1024
8 heads, 2 tails	2	9/2	45/1024
7 heads, 3 tails	3	8/3	120/1024
6 heads, 4 tails	4	7/4	210/1024
5 heads, 5 tails	5	6/5	252/1024
4 heads, 6 tails	6	5/6	210/1024
3 heads, 7 tails	7	4/7	120/1024
2 heads, 8 tails	8	3/8	45/1024
1 head, 9 tails	9	2/9	10/1024
0 heads, 10 tails	10	1/10	1/1024

||||| Students should, as an exercise, calculate the values of the k-statistics, and of g_1 and g_2, for the distribution given by multiplying the probabilities of Table II.17 by 1,024, i.e. for the case 1,024 $(\frac{1}{2} + \frac{1}{2})^{10}$, using as the values of X the number of heads (or number of tails) for the several combinations.

The binomial expansion may be extended from two categories to the general case of S mutually exclusive categories, known as the *multinomial expansion*. For N independent trials, the probability of occurrence of n_1 in the first category, n_2 in the second, and in general n_i in the ith category is the corresponding term in the multinomial expansion $(p_1 + p_2 + \ldots + p_i + \ldots + p_S)^N$, where $i = 1, 2, \ldots, S$, and p_i denotes the probability of occurrence for the ith category. The general term is

The general form of the model binomial distributions is illustrated in Figure II.1, for the two cases of $p = \frac{1}{2}$ and $p = \frac{1}{5}$. In the case of each, the distributions corresponding to several values of k have been included. Note that the distributions are always symmetrical when $p = \frac{1}{2}$, whatever the value of k, and rapidly approach a bell-shaped form as k increases. For the case $p = \frac{1}{5}$, on the other hand, the distributions are markedly skew even for moderately large values of k. As is evident from the steady change in shape as k is increased, however, even when p is not equal to $\frac{1}{2}$ the binomial distribution will approach a bell-shaped form as k becomes very large. As we pointed out above, the skewness becomes greater as p becomes smaller, and when p (or q) is very small the binomial distribution takes the simple form discussed in the next section.

The Poisson Distribution

More than a century ago, in 1837, Poisson derived the formula for the theoretical distribution now known as the *Poisson distribution*. It is a limiting form of the positive binomial distribution, arising when p (or q) is very small but k is sufficiently large so that the mean (kp) of the distribution is finite. Under these conditions, if we write $m = kp$ and denote by X the number of successes ($0 \leqslant X \leqslant k$), then the general term of the binomial becomes

$$\frac{e^{-m}m^X}{X!}$$

where e is the base of the natural logarithms.* The terms can be readily evaluated for the various values of X, since m is the only other term entering into the equation, but tables are available which give the probabilities for the several X values for values of m ranging from 0.1 to 15.0 by units of 0.1.† While there is, theoretically, no restriction on the value of m, in most situations for which the distribution is useful m is likely to be small.

The distribution is very skewed for small values of m, but it rapidly approaches a symmetrical bell-shaped form for even moderately large values of m (Fig. II.2). The most unusual feature of this theoretical distribution is, perhaps, that all the population values corresponding to the set of k-statistics discussed earlier are identically equal to m, i.e., $K_1 = K_2 = K_3 = K_4 = m$. Thus, the mean and the variance of the distribution are equal and both equal to m, the skewness measure, γ_1, is equal to $\frac{1}{\sqrt{m}}$, and the

---

$$P(n_1, n_2, \ldots, n_S) = \frac{N!}{n_1!\, n_2!\, \ldots n_S!} \, p_1{}^{n_1} + p_2{}^{n_2} + \ldots + p_S{}^{n_S}$$

where $p_1 + p_2 + \ldots + p_S = 1$ and $n_1 + n_2 + \ldots + n_S = N$. The binomial expansion is the special case for which $s = 2$.

* The value of e is 2.718, approximately.

† Karl Pearson, *Tables for Statisticians and Biometricians*, Part I (3rd ed.; London: Biometric Laboratory, University College, 1930), Table LI.

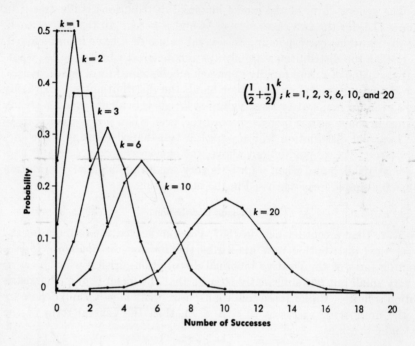

$$\left(\frac{1}{2}+\frac{1}{2}\right)^k ; k = 1, 2, 3, 6, 10, \text{ and } 20$$

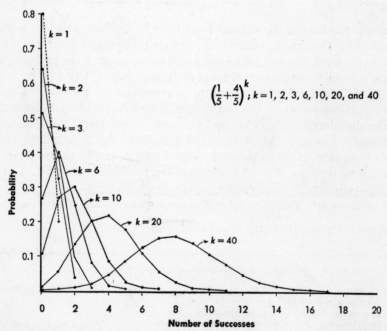

$$\left(\frac{1}{5}+\frac{4}{5}\right)^k ; k = 1, 2, 3, 6, 10, 20, \text{ and } 40$$

Figure II.1. THE BINOMIAL DISTRIBUTION

as k gets larger, regardless of the values of p + q, the distribution approaches the normal curve

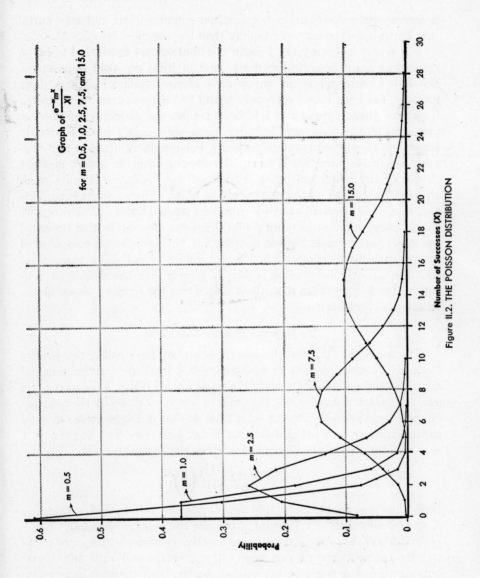

Graph of $\dfrac{e^{-m}m^x}{x!}$

for m = 0.5, 1.0, 2.5, 7.5, and 15.0

Figure II.2. THE POISSON DISTRIBUTION

kurtosis measure, γ_2, is equal to $\dfrac{1}{m}$. These last two results indicate that as m increases the distribution becomes more symmetrical and mesokurtic (the kurtosis decreasing more rapidly than the skewness for $m > 1$).

For nearly a century the Poisson distribution was considered to be no more than a mathematical curiosity and of little practical importance. But it has found numerous important biological applications and, more recently, has been found extremely useful in problems relating to deaths from rare diseases, road and telephone traffic, and accident and absence proneness among workers in industry, to mention only a few. We would expect, on theoretical grounds, to find a Poisson distribution in any situation where the variation is essentially discontinuous in nature and the chance of any individual being a "success" (or "failure") is quite small although the mean for the group would be finite. These are the conditions that do actually pertain to many situations studied but, in all fairness, we should point out that in quite a few situations the distribution observed resembles, not a simple Poisson distribution, but a compound composed of several such distributions with different values of m.‡ The variance in such a compound distribution is usually greater than the mean—an indication that factors other than those underlying the simple Poisson distribution are operating.

The Negative Binomial Distribution

The usual binomial distribution $(p + q)^k$, we have called the *positive* binomial distribution in order to distinguish it from the *negative* binomial distribution (of which apparently little was known before a decade or two ago). The latter distribution, the terms of which are given by the negative binomial expansion by algebra equivalent to that of the positive binomial expansion, may be written, following Fisher,‡ as $(q - p)^{-k}$ where $q = 1 + p$ and k is always positive, and for which the general term is

$$q^{-k} \frac{(k + X - 1)!}{X!(k - 1)!} \left(\frac{p}{q}\right)^x$$

Unlike the positive binomial, this term is positive for all positive values of X and for all values of k, integral or not (for the positive binomial, when k is not integral the expansion may give negative coefficients and, since negative frequencies have no meaning, will not correspond with any distribution). For the negative binomial, however, both p and k have to be estimated from the data.§

‡ R. A. Fisher, "The Negative Binomial Distribution," reprinted from the *Annals of Eugenics* in Paper 38 of *Contributions to Mathematical Statistics* (New York: John Wiley & Sons, Inc., 1950).

§ Readers interested in the most efficient method of estimating p and k should consult the following reference: Herbert S. Sechel, "The Estimation of the Parameters of a Negative Binomial Distribution with Special Reference to Psychological Data," *Psychometrika*, XVI, No. 1 (March, 1951), 107–27.

The shape of the negative binominal distribution may again be determined from the following expected values of the set of k-statistics.
$$K_1 = kp, \quad K_2 = kpq, \quad K_3 = kpq(q + p), \quad K_4 = kpq(1 + 6pq)$$

$$\gamma_1 = \frac{q + p}{\sqrt{kpq}} \qquad\qquad \gamma_2 = \frac{1 + 6pq}{kpq}$$

Since $0 \leqslant p \leqslant 1$, and $q = 1 + p$, it is obvious that the negative binomial distribution will always have a variance greater than the mean, will generally be quite skewed and leptokurtic, but will become more symmetrical and less leptokurtic as k increases. The distribution becomes mesokurtic much more rapidly than it becomes symmetrical, but it will remain moderately asymmetrical and leptokurtic even for fairly large values of k.

The terms of the negative binomial are relatively easy to evaluate, although it becomes a somewhat laborious process when k is large. Note that the first term, for $X = 0$, reduces to q^{-k} and that the ratio of the $(X + 1)$-th term to the Xth may be written

$$\frac{k + X}{X + 1} \cdot \frac{p}{q}$$

For small values of k, the simplest procedure is to evaluate the first term and calculate the others from it by successive multiplication, using the above factor. When k is large, however, it is better to evaluate a term near the middle of the distribution and calculate the others from it, using for values of X lower than the middle term selected the relationship of the $(X - 1)$-th term to the Xth, viz.

$$\frac{X}{k + X - 1} \cdot \frac{q}{p}$$

For an example, setting $p = 0.5$, for which the positive binomial is always symmetrical, we have the following values as k is increased:

STATISTIC	$k = 1$	$k = 3$	$k = 5$	$k = 10$	$k = 20$
K_1	0.50	1.50	2.50	5.00	10.00
K_2	0.75	2.25	3.75	7.50	15.00
γ_1	2.31	1.33	1.03	0.73	0.52
γ_2	7.33	2.44	1.47	0.73	0.37

As is evident from these values and the formulae, the distribution becomes mesokurtic much more rapidly than it becomes symmetrical but will remain moderately asymmetrical and leptokurtic even for fairly large values of k. Illustrations of the negative binomial distribution for the example considered above are shown in Table II.18: i.e. for $p = 0.5$; $k = 1, 3, 5, 10$,

TABLE II.18

ILLUSTRATIONS OF THE NEGATIVE BINOMIAL DISTRIBUTION
$p = 0.5, k = 1, 3, 5, 10, and 20$

VALUE OF X (no. of successes)	EXPECTED FREQUENCIES (*Probability* $\times$ 10,000)				
	$k = 1$	$k = 3$	$k = 5$	$k = 10$	$k = 20$
0	6,666.7	2,963.0	1,316.9	173.4	3.0
1	2,222.2	2,963.0	2,194.8	578.1	20.0
2	740.7	1,975.3	2,194.8	1,059.8	70.2
3	246.9	1,097.4	1,707.1	1,413.0	171.5
4	82.3	548.7	1,138.0	1,530.8	328.8
5	27.4	256.1	682.8	1,428.7	526.0
6	9.1	113.8	379.3	1,190.6	730.6
7	3.0	48.8	198.7	907.1	904.5
8	1.0	20.3	99.4	642.5	1,017.6
9	0.3	8.3	47.8	428.4	1,055.3
10	0.1	3.3	22.3	271.3	1,020.1
11	9,999.7	1.3	10.1	164.4	927.4
12		0.5	4.5	95.9	798.6
13		0.2	2.0	54.1	655.2
14		0.1	0.8	29.6	514.8
15		10,000.1	0.4	15.8	389.0
16			0.1	8.2	283.6
17			0.1	4.2	200.2
18			9,999.9	2.1	137.2
19				1.0	91.5
20				0.5	59.4
21				0.2	37.7
22				0.1	23.4
23				0.1	14.3
24				9,999.9	8.5
25					5.0
26					2.9
27					1.6
28					0.9
29					0.5
30					0.3
31					0.1
32					0.1
					9,999.8

and 20; and for $N = 10,000$ (the total number of trials or cases). The general term then becomes

$$(1.5)^{-k} \cdot \frac{(k + X - 1)!}{(X!)(k - 1)!} \cdot (1/3)^X \cdot (10,000)$$

The distributions are presented graphically in Figure II.3: note how the distributions become less skewed and less leptokurtic as k is increased.

In practice, the negative binomial distribution will arise under conditions that may be thought of as an extension of those which give rise to

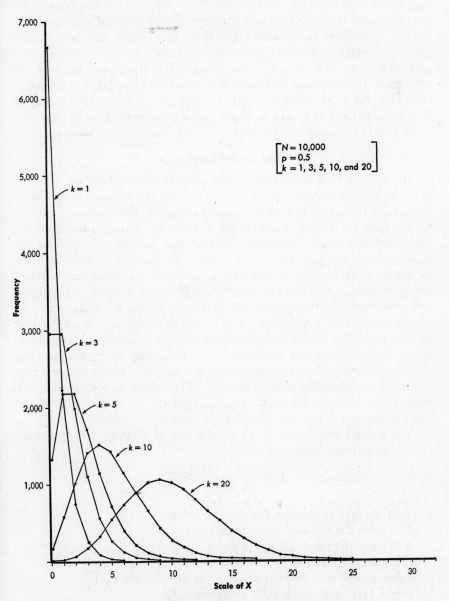

$$\begin{bmatrix} N = 10,000 \\ p = 0.5 \\ k = 1, 3, 5, 10, \text{ and } 20 \end{bmatrix}$$

Figure II.3. ILLUSTRATIONS OF NEGATIVE BINOMIAL DISTRIBUTIONS

(reg. binomial)

N.B.

the Poisson distribution. It is, in essence, a compound of a number of Poisson distributions with varying values of m. In studies of accidents and absences in industry, for instance, the value of m for the Poisson distribution may be considered as a measure of an individual's proneness or liability to accidents or absences, and this will normally vary widely from person to person. Similarly, in studies of errors made by school children in various tests, proneness to error varies widely from child to child. In such cases, the frequency distribution of number of accidents, absences, or errors for the total group is really a compound of a number of Poisson distributions, and it has been found that such distributions do resemble quite closely the negative binomial.

The Normal Distribution

It will have been noted that for the positive binomial the variance can never be greater than the mean, for the Poisson the variance must always be equal to the mean, and for the negative binomial the variance can never be less than the mean. Further, the Poisson and negative binomial distributions are always positively skewed and leptokurtic, whereas the positive binomial may vary from positive to negative in both of these measures. For the *normal distribution*, however, the mean and variance are quite independent and the distribution is always perfectly symmetrical and mesokurtic (neither peaked nor flattened, so that $K_3 = K_4 = 0$). Of all the theoretical distributions it is by far the most important for continuous variation, having properties that make it peculiarly well suited for use in both applied and theoretical statistics. For an amazingly large number of distributions encountered in practice, too, we find a form that is normal or reasonably close to normal. The almost universal use of this distribution has, unfortunately, long delayed the development of theory and practice in relation to other possible types of distributions.

The normal population distribution is one of a family of exponential curves, its formula being

height for normal curve

$$Y = \frac{N}{\sigma\sqrt{2\pi}}\, e^{-\frac{(X-\xi)^2}{2\sigma^2}}$$

a simplified (or derived) form → $y \leq (constant) e^{-x^2}$

where X denotes any one of the abscissa values
   Y denotes the ordinate for a given value of X
   N denotes the total number of cases
   ξ denotes the mean of the distribution (K_1)
   σ denotes the standard deviation of the distribution ($\sqrt{K_2}$)
   $\pi = 3.1416$, and $e = 2.7183$, approximately.

Note that, given the values of ξ and σ, the formula is completely determined for any X and N. Consequently the form of the normal distribution depends only upon the values of the parameters ξ and σ. It is a single

Positive Binomial: the variance can never be greater than the mean
Poisson: variance must always equal the mean
Negative Binomial: the variance can never be less than the mean.

humped distribution and is perfectly symmetrical about the mean, so that the mean, median, and mode are identically equal in value. The curve approaches the X axis asymptotically as X increases without limit $(-\infty \leqslant X \leqslant +\infty)$, but so rapidly that very few cases occur outside the limits $X \pm 3\sigma$.

The standard form of the normal curve is illustrated in Figure II.4.

It was through the formula for the positive binomial that De Moivre, in 1733, originally obtained the formula for the normal curve. He was interested in the case in which k is very large and for which the labor of expanding $(p + q)^k$ is prohibitive. He thought of his result as only a useful approximation to the positive binomial, never dreaming that the "approximation" was destined to become so important in its own right. Gauss derived the same formula some seventy years later, in connection with his work on the errors of observation in astronomy. Basically, his problem was to determine what theoretical distribution of errors would make the mean of a set of observations the best estimate of the true value to be measured (e.g. the true position of a star, in astronomy). Gauss assumed that any deviation from the true value, i.e. in his case any error of observation, would arise from the operation of a very large number of very small independent causes, each of which would produce a small disturbance. If these small disturbances are assumed to be equal, and positive and negative values equally likely, then the derivation of the distribution of the resulting errors proceeds in much the same fashion as that used by De Moivre—beginning with the positive binomial and allowing the exponent to increase without limit.‖ Gauss's derivation became so widely known that the normal curve is often called the *Gaussian distribution* or the *law of errors:* De Moivre's earlier derivation was completely overlooked, until Karl Pearson drew attention to it in 1924 (*Biometrika*, XVI).

Tables of the normal probability curve, giving ordinate and area values, have made it possible to use the normal distribution without the effort of evaluating the terms or integrals for each situation that arises. Laplace suggested as early as 1783 that such tables be prepared, and the first was published by Kramp in 1799. The best known and most widely used set today is the one published by Karl Pearson in Part I of *Tables for Statisticians and Biometricians*. We give in Appendix A an abbreviated form of the table of areas for the standard normal distribution, which is sufficient for most practical purposes, in the form of the area from the lower limit of the curve to any value of $z \geqslant 0$, for values of z, by intervals of 0.01, from 0.00 to 3.99. (The ordinate values [Y] are so seldom used that we deemed it unnecessary to present them.) Note that, since the normal curve is

‖ In deriving the formulae for a family of distributions, of which the normal is but one member, Karl Pearson used a different approach, beginning with the differential equation: $\dfrac{dy}{dx} = \dfrac{(d-x)y}{a + bx + cx^2}$.

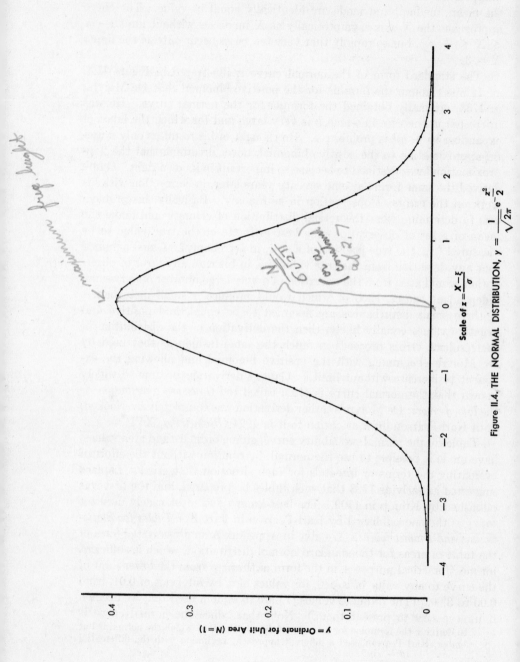

Figure II.4. THE NORMAL DISTRIBUTION, $y = \dfrac{1}{\sqrt{2\pi}} e^{-\frac{z^2}{2}}$

Scale of $z = \dfrac{X - \xi}{\sigma}$

y = Ordinate for Unit Area ($N = 1$)

freq. height

maximum

$\dfrac{N}{\sigma\sqrt{2\pi}}$

(average α & general 2.7)

perfectly symmetrical, the values for the other half of the distribution can be secured by simple subtraction from unity.#

To illustrate the use of the table of areas given in Appendix A, and also how closely the normal approximates to the other distributions although the variation is essentially discontinuous, we show in Table II.19 the calculation of the expected normal distribution frequencies for the case of a Poisson distribution where $m = 10$ and $N = 10,000$. The values of X and the corresponding Poisson frequencies are given in the first two columns. If the normal distribution is to be used, we must assume that the variation is continuous: this is equivalent to the assumption that each of the X-values represents the mid-point of an interval extending from half a unit below to half a unit above the tabled X-value. Thus, for $X = 4$, the corresponding interval is 3.5–4.5, and so on for the remaining values of X. The assumed upper and lower limits of the intervals, denoted by X', are shown in the third column of Table II.19. But, in order to enter the table in Appendix A, these X'-values must be transformed as follows:

$$z = \frac{X' - \xi}{\sigma}$$

where $\xi = 10$ and $\sigma = \sqrt{10}$. The corresponding z-values are given in the fourth column. Then, from the table in Appendix A, the area under the normal curve below each z-value is determined, for $N = 1$, as shown in the fifth column (using simple linear interpolation between the tabled values). Subtraction of adjacent values of column five yields the unit area in each interval shown in column six: multiplying each of these by $N = 10,000$ gives the normal distribution frequencies shown in the last column.

The normal frequencies do not total 10,000, but only 9,995.5, since we have ignored the portion of the normal curve below $X' = -0.5$, in amount equivalent to the missing 4.5 cases. Except for this discrepancy, the Poisson and normal frequencies, given in the second and in the final columns, agree remarkably well. The two distributions are presented graphically in Figure II.5, where the missing portion of the normal curve is indicated in the lower left corner (below $X = 0$). Note that even for $m = 10$ the Poisson distribution is still slightly skewed, but as regards kurtosis is practically indistinguishable from the normal. Obviously, however, we could in such a situation assume that our data are normally distributed, although in fact they are not, without any serious loss or distortion of the data. The fit, while far from perfect, is certainly good enough for all practical purposes.

The popularity and wide use of the normal distribution did not, however, arise mainly from the fact that it was the limiting form of such discrete distributions. As we indicated earlier, the astronomers found that

Illustrations of the use of these tables may be found in Johnson and Jackson, *op. cit.*

their distributions of errors of observation were of this single-humped and symmetrical form. Further, when measures and other observations of humans were collected—by Quetelet, Galton, and others—it was found that trait after trait was distributed in a form amazingly similar to the normal. Most of these early researchers, amazed and somewhat awed by this finding, concluded that the normal curve was the ideal to which all distributions would or should correspond if we only measured or observed properly. In this they were wrong, as we now know, but so striking was this apparent uniformity and conformity that one can easily understand why Galton was moved to comment that the normal "law," as he described it, "would have been personified by the Greeks and deified, if they had known of it. . . . It is the supreme law of Unreason." Even modern researchers, in spite of the fact that they know it is probably easier to find the proverbial needle in a haystack than to discover a variate for which

TABLE II.19

COMPARISON OF NORMAL AND POISSON DISTRIBUTIONS

$N = 10,000, \ m = \xi = \sigma^2 = 10$

X	POISSON FREQUENCY	ASSUMED INTERVAL LIMITS (X')	$z = \dfrac{X' - \xi}{\sigma}$	UNIT AREA BELOW z	UNIT AREA IN INTERVAL	NORMAL FREQUENCY
0	0.5	−0.5	−3.320	.00045		
					.00088	8.8
1	4.5	0.5	−3.004	.00133		
					.00226	22.6
2	22.7	1.5	−2.688	.00359		
					.00526	52.6
3	75.7	2.5	−2.372	.00885		
					.01109	110.9
4	189.2	3.5	−2.055	.01994		
					.02108	210.8
5	378.3	4.5	−1.739	.04102		
					.03635	363.5
6	630.5	5.5	−1.423	.07737		
					.05678	567.8
7	900.8	6.5	−1.107	.13415		
					.08032	803.2
8	1,126.0	7.5	−0.791	.21447		
					.10328	1,032.8
9	1,251.1	8.5	−0.474	.31775		
					.11948	1,194.8
10	1,251.1	9.5	−0.158	.43723		
					.12554	1,255.4
11	1,137.4	10.5	0.158	.56277		
					.11948	1,194.8
12	947.8	11.5	0.474	.68225		
					.10328	1,032.8
13	729.1	12.5	0.791	.78553		
					.08032	803.2

(Continued on following page)

TABLE II.19 Cont'd.

COMPARISON OF NORMAL AND POISSON DISTRIBUTIONS

$$N = 10,000, \ m = \xi = \sigma^2 = 10$$

X	POISSON FREQUENCY	ASSUMED INTERVAL LIMITS (X')	$z = \dfrac{X' - \xi}{\sigma}$	UNIT AREA BELOW z	UNIT AREA IN INTERVAL	NORMAL FREQUENCY
		13.5	1.107	.86585		
14	520.8				.05678	567.8
		14.5	1.423	.92263		
15	347.2				.03635	363.5
		15.5	1.739	.95898		
16	217.0				.02108	210.8
		16.5	2.055	.98006		
17	127.6				.01109	110.9
		17.5	2.372	.99115		
18	70.9				.00526	52.6
		18.5	2.688	.99641		
19	37.3				.00226	22.6
		19.5	3.004	.99867		
20	18.7				.00088	8.8
		20.5	3.320	.99955		
21	8.9				.00031	3.1
		21.5	3.637	.99986		
22	4.0				.00010	1.0
		22.5	3.953	.99996		
23	1.8				.00003	0.3
		23.5	4.269	.99999		
24	0.7				.00001	0.1
		24.5	4.585	1.00000		
25	0.3				—	
		25.5	4.902	—		
26	0.1				—	
Total	10,000.0	—	—	—	.99955	9,995.5

the distribution is perfectly normal, are upon occasion overawed by the apparent universality of this "law" and guilty of the crime of worshipping at its altar. But the equation of the normal distribution has proven to be so amenable to mathematical manipulation that they should perhaps be forgiven.

Researchers in education came closest to doing what Galton claimed the Greeks would have done, partly because of the almost incalculable influence of Galton on the development of educational statistics in America. For many generations in education the normal distribution has been enthroned and has held supreme sway: so much so, in fact, that any observed distribution that did not conform to the law was immediately suspect. Not only the physical but also the mental measurements of children yielded distributions that were surprisingly normal in form.** We show in Table

** Educationists have recognized, belatedly, that this occurred in the case of mental measurements because of the manner in which the tests and examinations were constructed, and probably for no other reason.

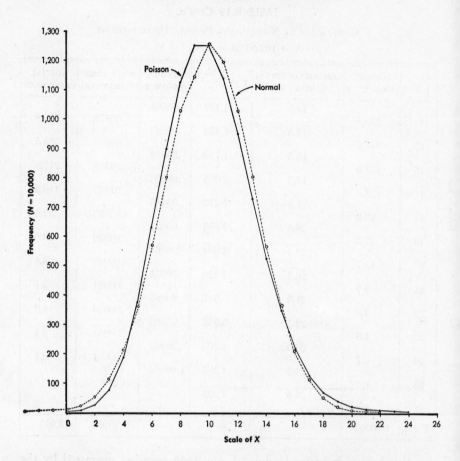

Figure II.5. POISSON (m = 10) AND CORRESPONDING NORMAL DISTRIBUTION ($\xi = \sigma^2 = m$)

II.20 an example of the form of distribution of test scores commonly observed in educational research and the corresponding expected frequencies obtained from the theoretical normal distribution. The correspondence between the observed and the expected frequencies is amazing—until we remember that this test (and others like it) was so constructed that the appearance of a single-humped and roughly symmetrical distribution of scores was inevitable. This leaves unanswered—and unanswerable—the question of the form in which the trait or ability is really distributed. Nevertheless, for this test and this situation we obviously can assume, for all practical purposes, that the distribution is normal in form.

The frequencies in the last column are those obtained for the negative binomial for which $k_1 = 9.0224$ and $k_2 = 12.73644$: the score scale must be transformed in this case, by subtracting the obtained score from 20, in

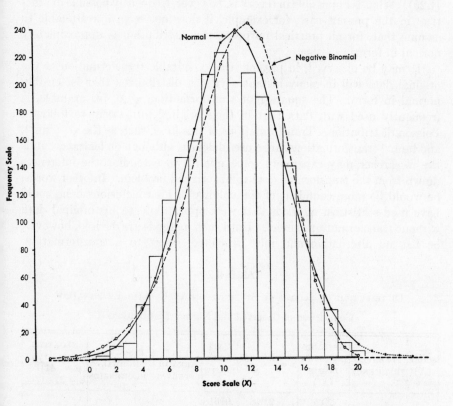

Figure II.6. COMPARISON OF OBSERVED DISTRIBUTION OF SCORES ON AN ENGLISH
EXAMINATION AND FITTED NORMAL AND NEGATIVE BINOMIAL DISTRIBUTIONS

order to secure a positive value for k_3 (as required for any negative binomial). Figure II.6 shows a histogram of the observed frequencies and
superimposed on it two frequency polygons, plotted from the expected
normal and negative binomial frequencies. Although either theoretical distribution yields a fairly good fit, inspection indicates that the normal is
probably the better of the two.

From a theoretical point of view, neither of these models can, strictly
speaking, be used. The actual scores, by virtue of the manner in which
the test was constructed and scored, cannot be less than zero nor greater
than 20, whereas the normal distribution varies without limit in both
directions and the negative binomial without limit to the left. The portions
of the theoretical distributions outside the possible range of scores are
shown in Figure II.6: these extensions account for the discrepancy between
observed total frequency ($N = 2{,}145$) and the total for the expected fre-

quencies (normal, $N = 2{,}135.4$, negative binomial, $2{,}137.8$—see Table II.20). What is impossible in theory is, however, frequently possible in practice: in the present case, for example, it does not seem unreasonable to assume that, for all practical purposes, the distribution is approximately normal in form.

It may be observed, in passing, that a suitable transformation of the original data will in many instances yield a distribution that is sensibly normal in form. The square root transformation, $\sqrt{X}$, for example, is frequently used with data that in their original form seem to follow a Poisson distribution. Transformations of this kind, such as the $\sqrt{}$, $\sin^{-1}$, and $\tanh^{-1}$ transformations, are a useful device, although on logical grounds the researcher may experience some qualms in extending the inferences drawn from the transformed data to his original problem. In other words, he would be more confident of the validity of his conclusions if he could have used statistical methods that were appropriate to his original data without transformation thereof. Until such methods are devised, however, he has no alternative and must, perforce, resort to a transformation.

TABLE II.20

DISTRIBUTION OF SCORES OF STUDENTS ON AN ENGLISH EXAMINATION

Comparison of Observed and Normal Distributions

SCORE (X)	OBSERVED FREQUENCY	ASSUMED INTERVAL LIMITS (X')	$z = \dfrac{X' - M}{S}$	UNIT AREA BELOW z	UNIT AREA IN INTERVAL	EXPECTED NORMAL FREQUENCIES	NEGATIVE BINOMIAL $p = .41165$ $k = 21.91765$
		20.5	2.668	.99618			
20	4				.00465	10.0	1.1
		19.5	2.388	.99153			
19	10				.00905	19.4	7.2
		18.5	2.108	.98248			
18	34				.01626	34.9	24.0
		17.5	1.828	.96622			
17	88				.02715	58.2	55.7
		16.5	1.547	.93907			
16	113				.04165	89.3	101.2
		15.5	1.267	.89742			
15	139				.05924	127.1	152.9
		14.5	0.987	.83818			
14	179				.07797	167.2	200.0
		13.5	0.707	.76021			
13	189				.09527	204.3	232.6
		12.5	0.426	.66494			
12	207				.10690	229.3	245.2
		11.5	0.146	.55804			
11	200				.11134	238.8	237.7
		10.5	−0.134	.44670			
10	222				.10726	230.1	214.3

(Continued on following page)

TABLE II.20 *Cont'd.*

DISTRIBUTION OF SCORES OF STUDENTS ON AN ENGLISH EXAMINATION

Comparison of Observed and Normal Distributions

SCORE (X)	OBSERVED FREQUENCY	ASSUMED INTERVAL LIMITS (X')	$z = \dfrac{X' - M}{S}$	UNIT AREA BELOW z	UNIT AREA IN INTERVAL	EXPECTED NORMAL FREQUENCIES	NEGATIVE BINOMINAL $p = .41165$ $k = 21.91765$
		9.5	−0.414	.33944			
9	206				.09560	205.1	181.3
		8.5	−0.694	.24384			
8	158				.07906	169.6	145.0
		7.5	−0.975	.16478			
7	146				.06004	128.8	110.4
		6.5	−1.255	.10474			
6	115				.04235	90.8	80.3
		5.5	−1.535	.06239			
5	74				.02763	59.3	56.0
		4.5	−1.815	.03476			
4	39				.01667	35.8	37.7
		3.5	−2.095	.01809			
3	11				.00934	20.0	24.5
		2.5	−2.376	.00875			
2	9				.00480	10.3	15.5
		1.5	−2.656	.00395			
1	2				.00229	4.9	9.5
		0.5	−2.936	.00166			
0	—				.00101	2.2	5.7
		−0.5	−3.216	.00065			
Total	2,145	—	—	—	.99553	2,135.4	2,137.8

$$s_1 = 23,547 \qquad\qquad S_2 = 27,306.926$$
$$s_2 = 285,797$$
$$k_1 = 10.9776 \qquad\qquad k_2 = 12.73644$$
$$S = \sqrt{k_2} = 3.5688$$
$$s_3 = 3,733,605 \qquad\qquad S_3 = 3,296.8$$
$$k_3 = -1.539$$

Readers interested in transformations suitable for use with Poisson, positive binomial, and negative binomial distributions, should consult the following paper: F. J. Anscombe, "The Transformation of Poisson, Binomial, and Negative Binomial Data," *Biometrika*, XXXV (1948), 246.

The Rectangular Distribution

In a number of problems in the social sciences, the data are in the form of ranks—either the ordinary variety using the integer numbers, or percentile ranks. In such cases the distribution will be *rectangular* in form, i.e. the frequency of occurrence of the several values is constant, being unity or greater depending on the circumstances. Moreover, several examples of continuous data (e.g. chronological age over a restricted range) are distributed in a form that is nearly rectangular, and any continuous distribution can be transformed into a rectangular form.

Such a population distribution is about the simplest it is possible to imagine, being always perfectly symmetrical and perfectly flat. Using n to denote the number of possible integer values, for instance, the measures of the first three population characteristics are *(10) as in a person's age with digits, 0-9 or 10 diff digits*

$$K_1 = \frac{n+1}{2} \; ; K_2 = \frac{n^2-1}{12} \; ; \text{and } K_3 = 0$$

but K_4 is an exceedingly complex expression in n and powers of n. Note that for indefinitely large values of n, K_1 approaches the value $\frac{n}{2}$ and K_2 the value $\frac{n^2}{12}$. Thus if we consider a distribution in the form of a rectangle with base of length l, but divided into a very large number, n, of equal elements, *(or variance)* the mean will be $\frac{l}{2}$ and the variance $\frac{l^2}{12}$.

Distribution of Statistics in Repeated Random Sampling††

We turn now to a discussion of the form in which statistics calculated from samples drawn at random from various populations distribute themselves in repeated sampling. The empirical and theoretical results presented will reveal the differences that may occur from sample to sample where the only factor operating is random selection from the population. These variations are known as *errors of sampling*, although they are not, strictly speaking, "errors" at all in terms of the layman's understanding of the word. They are probably better described as *chance deviations*.

Populations Sampled and Sampling Procedures

To illustrate samples drawn from a *positive binomial population*, we have selected tosses of ten coins simultaneously, recording for each such toss the number of heads appearing. In order to approximate as closely as possible to the rigid conditions of random sampling, we used ten undamaged dimes of roughly the same state of wear, placed them in a covered cardboard box of size sufficient to permit relatively unrestricted freedom of movement of the several coins, and for each toss shook the coins vigorously, with a twist and snap of the wrist, from one end of the box to the other exactly five times. A check was made at the end of the first two hundred tosses, by comparing observed and expected frequencies, in order to determine whether we had, in fact, set up a valid sampling procedure. The ten coins were tossed 1,000 times altogether, and the number of heads appearing on successive tosses were recorded in groups of 5. By combining adjacent

†† Students should be encouraged to secure samples of their own, thereby obtaining a better appreciation of what is meant by repeated sampling. They may toss coins, roll dice, or draw cards from one of the populations of numbered cards about to be described.

pairs of these 200 samples of size 5, we secured 100 samples of size 10, then 50 of size 20, 10 of size 100, and finally 1 of size 1,000. While this procedure does not yield independent samples in relation to size, the smaller being combined to yield the larger, this is somewhat of an advantage for the purpose of illustrating what occurs when the size of the sample is increased.

Since a *Poisson population* is hypothetical in nature and infinite in number we cannot, strictly speaking, sample directly from it. To overcome this difficulty, we set up a finite population of 1,000 small squares of cardboard, each one-half-inch square, with a number from 0 to 11 typed on each card, and then sampled from this "population" with replacement. The population represented by the frequencies of the numbers was as close as possible to the Poisson population for which $m = 3.5$. The small cards were placed in a fair-sized box, the box was shaken vigorously, opened, and one card extracted without looking at the cards. The number appearing on the card was then recorded, the card replaced, the box closed, and the procedure repeated for each draw. A check at the end of the first 1,000 draws, by comparing observed and expected frequencies, indicated that the conditions of repeated random sampling were well satisfied. In all, 3,000 draws were made, and the observations were recorded in groups of 10 to yield 300 samples of size 10. These were later combined, in groups of five, to yield 60 samples of size 50.

For a *normal population*, we compromised by setting up a finite population with discontinuous variation—adequate, although a far cry from the strict mathematical requirements. We used 1,611 cardboard squares, bearing one of the numbers from 1 to 25 on each, with frequency of occurrence so arranged that the population distribution was reasonably normal in form. The population mean was 13, and the population standard deviation was 3.5622. Samples were drawn in much the same fashion as for the Poisson population, i.e. sampling with replacement with a check on the validity of the procedure made for the first set of 1,000 cards drawn. Altogether 5,000 cards were drawn, yielding 500 samples of size 10, 250 samples of size 20, and 100 samples of size 50.

For a *rectangular population* we adopted a similar procedure, using cards drawn from a box rather than, for instance, rolls of a die. The population consisted of a set of 1,000 cards with the numbers from 0 to 19, both inclusive, typed on them (exactly 50 cards for each of the possible 20 numbers). The population measures had the following values: $K_1 = 9.5$; $K_2 = 33.25$; $K_3 = 0$; and $K_4 = -1,333.325$. In all, 2,000 cards were drawn (again with replacement), yielding 200 samples of size 10 and 40 of size 50.

Distribution of Means of Samples
(normal, circular, skewed, etc.)

Whatever the shape of the population, the sample distribution form will be the same as that of the parent—save for chance deviations—in any sample drawn at random from it. In most researches, however, we are only indirectly interested in the shape of the sample distribution, i.e. we may wish only to check or to determine the type of population from which it was drawn. Our prime interest is generally in certain statistics calculated from the sample data and the manner in which they are distributed in repeated random sampling. In this section we will consider the distribution of the mean in repeated random sampling from the various populations discussed in the preceding section. The actual sampling results secured through the procedures explained earlier will be used to illustrate the concepts and theoretical results introduced.

For each of the hundreds of actual samples referred to earlier, we calculated the mean. When presented in tabular or graphical form, these provide an empirical demonstration of the distribution of means in repeated sampling. For each such distribution, we can again calculate measures of central position, variability, skewness, and kurtosis. The second of these is of particular importance in sampling theory: the standard deviation (the square root of the variance) of the distribution of the statistic measures the magnitude, on the average, of the variation of that statistic when the only factor operating is the random errors of sampling. Accordingly, this standard deviation is called the *standard error of sampling* of the statistic concerned.

To consider the general case first, since it enables us to anticipate the specific finding for samples drawn from the various populations to be considered, let us denote by K_1 the mean of the population and by K_2 its variance. In general, i.e. for samples drawn from any type of population, the distribution of means secured in repeated random sampling will, as the number of samples increases without limit, have a mean of K_1 and a standard deviation of $\sqrt{K_2/N}$, where N is the size of the sample. The standard error of the mean is, therefore, a function of the population standard deviation and of the size of the sample: it varies directly with the square root of the population variance and inversely with the square root of the sample size. This finding is, of course, in accord with what common sense, or experience, would lead us to expect, viz. that in repeated random sampling the variation in means will be greater for a more variable population and will steadily decrease in magnitude as the size of the sample is increased. In regard to skewness and kurtosis of the distribution of means, by virtue of the central limit theorem we may state that the mean of N independent random variables, no matter what form their distribution may take, tends to the normal form of distribution when N becomes large. As a matter of fact, the normal distribution is the limiting form of the sampling distributions of a large number of statistics, as we shall see in subsequent sections. And for all practical purposes, fortunately, the sampling distributions are approximately normal in form even for moderate values of N.

N is a constant

To summarize the theory of the sampling distribution of means, we may state that the distribution of means of samples of size N drawn‡‡

(1) from the binomial $(p + q)^k$ is the binomial $(p + q)^{Nk}$, with an interval *& dist. of means of samples of size N* of $\frac{1}{N}$ instead of unity;

(2) from the Poisson $\frac{e^{-m}\, m^X}{X!}$ is the Poisson $\frac{e^{-Nm}(Nm)^X}{X!}$ with an interval of $\frac{1}{N}$;

(3) from the normal distribution of mean ξ and standard deviation σ is the normal distribution of mean ξ and standard deviation $\frac{\sigma}{\sqrt{N}}$;

(4) from a rectangular distribution is the symmetrical but, for small samples, somewhat platykurtic distribution of mean $\frac{n+1}{2}$ and standard deviation $\sqrt{\frac{n^2-1}{12N}}$.

Students should observe that, in general, the means tend to have the same form of distribution as occurs in the population from which the samples concerned were drawn. The measures of the characteristics of the distribution of means are as given in the following table:

CUMULANTS OF DISTRIBUTION OF MEANS	BINOMIAL	POISSON	NORMAL	RECTANGULAR
κ_1 (mean)	kp	m	ξ	$\frac{n+1}{2}$
κ_2 (variance)	$\frac{kpq}{N}$	$\frac{m}{N}$	$\frac{\sigma^2}{N}$	$\frac{n^2-1}{12N}$
κ_3 (higher orders of k)	$\frac{kpq\,(q-p)}{N^2}$	$\frac{m}{N^2}$	0	0
κ_4	$\frac{kpq\,(1-6pq)}{N^3}$	$\frac{m}{N^3}$	0	Order of $\frac{1}{N^3}$

For the positive binomial population for which we had samples, $k = 10$ and $p = q = \frac{1}{2}$; for the Poisson population $m = 3.5$; for the normal population $\xi = 13$ and $\sigma = 3.5622$; and for the rectangular population $n = 20$. Knowing these quantities, the values of the cumulants for any given sample size can be readily determined from the above table. Students will be able to prove, for instance, that the sampling distribution of means tends to become mesokurtic more quickly than symmetrical as the size of the sample is increased. For their guidance, they may wish to work out the formulae

‡‡ See, for instance, Maurice G. Kendall, *The Advanced Theory of Statistics* (London: Charles Griffin and Company, 1947), Vol. 1.

for the expected values of the measures of skewness and kurtosis for the distribution of means of samples from the binomial and Poisson populations.

To illustrate the form of sampling distribution, and to show the agreement between observed and expected values of the first two cumulants, we present in the following set of tables, Tables II.21 A–D, the results secured for the means of the samples drawn from the four populations discussed above. In each case, the main body of the table gives the observed frequencies; the last four rows show the observed and expected means and variances of these distributions (the observed values were calculated from the original ungrouped data). The agreement between the two sets of the latter is so good that these data yield an impressive empirical verification of the theoretical results stated above without proof. Observation of the distributions indicates, also, that they do in fact tend to become symmetrical and mesokurtic as the sample size is increased.

Two special points are of interest in connection with the samples drawn

TABLE II.21

DISTRIBUTIONS OF MEANS IN REPEATED RANDOM SAMPLING

A: BINOMIAL POPULATION (# OF HEADS)					B: POISSON POPULATION		
Class Interval	Sample Size				Class Interval	Sample Size	
	5	10	20	100		10	50
6.65–6.84	1				5.60–5.79	1	
6.45–6.64	2				5.40–5.59		
6.25–6.44	2				5.20–5.39	1	
6.05–6.24	5				5.00–5.19	3	
5.85–6.04	7	3	1		4.80–4.99	1	
5.65–5.84	10	6	2		4.60–4.79	7	
5.45–5.64	20	6	1		4.40–4.59	12	
5.25–5.44	17	14	8	1	4.20–4.39	23	
5.05–5.24	27	16	16	2	4.00–4.19	27	2
4.85–5.04	22	19	7	4	3.80–3.99	28	8
4.65–4.84	30	17	6	3	3.60–3.79	34	11
4.45–4.64	14	7	3		3.40–3.59	38	21
4.25–4.44	12	3	4		3.20–3.39	38	10
4.05–4.24	10	6	2		3.00–3.19	31	6
3.85–4.04	8	2			2.80–2.99	19	2
3.65–3.84	5	1			2.60–2.79	17	
3.45–3.64	5				2.40–2.59	11	
3.25–3.44					2.20–2.39	6	
3.05–3.24	2				2.00–2.19	3	
2.85–3.04	1						
Total	200	100	50	10	Total	300	60
Expected Mean	5.000	5.000	5.000	5.000	Expected Mean	3.500	3.500
Observed Mean	4.998	4.998	4.998	4.998	Observed Mean	3.507	3.507
Exp. Variance	0.500	0.250	0.125	0.025	Exp. Variance	0.350	0.0700
Obs. Variance	0.470	0.223	0.154	0.033	Obs. Variance	0.394	0.0663

TABLE II.21

DISTRIBUTIONS OF MEANS IN REPEATED RANDOM SAMPLING (CONT'D.)

C: NORMAL POPULATION

Class Interval	Sample Size		
	10	20	50
16.80–17.09	1		
16.50–16.79	2		
16.20–16.49			
15.90–16.19	2		
15.60–15.89	5	1	
15.30–15.59	4	1	
15.00–15.29	10	3	
14.70–14.99	17	1	
14.40–14.69	25	6	
14.10–14.39	29	12	2
13.80–14.09	53	17	5
13.50–13.79	42	37	16
13.20–13.49	48	32	21
12.90–13.19	51	33	18
12.60–12.89	44	40	23
12.30–12.59	44	30	9
12.00–12.29	47	21	6
11.70–11.99	26	13	
11.40–11.69	24	2	
11.10–11.39	15	1	
10.80–11.09	7		
10.50–10.79	2		
10.20–10.49	1		
9.90–10.19			
9.60– 9.89	1		
Total	500	250	100
Expected Mean	13.00	13.00	13.00
Observed Mean	13.09	13.09	13.09
Exp. Variance	1.269	0.634	0.254
Obs. Variance	1.253	0.596	0.231

D: RECTANGULAR POPULATION

Class Interval	Sample Size	
	10	50
15.00–15.39	1	
14.60–14.99	1	
14.20–14.59		
13.80–14.19		
13.40–13.79	1	
13.00–13.39		
12.60–12.99	5	
12.20–12.59	8	
11.80–12.19	7	
11.40–11.79	12	1
11.00–11.39	15	3
10.60–10.99	12	1
10.20–10.59	14	6
9.80–10.19	19	6
9.40– 9.79	18	9
9.00– 9.39	20	7
8.60– 8.99	13	
8.20– 8.59	10	2
7.80– 8.19	8	2
7.40– 7.79	11	3
7.00– 7.39	9	
6.60– 6.99	5	
6.20– 6.59	6	
5.80– 6.19	3	
5.40– 5.79	1	
5.00– 5.39		
4.60– 4.99	1	
Total	200	40
Expected Mean	9.50	9.50
Observed Mean	9.62	9.62
Exp. Variance	3.325	0.665
Obs. Variance	3.383	1.020

from the binomial population. First, in some situations the researcher may be interested in the *proportion*, p, rather than the *number* of successes (heads). However, since the proportion is secured from the number by dividing by N, where N is the number of cases upon which p is based, it is obvious that the sampling distribution will be altered only in central position and variability. The expected mean of the sampling distribution of proportions must, of course, be the value of the population p, and the expected variance of that distribution will be pq/N. In a similar fashion, the sampling distribution of *percentages* is linked to that of proportions by the factor of 100. Thus the expected mean will be $P = 100p$ and the expected variance will be PQ/N, where N is the number of cases upon which P is based.

Distribution of Variances of Samples

For each of the samples from each of the populations referred to above, we calculated the value of the variance. The distributions for samples of various size have been shown in Tables II.22 A–D. For any population, the general formulae for the expected mean and variance of the sampling distribution of variances are, using the original population measures:

Expected mean variance $= K_2$

Expected variance of variances $= \dfrac{K_4}{N} + \dfrac{2K_2^2}{N-1}$

Substituting in these formulae, for each population and sample size in turn, yields the expected values shown in the rows at the bottom of each part of

TABLE II.22

DISTRIBUTION OF VARIANCES IN REPEATED RANDOM SAMPLING

A: BINOMIAL POPULATION					B: POISSON POPULATION		
Class Interval	Sample Size				Class Interval	Sample Size	
	5	10	20	100		10	50
10.13–10.62	1				10.00–10.49	1	
9.63–10.12	1				9.50– 9.99		
9.13– 9.62	1				9.00– 9.49	3	
8.63– 9.12					8.50– 8.99		
8.13– 8.62		1			8.00– 8.49	1	
7.63– 8.12	2				7.50– 7.99	2	
7.13– 7.62	2				7.00– 7.49	3	
6.63– 7.12	4				6.50– 6.99	4	
6.13– 6.62	1	1			6.00– 6.49	8	
5.63– 6.12	3	1			5.50– 5.99	12	1
5.13– 5.62	2				5.00– 5.49	20	2
4.63– 5.12	9	3	1		4.50– 4.99	21	5
4.13– 4.62	7	4			4.00– 4.49	29	9
3.63– 4.12	17	5	2		3.50– 3.99	18	14
3.13– 3.62	15	14	6		3.00– 3.49	34	10
2.63– 3.12	19	9	16	3	2.50– 2.99	36	11
2.13– 2.62	22	20	8	5	2.00– 2.49	43	8
1.63– 2.12	27	17	7	2	1.50– 1.99	35	
1.13– 1.62	23	17	10		1.00– 1.49	19	
0.63– 1.12	30	8			0.50– 0.99	11	
0.13– 0.62	14						
Total	200	100	50	10	Total	300	60
Expected Mean	2.50	2.50	2.50	2.50	Expected Mean	3.500	3.500
Observed Mean	2.59	2.58	2.51	2.53	Observed Mean	3.402	3.518
Exp. Variance	2.875	1.264	0.595	0.114	Exp. Variance	3.072	0.570
Obs. Variance	3.55	1.59	0.63	0.17	Obs. Variance	2.975	0.714

TABLE II.22

DISTRIBUTION OF VARIANCES IN REPEATED RANDOM SAMPLING (CONT'D.)

C: NORMAL POPULATION				D: RECTANGULAR POPULATION		
Class Interval	Sample Size			Class Interval	Sample Size	
	10	20	50		10	50
40–41.99	1			60–61.99	2	
38–39.99				58–59.99	1	
36–37.99	1			56–57.99		
34–35.99				54–55.99	2	
32–33.99				52–53.99	2	
30–31.99	3			50–51.99	5	
28–29.99	3			48–49.99	6	
26–27.99	5			46–47.99	7	
24–25.99	9	3		44–45.99	7	
22–23.99	11	4		42–43.99	16	2
20–21.99	16	9		40–41.99	10	1
18–19.99	33	10	2	38–39.99	10	4
16–17.99	49	16	9	36–37.99	11	7
14–15.99	37	34	14	34–35.99	22	3
12–13.99	62	44	26	32–33.99	20	8
10–11.99	72	56	32	30–31.99	6	4
8– 9.99	75	38	13	28–29.99	15	6
6– 7.99	63	26	3	26–27.99	10	4
4– 5.99	44	9	1	24–25.99	11	1
2– 3.99	15	1		22–23.99	10	
0– 1.99	1			20–21.99	10	
				18–19.99	3	
Total	500	250	100	16–17.99	3	
				14–15.99	5	
Expected Mean	12.69	12.69	12.69	12–13.99	4	
Observed Mean	12.37	12.38	12.37	10–11.99	1	
Exp. Variance	35.78	16.95	6.57	8– 9.99	1	
Obs. Variance	35.73	17.65	6.35			
				Total	200	40
				Expected Mean	33.25	33.25
				Observed Mean	33.75	33.42
				Exp. Variance	112.35	18.46
				Obs. Variance	109.82	20.81

Table II.22: again, the observed values are in reasonably close agreement. Note the spread of the variances decreases fast as the size of the sample is increased, but that the distribution tends to be quite skewed and lepto-kurtic for small samples, although this obviously becomes less pronounced as the size of the sample is increased. It seems evident that the distribution of the variance will approach the normal in form as the sample size becomes large.

The theoretical sampling distribution of the variance, v, is known for samples drawn from a normal population. For samples of size N from a normal population of standard deviation σ, the quantity $\dfrac{(N-1)v}{\sigma^2}$ is distributed as the statistic χ^2 (pronounced chi-square). The distribution of chi-square is of the form

[handwritten: for $n > 30$, the χ^2 distrib. becomes more like the normal]

[handwritten: constant]

$$p(\chi^2) = \frac{1}{2^{\frac{N-1}{2}}\ \overline{\left|\ \frac{N-1}{2}\right.}}(\chi^2)^{\frac{N-1}{2}-1}\exp\left(-\frac{\chi^2}{2}\right)$$

(where Γ denotes the gamma function). *[handwritten: generalizes factorial to include fractional pos. values]*
This distribution function has been evaluated and tables prepared, of which the table by Fisher and Yates of Appendix B is a well-known example. We may note in passing that the expected mean value of χ^2 in repeated random sampling is $(N-1)$ and of its variance is $2(N-1)$. Also, the skewness of the distribution of the variance will be of order $\dfrac{8}{N-1}$ and the kurtosis of order $\dfrac{12}{N-1}$, so that for even moderately large samples the distribution will be reasonably normal in form.

Except for samples from the rectangular population, for which the variance distribution is markedly different for small samples, the χ^2 distribution yields a fair approximation for the distribution of variances in repeated random sampling from the other populations previously considered. Using the formula $\chi^2 = \dfrac{(N-1)(v)}{\sigma^2}$ and the tables of χ^2, we can obtain the comparison of observed and expected frequencies given in Table II.23 (using for values of σ^2 the quantities 12.689 for the normal, 2.5 for the binomial, 3.5 for the Poisson, and 33.25 for the rectangular population). Our sampling results do, therefore, yield empirical evidence that even for variates far from normally distributed the variance in repeated random sampling will have a distribution form resembling that of χ^2.

Standard Errors of Other Statistics

Not very much is known about the sampling distributions of many of the commonly-used statistics, even for samples from a normal population. Some of the distributions appear to be most peculiar and more or less unmanageable: unlike the statistics considered earlier, some of them may not have a limiting form of distribution as the size of the sample is increased, and even if a limiting form does exist it may not be normal in form. The distribution of the range (difference between the largest and smallest values in the sample), for instance, departs steadily *from* the normal form as the size of the sample is increased.§§

§§ Readers interested in the distribution of the range should consult the papers by E. S. Pearson and H. O. Hartley, published in *Biometrika* in 1942 and 1943, and L. H. C. Tippett's paper in the same publication in 1925. Note that for samples from the same population, the range increases with the sample size—an inconvenient characteristic.

[handwritten: $\chi^2 = \sum \dfrac{(S_0 - S_f)^2}{S_f}$ as a special form of $\chi^2 = \dfrac{\sum_{i=1}^{m} X_i^2}{\sigma^2}$ m = degrees of freedom]

TABLE II.23

COMPARISON OF EXPECTED AND OBSERVED FREQUENCY OF OCCURRENCE OF VARIANCES IN REPEATED RANDOM SAMPLING FROM A NORMAL, POSITIVE BINOMIAL, POISSON, AND RECTANGULAR POPULATION

Expected (χ^2)	χ^2	4.168	6.393	8.343	14.684	16.919	21.666
	Percentage $\geq \chi^2$	90	70	50	10	5	1
Observed (Normal)	V	5.876	9.013	11.763	20.703	23.854	30.547
	Percentage $\geq V$	88.2	66	48.2	8.6	4.4	0.9
Observed (Positive Binomial)	V	1.158	1.776	2.318	4.079	4.700	6.018
	Percentage $\geq V$	92	71	50	11	6	2
Observed (Poisson)	V	1.621	2.486	3.245	5.710	6.580	8.426
	Percentage $\geq V$	86.00	64.67	45.33	10.33	4.33	1.33
Observed (Rectangular)	V	15.398	23.988	30.822	54.249	62.505	80.043
	Percentage $\geq V$	95	81.5	61.5	2.5	0	0

The formulae for the standard errors given below apply *only to large samples drawn from a normal population*. They are, therefore, approxi-

STATISTIC	STANDARD ERROR
Median	$1.25 \times \dfrac{\sigma}{\sqrt{N}}$
Quartiles	$1.36 \times \dfrac{\sigma}{\sqrt{N}}$
Deciles 4, 6	$1.27 \times \dfrac{\sigma}{\sqrt{N}}$
3, 7	$1.32 \times \dfrac{\sigma}{\sqrt{N}}$
2, 8	$1.43 \times \dfrac{\sigma}{\sqrt{N}}$
1, 9	$1.71 \times \dfrac{\sigma}{\sqrt{N}}$
Standard deviation	$\dfrac{\sigma}{\sqrt{2N}}$
Semi-interquartile range	$0.787 \dfrac{\sigma}{\sqrt{N}}$
Skewness	$\dfrac{6}{N}$
Kurtosis	$\dfrac{24}{N}$

mations of limited value, but at least they do indicate something of the magnitude of the sampling variation involved. Partly because of the intractability of their sampling distributions, they are not used very often in sampling theory and tests of significance.

Inapplicability of the Classical or Large-Sample Theory in Many Practical Problems

Owing partly to the influence of Gauss and other astronomers who were concerned only with measurements distributed more or less in the normal form, and partly to the influence of Quetelet, Galton, and others who dealt only with very large samples, practically all of the early work on sampling theory and tests of significance was based on the assumptions of normal variation and large samples. The formulae for the standard errors, subject to these assumptions, for a multitude of statistics were developed, reported, and used. An additional, and more serious, assumption was made that each statistic itself was normally distributed in repeated random sampling: thus, given the expected mean and the standard error, the distribution in random sampling would be completely specified if it were normal in form.

The confusion was deepened, and the errors compounded, through the introduction of the probable error concept. The probable error is derived from the standard error, being a multiple thereof ($\frac{2}{3}$, or, more exactly, 0.6745), and used and interpreted in much the same fashion. A glance at the table of areas of the normal distribution will reveal that 50% of the area under the curve lies between the points $\xi - 0.6745\sigma$ and $\xi + 0.6745\sigma$. It follows that any particular value selected at random from such a distribution has a 50-50 chance of lying within the section of the scale $\xi \pm 0.6745\sigma$: hence the origin of the use of the word probable, from equally probable. But note that this fraction, 0.6745, is applicable only for the normal distribution: for any other form of distribution a probable error so defined has not the interpretation usually ascribed to it. Thus, the probable error was calculated from the standard error on the assumption of normality, employed on the assumptions of normality and large samples, and the conclusions obtained through its use were erroneous save only where the assumptions of normality and indefinitely large samples were justified. It is now realized that the probable error concept is of little value, and students will find no reference to it in most modern texts on statistical methods. We mention it here only to warn against its use: in some of the social sciences, unfortunately, it has a form of sanctity bestowed through long usage (undeservedly, at that).

To return to the standard error and the assumptions of normality and large samples underlying its use, students will be aware from our discussion of types of populations that a truly normal population is extremely rare in practice. As we pointed out, also, a particular statistic (e.g. the variance) may not be normally distributed in repeated sampling even though the parent population is so distributed. When we reflect on the fact that in the practical problems a researcher normally encounters, the samples are small and the form of the population distribution is unknown and is quite likely not normal in any event, it will be realized that the classical or large-sample theory of sampling and tests of significance of experimental results is quite inappropriate. Upon occasion it led to the acceptance of a hypothesis as true when the conclusion should have been that it was false, or —as more frequently happened with small samples—to the conclusion that the hypothesis was false when the conclusion should have been drawn that it must be accepted as true. In most cases, of course, a researcher would not know which type of error he was committing: indeed an exasperating and frustrating situation in which to be placed, although—perhaps fortunately—most researchers were blissfully unaware that they were involved in such a predicament.

Student and Fisher, as we noted in Chapter I, did see the predicament and led the way in the development of exact sampling distributions of statistics for both large and small samples. This was an advance of the utmost importance, making unnecessary the assumptions of indefinitely large samples and normality of the distribution of statistics in repeated random sampling, and largely resolved the predicament. Their work, together with that of others on the sampling distributions of statistics for non-normal populations, has made it possible for the statistician to reach conclusions with reasonable confidence that he is not seriously in error. Much remains to be done, of course, but at least the foundation has been well and truly laid, and most researchers are now fully aware of the pitfalls underlying the use of the classical theory. Naturally, absolute certainty of the validity of the conclusions has not and never will be attained, as we shall see in subsequent chapters, but the statistician of today is in the happy position of being able to avoid most of the errors of his forefathers.

EXERCISES

1. Select 5 dimes of roughly the same vintage, all in apparently perfect condition without undue wear or distortion, and place them in a container suitable for proper tossing. Set up the conditions you deem necessary to insure drawing a random sample from the hypothetical population of tosses of 5 coins, and toss and record for each toss the number of heads appearing in 500 tosses under like conditions.

2. For the data of Question 1,
   (a) Compare the observed and expected frequency of occurrence of 0 heads, 1 head, 2 heads, 3 heads, 4 heads, and 5 heads.
   (b) Combine adjacent values to yield 100 samples of size 5, and for each such calculate the mean and variance for the distribution of number of heads.
   (c) For each toss, calculate the *proportion* of heads appearing and for each sample

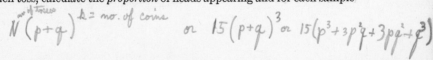

of 5 tosses calculate the *percentage* of 2 or 3 heads appearing in tosses of 5 coins.

(d) Draw the graphs of the distributions in (b) and (c), above, and compare the observed and expected distributions in terms of measures of their characteristics.

3. Select and actually construct a "population" of 1,000 cards for

    (a) a Poisson distribution for which $m = 4.0$;

    (b) a normal distribution for which $\xi = 20$ and $\sigma = 5$;

    (c) a rectangular distribution with exactly 50 cards for each of the 20 numbers (10 to 29, inclusive).

4. Following the procedure outlined in the text, sampling with replacement, secure for each of the above populations 500 samples of size 5 and for each case set up for your sample results the distributions and comparisons given in the text.

CHAPTER III

Theory of Tests of Statistical Hypotheses

Nature and Use of Hypotheses in Reasoning

One of the distinguishing characteristics of the scientific method is the formulation and testing of hypotheses. The hypotheses are used to guide, control, and assist in the investigation or search for truth: the root word is the Greek *hypothesis*, meaning foundation, and in a very real sense hypotheses are the "foundation" of scientific reasoning. It matters little whether a hypothesis is true or false; it is merely a supposition (i.e. something held to be true and taken as the basis of an argument) made as a starting point for investigation or as a basis for reasoning. They should be considered as islands in the uncharted seas of thought, to be used as bases for consolidation and recuperation as we advance into the unknown.

Hypotheses occur in both deductive and inductive reasoning. Given a theory or set of laws or principles, we may deduce that a certain set of events will occur in a particular way. This constitutes a hypothesis, which we may test by comparison with observed facts or phenomena. If we accept the hypothesis, we may (or may not) go on with our line of reasoning to further hypotheses; if we reject the hypothesis, we may question the validity of either the theory or the reasoning that led to the formulation of that specific hypothesis, and possibly change one or the other. Similarly, a hypothesis or a group of related hypotheses may, when confirmed, be used as a theory—an example of inductive reasoning. In most scientific investigations there is a combination of deductive and inductive reasoning, and the chain of reasoning may pass back and forth between theory and hypothesis at any time and at any point. Note that in the sense in which we have used the terms here, the term *theory* relates to the general explanation and the term *hypothesis* to the specific supposition under a given set of circumstances. Normally there will be many hypotheses (not necessarily independent) associated with any given theory; also, it may be that upon closer examination of a particular hypothesis we will discover that it is actually composed of a number of clearly distinguishable hypotheses. Thus, for any given research problem we may have a single hypothesis or a set of hypotheses, and any specific hypothesis may itself be either simple or complex.

Statistical Hypotheses

Any theory, and likewise any hypothesis, is normally stated in general terms, at least in the first instance. When expressed in this form, there is little we can do statistically about a *test* of the hypothesis. We must continue our chain of deductive reasoning and transform the general hypothesis into a very specific, and generally numerical, equivalent before we can apply a statistical test to it. Such specific hypotheses are called *statistical hypotheses*, in order to distinguish them from the *general hypotheses* and also to denote that the form is suitable for the application of statistical tests. Note that this process of deductive reasoning, from theory to general hypothesis to statistical hypothesis, and the corresponding process of inductive reasoning, from the test of the statistical hypothesis to the general hypothesis to the theory, is an exercise in logic rather than in statistical methods. The statistical tests we are about to illustrate apply, strictly speaking, only to the test of the statistical hypothesis and its acceptance or rejection, not to the process of deductive reasoning whereby we were led to the formulation of that specific statistical hypothesis, nor to the process of inductive reasoning that leads from the results of the test of the statistical hypothesis to the conclusions regarding the general hypothesis and the theory. An error in deductive reasoning will lead to the formulation of a completely inappropriate statistical hypothesis: an error in inductive reasoning may lead to conclusions quite at variance with the observed facts. Neither of these errors can properly be blamed on statistical methodology (although they frequently are), since the latter is concerned solely with an appropriate test of the statistical hypothesis.*

The test of a statistical hypothesis is based on a comparison of the observed facts with those expected on the basis of repeated random sampling† from a specified population if the hypothesis were, in fact, true. Note the implication or requirement that variation exist in the population to which the hypothesis has reference. While it is possible to set up a general hypothesis relating to a population in which there is known to be no variation, in such case there is no place for a statistical hypothesis or for a test thereof. The study of a single individual from that population will give complete information concerning it and permit an unequivocal acceptance or rejection of any hypothesis about the population. There can be no variation in the sample results, no matter how small or large the number of cases may be. On the other hand, where variation exists in the population we expect our sample results to vary also. This gives rise to un-

* Save that statistics, like any other branch of science, has a general responsibility for the development of an ability to think logically and consistently—and also persistently!

† Or some other form of sampling, depending on the circumstances.

Deductive Reasoning: From theory, to general hypothesis, to statistical (numerical) hypothesis.

Inductive Reasoning: From test of statistical (numerical) hypothesis, to general hypothesis, to theory.

certainty, since the observed results may solely by chance differ somewhat from those expected, and consequently a statistical hypothesis may quite properly be postulated and tested.

The basis for the test of a statistical hypothesis is in agreement with the axiom of the logicians that it is needless to postulate a complex structure of causes when a simple one will serve. In terms of the statistical hypothesis, the simplest explanation of any differences between observed and expected results is that they arose through errors of random sampling. If the differences are no greater than sampling errors, a point which we will define more exactly in subsequent paragraphs, why do other than accept the hypothesis? Logically and intuitively we seem to be on sound ground in so deciding, in that we accept a simple structure of causes unless we have good reason for rejecting it. What explanation could be simpler, or better, than that of sampling errors or chance, if it suffices to explain what we have observed?

It is important to note that the general hypothesis implicitly or explicitly refers to a population and actually defines it in general terms. Lack of recognition of this characteristic of a hypothesis leads to serious errors on the part of the researcher: to a lack of definiteness in his statement of the problem, for instance, and to vague and indefinite, often erroneous, conclusions that result because of gaps and incomplete links in the chain of deductive-inductive reasoning. Perhaps even more serious is the fact that unless the researcher has clearly in mind the population he is considering, he will be completely unable properly to formulate and to test the statistical hypothesis. The latter is the numerical equivalent of the general hypothesis and expresses it in terms of the parameters that define the population. For a positive binomial population, for instance, the statistical hypothesis will specify the value of p; for a normal population, the statistical hypothesis will specify the value of ξ or of σ, or the values of both ξ and σ. It is surely self-evident that the researcher will get woefully lost in the jungle of deductive and inductive reasoning if he does not in the beginning define exactly and explicitly the population to which his arguments are directed.

Kinds of Statistical Hypotheses

Let us examine more carefully this logic-creature called a statistical hypothesis. In the first place, the statistical hypothesis may be either *simple* or *composite*. By definition, a *simple* statistical hypothesis is one that specifies, or otherwise determines completely, the values of all the parameters that relate to the population. Where p and k are known, for example, the positive binomial population is completely determined; since k is determined by the situation, any statistical hypothesis that specifies the value of p will be simple. So also, by similar argument, will any statistical hypothesis relating to a normal population that specifies values of both ξ and σ. If, on the other hand, the statistical hypothesis for a normal population specifies the value of ξ but not σ (or σ but not ξ), the population is not completely determined, and in such case the statistical hypothesis is called *composite*. In point of fact, a composite statistical hypothesis is not necessarily "complex" in the sense of "complicated," but it is composed of a set (in some cases, infinite in number) of statistical hypotheses which, in turn, may be either simple or composite. For the normal population referred to above, for example, the statistical hypothesis might only specify that the mean, ξ, has a specific value ξ_o. Since the value of the standard deviation, σ, is not specified, there exists not one but a set of statistical hypotheses corresponding to the various possible values of σ. In such event the statistical hypothesis is a composite one, composed in this instance of a set of simple statistical hypotheses. For any population with more than two parameters, for which the value of only one is specified by the statistical hypothesis to be tested, clearly the composite statistical hypothesis would comprise a set of possible composite statistical hypotheses. In the light of these circumstances, it will be readily appreciated how important it is that the researcher state clearly his hypothesis before he applies a statistical test to it and attempts to interpret his results.

The researcher must also determine beforehand what particular statistical hypothesis or hypotheses are alternative to the one to be tested. He may be concerned with only one set of alternative hypotheses, not with all possible sets, or he may deem one set to be of greater importance than the remainder. A manufacturer whose product must meet the standard set by a government agency, for instance, may be far more concerned in any routine test of his product that it does not fall below this minimum standard than that it may exceed the standard.‡ In many tests of experimental results, on the other hand, the possible alternative hypotheses may be of equal importance, and many of the statistical tables we shall use later are set up on the assumption that this is the case. The researcher cannot, however, blithely assume that this holds in each and every situation he may encounter. In comparing the yields of a new variety of wheat or the results attained through the use of a new teaching technique with those of a standard variety of wheat or teaching method, for example, we are normally not particularly interested in the possibility that the new may be poorer than the old. In both cases we are looking for something better in some defined particular, and accordingly must design our statistical test so that it operates in the manner we desire.

‡ In our democracies, as another example, the scales of justice are tilted in a comforting fashion: the accused is deemed to be innocent unless it can be demonstrated beyond reasonable doubt that this hypothesis must be rejected.

Logical Basis of Tests of Statistical Hypotheses   *N. B.*

In testing a statistical hypothesis, we use a combination of deductive and inductive reasoning. Our argument runs as follows: if the hypothesis to be tested is in fact true, then in repeated random sampling from the population defined by the statistical hypothesis we will obtain the results illustrated in the previous chapter. If, on the other hand, the hypothesis to be tested is in fact false (i.e. not true) and one of the alternative hypotheses is true,§ then in repeated random sampling from the population defined by the alternative hypothesis that is true, we will obtain results that differ from those that would be obtained if the hypothesis to be tested were true. To this point, the argument is a simple example of deductive reasoning, by means of which we have set up two models of what to expect in repeated random sampling: first, when the hypothesis to be tested is true; and, second, when the hypothesis to be tested is false and one of the alternative hypotheses is true. But in practice all we have is a set of observed facts—obtained through experimentation or by some other means —and we simply do not know to which population the observed data relate.‖ How, then, in such a state of uncertainty may we draw any conclusion concerning the truth or falsity of the statistical hypothesis (and the corresponding general hypothesis) to be tested?

We proceed by arguing from the set of observed facts to the hypotheses, using what we know about random sampling and sampling errors (or variation) in the following manner. We compare the observed facts with the results expected in repeated random sampling from the population defined by the hypothesis to be tested and with those from the population defined by the alternative hypothesis (or set of alternative hypotheses). On the basis of the difference between the observed and expected results in the two cases, we reach a conclusion regarding the truth or falsity of the hypothesis to be tested. Common sense or intuition (and statistical reasoning, as we shall see, is essentially common sense operating within a well-defined framework) would indicate that if our observed results are such that we could frequently obtain as extreme, or even more extreme, results in repeated random sampling from the population defined by the statistical hypothesis to be tested, then we have really no sound grounds for rejecting that hypothesis. We would, in fact, be inclined to accept it, i.e. conclude that the hypothesis to be tested is true. Our justification for such a conclusion is that we can explain the difference between the observed and expected results on the basis of sampling errors alone, and it would be rather foolish to postulate any conclusion other than this simple one (i.e.

§ Readers will note that it is essential to consider the alternative hypotheses even at this initial stage of logical (as contrasted with statistical) reasoning about the problem.

‖ And we never do know beyond all shadow of doubt, although we may have excellent reasons for concluding that the hypothesis to be tested is true (or false).

conclude that the hypothesis to be tested was false). But, on the other hand, if the divergence between the observed results and those expected in repeated random sampling from the population defined by the statistical hypothesis to be tested is so great that the simple explanation of sampling errors as the sole factor operating is not very plausible, whereas the divergence is not so great for the population corresponding to the alternative hypotheses, then we would apparently be justified in concluding that the hypothesis to be tested is false, i.e. that the alternative hypothesis (or one of the set of possible alternative hypotheses) is in fact true. In short, what we have observed doesn't seem to belong to the population defined by the hypothesis to be tested, so we conclude that the hypothesis is unacceptable. Accordingly, we reject the hypothesis to be tested in favor of the alternative or alternatives.

Coin-Tossing Illustration

This is about as far as a general discussion can take us because some complications arise when the alternative statistical hypotheses specify values not greatly different from those specified by the hypothesis to be tested, and we need to define more exactly our terms and concepts before we can deal with such difficulties. It is convenient to introduce these refinements through a discussion of some tests relating to results of simple coin-tossing, for which both actual and theoretical sampling results were secured in the preceding chapter. It will be remembered that the situation was tossing 10 coins simultaneously, so that the corresponding population was the positive binomial $(p + q)^{10}$. For purposes of argument, we shall state that the hypothesis to be tested is that the coins are unbiased: the corresponding statistical hypothesis, which may for convenience be denoted by H_o, will be that in the population $p = \frac{1}{2}$. To introduce a procedure to be followed later, we shall express the statistical hypothesis to be tested in this form

$$H_o : p = \frac{1}{2} \quad \left(\text{a simple stats. hyp., completely defined} \right)$$

Since the population is thereby completely defined, H_o is a *simple* statistical hypothesis.

Now consider the alternative general hypothesis, which we may conveniently express in the statement that not all the coins are unbiased or, if preferred, that at least one of the 10 coins is biased. Note, however, that the alternative general hypothesis does not specify how many of the coins are biased nor whether the bias favors the appearance of heads or tails. What we have, therefore, is a set of alternative statistical hypotheses— very large in number#—which we may conveniently denote, using H to represent the set, as follows:

$$H : p \neq \frac{1}{2}$$

\# Can the number be infinite in this particular situation? *(No, because there must always be a number regardless of the combinations, permutations, etc.)*

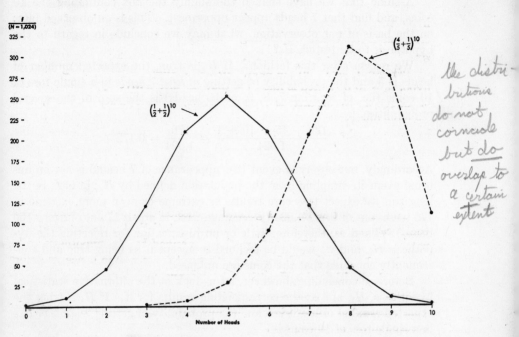

*the distri-
butions
do not
coincide
but do
overlap to
a certain
extent*

Figure III.1. POSITIVE BINOMINAL POPULATIONS $\left(\frac{1}{2}+\frac{1}{2}\right)^{10}$ AND $\left(\frac{4}{5}+\frac{1}{5}\right)^{10}$

where the symbol $\neq$ denotes "not equal to." For illustrative purposes we shall select one of the alternative statistical hypotheses, although we will return later to a discussion of the results for the whole set. Assume that each of a number of the coins are weighted so as to favor the appearance of a head, and in such a manner that the single alternative statistical hypothesis, H_1, is true, where

$$H_1 : p = \frac{4}{5}$$

and the corresponding positive binomial population will therefore be

$$\left(\frac{4}{5} + \frac{1}{5}\right)^{10}$$

These two populations are illustrated graphically in Figure III.1; observe, in particular, the overlap of the two population distributions. Where the populations corresponding to H_o and H_1 are not well separated, it is not surprising that difficulty is experienced in controlling the errors associated with our conclusions regarding the hypothesis to be tested—a point we discuss in some detail in subsequent sections.

Assume that we have shaken thoroughly the box containing the 10 coins, and find that 7 heads appear uppermost. This is an observed fact: on the basis of our observation, what may we conclude in regard to the hypothesis to be tested, H_o?

We reason after this fashion. If H_o is true, the expected number of heads is 5 and the probability of getting *at least 7 heads* in a single toss of 10 coins (i.e. of securing 7, 8, 9, or 10 heads) is the sum of the several probabilities, i.e.

$$\frac{120 + 45 + 10 + 1}{1,024} = \frac{176}{1,024} = 0.172$$

Accordingly, our observed event (the appearance of 7 heads) is not an unusual event in sampling from the population defined by H_o; in fact, in the long run we expect to secure results as extreme or even more extreme in 176 tosses out of every 1,024 (percentage-wise, in about 17 out of every 100 tosses). There is, therefore, little or no justification for rejecting the hypothesis H_o, and we would be inclined to accept it as being true and consequently conclude that the coins are unbiased.

Before so concluding, however, let us look at the alternative statistical hypothesis, H_1, and at the corresponding results for it. If H_1 is true, the expected number of heads is 8 and the probability of getting *7 heads or less* in a single toss of 10 coins is

$$\frac{330}{1,024} = 0.322$$

Accordingly, the observed event is not an unusual one (in fact, even less unusual than for the previous case) in sampling from the population defined by H_1. Obviously, on the basis of this single observed event we cannot be too confident about any conclusion we may reach. But we certainly have no reason to reject H_o, and probably the only justifiable conclusion to make —no matter how uncertain or unhappy we may be about it—is that H_o is, in fact, true.

Consider a rather different situation, however, where the choice between H_o and H_1 is not so difficult to make. Let us assume that our toss of the 10 coins revealed only 3 heads: what now are the probabilities corresponding to those considered above? For H_o, the probability of getting *3 heads or less* in a single toss of 10 coins is obviously the same as getting 7 heads or more, i.e. $\frac{176}{1,024}$. For H_1, however, the appearance of 3 or fewer heads is obviously a very unusual event, the probability being slightly less than $\frac{1}{1,024}$. Again we have no reason to reject H_o, but in this case in accepting it we can be reasonably confident that H_1 is not true (we can never be *certain* of this, by the way) and that, at least as between H_o and H_1, we are quite justified in accepting H_o as true and concluding that the coins are unbiased.

If we had observed 9 heads on the single toss, on the other hand, we would be inclined to reject H_o in favor of H_1. Our reasoning would be somewhat as follows: if H_o were true, the probability of 9 or 10 heads appearing is very small (about 1 in 100); if H_1 were true, the probability of 9 or 10 heads appearing is quite large (about 38 in 100). The odds or chances are against H_o and in favor of H_1. But it is important to note that the observed event could occur if H_o were true, with a probability of approximately 1 in 100 of securing an event as extreme or even more extreme (i.e. 9 or 10 heads).**

Now the ordinary individual would be rather suspicious about conclusions based on a single toss of even 10 coins, and would quite properly propose that the coins be tossed a few more times before any conclusions were finally formulated. Let us see what sampling theory has to say about this request, using the mean number of heads appearing in 5 tosses of the 10 coins as illustrative material. For instance, let us say that in the 5 tosses, 30 heads appeared so that the mean number of heads appearing per toss is 6. The sampling distribution of the mean of N values from a binomial population is

$$(p + q)^{kN}$$

where the interval is $\frac{1}{N}$ instead of unity. For our case, $k = 10$ and $N = 5$, so the distribution of the mean number of heads in 5 tosses will be

$$(p + q)^{50}$$

with an interval of 0.2 instead of unity. For $p = \frac{1}{2}$ and $p = \frac{4}{5}$, corresponding to the hypotheses H_o and H_1 respectively, we have the expected sampling distributions shown in Figure III.2.††

A comparison of Figures III.1 and III.2 reveals that we have gained considerably by taking 5 tosses instead of 1: note that in the latter the sampling distributions are well separated. For larger samples the two sampling distributions would overlap very little if at all. All of which is nothing more than a comforting theoretical justification of the layman's hunch that a few more tosses of the coins would enable us to reach conclusions in which we could place considerable confidence.

But to return to our test of H_o, we observed a mean number of heads in 5 tosses equal to 6: what information may we glean from these sampling distributions? We first note that if H_o were true, the probability of obtaining a mean of 6 or greater in 5 repeated tosses of 10 coins is approxi-

** Students are invited to figure out what conclusion they would reach if only 1 head had appeared!

†† As a matter of interest, students will find these expected frequencies easy to calculate from the above formula $(p + q)^{50}$, if the interval adjustment is made at the final stage (essentially, a simple transformation of the 0–50 point scale).

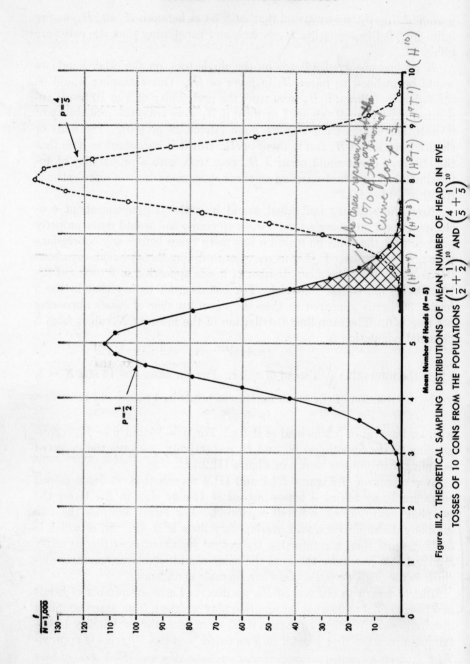

Figure III.2. THEORETICAL SAMPLING DISTRIBUTIONS OF MEAN NUMBER OF HEADS IN FIVE TOSSES OF 10 COINS FROM THE POPULATIONS $\left(\frac{1}{2} + \frac{1}{2}\right)^{10}$ AND $\left(\frac{4}{5} + \frac{1}{5}\right)^{10}$

mately $\frac{1}{10}$ (for the empirical results of the previous chapter, we observed 17 out of 200). Similarly, if H_1 were true, the probability of observing a mean of 6 or less in 5 repeated tosses of 10 coins is about $\frac{1}{1,000}$. The event we actually observed, a mean of 6 heads, is therefore not unusual when H_o is true, but is a rather unlikely event when H_1 is true. Accordingly, we would be inclined, and with reasonable justification, to accept H_o rather than the alternative H_1, and consequently conclude that the coins were unbiased. Of course, we are not absolutely certain of the validity of our conclusion, but it does seem to be reasonable in view of what we know about the situation.

Basis Proposed by Neyman and Pearson for Tests of Statistical Hypotheses

With this simple illustration in mind, we are now in a position to define more exactly the procedure to be followed in a test of a statistical hypothesis. We will follow as closely as possible the logical and mathematically elegant arguments first expounded by J. Neyman and E. S. Pearson in the early 1930's, of which a good example may be found in two papers in Volume I of *Statistical Research Memoirs* (June, 1936: Department of Applied Statistics, University of London). We first observe that there are two courses open to us: we may reject the statistical hypothesis to be tested, i.e. H_o, or we may accept it.‡‡ We observe, next, that there are two kinds of errors which we may commit:

1. We may reject H_o as false when it is in fact true, which is called an *error of the first kind*. To complete this phase of the argument, note that if we reject H_o when it is in fact false we do not commit an error —of any kind.

2. We may accept H_o as true when it is in fact false, that is, when some alternative hypothesis H_1 is in fact true, which is called an *error of the second kind*. Note, again, that if we accept H_o when it is in fact true we do not commit an error. **

In any given practical situation we never do know whether we have or have not committed an error, or which kind of error, if any, we have committed. But we can at least calculate (exactly or approximately, depending upon the circumstances) the *probability* of committing an error, and report the corresponding probability along with our decision about the rejection or acceptance of H_o. *(the real philosophy of modern statistics)*

These probabilities of committing an error are calculated on the basis of sampling theory. To illustrate, let us return to the coin-tossing example

‡‡ Students should at each step in the argument return to the illustration of coin-tossing and think their way through an actual example. This type of reasoning, while logical and sound enough, seems foreign to our usual mode of thought, and a student will founder in the seas that follow unless his mental boat is made seaworthy now.

** The third possibility: We may neither accept nor reject but we may decide to test further by usually enlarging further. (i.e. defer judgement)

of the preceding pages. Our statistical hypothesis to be tested was H_o : $p = \frac{1}{2}$. We observed a mean of 6 heads in 5 tosses, and may direct our attention to Figure III.2 where the simple alternative hypothesis, H_1, is the only one to be considered. We either reject H_o or accept it on the basis of the observed result: let us determine the consequences of each of these two possible decisions. Assume that we decide to reject H_o, in which case we may commit an error of the *first* kind: what is the probability of committing an error of the first kind in this situation? Our decision to reject H_o because the mean number of heads in the 5 tosses proved to be 6, is equivalent to the general rule that in any set of 5 tosses of these 10 coins we will reject H_o when the mean number of heads is 6 or greater (if we reject at 6, we would obviously reject for any value greater than 6). But if H_o is in fact true, we can obtain a mean of 6 or greater in sets of 5 repeated tosses of the 10 coins in approximately 1 out of every 10 sets (see the cross-hatched portion of the $p = \frac{1}{2}$ distribution of Figure III.2). Therefore, if we reject H_o according to this rule, we will commit an error of the first kind rather frequently—in fact, in approximately 10 per cent of such cases. This is the probability of an error of the first kind (generally expressed as either 10 per cent or as 0.1), and it is rather large—large enough, probably, to cast some doubt on the wisdom of the decision to reject H_o, since no one would wish willingly to adopt a course of action for which the risk of being in error is this great.

Assume, on the other hand, that we decide to accept H_o, in which case we may commit an error of the *second* kind: what is the probability of committing an error of the second kind in this situation? Our decision to accept H_o, because the mean number of heads in the 5 tosses was 6, is equivalent to the general rule (in this situation) that in any 5 tosses of these 10 coins we will accept H_o when the mean number of heads is 6 or less (if we accept at 6, we will clearly accept at less than 6).§§ But if H_o is in fact false, then H_1 must be true: if H_1 is true, we can obtain means of 6 or less in sets of 5 repeated tosses of the 10 coins in approximately 1 out of every 1,000 sets (see the shaded portion of the $p = \frac{4}{5}$ distribution of Figure III.2, to the left of 6). It follows that if we accept H_o according to the rule of 6 or less,§§ we will commit an error of the second kind only infrequently—the probability of an error of the second kind in the situation depicted being about 1 in 1,000. Accordingly, we would be inclined to accept H_o with an easy conscience: while we may commit an error of the second kind, the probability of doing so is comfortably small.

When we realize that in real-life situations, like the industrial or the agricultural problem referred to earlier, our arguments are similar to those used in this simple example of coin-tossing, it will be appreciated how

§§ The red light flashes at the lower end of the distribution for $p = \frac{1}{2}$ in Figure III.2, but we ignore it for the moment since we are considering only one alternative statistical hypothesis, namely, $H_1: p = \dfrac{4}{5}$.

important sampling theory and a knowledge of exact sampling distributions really are. We must make a decision, i.e. reject or accept H_o, and we know that in doing so we may (in most cases, must) commit an error of the first kind or of the second kind, depending upon the decision. To be able to calculate and state the probability of the error is essential, and this is what sampling theory enables us to do.‖‖

The General Theory of Tests of Significance

We are now in a position to state the general theory of tests of statistical hypotheses, or *statistical tests of significance* as they are frequently called. The fundamental concept or principle is that a statistical test must minimize the probability of errors, or, as it is sometimes expressed, that the efficiency of a statistical test may be assessed by the manner in which it controls those two sources of error. This provides a criterion, therefore, on the basis of which we may select the best (most efficient) statistical test in any given situation. Neyman and Pearson used this principle, as did numerous others who followed their lead, in evaluating existing statistical tests and in devising new and more efficient ones. They demonstrated that any test of a statistical hypothesis H_o is equivalent to the rule of rejecting H_o whenever the sample point falls within a specified region, denoted by w and called the critical region, and of accepting H_o in all other cases. In the example just considered, we could define w as the region consisting of means of 6 or more heads in samples of 5 tosses of 10 coins—i.e. the part of the horizontal scale beginning at the point 6 and extending to the right, in which case we would accept H_o whenever the mean number of heads was less than 6 and reject it whenever the mean was 6 or greater.

In general, we may consider a system of variables $X_1, X_2, \ldots, X_N$, the values of which can be obtained by observation, and the N-dimensional space W corresponding to this system of variables. For any given sample of N values of these X's, there will correspond a sample point E in the sample space W. For the coin-tossing situation, the sample space W is a line extending from 0 to 10 and the sample point E is a point on this line. The sample space W, however, may have any number of dimensions (i.e. consist of a line, surface, or volume), depending on the circumstances, but in each case the sample point E will be a point in the sample space. Similarly, the critical region w will be some defined part of W, and any given sample point E will fall either in w or in the rest of the sample space, which we may denote by $W-w$. Any test of the statistical hypothesis H_o, therefore, consists in the rule of rejecting H_o whenever E falls in w and of accepting H_o whenever E falls in $W-w$.

It is assumed that the variables $X_1, X_2, \ldots, X_N$, are such that we can calculate the probability (either exactly or at least approximately) that

‖‖ If not the exact probability, at least a fair approximation thereto that will be sufficient for all practical purposes.

Read to size it up

terminology only

the sample point E will fall within w, and consequently the probability that the sample point E will fall outside w (i.e. within $W-w$), whether the statistical hypothesis to be tested be true or false. ## The first probability may be denoted by $P\{E\epsilon w\}$—read the "probability that E is an element of (or within) w"—and the second by $P\{E\epsilon(W-w)\}$. If the hypothesis to be tested is true, the probability that E is within w may be written $P\{E\epsilon w/H_o\}$, and this is the probability of an error of the first kind—i.e. of rejecting H_o when it is in fact true. Neyman and Pearson have defined this as the *size* of the corresponding critical region w, and have denoted the size by the Greek letter α (alpha). Similarly, the probability of an error of the second kind—of accepting H_o when it is in fact false and some alternative hypothesis H_1 is true—may be written

$$P\{E\epsilon(W - w)/H_1\}   \text{or}   1 - P\{E\epsilon w/H_1\}$$

terminology only

The probability of rejecting H_o when the true hypothesis is an alternative simple hypothesis H_1, i.e. $P\{E\epsilon w/H_1\}$, has been termed the *power* of the test with regard to H_1. The most powerful test for H_o with regard to H_1 is that for which $P\{E\epsilon w/H_1\}$ is greatest, and the corresponding critical region w has been called the best critical region for H_o with regard to H_1. For a set of admissible alternative hypotheses, a test of H_o has been called uniformly most powerful if it is the most powerful test with regard to every alternative hypothesis in that set.

The choice of a critical region, w, to use in the test of a statistical hypothesis is, therefore, based upon the common-sense principle that we should control and minimize the probabilities of error—of the second kind as well as the first. We wish to reject H_o when it is true as infrequently as possible, and reject H_o when it is false as frequently as possible. In other words, we want the most powerful test we can get which will, at the same time, control the probability of errors of the first kind at a desired and specified level.

It is of some historical interest to note that originally Neyman and Pearson suggested a likelihood principle from which tests of statistical hypotheses could be derived.*** They observed that the statistical tests commonly employed seemed to be based on the principle that we are inclined, intuitively, to reject the hypothesis tested, H_o, when among the possible alternative hypotheses there exists one or more that ascribe to the observed event, E, a probability much larger than that ascribed by the hypothesis to be tested. If we denote by $P\{E/H_o\}$ the probability of the observed event when the hypothesis to be tested is true, and by $P\{E/H\}_{max}$ the upper bound (maximum) of the probabilities of the observed event cor-

Neyman and Pearson have defined the variables that have this property as *random variables*, where the probability can be determined exactly.

*** J. Neyman and E. S. Pearson, "On the Use and Interpretation of Certain Test Criteria for Purposes of Statistical Inference," *Biometrika*, XXA (1928), 175–240 and 264–94.

responding to all the admissible alternative hypotheses, ††† then if these hypotheses are simple hypotheses the likelihood ratio λ (the Greek letter lambda), where

$$\lambda = \frac{P\{E/H_o\}}{P\{E/H\}_{\max}}$$

may be used as a suitable criterion for testing the hypothesis H_o. If λ is small, then we are intuitively inclined to reject H_o because there exists among the alternative hypotheses at least one that makes the observed event much more probable than does H_o. On the other hand, if λ is not small we are inclined intuitively to accept H_o since the associated probabilities do not indicate any good reason for doing otherwise. Here the critical region will be defined in the form $\lambda < \lambda_o$, or its equivalent, where λ_o $(0 < \lambda_o < 1)$ is fixed at a point such that the probability of errors of the first kind is equal to some specified value ϵ, i.e. $P\{\lambda < \lambda_o/H_o\} = \epsilon$. The likelihood ratio will, at least where the hypotheses are simple, yield a statistical test for which the probability of errors of the first kind is controlled at a specified level *and* that will ensure rejection of H_o when among the alternative hypotheses there exists at least one which ascribes to the observed event a probability greater than that ascribed to it by H_o. Observe that the probability of errors of the second kind is fixed by the process, although this probability is not taken into account directly when the critical region is determined.

This lack of control over the size of the probability of errors of the second kind proved upon further investigation to be so important, that Neyman and Pearson later suggested that tests of statistical hypotheses should have the properties noted above, viz. control of the first-kind errors at a fixed probability level and reduction of the probabilities of second-kind errors to as low a level as possible. They showed that the desired statistical test, i.e. the critical region w, is defined by the inequality, where $p(X_1, \ldots, X_N)$ denotes the elementary probability law of the X's,

$$p(X_1, \ldots, X_N/H_1) \geqslant kp(X_1, \ldots, X_N/H_o) \text{ inside } w$$

and $\quad p(X_1, \ldots, X_N/H_1) \leqslant kp(X_1, \ldots, X_N/H_o) \text{ outside } w$

where k is a constant determined so that

$$p\{E\epsilon w/H_o\} = \alpha$$

is satisfied. A variation has been suggested by Jackson,‡‡‡ to determine what he called the "most stringent" statistical test, where the region of acceptance for H_o would be as broad as possible and the total probability of error (of any kind) would be less than a fixed value determined in advance.

For the simple hypotheses considered above in relation to the tosses of

††† With only one alternative hypothesis, H_1, this will be simply $P\{E/H_1\}$.

‡‡‡ Robert W. B. Jackson, "Tests of Statistical Hypotheses in the Case when the Set of Alternatives is Discontinuous, Illustrated on Some Genetical Problems," *Statistical Research Memoirs* (London: Department of Statistics, University College, University of London, 1936), Vol. I, pp. 138–61.

10 coins, the same test is suggested no matter which of the two methods of Neyman and Pearson is employed. For the single toss, for example, the lambda criterion suggests that we would be inclined intuitively to accept H_o when the number of heads is less than about 6.6, and reject H_o in favor of H_1 when the number of heads is greater than this value, and reference to the distributions of Figure III.1 shows that this is the point where the two curves cross. Students are invited to apply the same procedure to the case of the mean of 5 tosses of the 10 coins, determine the point where $\lambda = 1$, and determine also the boundaries of the critical region w for several values of α (using the fact that the interval is $\dfrac{1}{N}$ at the final stage).

The critical region, w, is frequently called the *region of significance*, and the region $W - w$ the *region of non-significance* or the *region of acceptance*. The word *significance*, as used here, has a special or technical meaning quite different from the ordinary meaning. *Significance* and *non-significance* refer to the hypothesis to be tested, H_o, and to its rejection or acceptance (or non-rejection), and that is all, as we indicated earlier. The student will find the discussion easier to follow, and will be less apt to make errors of interpretation, if he remembers that the critical region, w, the region of significance, is really the *region of rejection* for the hypothesis H_o, since we *reject* H_o whenever the sample point, E, falls within the region w. Similarly, the region $W - w$, the region of non-significance, should be thought of as the *region of acceptance* for the hypothesis H_o, since we *accept* (in the sense of non-reject) H_o whenever the sample point, E, falls within the region $W - w$. Thus, when we say our observed results (from an experiment, for instance) are *significant*, we mean—strictly speaking—not that the results are necessarily "important," but that the sample point E falls within the critical region, w, and, consequently, that the hypothesis H_o is to be *rejected*. Similarly, when we say that our observed results are *not significant*, we mean, not that the results are "not important"—they may, in fact, be extremely important—but that the sample point E falls within the region $W - w$ and, consequently, that the hypothesis H_o is to be *accepted*.

N.B.

The statistical test of significance leads only to the rejection or acceptance of the hypothesis to be tested. Any conclusion in regard to the importance or otherwise of the results is an inference based on the statistical test, but is not actually a part of the test of the statistical hypothesis. This distinction and these limitations of statistical tests are essential points that the student and researcher must never forget. Moreover, in this final step of inductive reasoning, it will be of the utmost assistance to the researcher if he has formulated, not only the statistical hypothesis to be tested, H_o, but also the set of alternative hypotheses that are admissible under the circumstances of his problem. Then, whether he rejects H_o or accepts it, he will have a proper guide for whatever inferences he may wish to make and which his data warrant.

EXERCISES

1. For a problem in your own field of interest, preferably an experimental one, give an example of (a) a null hypothesis, (b) an admissible alternative hypothesis, (c) an error of the first kind, (d) an error of the second kind, (e) a one-sided test of the null hypothesis, and (f) the complete set of alternative hypotheses.

2. Express in your own words the intuitive or logical basis of a test of a statistical hypothesis. Why, in general, would you prefer to reduce to as low a level as possible the probability of an error of the first kind? Would you do so even if it meant that the probability of an error of the second kind would be substantial? Why?

3. Why is it that hypotheses in the social sciences, at least as originally stated, are seldom if ever in the form of "null" hypotheses?

4. Express the following in your own words:
   "If I reject, the probability of an error of the first kind is 15 per cent; whereas if I accept, the probability of an error of the second kind is 75 per cent."

5. With reference to the coin-tossing experiment discussed in the text, illustrate what you think is the meaning of the following statement:
   "A test of significance cannot prove the truth or falsity of the null hypothesis; it can only demonstrate its improbability."

CHAPTER IV

Tests of Statistical Hypotheses Expressed in Terms of
Proportions or Percentages

In a very large number of problems, the statistical hypothesis to be tested, H_o, and the set of admissible alternative hypotheses, H, may be most conveniently expressed in terms of either proportions or percentages. The general hypothesis may or may not include a reference to proportions or percentages, but normally will not do so. Actually, we need not make any real distinction between proportions and percentages, at least in the development of an appropriate statistical test, since we can shuttle back and forth between the two sets of units on the factor of 100 (or by shifting the decimal point two places in the appropriate direction). Accordingly, we shall in the illustrations that follow confine our attention to proportions, the corresponding statistical hypotheses, and the tests thereof. Readers may, if they need to do so, very easily make the necessary adjustments in the calculations and develop the argument for percentages.

Case 1: Proportion of a Single Sample (*universe + observed value*)

In one of the Dominion Tests of Silent Reading,* a pupil is required on each of 28 items to read a short paragraph and then mark that one of four accompanying pictures which most closely corresponds to the story. A pupil can obtain, on the average, one item correct in every four by marking one picture at random in each set. As we write we have before us a test on which a pupil had only 9 items correctly marked: should we conclude that he answered the test items by guessing?

The most convenient hypothesis to test is that the pupil did answer by guessing, and the set of admissible alternative hypotheses will then be that he had some knowledge of reading and used it, i.e. did not guess. The population we have in mind in setting up the sampling model will be the positive binomial $(p + q)^{28}$ and we may write the statistical hypotheses to be tested, H_o, in the form $H_o : p = \frac{1}{4}$ and the set of admissible alternative statistical hypotheses, H, in the form $H : p > \frac{1}{4}$. Note that we are not interested in the set of possible statistical hypotheses corresponding to $p < \frac{1}{4}$, since they have no meaning here, but in other situations our set

* Prepared by the Department of Educational Research, University of Toronto. The particular test referred to is the Paragraph Reading Test for Grade I.

1 item correct in every 4   with 28 items will get 7 correct out of 28 , $\frac{7}{28} = \frac{1}{4}$ $H_o : p = \frac{1}{4}$

of admissible alternative hypotheses could be either $p \neq \frac{1}{4}$, i.e. both $p > \frac{1}{4}$ and $p < \frac{1}{4}$, or even the group $p < \frac{1}{4}$ alone.

The critical region will consist of that part of the scale of number of items correct for which the probability of an error of the first kind is at the desired level. Assuming that H_o is true, we find by direct calculation or from the *Tables of the Binomial Probability Distribution*† that the probability of obtaining r or more items correct, is as follows, beginning with $r = 9$:

r	Probability of r or more items correct
9	0.2499
10	0.1385
11	0.0679
12	0.0294
13	0.0112
14	0.0038

Our selection of a level depends on the risk of rejecting the hypothesis tested, H_o, when it is in fact true that we are willing to accept as permissible under the circumstances. Setting the level at 1 per cent, or as close to it as we can get (with discrete values, the exact levels can seldom be secured), defines the size of the critical region, w, as $13 \leqslant r \leqslant 28$, and we may use the customary designation of 13 as the approximate 1 per cent *point*. We reject H_o whenever the sample point, E, falls in w, i.e. whenever the number of items correct is 13 or more, and accept H_o in all other cases.‡ Since our observed event, E, was 9 items correct, we accept H_o and conclude that the pupil answered by guessing.

Let us consider, next, the critical region w in light of the probability of errors of the second kind, i.e. of accepting H_o when it is in fact false. Observe, first, that the amount of reading ability a pupil may use in answering the items can vary from zero to the (unknown) maximum of which he is capable. It follows that our set of admissible alternative hypotheses, H, could have for the value of p any value greater than $\frac{1}{4}$ and differing from it by any amount less than $\frac{3}{4}$. Let us assume for purposes of argument that the pupil used just enough of his reading ability to make the value of p equal to 0.26.§ Referring again to the tables, we find that the probability of the sample point, E, falling within the region of acceptance, $W-w$, is approximately 98.4 per cent! In fact, as Neyman and Pearson have

† "Applied Mathematics Series" 6, National Bureau of Standards, United States Department of Commerce.

‡ It is common practice to set up three regions: the region of rejection defined by the 1 per cent level; the *region of acceptance* defined by the 5 per cent level; and a *region of doubt or non-decision* between the above two. This is an arbitrary, but convenient and generally accepted, rule that makes some allowance for errors of the second kind.

§ Unfortunately our argument runs foul of the facts, since the items vary in difficulty and p will not be constant for this particular test although it might be for some others. We really have a multinomial model for these admissible alternative hypotheses.

shown for other and similar situations, for an alternative hypothesis, H_1, that differs only slightly from the one to be tested, H_o, the probability of an error of the second kind is approximately equal to the difference between unity and the probability of an error of the first kind. Such a large value for the probability of an error of the second kind may lead to a reconsideration of the size of the critical region, w. Should we make it a bit bigger, thereby increasing the probability of an error of the first kind, in order to have a smaller region of acceptance, which will mean a decrease in the probability of an error of the second kind? There is no general rule that will resolve this dilemma: a researcher must in each problem make the choice in the light of circumstances, balancing one risk against the other with whatever system of weights he feels may be necessary. In the above problem we would be inclined to stress the importance of errors of the first kind, rather than run the risk of assigning a comforting reading grade to a pupil who answered the reading test by guessing.||

An approximate solution to the original problem could have been secured rather simply and quickly by reference to the standard error of the proportion p. We observed 9 items correct out of 28, i.e. a proportion $p_o = \dfrac{9}{28}$ = 0.3214 instead of the expected proportion $p = \frac{1}{4}$. Since the standard error of p will be, because $k = 28$ and H_o specifies the value $p = \frac{1}{4}$,

$$SE_p = \sqrt{\frac{pq}{k}} = \sqrt{\frac{3}{448}} = 0.0818$$

the difference between the observed and expected value of p, i.e. .3214 − .2500 = .0714, is slightly less than the standard error and is quite clearly *not significant* in the statistical sense of that phrase. Students should observe, however, that this method does not provide estimates of the probabilities of the two kinds of error, although it does indicate that if we reject H_o the probability of an error of the first kind will be quite large. For a quick preview or peek at our statistical results, this use of the standard error can be justified.

Another approximate method, which does give an estimate of the magnitude of the probability of an error of the first kind (and when k is reasonably large, or p approximately $\frac{1}{2}$, a very good estimate indeed), consists in the use of the normal distribution. The assumption is made that the latter will be a fair approximation to the positive binomial, with an appropriate adjustment to compensate for the discontinuous nature of the data. For this particular problem of the reading test we would have for the corresponding normal population $\xi = kp = 28(\frac{1}{4}) = 7$ and $\sigma = \sqrt{kpq} =$

|| Those who construct such mental tests often advocate a "correction for guessing," based on the number of wrong answers and designed to give the "pure" guesser a zero score *on the average*. But, in practice, the results are often not too happy for either the examiner or the student.

$\sqrt{(28)(\frac{1}{4})(\frac{3}{4})} = 2.2913$, from which we secure the following values for the probability of getting r or more items correct:

r	EXACT BINOMIAL PROBABILITIES	ADJUSTED VALUE OF r' FOR NORMAL	$\left(\dfrac{r'-7}{2.29}\right)$	NORMAL PROBABILITIES
9	0.2499	8.5	0.655	0.2562
10	0.1385	9.5	1.091	0.1376
11	0.0679	10.5	1.528	0.0633
12	0.0294	11.5	1.964	0.0247
13	0.0112	12.5	2.400	0.0082
14	0.0038	13.5	2.837	0.0023

[handwritten margin notes: $r' = 8.5$; $\frac{8.5-7}{2.29}$; .655 ; app. p. .499 ; value is .7438   1.0000 - .7438 = .2562]

While the agreement is far from perfect, and would be even less satisfactory for smaller values of k or p, yet for an approximate method the estimates of the probabilities are fair—probably sufficiently accurate for a preliminary canter over the field and to serve until the exact values are required.

Another example of the use of the normal approximation, and one where the labor of calculating exact probabilities would be prohibitive and unnecessary, may be found in the data of Table IV.1 relating to gastric disorder.

TABLE IV.1 *[handwritten: not a random sample]*

EXAMPLE OF CATEGORICAL DATA: MULTIPLE CLASSIFICATION
Cases of Gastric Disorder Dismissed from Hospitals
in Oxford Area during 1945

[handwritten margin: data here is actual but crude data. don't know here what qualification there are, if any. The school at Oxford is an all male school]

GASTRIC DISORDER	SEX OF PATIENT	
	Male	Female
Gastric ulcer	22	9
Duodenal ulcer	52	5
Other gastric disorders	535	415
Total	609	429

Source, H. Cotton, "The Collection of Morbidity Data from Hospitals," *Journal of the Royal Statistical Society*, Series A (General), CXI, Part I (1948), 17.

The observed event (using the totals of all cases of gastric disorder) was 609 male patients to 429 female patients, or an observed proportion of 0.5867 males. May we conclude from these data that males are more susceptible than are females to gastric disorders? For the total population aged 30 and over (the major group subject to gastric disorders), the proportion of males is 0.51, so our model for H_o is the positive binomial

$$(.51 + .49)^{1038}$$

and for the normal approximation thereto, we have $\xi = 529.38$ and $\sigma =$

[handwritten: $(.51)(1038)$]

529.38 [handwritten]

16.106. The normal deviate, $\dfrac{608.5 - \xi}{\sigma \ 16.1}$, corresponding to the observed

(.49)(.51)($\sqrt{1038}$) [handwritten, left margin]

event is 4.91 and, consequently, the probability of securing a value as great or greater than this in repeated random sampling from the defined population is between 4 and 5 in 10,000,000. We would, therefore, be willing to reject H_o with considerable confidence and conclude that males are considerably more susceptible than females to gastric disorders. Students should observe that we did not actually set up a critical region, w, in making this test, although, by calculating the probability as we did, we used the same concept of level of probability of an error of the first kind. For this situation, where we considered only the set of alternative hypotheses H : $p > 0.51$,# the normal deviate $\dfrac{X - \xi}{\sigma}$ corresponding to the 1 per cent level of probability of errors of the first kind is 2.3263, and our observed event, E, obviously falls within the critical region, w. These are not two different tests of the statistical hypothesis, H_o, but merely two different, although equivalent, ways of expressing it.

This form of hypothesis and statistical test arises frequently in medical statistics, although in many situations involving the occurrence of diseases the population to which the sample belongs is a Poisson or a negative binomial. A rather simple example which was brought to our attention concerned the incidence of cancer in a group of patients suffering from a disease that a surgeon suspected might be related to cancer. In a group of 114 patients, autopsies revealed the existence of primary cancers in 22 patients. It is known that in the general population of the same age group and sex, the incidence of cancer is approximately 16 in 1,000. May it be concluded that the sample of 114 patients is a random sample from the general population in regard to incidence of cancer?

Since p is so small, we clearly must use the Poisson distribution in answering this question. For $N = 114$ and $p = 0.016$, we have for the Poisson population a value of $m = 1.824$. From the tables for the corresponding distribution, i.e. for $m = 1.8$, we find that the probability of finding even 11 or more patients suffering from cancer in a random sample of 114 from the general population is about 3 in 1,000,000. The observed event, of 22 patients in 114 suffering from cancer, is so improbable an event under these conditions, therefore, that we must reject the hypothesis tested and conclude that our observed sample is from a population in which the incidence of cancer is much higher than in the general population. Our statistical test does not, of course, "prove" that cancer is the cause of the other disease, but it does suggest that it might be worthwhile to investigate

There is obviously little point in considering the other set of alternative hypotheses, H' : $p < 0.51$, in this situation. As we shall see later, however, we must admit and consider both sets of possible alternative hypotheses and use a different critical region, w, in certain situations.

$m = Kp = (114)(.016) = 1.824$ [handwritten]

(medically) the reason for the high incidence of cancer in patients suffering from this particular disease.

(only have sample info. here)

Case 2: Difference Between Proportions of Two Independent Samples

By the term "independent" we mean in this situation that the proportions have been calculated for samples or groups that are not related in any way; the contrary case, considered in the next example, occurs rather frequently in experiments in education and psychology because the same or matched individuals are often used in the two groups. We may, for instance, make observations of a group of individuals before and after an experiment, or use matched individuals in a control and in an experimental group, and since the same or equated individuals occur in both groups our proportions calculated therefrom must obviously be related. The situation is quite different, of course, if one group contains males and the other females, or if in some other way the individuals (or objects) in the two groups have no members in common.

The discussion in this example and the next will be restricted to the calculation and use of the standard error as an approximate method, with estimates of the probability of an error of the first kind, if desired, calculated from the tables of the normal distribution. In the next chapter we shall give a general method (the chi-square, χ^2, test) that, subject to certain limitations and conditions, is applicable to these and related situations and for which the probabilities have been tabled in an extremely convenient form. While this χ^2-test yields only approximations to the probabilities, they are quite good enough for all practical purposes provided the samples are not too small. We should perhaps add that one disadvantage of the χ^2-test is that, being a general test, it is difficult at times to unscramble and to specify exactly for a particular situation the hypothesis to be tested, H_o, and the set of admissible hypotheses, H.

As an example,** let us consider again the data of Table IV.1 but now focus attention on the incidence of ulcers in these two groups (male and female) of gastric disorder patients. We observe the proportion of *patients* with gastric or duodenal ulcers is as follows:

$$\text{Male: } \frac{74}{609} = 0.1215$$

$$\text{Female: } \frac{14}{429} = 0.0326$$

$$\text{Total: } \frac{88}{1,038} = 0.0848$$

Are the male patients more subject to ulcers than the female patients?

** Many similar examples, expressed in percentage form, may be found in the results of public opinion polls.

In transforming this general hypothesis into the corresponding statistical one, attention must be paid to three points. First, the population we now have in mind is not the general population of males and females, but the subpopulation of males and females suffering from gastric disorders. Second, our problem is to compare two observed proportions and test the significance of the difference between them. Third, we do not know the population values for the several proportions: all we have is a sample of male patients and a sample of female patients from a population, or populations, with unknown value(s) of p. How, then, may we phrase our statistical hypothesis to be tested, H_o, and the set of admissible hypotheses, H, and test H_o?

We begin by defining two populations: one for male patients in the form of a positive binomial with $k = 609$ and an unknown value of p, say $\hat{p}_M$, and another for female patients of the same form with $k = 429$ and an unknown value of p, say $\hat{p}_F$. The simplest statistical hypothesis to be tested, H_o, that we can formulate—simplest from the point of view of sampling theory as well as of interpretation—is that our samples are independent samples of size 609 and 429 drawn from the same positive binomial population with an unknown value of p, say $\hat{p}$, i.e. in symbols

$$H_o: \hat{p}_M = \hat{p}_F = \hat{p}$$

As for the alternative hypotheses, H, there are two possible sets: the first set, denoted by H_1, may be expressed in the form

$$H_1: \hat{p}_M > \hat{p}_F$$

and the second set, denoted by H_2, may be expressed in the form

$$H_2: \hat{p}_M \neq \hat{p}_F$$

Students should note that the set H_2 includes the set H_1. In view of the phrasing of the general hypothesis, the set of admissible alternative hypotheses will be H_1, not H_2. We require a critical region, w, such that if we reject H_o we will do so in favor of H_1. But our general hypothesis might well have been phrased differently, so that the set of admissible alternative hypotheses would be H_2: we might, for example, have phrased the original question in the form, "Are male and female patients equally subject to ulcers?" and would then have to admit the two possibilities, $\hat{p}_M > \hat{p}_F$ and $\hat{p}_M < \hat{p}_F$.

The next step is to turn to sampling theory to determine what will happen in repeated random sampling from a population defined by the hypothesis to be tested, H_o, so that we may calculate the probability of errors of the first kind. If we know the value of $\hat{p}$, the standard error of the difference between two proportions when H_o is true will be††

†† When H_o is false, i.e. one of the set of alternative hypotheses is true, the formulae must be written

$$\sqrt{\frac{p_1 q_1}{N_1} + \frac{p_2 q_2}{N_2}}$$

$\hat{p}$; estimate of universe prop. of ulcer cases.

$\hat{p}_M$ = an unknown value of the prop. of male pop. with ulcers.

$$SE_{D_p} = \sqrt{\hat{p}\,\hat{q}\left(\frac{1}{N_1} + \frac{1}{N_2}\right)}$$

where N_1 is the number in the first sample, and N_2 the number in the second sample, upon which the proportions are based.‡‡ But we do not know the value of $\hat{p}$. All we can do is estimate it from our observed results—not for each sample but for the two combined, since we assume that H_o is true. If p_1 denotes the observed proportion in the first sample, and p_2 the observed proportion in the second sample having the desired characteristic, then the best estimate of $\hat{p}$, which we may denote by p, is

$$p = \frac{N_1 p_1 + N_2 p_2}{N_1 + N_2} \quad \rightarrow a\ weighted\ prop.$$

which reduces to $p = (p_1 + p_2)/2$ when $N_1 = N_2 = N$. Accordingly, our estimate of the standard error of the difference in proportions will be

$$SE_{Dp} = \sqrt{pq\left(\frac{1}{N_1} + \frac{1}{N_2}\right)} \quad \text{§§}$$

How much in error may we be in using SE_{Dp}^1 as an estimate of the true value SE_{Dp}? Using the coin-tossing data of Chapter II, for the case $N_1 = N_2 = 100$ and $\hat{p} = \frac{1}{2}$, we find that for samples of this size from this population, the use of our estimate of the standard error of the difference between proportions is quite justified. At most, SE_{Dp}^1 will differ from SE_{Dp} only in the second significant figure, and even then rather infrequently and generally by not more than 1 or 2 points.

As for the distribution of $D_p = p_1 - p_2$ when H_o is true, observe that the distribution of D_p must in this event always be symmetrical in form—since plus and minus differences are equally likely to occur—and is unlikely to depart greatly from the normal form when the sample is moderately large, say 100 or more cases. Accordingly, we will not be greatly in error, even for fairly small samples, if we assume that D_p is normally distributed about a mean of zero with standard deviation estimated by SE_{Dp}^1, or, in other words, that $\dfrac{Dp}{SE_{Dp}^1}$ is a normal deviate with zero mean and unit standard deviation, when H_o is true.

We are now in a position to complete the test of the hypothesis H_o for the problem originally enunciated for this example. We had

‡‡ $D_p = p_1 - p_2$, the observed difference in proportions.
§§ This formula is consistent with the hypothesis to be tested, H_o: the other form commonly used, namely,

$$\sqrt{\frac{p_1\,q_1}{N_1} + \frac{p_2\,q_2}{N_2}}$$

is not, and it should not be used in relation to H_o. It applies only to the hypotheses alternative to H_o.

$$N_1 = 609$$
$$N_2 = 429$$
$$p_1 = 0.1215$$
$$p_2 = 0.0326$$
$$p = 0.0848$$

Whence we obtain

$$Dp = 0.0889$$

$$SE'_{Dp} = \sqrt{(.0848)(.9152)\left\{\frac{1}{609} + \frac{1}{429}\right\}} = 0.01756$$

The ratio $\dfrac{Dp}{SE'_{Dp}}$ is equal to 5.06, and if we consider only the set of alternative hypotheses H_1, then the probability of an error of the first kind if we reject H_o (equivalent to fixing the lower bound of the critical region, w, at 5.06) will be approximately 2 in 10,000,000. For the set of alternative hypotheses H_2, on the other hand, fixing the critical region, w, in the form

$$-5.06 \geqslant \frac{Dp}{SE'_{Dp}} \geqslant 5.06, \quad \text{or} \quad \left|\frac{Dp}{SE'_{Dp}}\right| \geqslant 5.06$$

the probability of an error of the first kind will be approximately 4 in 10,000,000. In either event, of course, we would reject H_o with considerable confidence. Our conclusion would be, in terms of the general hypothesis, that male patients (of gastric disorders) are more subject to ulcers than are female patients, i.e. we reject H_o in favor of the set H_1.

The hypothesis H_o, $H_o : \hat{p}_M = \hat{p}_F = \hat{p}$ is generally called the *null hypothesis*, as are others similarly expressed, by virtue of the fact that it may be written $H_o : \hat{p}_M - \hat{p}_F = 0$. Thus, the *null* hypothesis is really the hypothesis of zero difference, and is the one normally postulated and subjected to test.

Case 3: Difference Between Proportions of Dependent Samples

Wherever the same or paired (identical twins, other siblings, or matched) individuals or objects occur in the two groups, the proportions calculated on the basis of the appearance of some specified characteristic must obviously be related and the standard error formula used in the immediately preceding case cannot fit the situation. Consider, for instance, the rather common problem of determining whether two items on a mental test differ in difficulty, defined in terms of the proportion (or the percentage) of correct responses, or that of determining whether the expressions of attitude differ on two items of a questionnaire, defined in terms of the proportion (or the percentage) of "like" or "favorable" responses. From the point of view of a sampling model, it is important to distinguish between the case where the same (or paired) individuals answer the two items and the case where the items are answered by two groups of individuals randomly selected. Intuitively, we would expect greater variation in the responses in the latter than in the former case, because of the general "halo" effect of the ability or opinion, as the case may be, where the same individual responds to the two items. With reference to the coin-tossing experiment, for correlated proportions it is almost as if we had between tosses made the lower surface of a number of the coins adhesive so that the number (or proportion) of heads appearing on the second toss would be related to the number appearing on the first.

The data in the following table show the responses made by 200 children to two items on a mental test, arranged to show the number of cases in the four possible combinations of responses on the two items, namely, taking the first item first,

$$\text{correct—correct}$$
$$\text{correct—wrong}$$
$$\text{wrong—correct}$$
$$\text{wrong—wrong}$$

		SECOND ITEM		
Response		*Correct*	*Wrong*	*Total*
FIRST ITEM	Correct	131 (a)	20 (b)	151
	Wrong	0 (c)	49 (d)	49
	Total	131	69	200

response between one item + another is related (like a sequence of cards)

For the first item the proportion correct, p_1, is

$$p_1 = \frac{151}{200} = 0.755$$

for the second item the proportion correct, p_2, is

$$p_2 = \frac{131}{200} = 0.655$$

the number of cases, $N = 200$, being the same for both, of course. Likewise, if the hypothesis to be tested, H_o, is the null hypothesis

$$H_o : \hat{p}_1 = \hat{p}_2 = \hat{p}$$

the best estimate of $\hat{p}$, denoted by p, will be

$$p = \frac{p_1 + p_2}{2} = 0.705$$

Ignoring the fact that the same individuals answered both items, or assuming that the proportions are independent,|||| the standard error of the difference, $D_p = p_1 - p_2 = 0.100$, would be, since we do not know the value of $\hat{p}$ and must use the estimate p,

$$SE_{Dp}^1 = \sqrt{pq\left(\frac{1}{N_1} + \frac{1}{N_2}\right)}$$

|||| Which is wrong, because we know they are related.

$$= \sqrt{(.705)(.295)\left(\frac{1}{200} + \frac{1}{200}\right)} = 0.0456$$

and the normal deviate, Dp/SE_{Dp}^{1}, is equal to 2.19.## The corresponding probabilities are, considering the set of alternative hypotheses $H_1 : \hat{p}_1 > \hat{p}_2$, approximately 14 in 1,000, and, considering the set of alternative hypotheses $H_2 : \hat{p}_1 \neq \hat{p}_2$, approximately 28 in 1,000.

But observe what occurs when we do take into account the fact that the same individuals answered both items. The formula for the standard error of the difference between the proportions now becomes, when H_o is true,

$$SE_{Dp}^{11} = \sqrt{\frac{b + c}{N^2}} \text{ ***}$$

where $b = 20$ and $c = 0$ are the entries in the table as indicated, and $N = 200$. We have

$$SE_{Dp}^{11} = \sqrt{\frac{20 + 0}{(200)^2}} = \sqrt{\frac{1}{2,000}} = 0.02236$$

(just less than half the value of SE_{Dp}^{1}), and the corresponding normal deviate is 4.47. The appropriate values of the two probabilities considered immediately above are approximately 4 and 8 in 1,000,000—a very significant result. We would reject H_o and conclude that the two items differ significantly in difficulty.

Students interested in algebraic manipulation, and researchers interested in a formula that simplifies the calculations, should note—and prove, if they so desire—that we may write

$$\frac{Dp}{SE_{Dp}^{11}} = \frac{b - c}{\sqrt{b + c}}$$

which for our example reduces to $\frac{20}{\sqrt{20}} = \sqrt{20} = 4.47$. The only disadvantage of the formula expressed in this way is that it effectually hides any indication of the process involved, but perhaps this is more than compensated for by the ease with which the calculations may be performed.

Those interested in the derivation of the formula for the standard error of the difference between correlated proportions may be assisted by the following simple approach to the problem.††† Consider that the N pairs of responses are set forth in two columns, one for the first item and the

The normal approximation works fairly well in practice provided that, in the case of independent proportions, no cell entry is less than 5 and, for correlated proportions, the sum $b + c$ is not less than 10.

*** This formula was first given, although not exactly in this form, by Quinn McNemar, *Psychological Statistics* (New York: John Wiley & Sons, Inc., 1949), p. 80. For the derivation of the formula, and of related formulae, see subsequent paragraphs of this section.

††† For an extension to more than two columns, see the general formula in W. G. Cochran, "The Comparison of Percentages in Matched Samples," *Biometrika*, XXXVII, Parts 3 and 4 (December, 1950), 256–66.

other for the second item, with a "correct" response denoted by a 1 and a "wrong" response by a 0.‡‡‡ Without specifying for the moment any particular hypothesis to be tested, and consequently any particular arrangement of the responses in relation to each other, consider the differences that occur when we subtract the response values for each individual, say the second from the first, for each item. We can have the following response patterns: $1 - 1 = 0$; $1 - 0 = 1$; $0 - 1 = -1$; and $0 - 0 = 0$, corresponding to the cells a, b, c, and d, respectively, of the table shown earlier. Using $\hat{b}$ and $\hat{c}$ to denote the population or expected values of b and c, clearly the expected mean of the differences must be, excluding the trivial case $\hat{b} = \hat{c} = 0$,

$$\xi_D = \frac{\hat{b} - \hat{c}}{N} = \hat{p}_1 - \hat{p}_2$$

and likewise the standard deviation of the distribution of differences (for the population to which any observed set of differences may relate) will be

$$\sigma_D = \sqrt{\frac{\hat{b} + \hat{c}}{N} - \left(\frac{\hat{b} - \hat{c}}{N}\right)^2}$$

since the sum of squares of the differences must be equal to $\hat{b} + \hat{c}$. Consequently the standard error of the mean D in repeated random sampling will be

$$SE_D = \frac{\sigma_D}{\sqrt{N}} = \sqrt{\frac{1}{N}\left\{\frac{\hat{b} + \hat{c}}{N} - \left(\frac{\hat{b} - \hat{c}}{N}\right)^2\right\}}$$

This is the general formula for the standard error of the difference between two correlated proportions, when no hypothesis is made which specifies a relation between them. Observe, next, that for ξ_D to be zero, we must have $\hat{b} - \hat{c} = 0$, which yields for the standard error

$$SE_D^1 = \sqrt{\frac{\hat{b} + \hat{c}}{N^2}}$$

Using the sample or actual values as estimates of $\hat{b}$ and $\hat{c}$, which is satisfactory enough when $b + c$ is greater than 10, the appropriate normal deviate will be $\dfrac{b - c}{\sqrt{b + c}}$, as we stated earlier without proof.§§§

Comparison of Changes in Proportions in Two Groups

These statistical tests can be extended without difficulty to the comparison of changes in an experimental group and a control group.‖‖ This

‡‡‡ Any values could probably be used, but these are the simplest and yield the simplest result.

§§§ See the next chapter for the test of the related hypothesis of a *proportional change.*

‖‖ See McNemar, *op. cit.*, pp. 80–82.

is an important consideration in education and psychology, in particular, because of the almost inevitable changes that occur in individuals whether or not they are subject to the influence of an experimental factor. In an experimental-control-groups situation, we may be interested in the difference in the changes in the proportions in the two groups of individuals. If the experimental factor has no effect, then the change in the proportions for the experimental group will not be significantly different from the change in the proportions for the control group: if the experimental factor has an effect, then the change for the experimental group will be significantly different from the change for the control group.

Using Δ_E to denote the change in the proportions for the experimental group, and Δ_C to denote the change in the proportions for the control group, then in the population

$$\Delta_E = \hat{p}_{1E} - \hat{p}_{2E} \quad \text{and} \quad \Delta_C = \hat{p}_{1C} - \hat{p}_{2C}$$

The hypothesis to be tested, H_o, will be

$$H_o : \Delta_E - \Delta_C = 0$$

and the set of admissible alternative hypotheses will be

$$H : \Delta_E - \Delta_C \neq 0$$

It may be that in a particular problem the set of admissible alternative hypotheses would be

$$H_1 : \Delta_E - \Delta_C > 0$$
$$\text{or} \quad H_2 : \Delta_E - \Delta_C < 0$$

but this can be easily taken care of in the calculation of the probability of an error of the first kind by using only one end of the distribution of the normal deviate. Otherwise no change need be made in the procedure or in the formulae.

In developing the appropriate test of H_o, we must again distinguish between two possible experimental situations. In the first, which has been considered by McNemar,### the experimental and control groups comprise different individuals that are not paired or matched in any way, i.e. the two groups may be considered as independent samples. But researchers frequently use the same or paired (matched, sibs, or identical twins) individuals in the experimental and control groups, for the obvious reason that the gain in precision of the experiment and in simplicity of interpretation makes it worth while to design the experiment in this fashion. The formula given by McNemar is appropriate for use in the first case but not in the second (as it happens, the latter situation is simpler and probably more important than the former). In the following discussion, we will treat each of these cases separately.

Independent Experimental and Control Groups

The test of H_o is not very difficult to devise in this case, although as we shall see certain complications may occur because the test of the differ-

Ibid.

ence between the groups is not independent of the subsidiary, or perhaps basic, test of significance of the change within each group. Denoting by d_E the sample estimate of Δ_E, based on the sample proportions, and by d_C the sample estimate of Δ_C, then an appropriate test of H_o will be in the form

$$\frac{d_E - d_C}{SE_{d_E - d_C}}$$

Now the denominator, for independent samples, will be simply $\sqrt{\sigma^2_{\Delta_E} + \sigma^2_{\Delta_C}}$ and since we have already derived the formulae for $\sigma^2_{\Delta_E}$ and $\sigma^2_{\Delta_C}$ the problem is solved.* The only question is which of the two possible formulae for each of the components should be used. It will be remembered that for the general case the appropriate formula is

$$SE_D = \sqrt{\frac{1}{N}\left\{\frac{\hat{b} + \hat{c}}{N} - \left(\frac{\hat{b} - \hat{c}}{N}\right)^2\right\}}$$

whereas, when the hypothesis that there is no change in the proportions within the group is true, this formula reduces to

$$SE_D^1 = \sqrt{\frac{\hat{b} + \hat{c}}{N^2}}$$

To be consistent, we should test each of the subsidiary hypotheses first ($\Delta_E = 0$ and $\Delta_C = 0$), and then use SE_D if the hypothesis is rejected and SE_D^1 if it is accepted. We may note, parenthetically, that SE_D and SE_D^1 will differ considerably when $\hat{b}$ is much larger (or smaller) than $\hat{c}$.

As an illustration, consider the data reported by McNemar for comparing changes in length-of-war estimates.† Using our notation, he had the following observed values:

CONTROL GROUP ($N = 181$)

$a = 107$	$c = 14$
$b = 8$	$d = 52$

EXPERIMENTAL GROUP ($N = 205$)

$a = 135$	$c = 34$
$b = 0$	$d = 36$

For the control group, we have for the test of $H_o : \Delta_C = 0$,

$$\frac{Dp}{SE_D^1} = \frac{b - c}{\sqrt{b + c}} = -1.28$$

and we would accept the hypothesis tested and consequently use as an estimate of σ_{Δ_C} the value $\sqrt{\dfrac{b + c}{N^2}} = 0.0259$. For the experimental group, on

---

* We shall consider only the hypothesis postulated by McNemar ($H_o: b - c = 0$).
† Op. cit., Table 12, p. 81. Adapted with permission of the publishers.

the other hand, we have for the test of $H_o : \Delta_E = 0$,

$$\frac{Dp}{SE_D^i} = \frac{b - c}{\sqrt{b + c}} = -5.83$$

and we would reject the hypothesis tested and consequently use as an estimate of σ_{Δ_E} the value

$$\sqrt{\frac{1}{N} \left\{ \frac{b + c}{N} - \left(\frac{b - c}{N} \right)^2 \right\}} = 0.0260$$

(instead of the value of 0.029 given by McNemar). Substituting these values in the formula for $SE_{d_E - d_C}$, we have

$$SE_{d_E - d_C} = \sqrt{(0.0260)^2 + (0.0259)^2} = 0.0367$$

(McNemar obtained 0.039). Now

$$d_E - d_C = 0.132$$

so our normal deviate is $\dfrac{0.132}{0.0367} = 3.60$ (as compared with the value of 3.38

given by McNemar). Accordingly, we reject the hypothesis $H_o : \Delta_E - \Delta_C = 0$ and conclude that the change in the experimental group was significantly different from the change in the control group.‡

Equated Experimental and Control Groups

The formulae about to be derived are general and apply to any comparison of the difference between changes in the proportions in two groups when the individuals are either the same or paired. We may or may not have experimental and control groups, and in fact in the illustration to be used we have not, because we are concerned with the difference between pairs of responses on an interest inventory where the 4 responses concerned were made by the same individuals.§ The most interesting feature of the proposed test is that we may proceed directly to the test of the hypothesis $H_o : \Delta_E - \Delta_C = 0$ without reference to the subsidiary or basic hypotheses that it was necessary to consider in the previous case.

Following the schematic representation of the responses used earlier,‖ assigning a 1 for a favorable response and a 0 for an unfavorable response, we can set up the following pattern of responses (see page 113).

We have, of course, indicated only the 4 possible types of differences for Δ_F and Δ_S (differences for first and second pair of items, respectively), although in practice we must record the responses in this form for each of the N individuals. This table of 6 by N entries can be neatly summarized

‡ For this particular example, where $b = 0$, the same decision is made (to reject $H_o : \Delta_E - \Delta_C = 0$) regardless of the formula used.

§ Analogous to the situation considered by McNemar, *op. cit.*, in Table 31, p. 201.

‖ Which, with a suitable adaptation, will fit any such case of a twofold classification of responses.

INDIVIDUAL	FIRST PAIR OF ITEMS			SECOND PAIR OF ITEMS		
	First Response	*Second Response*	*Difference* Δ_F	*First Response*	*Second Response*	*Difference* Δ_S
1	1	1	0	1	1	0
2	1	0	1	1	0	1
3	0	1	−1	0	1	−1
4	0	0	0	0	0	0
.	.	.	.	.	.	.
.	.	.	.	.	.	.
.	.	.	.	.	.	.
N		.	.	.	.	.

by the following schema, where the letters $a, b, \ldots, i$, denote frequencies of occurrence of the corresponding pattern of responses:

		Δ_S	SECOND PAIR OF ITEMS		
	Δ_F		$(10) = +1$	$(11), (00) = 0$	$(01) = -1$
FIRST PAIR OF ITEMS	$(10) = +1$		$a\ (1010 = 0)$	$b \begin{pmatrix} 1011 = +1 \\ 1000 = +1 \end{pmatrix}$	$c\ (1001 = +2)$
	$(11), (00) = 0$		$d \begin{pmatrix} 1110 = -1 \\ 0010 = -1 \end{pmatrix}$	$e \begin{pmatrix} 1111 = 0 \\ 1100 = 0 \\ 0011 = 0 \\ 0000 = 0 \end{pmatrix}$	$f \begin{pmatrix} 1101 = -1 \\ 0001 = -1 \end{pmatrix}$
	$(01) = -1$		$g\ (0110 = -2)$	$h \begin{pmatrix} 0111 = -1 \\ 0100 = -1 \end{pmatrix}$	$i\ (0101 = 0)$

The peculiar-looking system of numbers (like a binary notation) represents the pattern of responses on the four items and the corresponding value of $\Delta_F - \Delta_S$: for example, the responses of the first hypothetical individual in the preceding table would be written $1\,1\,1\,1 = 0$ since $\Delta_F = 1 - 1 = 0$, $\Delta_S = 1 - 1 = 0$, and $\Delta_F - \Delta_S = 0$.

Consider now the differences $\Delta = \Delta_F - \Delta_S$. It will be seen that, using the circumflex to denote population values,#

$$N\xi_\Delta = (\hat{b} + 2\hat{c} + \hat{f}) - (\hat{d} + 2\hat{g} + \hat{h})$$

and $\sigma_\Delta = \dfrac{1}{N} \sqrt{N\{N + [3(\hat{c}+\hat{g}) - (\hat{a}+\hat{e}+\hat{i})]\} - \{(\hat{b}+2\hat{c}+\hat{f}) - (\hat{d}+2\hat{g}+\hat{h})\}^2}$

When the hypothesis to be tested is true, i.e. $H_o : \Delta_F - \Delta_S = 0$, then $\xi_\Delta = 0$ and

$$\hat{b} + 2\hat{c} + \hat{f} = \hat{d} + 2\hat{g} + \hat{h}$$

and $\sigma_\Delta = \sqrt{\dfrac{N + [3(\hat{c}+\hat{g}) - (\hat{a}+\hat{e}+\hat{i})]}{N}}$

\# These formulae have been set up for simplicity in calculation, not for elegance or ease of algebraic manipulation.

and the standard error of the mean difference will be $\dfrac{\sigma_\Delta}{\sqrt{N}}$, which becomes

$$SE_{\text{Mean}_\Delta} = \frac{\sqrt{N + [3(\hat{c} + \hat{g}) - (\hat{a} + \hat{e} + \hat{\imath})]}}{N}$$

The appropriate approximate test of our hypothesis $H_o : \Delta_F - \Delta_S = 0$ will therefore, be given by use of the normal deviate (using observed values as estimates)

$$\frac{D_D}{SE_{D_D}} = \frac{(b + 2c + f) - (d + 2g + h)}{\sqrt{N + [3(c + g) - (a + e + i)]}} \quad **$$

and the tables of the normal distribution areas.††

The two questions selected as an illustration from the interest inventory were as follows:

"118. Do work in which you become acquainted with many people.

119. Do work requiring planning and organizing."

to each of which the student responded in terms of his interest and of his participation. It was felt, on *a priori* grounds, that there might be a significant difference in interest versus participation (in terms of favorable responses) on the two items.‡‡ Upon recording the responses of 113 grades 11 and 12 students in an Ontario secondary school, the following observed values were obtained:

$a =$	1	$f =$	19
$b =$	9	$g =$	1
$c =$	1	$h =$	19
$d =$	2	$i =$	13
$e =$	48	Total $=$	113

The double-pattern schema is as shown below,

1	9	1
2	48	19
1	19	13

and, intuitively, one would not expect any significant difference to appear

** As a check, note that these formulae reduce to those used earlier to test the hypothesis $H_o : \Delta_F = 0$ if we set equal to zero all the unnecessary letters and make the other appropriate changes in notation.

†† The test will not work very well if the total $b+c+f+d+g+h$ is less than about 10.

‡‡ Permission to use these items and the data relating to them was very kindly granted by the author of the interest inventory, Professor H. M. Fowler of the Department of Educational Research, University of Toronto.

because the table is roughly symmetrical about the *aei* diagonal. Making the substitutions in the formula, we find

$$\frac{D_D}{SE_{D_D}} = \frac{7}{\sqrt{57}} = 0.93$$

and, accordingly, we would accept the hypothesis $H_o : \Delta_F - \Delta_S = 0$ and conclude that there is no significant difference in interest versus participation on the two items.

We hasten to add that we have not by this test extracted all the possible information from our data. The four subsidiary tables of most interest, and that reveal why the above result was not significant, are given below with the responses as indicated.

ITEM	RE-SPONSE	INTEREST 119		TOTAL
		1	0	
Interest	1	16	37	53
118	0	3	57	60
Total		19	94	113

$$\frac{b - c}{\sqrt{b + c}} = \frac{34}{\sqrt{40}} = 5.38$$

ITEM	RE-SPONSE	PARTICI-PATION 119		TOTAL
		1	0	
Partici-pation 118	1	42	33	75
	0	6	32	38
Total		48	65	113

$$\frac{b - c}{\sqrt{b + c}} = \frac{27}{\sqrt{39}} = 4.32$$

ITEM	RE-SPONSE	PARTICI-PATION 118		TOTAL
		1	0	
Interest	1	42	11	53
118	0	33	27	60
Total		75	38	113

$$\frac{b - c}{\sqrt{b + c}} = \frac{-22}{\sqrt{44}} = -3.32$$

ITEM	RE-SPONSE	PARTICI-PATION 119		TOTAL
		1	0	
Interest	1	15	4	19
119	0	33	61	94
Total		48	65	113

$$\frac{b - c}{\sqrt{b + c}} = \frac{-29}{\sqrt{37}} = -4.78$$

The appropriate test for the hypothesis $H_o : \hat{p}_1 = \hat{p}_2$ is indicated below each table: in all cases we would reject H_o. But note that the pattern of responses, when items 118 and 119 are compared, is roughly the same, which explains why we did not find any significant difference when changes in the two items were compared.§§

§§ Despite the improbability of an "Irishism" with a Norwegian accent, we may state that the items are different although they are the same! They differ in their differences in the same direction, and consequently do not differ significantly.

We should probably point out that the formulae we have derived above apply also to the test of the hypothesis $H_o: \hat{p}_1 = \hat{p}_2$ where the responses to each item, or part of each item, are coded in three categories, $+1$, 0, and -1. The interpretation is not the same, of course, and indeed is very difficult to express in terms of proportions. Moreover, it is a relatively simple matter to extend the general method we used in the development of these formulae to derive the appropriate formula for almost any type of situation of this kind. The number of possible developments is legion, and we have not thought it worth while to record them. Where the circumstances require a more complex classification of the responses—into four or five categories, for example—it is probably simpler to assign numerical equivalents to the categories and treat the values as if they were continuous variables, although they are not, and express the hypothesis in terms of means. The appropriate methods and statistical tests for this type of situation are considered in Chapter VI.

EXERCISES

1. If one of your subjects got two items correct in a 20-item true-false test, what conclusion would you reach? Why?

2. In a "blindfold" test of two brands of cigarettes, 4 cigarettes of each brand were selected and the 8 presented in random order to the subject, who was required to "take a few puffs" from each and name the brand. He named 7 of the 8 correctly. Would you conclude that the subject could, in fact, distinguish between the two brands of cigarettes?

3. State the null statistical hypothesis and the set of admissible alternative hypotheses for each of questions 1 and 2, and perform the approximate tests of the null hypotheses described in the text.

4. (a) The executives of a company have had a total of 114 children, but of these 75 have been boys and 39 girls. For the United States as a whole, however, there are 51 boys born to every 49 girls. Is there an unexpected characteristic of executives?

   (b) Did you use a one-tailed or a two-tailed test of the null hypothesis? Justify your action.

5. Would you conclude from the following data that women drivers have been unjustly accused?

NUMBER OF ACCIDENTS	WOMEN DRIVERS	MEN DRIVERS
None	9	44
One or more	6	6

6. If a political issue is favored by 55 per cent of a sample of 200 Republicans and by 46 per cent of a sample of 250 Democrats, what would you conclude, in general, about the opinions of the two parties? Justify your conclusion, if you can.

7. A total of 120 subjects was used to test the effect of practice on a highly complex coordination exercise. On the first trial, 40 of the subjects were successful, whereas on the final trial 50 subjects were successful. Over the period of practice, 20 subjects showed improvement as compared with 10 who enjoyed a loss in skill. What would you conclude about the effect of practice on success in this exercise?

8. If 42 of 60 rats turn to the right at a critical point in a maze *before* conditioning, but only 35 do so *after* conditioning, and of which only 30 belonged to the original group of "right-turners," did the conditioning have a significant effect?

9. The responses of 100 persons to two items on an interest inventory yielded the following results. May we conclude that the two items were of equal interest?

ITEM		SECOND ITEM	
	Response	*Interested*	*Not Interested*
FIRST ITEM	Interested	24	25
	Not Interested	8	43

10. The following reactions were observed in a group of soldiers before and after a pep-talk by a senior officer. What should he have done?

		BEFORE TALK		
		Grumblers	*Non-Grumblers*	*Total*
AFTER TALK	Grumblers	70	10	80
	Non-Grumblers	0	70	70
	Total	70	80	150

11. As a control or check, a group of 200 soldiers in another camp were observed in the same fashion as those in Question 10, but were not subjected to the pep-talk. Their pattern of reactions was as follows:

		FIRST OBSERVATION PERIOD		
		Grumblers	*Non-Grumblers*	*Total*
SECOND OBSERVATION PERIOD	Grumblers	80	25	105
	Non-Grumblers	18	77	95
	Total	98	102	200

Was there a significant change in this group between the two periods?

12. Compare the two groups of soldiers of questions 10 and 11 on the following bases:

    (a) at first observation period

    (b) at final observation period

    (c) on difference in changes between the two periods.

13. (a) The pattern of responses on two other pairs of items (pair being interest and participation) on Fowler's interest inventory (see p. 114) yielded the following pattern:

$$
\begin{array}{ll}
a = 19 & f = 15 \\
b = 21 & g = 1 \\
c = 13 & h = 2 \\
d = 2 & i = 16 \\
e = 24 & \overline{N = 113}
\end{array}
$$

    Did the interest-versus-participation patterns differ on the two items?

    (b) For the first item, the values required for the interest versus participation test are $b = 53$ and $c = 19$; for the second, the corresponding values are $b = 22$ and $c = 44$. Test the corresponding hypotheses, as in the examples discussed in the text, and decide whether the results agree in the (a) and (b) parts of this question.

CHAPTER V

Tests of Statistical Hypotheses Expressed in Terms of Frequencies

In a very wide variety of problems in many fields, we cannot measure on any scale but must rest content with a classification or categorization of the data. Under these conditions, and in a limited number of other situations, our observations consist essentially of the frequencies occurring in the various cells or compartments of a table of simple or multiple classification. Generally it is possible, and convenient, to express the hypothesis to be tested in terms of the *expected* frequencies pertaining to the cells. No matter what the underlying situation may be, although this is of prime importance in the interpretation of the results, the basic problem is a comparison of the *observed* and *expected* frequencies in each cell and the determination of acceptable limits within which the observed frequencies may diverge from the expected due solely to errors of repeated random sampling from the parent population.

Consider, for example, the jth of a set of cells for the parent population in which the *proportion* of members of the population is $\hat{p}_j$. Now, in a sample of size N we observe a proportion p_j in that cell, so that we have an observed frequency, which we may denote by O_j, of $O_j = Np_j$ and an expected frequency, which we may denote by E_j, of $E_j = N\hat{p}_j$, and a difference between observed and expected frequencies of

$$O_j - E_j = Np_j - N\hat{p}_j = N(p_j - \hat{p}_j)$$

How great will these differences, $O_j - E_j$, be in repeated random sampling? Students will see a clue to the solution in terms of our earlier discussion of proportions if they observe that the difference between O and E depends, for any specified value of N, only on the difference between p_j and $\hat{p}_j$—the observed and expected *proportion* of observations in the jth cell. The general solution to the problem for k cells and samples of size N is found, in fact, in the multinomial distribution, since the probability of getting n_1 in the first cell, n_2 in the second cell, and so on to n_k in the kth cell, will be the corresponding term in

$$(\hat{p}_1 + \hat{p}_2 + \ldots + \hat{p}_k)^N$$

which, of course, reduces to the binomial form when $k = 2$. But it is an exceedingly laborious matter to evaluate the terms of the multinomial, and hence the calculation of the exact probabilities of errors of the first kind is not practicable. Fortunately, an approximation due to Pearson (1900) is available that yields in most cases probabilities that are exact enough for all practical purposes. Provided the theoretical frequencies, E, are not small*—the generally accepted minimum being 5—then we can get a fair approximation to the probabilities by using the statistic

$$\chi^2 = \sum_{j=1}^{k} \frac{(O_j - E_j)^2}{E_j}$$

which has the distribution of the sum of squares of $k-1$ independent normal variates of unit variance.

Pearson, Yule, Fisher, and others have provided tables of the χ^2 distribution, from which the desired probabilities of errors of the first kind may be easily read, i.e. $P(\chi^2 > \chi_o^2)$. Fisher's table of χ^2, reproduced in Appendix B, is probably the most convenient for tests of statistical hypotheses. To use this table, however, one must first determine the *number of degrees of freedom*, which Fisher denotes by n. For values of n greater than 30, Fisher suggests that the probabilities be obtained by assuming the quantity $\sqrt{2\chi^2} - \sqrt{2n-1}$ is a normal deviate with unit variance, yielding an approximation to the χ^2 probabilities. We must examine these two points in more detail before we illustrate how the table may be used in tests of statistical hypotheses.

Consider, first, the concept of *degrees of freedom* as it applies in this particular situation. Let us assume that we have k cells or compartments *after* whatever regrouping may be necessary to secure that no value of E_j is less than 5.† The number of degrees of freedom is then equal to the number of *independent* differences $O_j - E_j$; or, to state it in another way, equal to k minus the number of conditions or constraints that we impose on these differences. Two quite distinct situations arise in practice: (1) the E's may be completely determined, except for the value of N, by some law, principle, or theory, quite independent of the observed set of frequencies; (2) the E's may be determined in part by the observed set of values, i.e. constrained in one or more ways to agree with them. For instance, if the theory specifies that a distribution is normal with mean ξ and standard deviation σ,‡ then the theoretical frequencies are quite independent of the observed save for the fact that both totals must equal N. But we may require that

---

* Equivalent to the assumption, for the basic binomial form, that the frequencies form a normal system of variates.

† It has been indicated that a minimum of 5 is too conservative: see William G. Cochran, "Some Methods for Strengthening the Common χ^2 Tests," *Biometrics*, X (December, 1954), 417–51.

‡ For an intelligence test, for example, the theory might specify that $\xi = 100$ and $\sigma = 16$ I.Q. points.

ξ and σ agree with the observed values of the mean and standard deviation, respectively, and it is now obvious that we have forced our distributions of O's and E's to agree in number, mean, and standard deviation. Note that we have used the estimates derived from the sample, not the values of the population parameters, in calculating the E's in the latter situation. Fisher has shown for this second case that, if the sample and each cell-frequency are large, if the number of degrees of freedom is reduced by one for each such parameter estimated from the sample data, and if maximum likelihood estimates are used,§ we may use the same table of χ^2 for testing the corresponding statistical hypothesis. These conditions are reasonably well satisfied in a very large number of problems.

In regard to the approximation suggested by Fisher for n greater than 30, it is quite good and may be sufficiently accurate for most practical situations. However, a closer approximation—although slightly more difficult to use—has been suggested by Wilson and Hilferty,‖ namely that we use as a normal deviate (of zero mean and unit standard deviation) the quantity

$$\left\{ \left(\frac{\chi^2}{n}\right)^{\frac{1}{3}} + \frac{2}{9n} - 1 \right\} \left\{ \frac{9n}{2} \right\}^{\frac{1}{2}}$$

whenever n is greater than 30. Actually, the Wilson-Hilferty approximation gives amazingly accurate results for values of n as low as 20, as students may very easily determine from the above formula and the tabled values of χ^2.

In summary, then, we have in the chi-square distribution a very useful tool to use in tests of any statistical hypotheses that are, or may be, expressed in terms of expected frequencies. The greatest advantage of it is that the distribution function of χ^2 depends only on the number of degrees of freedom, which we always know or can determine, not on the form of the distribution, nor any of its parameters, to which the frequencies apply. It is a non-parametric or distribution-free test, therefore, which is a very important consideration.# It must always be remembered, however, that the probabilities obtained through it are only approximations to the exact (and generally unknown) probabilities of errors of the first kind.

Perhaps it is worth while to digress for a moment and compare the exact and approximate probabilities for the simple case of coin-tossing, where we can calculate the exact probabilities without too much difficulty. Further, let us first consider the case $N = 10$, where the expected frequencies, E, are at the minimum value of 5, and we have 1 degree of freedom—something

§ See Chapter X for a discussion of methods of estimation of population parameters.

‖ E. B. Wilson and M. M. Hilferty, "The Distribution of Chi-square," *National Academy of Science*, XVII (1931), 694.

Chapter IX deals with non-parametric tests.

of an extreme test of the accuracy of our approximation. Just how exacting and revealing is this empirical test will become apparent in the sequel.**

Assuming that our coin is unbiased, the expected number of heads—and of tails—in 10 tosses of the coin will be exactly 5. For each sample of size 10, we have only two compartments or cells (heads and tails), so that our value of χ^2 may be expressed, denoting the number of heads by H and the number of tails by T,

$$\chi^2 = \frac{(H-5)^2}{5} + \frac{(T-5)^2}{5} = \frac{2}{5}(H-5)^2$$

Observe, next, that the number of heads that can occur will vary by integer values from 0 to 10, so that we have the following limited number of *possible* values of χ^2 in this situation:

Number of Heads	10	9	8	7	6	5	4	3	2	1	0
Corresponding χ^2	10.0	6.4	3.6	1.6	0.4	0	0.4	1.6	3.6	6.4	10.0

Two points are evident from this table of possible values: (1) that not all values of χ^2 can occur in this case, although required to do so by the continuous nature of χ^2; and (2) that χ^2 has the same value for 6 and 4 heads, 7 and 3 heads, and so on, and does not in itself distinguish between these situations. Since we have previously calculated the probabilities for this particular binomial case, we may refer directly to the comparison in the following table:

COMBINATION OF HEADS	EXACT (BINOMIAL) CUMULATIVE PROBABILITY	VALUE OF χ_o^2	$P\{\chi^2 > \chi_o^2\}$††
5	1.0000	0	1.0000
4 and 6	0.7539	0.4	0.5271
3 and 7	0.3438	1.6	0.2059
2 and 8	0.1094	3.6	0.0578
1 and 9	0.0215	6.4	0.0114
0 and 10	0.0020	10.0	0.0016

Quite clearly the approximation to the exact probabilities leaves much to be desired, so that for discrete data of this type and with small samples any critical region defined in terms of χ^2 may not be altogether satisfactory.

** The chi-square test is often referred to as an *exact* test, because the form of distribution of χ^2 is known. But students should be aware that this does not necessarily mean that it is an exact test of a particular statistical hypothesis, since from it we may be able only to approximate the required probabilities of errors.

†† In this and the next table, the chi-square probabilities were obtained from supplementary tables of χ^2 for 1 degree of freedom, first prepared by G. Udny Yule (see *An Introduction to the Theory of Statistics* [London: Charles Griffin and Company, 1929], pp. 388–89).

The agreement is better when $N = 20$, as the following table reveals, although still far from perfect. But we will not be too greatly in error if we use the chi-square probabilities, certainly not for samples of 50 and greater, provided that we remember the statistical test we are using is an approximation. The saving in labor will more than compensate for the lack of exactness in our probability estimates.

COMBINATION OF HEADS	EXACT (BINOMIAL) CUMULATIVE PROBABILITY	VALUE OF χ_o^2	$P\{\chi^2 > \chi_o^2\}$
10	1.0000	0	1.0000
9 and 11	0.8238	0.2	0.6547
8 and 12	0.5034	0.8	0.3711
7 and 13	0.2631	1.8	0.1797
6 and 14	0.1153	3.2	0.0736
5 and 15	0.0414	5.0	0.0254
4 and 16	0.0118	7.2	0.0073
3 and 17	0.0026	9.8	0.0017
2 and 18	0.0004	12.8	0.0004
1 and 19	0.00004	16.2	0.00006
0 and 20	0.000002	20.0	0.000008

The form of the chi-square distribution requires some explanation. It will be seen from the definition of χ^2 that it can never be less than zero but may vary (at least theoretically) in the positive direction without limit. For convenience, we may write the formula for its distribution in terms of the number of degrees of freedom, denoted by n, as follows:

$$y = p(\chi^2) = \frac{1}{2^{\frac{n}{2}} \overline{\left| \frac{n}{2} \right.}} (\chi^2)^{\frac{n}{2} - 1} \exp\left(-\frac{\chi^2}{2} \right)$$

$\rightarrow$ Gamma Function

which is known in calculus as an incomplete gamma function. For 1 degree of freedom the curve is asymptotic to the y-axis, dropping off very quickly as χ^2 increases, since the formula for this case reduces to

$$\frac{1}{\sqrt{2\pi\chi^2}} e^{\frac{-\chi^2}{2}}$$

For 2 degrees of freedom, the formula reduces to $\dfrac{e^{\frac{-\chi^2}{2}}}{2}$, so that the curve starts at 0.5 and again drops off rapidly as χ^2 increases. For 3 degrees of freedom, and all higher values of n, the curve starts at zero, rises to a maximum and then decreases slowly (the distribution is always single-humped), with the maximum ordinate (save for $n = 1$) at the value $\chi^2 = n - 2$. The distribution tends to normality as n increases, but very slowly.

After this discussion of χ^2, its distribution form, and its limitations or inaccuracies under certain conditions, we are in a position to illustrate its use in tests of statistical hypotheses. In doing so, we will consider, first, the examples where the expected frequencies are determined by some theory, law, or principle, and, second, the examples where the expected frequencies are determined in part by the observed data, i.e. constrained in a number of ways to fit the observed set of frequencies.

Case 1: Use of χ^2-test Where the Only Constraint is $\Sigma E = \Sigma O = N$

In each of the following examples, the number of degrees of freedom will be $n = k - 1$, where k is the number of compartments or cells. This is a simple and straightforward application of the method, the only point requiring care is the imposed condition that in no cell or compartment shall the expected frequency be less than 5.‡‡

Coin-tossing and Die-rolling Examples

As a first illustration, let us consider the 50 tosses of 10 coins made by a group of our students, for which we raised the question of whether they had followed their instructions. Assuming that the coins used were un-

TABLE V.1

ILLUSTRATION OF USE OF χ^2-TEST: OBSERVED AND EXPECTED FREQUENCIES FOR 50 TOSSES OF 10 COINS SIMULTANEOUSLY

NUMBER OF HEADS	EXPECTED FREQUENCY (E)	OBSERVED FREQUENCY (O)	$O - E$	$\dfrac{(O - E)^2}{E}$
10	⎧ 0.049	⎧		
9	8.593 ⎨ 0.488	5 ⎨	−3.593	1.50
8	2.197			
7	⎩ 5.859	⎩ 5		
6	10.254	16	+5.746	3.22
5	12.305	13	+0.695	0.04
4	10.254	10	−0.254	0.01
3	⎧ 5.859	⎧ 5		
2	8.593 ⎨ 2.197	6 ⎨ 1	−2.593	0.78
1	0.488			
0	⎩ 0.049	⎩		
Total	49.999	50	0.001	($\chi^2 =$) 5.55

‡‡ We are aware of the fact that recent studies have indicated that the rigid application of this rule may be harmful and that, for continuous frequency distributions at least, we should probably use many more class intervals—using class intervals of unequal width—than has been customary, in order to avoid the lack of sensitivity that arises when the expected frequencies are very high. Readers interested in these developments will find an excellent summary in the following reference: W. G. Cochran, "The χ^2 Test of Goodness of Fit," *The Annals of Mathematical Statistics*, XXIII, No. 3 (September, 1952). But the proper use of such refinements requires a background of experience in statistical methods far beyond that possessed by most students.

biased and the instructions were followed exactly, we can calculate the expected frequencies of occurrence from the terms of

$$50(\tfrac{1}{2} + \tfrac{1}{2})^{10}$$

and compare them with the observed frequencies. The results, and the necessary calculations, are given in Table V.1.

Note the grouping of expected frequencies to satisfy the condition that no E shall be less than 5. For a value of $\chi_o^2 = 5.55$, with 4 degrees of freedom, the probability (approximate) of an error of the first kind, $P(\chi^2 > \chi_o^2)$, is 20 in 100. The agreement between observed and expected frequencies is fair, therefore, and we would accept the statistical hypothesis $H_o : p = \tfrac{1}{2}$ since there is no good reason to conclude otherwise than that we have a sample drawn at random from that hypothetical population. In terms of our general hypothesis, we must conclude that in suspecting the students of "cooking" the results we were unjust. We have no evidence that they used biased coins or did not follow their instructions in tossing the coins.

As a second illustration, consider the results of 60 rolls of a die given below:

Face	1	2	3	4	5	6
Frequency	16	10	7	17	4	6

If the die were a true one and properly rolled, the expected frequency of occurrence of each face would be exactly 10. May we conclude from the data that the die was either biased or rolled improperly?§§ Applying the χ^2-test, we have $\chi_o^2 = 14.6$ with 5 degrees of freedom. The observed event is a somewhat unlikely one, since the probability of securing in random sampling a value of χ^2 greater than 14.6 for $n = 5$ is just slightly greater than 1 in 100. Accordingly, we would be inclined to reject the hypothesis H_o. As for the general hypothesis, we would probably conclude that the die was either biased or improperly rolled. (These data, alone, do not of course tell us which of the alternatives should be accepted.)

Questionnaire-Analysis Example

Students will realize that this method can be applied in a wide variety of situations, such as in analyzing replies to items on a questionnaire or to opinions expressed in an interview, wherever the general hypothesis (which may or may not be a law or principle) is such that the expected frequencies can be independently determined. For the data given by Gleason,‖‖ for

§§ These data were obtained through the efforts of the six-year-old son, Peter, of one of the authors. It was thought that his throws might not be made in a proper manner, owing to a lack of experience.

‖‖ John G. Gleason, "Attitude vs. Information on the Taft-Hartley Law," *Personnel Psychology*, II, No. 3 (Autumn, 1949), 295.

instance, the observed frequencies of expressed attitude toward the Taft-Hartley Law of 1,088 industrial production workers were as follows:

ATTITUDE	FREQUENCY
Favor	323
Oppose	453
No Opinion	312
Total	1,088

Assuming that the sample was a representative one, what conclusions may be reached concerning the attitudes of industrial production workers in general toward the Taft-Hartley Law?

The first question should properly be, do the workers hold definite opinions (of any kind) in regard to this law? Setting up the null hypothesis of a 50-50 division for with-opinion versus no-opinion, we have the observed and expected frequencies indicated below:##

	WITH OPINION	NO OPINION	TOTAL
Observed Frequency	776	312	1,088
Expected Frequency	544	544	1,088

The corresponding χ^2-test yields a value of $\chi_o^2 = 197.88$ with 1 degree of freedom: under the condition stipulated, we must reject this null hypothesis and, in view of the data, conclude that the majority of these workers hold a definite opinion in regard to the Taft-Hartley Law. Students may, as an exercise, by a suitable classification of the data and calculation of the corresponding value of χ_o^2, check the validity of the following general conclusions:***

1. A majority of the workers do not definitely oppose the Taft-Hartley Law (*oppose* versus *not*-oppose:††† $\chi_o^2 = 30.44$).
2. Of the workers who have a definite opinion, a majority oppose the Taft-Hartley Law (*oppose* versus *favor*: $\chi_o^2 = 21.78$).

We need not give further illustrations in order to stress the need to specify exactly the hypothesis being tested and also the set of admissible alternative hypotheses. The need to phrase the conclusions, specific and general, carefully should be self-evident: if it is not, a little practice in rephrasing the above two conclusions into several forms will be sufficient to demon-

Students should determine what conclusion they would draw if the hypothesis were that the workers assigned responses at random to the three categories.

*** Obviously the statistical results may easily be manipulated to support either or both sides in this case, i.e. by omitting the essential qualifying words and phrases.

††† *Favor* plus *no opinion* groups.

strate how many traps are scattered around awaiting the tender feet of the unwary.

Example of Goodness of Fit of Observed and Expected Frequency Distributions

As a final illustration, in this case of what is generally called "goodness of fit," we turn to the rough check of the validity of the sampling procedures followed in an earlier chapter, using the results for the first 1,000 draws from the Poisson population.‡‡‡ The observed and expected frequencies, and the necessary calculations, are shown in Table V.2. For a value of $\chi_o^2 = 4.98$ and 9 degrees of freedom, we find that $P(\chi^2 > \chi_o^2)$ is approximately 0.83, which is a result that may at first sight occasion the

TABLE V.2

ILLUSTRATION OF USE OF χ^2-TEST:
GOODNESS OF FIT OF SAMPLE (OBSERVED) AND POPULATION (EXPECTED)
POISSON FREQUENCIES OF 1,000 DRAWS

NUMBER	EXPECTED FREQUENCY (E)	OBSERVED FREQUENCY (O)	$O - E$	$\dfrac{(O-E)^2}{E}$
0	30	22	−8	2.13
1	106	104	−2	0.04
2	185	194	9	0.44
3	216	215	−1	—
4	189	189	0	—
5	132	126	−6	0.27
6	77	84	7	0.64
7	38	39	1	0.03
8	17	14	−3	0.53
9	7⎫	11⎫		
10	2⎬10	2⎬13	⎱3	⎱0.90
11	1⎭	0⎭		
Total	1,000	1,000	0	4.98 ($=\chi_o^2$)

student some difficulty in interpretation. A review of the discussion of the form of the chi-square distribution, however, will reveal that our observed value, χ_o^2, is to the *left* of the maximum ordinate—at a point on the χ^2-scale such that 83 per cent of the area under the curve lies to the right and 17 per cent to the left. Accordingly, our discrepancies $O - E$ are somewhat smaller than expected, but not suspiciously so since in repeated random sampling we will have χ^2 less than $\chi_o^2 = 4.98$ (for 9 degrees of freedom) in 17 per cent of cases. We accept the statistical hypothesis, therefore, and conclude that our sampling procedure was valid.

‡‡‡ As noted earlier, the χ^2-test is independent of the form of the parent population and its parameters.

Students should note the importance in any χ^2-test of considering the two sets of admissible alternative hypotheses, although normally we are concerned with only one set. The fit may be too good—i.e. the differences $O - E$ may be *smaller* than those which could arise in random sampling— or the fit may be too poor—i.e. the differences $O - E$ may be *larger* than those which could arise in random sampling. We must reject the hypothesis to be tested (i.e. $H_o : O - E = O$) whenever $P (\chi^2 > \chi_o^2)$ or $P (\chi^2 < \chi_o^2)$ is less than the probability of errors of the first kind that we are willing to accept. The important thing to remember is that *too good a fit* is just as unlikely an event in repeated random sampling as *too poor a fit*. When the fit is too good, we suspect that the O's and the E's have been forced in some manner to agree; when the fit is too poor, we suspect the validity (or acceptability) of the theory upon which the E's are based.

A classic example of the misinterpretation of the results of the χ^2-test in this situation may be found in one of the textbooks in educational psychology written by the late Professor Sandiford.§§§ In a discussion of the form of the distribution of intelligence in humans, he quoted Thorndike's data where observed and expected (normal) frequencies were compared and the "goodness of fit" tested, as in Table V.2. For 4 groups of individuals the values of $P(\chi^2 > \chi_o^2)$ were as follows: 0.999999; 1.000000; 0.999911; and 0.999988.

Sandiford went on to conclude,

> Since a perfect fit is represented by unity these results present an impressive verification of the normal distribution of intelligence. So much so, that if results are obtained which show deviations from the normal distribution, we are justified in believing that they are due either to the limitations of the [mental] test or to the selective nature of the sampling. (p. 162)

Now of course the results prove nothing of the sort: the values of $P (\chi^2 < \chi_o^2)$ secured by subtracting the above values from unity, indicate that the "fit" was far *too good*. Somewhere along the production line, either in the construction of the mental test, or more likely in the subsequent manipulation of the scores, the observed frequencies were forced to correspond with the expected. The results indicate no more than an "impressive verification" of the hypothesis that test constructors are able to force the distribution of test scores into the form of a normal distribution.

Case 2: Use of the χ^2-test Where More Than One Constraint Is Imposed on the Data

This type of application of the χ^2-test is much the same as that illustrated in the previous section, except that the number of degrees of freedom

§§§ Peter Sandiford, *Educational Psychology* (New York: Longmans, Green and Company, 1938), pp. 160–62.

is correspondingly altered and the additional conditions specified earlier must be satisfied. We may add, parenthetically, that most of the problems encountered in practice in the social sciences that may be solved through the use of the χ^2-test are of the type where more than one constraint is imposed. For convenience we shall distinguish between three main classes of problems that may arise. Such a classification is useful to the researcher, since from it he can readily determine the form of the χ^2-test applicable to any particular situation he may encounter.

Goodness of Fit

On the face of it, this application seems to be the same as that considered in Table V.2. But there is one essential point of difference. In the previous case the expected frequencies were determined from a specified population and were required to conform to the observed frequencies only in the total number of cases. In the case about to be considered, on the other hand, we require not only that the totals shall be the same, but that the observed and expected frequencies shall yield the same values for certain statistics calculated therefrom (equivalent to using as estimates of the unknown, or unspecified, population parameters the estimates calculated from the observed data). Observe that this consists essentially in a change in the hypothesis to be tested, H_o. The question becomes, not whether the observed frequencies could occur in random sampling from a population defined beforehand, but from a population defined after the event and forced to agree in certain respects with the observed event. Consider, for example, the problem relating to the data of Table V.3, the distribution of

TABLE V.3

ILLUSTRATION OF THE USE OF χ^2-TEST: GOODNESS OF FIT OF
OBSERVED FREQUENCIES AND NEGATIVE BINOMIAL FREQUENCIES

NUMBER OF ERRORS	OBSERVED FREQUENCY (O)	EXPECTED FREQUENCY (E)	$O - E$	$\dfrac{(O - E)^2}{E}$
0	30	27.86	+2.14	0.16
1	21	24.65	−3.65	0.54
2	18	16.41	+1.59	0.15
3	10	9.75	+0.25	0.01
4	3	5.42	−2.42	1.08
5	4	2.90		
6	8 { 3	1.51		
7	1	0.77		
8		0.39	+2.08	0.73
9	5.92	0.19		
10		0.09		
11		0.04		
12		0.02		
13		0.01		
Total	90	90.01	−0.01	2.67 ($= \chi_o^2$)

errors on a spelling test. To calculate the expected frequencies for the negative binomial, we must know the values of N, k, and p. The situation requires that $N = 90$, but the values of k and p are completely unspecified since, in effect, all we ask is whether these data can be assumed to be adequately represented by *a* negative binomial distribution.‖‖‖ We estimate k and p from the observed frequency distribution, obtaining $k = 1.978$ and $p = 0.809$, by forcing the population values of the mean and variance to agree with the observed values of these statistics. Since we have thereby imposed two additional constraints on the expected frequencies, the number of degrees of freedom for our χ^2-test will be 3 less than the number of compartments (or frequency groups) used in the calculation of the value of χ_o^2. The observed and expected frequencies are shown in Table V.3, together with the necessary calculations.

For the χ^2-test we have $\chi_o^2 = 2.67$ and $n = 3$, so we accept the hypothesis $H_o : O - E = 0$, and conclude that this observed distribution of errors can be adequately described by a negative binomial.

Students should note that the χ^2-test in this situation, as in the earlier test of goodness of fit, is a type of omnibus test of agreement over the whole distribution. In this respect it is quite different from the tests to be considered later, which are concerned only with hypotheses expressed in terms of measures of specific characteristics of the distribution—such as tests relating to means or standard deviations. The second point to note is that we do not by the χ^2-test *prove* that the variates are distributed in the negative binomial, Poisson, normal, etc. form. We have no reason to reject the hypothesis, so we accept it, but this does *not* imply proof.

Tests of Independence (Independent Samples)

In his original work on this type of problem, Professor Karl Pearson (1901) used the word "contingency" as a descriptive phrase because, as we shall see later, the expected frequencies are calculated on the basis of the hypothesis of "chance occurrence." Sheppard, in 1899, had proposed a similar test, which he called a test of independence of two distributions. The same tests are also called tests of homogeneity, meaning tests of whether the observations are all "of the same kind" (from the same population or from identical populations). They also include tests of the differences between proportions, since the hypothesis to be tested may be expressed in terms of frequencies and the χ^2-test applied. The general use of the term *tests of independence* to describe the whole set of problems of this kind is due largely to R. A. Fisher, who has pointed out that in all

‖‖‖ For intelligence test scores, on the other hand, we might ask whether the observed frequencies could occur in a random sample from a normal population with $\xi = 100$ and $\sigma = 16$, not simply from *any* normal population. Even in the above case, some theory or past experience might have enabled us to specify values of k and p beforehand.

these cases the basic hypothesis is really that the two (or more) classifications are independent.

In the discussion of this section we have restricted attention to the case of independent samples. The problem of correlated proportions (two dependent samples) is considered in the next section. It is convenient to separate the treatment of these two types for instructional and reference purposes because, while the basic problem is not changed, the expression of the hypothesis and of the corresponding χ^2-tests are quite different.

We will begin with the simplest case, which consists of two classifications for each of which we have a dichotomy. This is equivalent to the test of the difference between two independent proportions (i.e. proportions from independent samples), as we shall see. The general hypothesis, phrased to correspond with the null statistical hypothesis, is that the two classifications of the same group of individuals are independent. As an illustration, consider the following classification of 1,038 gastric disorder patients by sex and type of gastric disorder.###

| GASTRIC DISORDER | SEX | | TOTAL |
	Male	*Female*	
Ulcers	74	14	88
Other gastric disorders	535	415	950
Total	609	429	1,038

The test of independence in this situation is essentially a test of significance of a sex difference in type of gastric disorder, and is the same as the test of the statistical hypothesis earlier considered, viz. $H_o : \hat{p}_M - \hat{p}_F = 0$, of zero difference between the male and female proportions of ulcer patients. But how may we translate the hypothesis to be tested, of independent classifications, into expected frequencies?

The reasoning is as follows. We have a total of 1,038 gastric disorder patients, of whom 609 are male and 429 female, and of whom 88 are ulcer patients and 950 are not-ulcer patients. These values, which are the marginal totals, are fixed by the situation and cannot be varied. But we can secure exactly the same set of marginal totals by varying the entries in the double-classification part of the table in any one of many ways. If the hypothesis to be tested is true, i.e. the two classifications are independent, the division in each row into males and females will be in exactly the proportion of the bottom row of marginal totals, viz. $\dfrac{609}{1,038}$ to $\dfrac{429}{1,038}$ or roughly 6 to 4. Similarly, the division in each column into ulcer and not-ulcer will

H. Cotton, "The Collection of Morbidity Data from Hospitals," *Journal of the Royal Statistical Society*, Series A (General), CXI, Part I (1948), 17.

be in exactly the proportion of the column of marginal totals, viz. $\dfrac{88}{1,038}$ to $\dfrac{950}{1,038}$ or roughly 1 to 9. Accordingly, the expected frequencies may be calculated as shown below.*

$\dfrac{(609)\,(88)}{1,038} = $ 51.63	$\dfrac{(429)\,(88)}{1,038} = $ 36.37	88.00
$\dfrac{(609)\,(950)}{1,038} = $ 557.37	$\dfrac{(429)\,(950)}{1,038} = $ 392.63	950.00
609.00	429.00	1,038.00

Note that the marginal totals for the expected frequencies are exactly the same as those for the observed frequencies.

The calculation of the value χ_o^2 is now quite straightforward, since we have four pairs of O and E values, one pair for each cell. Applying the formula for χ^2 directly, we have the following values:

CELL	O	E	$O - E$	$\dfrac{(O-E)^2}{E}$
a	74	51.63	+22.37	9.69
b	14	36.37	−22.37	13.76
c	535	557.37	−22.37	0.90
d	415	392.63	+22.37	1.27
Total	1,038	1,038.00	0	25.62 ($=\chi_o^2$)

The $O - E$ differences have exactly the same value, save for sign, because there is in such cases only one degree of freedom, i.e. only one independent difference $O - E$. It is true that there are four cells, but we have imposed three constraints on the four expected frequencies. (Of the five possible constraints—the four marginal totals and the grand total—only three are necessary and independent.)

Our value χ_o^2 is 25.62, and for 1 degree of freedom $P\{\chi^2 > \chi_o^2\}$ is approximately 5 in 10,000,000. Our earlier test of two independent proportions for the same data, considered in Chapter IV, yielded the value $\dfrac{D_p}{SE'_{D_p}} = 5.06$ and the corresponding probability of approximately 4 in 10,000,000.† Note, first, that $\chi_o = \sqrt{25.62} = 5.06$, i.e. the results are nu-

* Students calculating such expected frequencies for a 2 × 2 contingency table will soon realize that when any one of the entries has been calculated, the others can be obtained by subtraction from the marginal totals.

† Note that the critical region corresponding to $\chi^2 > \chi_o^2$ is $- 5.06 > \dfrac{D_p}{SE'_{D_p}} > 5.06$, not just one tail of the distribution.

merically equivalent. This always holds true for a 2×2 contingency table. Observe, next, that the probabilities of an error of the first kind must be exactly equal in the two cases, save for discrepancies caused by interpolation and rounding off.

This method of calculating the value of χ_o^2 is unnecessarily cumbersome and lengthy for a 2×2 contingency table. Students may prove, as an exercise in algebra, that if we denote the *observed frequencies* in the double-classification part of the table as follows:

a	b
c	d

then $\chi_o^2 = \dfrac{(ad - bc)^2 N}{(a + b)(c + d)(a + c)(b + d)}$. For the above exam-

ple we have $\chi_o^2 = \dfrac{\{(74)(415) - (14)(535)\}^2 \{1{,}038\}}{(88)(950)(609)(429)} = 25.62$. This formula

is, of course, designed for machine calculation and does save time and effort. The one disadvantage it possesses, from the point of view of instruction, is that it effectively hides any trace of the hypothesis to be tested and of the set of admissible alternative hypotheses.

Upon occasion a researcher has no choice but to analyze the results of a 2×2 contingency table even when the expected frequencies in one or more cells are less than 5. The data of the following table, relating to qualifications and marital status of a small group of women teachers, will serve to illustrate the problem and its possible solutions. One of the ex-

CERTIFICATE	MARITAL STATUS		TOTAL
	Single	Married	
First	10	7	17
Second	2	7	9
Total	12	14	26

pected frequencies is slightly less than 5, another is just slightly greater than 5, and the question arises of the accuracy of the probability values obtained if we use the above formula for χ_o^2. The value of χ_o^2 is

$$\frac{\{(10)(7) - (7)(2)\}^2 \{26\}}{(17)(9)(12)(14)} = 3.17$$

and the corresponding probability, $P\{\chi^2 > \chi_o^2\}$, is 0.0750. Yates proposed that a "correction for continuity" be applied in such cases of 2×2 contingency tables (to compensate for the imposition of the continuous χ^2-distribution on a discrete variable), which consists in using the formula

$$\chi_{oY}^2 = \frac{\left\{|ad - bc| - \dfrac{N}{2}\right\}^2 \{N\}}{(a + b)(c + d)(a + c)(b + d)}$$

which for our example becomes

$$\chi^2_{oY} = \frac{(43)^2(26)}{(17)(9)(12)(14)} = 1.87$$

with $P\{\chi^2 > \chi^2_{oY}\} = 0.1716$. The probability values differ greatly: there might be some question about accepting the hypothesis if χ^2_o were used, but none at all if χ^2_{oY} were used. Which method gives the best estimate of the true probability?

Fortunately, in the case of 2×2 contingency tables of this kind it is not too difficult to calculate the exact probability. As Fisher has shown,[‡] given the marginal totals, the probability of any observed set of entries is

$$\frac{(a+b)!\,(c+d)!\,(a+c)!\,(b+d)!}{N!} \qquad \frac{1}{a!\,b!\,c!\,d!}$$

The observed set of frequencies and the two more extreme for the above example are, therefore,

10	7
2	7

;

11	6
1	8

; and

12	5
0	9

Accordingly, the probability of observing an event as extreme as, or even more extreme than, the event which did occur is the sum of the probabilities of these three possibilities. Making the necessary calculations,[§] we find that the exact probability of obtaining in random sampling a result as extreme as, or even more extreme than, that observed is 0.0846. Taking half the χ^2-probabilities reported above in order to get a comparable one-sided statistical test, we have the following comparable probability values:

Ordinary χ^2 : 0.0375
Corrected χ^2 : 0.0858
Exact Test : 0.0846

Obviously, even for this rather extreme case, Yates' correction for continuity yields an approximation that is highly satisfactory—so much so, in fact, that we seldom bother to calculate the exact probabilities although it is not too onerous a chore to do so.

It is a simple matter to extend the χ^2-procedure to a manifold classification of one or both variables, calculate the value of χ^2_o, and test its significance. For k categories of one variable and l of the other we have kl cells or terms involved in the calculation of the value of χ^2_o, with $(k-1)$ $(l-1)$ degrees of freedom. When k and l are large, greater than 5, say, this is a time-consuming, although not otherwise difficult, process. In a fine classification, however, unless N be very large, we will not be able to

[‡] R. A. Fisher, *Statistical Methods for Research Workers*, p. 102. See also the tables given by Finney in *Biometrika*, XXXV (1949), 145–56; and P. Armsen, "Tables for Significance Tests of 2×2 Contingency Tables," *Biometrika*, XLII (December, 1955).

[§] The simplest method is to use tables giving the logarithms of factorials.

satisfy the condition that the expected frequency in any cell must not be less than 5.|| The only solution is to reclassify the original data, either by establishing a completely new set of coarser categories or by combining adjoining classes.

The following data relating to the skill and adjustment of 180 West Indian technicians, may be used to illustrate both the procedure and the difficulty.#

SKILL	ADJUSTMENT					TOTAL
	Excellent	Good	Average	Poor	Very bad	
Very skilled	24	7	3	2		36
Good	17	43	27	6		93
Average		9	13	13	2	37
Poor			2	6		8
Very bad				3	3	6
Total	41	59	45	30	5	180

In order to satisfy the condition, we may combine the classes "Average," "Poor," and "Very bad" for the Skill variable, and combine the categories "Poor" and "Very bad" for the Adjustment variable, thus reducing the table to a 3 × 4 form. We have thereby lost some of the information, it is true, but we have probably not done too great violence to the data. The revised set of frequencies is given below:

$$\begin{array}{cccc} 24 & 7 & 3 & 2 \\ 17 & 43 & 27 & 6 \\ - & 9 & 15 & 27 \end{array}$$

Calculating the expected frequencies for each of the 12 cells, and substituting the observed and expected frequencies in the usual formula, we obtain the value $\chi_o^2 = 99.61$. For 6 degrees of freedom this observed value is well outside the range of the tables and we may reject the null, or independence, hypothesis with considerable confidence. We would therefore conclude that the two variables are related, not independent. As is evident from the pattern of observed frequencies, the skilled technicians tend to be better adjusted than the unskilled.

For a 2 × k table, Brandt and Snedecor have proposed a useful variation of the general formula which shows the contribution of each pair of values to the total χ_o^2. Denoting by a and b any pair of observed frequencies, and the corresponding totals by N_a and N_b, we calculate for each pair the

|| We cannot apply any simple correction for continuity, when k and l are greater than 2, but an exact test has been given by Freeman and Halton in *Biometrika*, XXXVIII (1951), 141–49.

A. H. Richmond, "Relation Between Skill and Adjustment of a Group of West Indian Negro Workers in England," *Occupational Psychology*, XXV, No. 3 (July, 1951), 161.

quantity $p = \dfrac{a}{a + b}$, and for the totals $\bar{p} = \dfrac{N_a}{N_a + N_b}$ and $\bar{q} = 1 - \bar{p}$. From

these values we may calculate the value of χ_o^2 from the following formula:

$$\chi_o^2 = \frac{\Sigma(ap) - N_a\bar{p}}{\bar{p}\bar{q}}$$

As an illustration, let us use the following data from Cotton, relating to gastric disorders in male and female patients (the calculations are given below the table):**

GASTRIC DISORDER	MALE a	FEMALE b	TOTAL $a + b$	RATIO $p = \dfrac{a}{a+b}$	$\left(= \dfrac{a^2}{a+b}\right)$ ap
Gastric ulcer	22	9	31	.70967742	15.61290
Duodenal ulcer	52	5	57	.91228070	47.43860
Other gastric disorders	535	415	950	.56315789	301.28947
Total	609	429	1,038	.58670520	364.34097

$$\bar{p}\bar{q} = 0.24248221$$
$$N_a\bar{p} = 357.30347$$
$$\text{and } \chi_o^2 = 29.02$$

which, for 2 degrees of freedom, is a highly significant result. A comparison of the pair-ratios reveals immediately that the large discrepancies occur in the two ulcer classes, and in particular in the duodenal ulcer category.

Tests Based on Correlated Proportions (Dependent Samples)

As we pointed out in the previous chapter, it is difficult to overemphasize the importance of tests of this type, particularly in education and psychology where we so often use equated individuals in the experimental and control groups in order to secure precision in our experiments and ease of interpretation of our results. We begin with the simple case of the responses of 200 individuals to two items on a mental test, which we used as an illustration in Chapter IV. The frequencies for the 2×2 table were $a = 131, b = 20, c = 0, d = 49$, and the marginal totals were 151, 49, 131, and 69. If we use the formula appropriate for a test of independence, obviously inappropriate in this situation, we must rewrite the table as follows (as if we had, in fact, two different groups but each of 200 persons):

** The ratios must be calculated to 7 or 8 places in order to secure an accurate value; it is more convenient to calculate the value by using the formula indicated in parentheses in the last column of the table.

CLASSIFICATION	CORRECT	WRONG	TOTAL
First Item	151	49	200
Second Item	131	69	200
Total	282	118	400

from which we obtain

$$\chi_o^2 = \frac{\{(151)(69) - (131)(49)\}^2(400)}{(200)(200)(282)(118)} = 4.81$$

But the usual test of independence doesn't make sense in this situation: we had 200 individuals, not 400, and each individual responded to both items. We must rephrase our hypothesis to be tested so that it takes into account directly the fact that the same (or paired) persons responded to both items. For these two test items, the only question in which we are interested is whether or not they are of equal difficulty. This was phrased, in our discussion of this case in the previous chapter, in the form of the null hypothesis that the proportion, $\hat{p}$, of correct responses was the same for the two items. Translated into terms of frequencies, this means that $\hat{a} + \hat{b}$ must equal $\hat{a} + \hat{c}$, which requires that $\hat{b}$ must equal $\hat{c}$. Our hypothesis to be tested, the null hypothesis, may therefore be written in the form $H_o : \hat{b} = \hat{c}$ and the set of alternative hypotheses will be $H : \hat{b} \neq \hat{c}$, of which there are two distinct sets, namely, $H_1 : \hat{b} > \hat{c}$ and $H_2 : \hat{b} < \hat{c}$.

It is now a simple matter to derive an appropriate statistical test of significance. As McNemar has shown,[††] we have for each of the observed changes b and c an expected value of $(b + c)/2$ and, after a simple algebraic manipulation, we obtain from the usual formula for chi-square the value

$$\chi_{oMc}^2 = \frac{(b - c)^2}{b + c}$$ with 1 degree of freedom. For our example, $b = 20$ and

$c = 0$, so we obtain $\chi_{oMc}^2 = 20$, identically equal to the square of the normal deviate (4.47) that we secured for the test of correlated proportions in the previous chapter. The corresponding probability of an error of the first kind in terms of the critical region required by H_1 is 78 in 10,000,000, and in terms of the critical region required by H_1 is one-half of that amount. (In this particular situation, since $c = 0$, the set H_2 would hardly be considered as admissible.) We would reject the hypothesis of equal change $(b = c)$, and consequently the hypothesis of equal proportions, and conclude that the second item is significantly more difficult than the first.

Students should note that for the above chi-square probability to be an accurate estimate of the required positive binomial probability (for $p = \frac{1}{2}$

[††] *Psychological Statistics*, p. 205.

and $k = b + c$), the total change $b + c$ should not be less than 20. A correction for continuity, analogous to Yates' correction for continuity for a 2×2 contingency table, consists in reducing the absolute difference between b and c by unity before squaring, or in the form given by McNemar:

$$\chi^2_{oMc} = \frac{(|b - c| - 1)^2}{b + c}.$$ When the total change is small, however, the exact

probability can be determined about as easily as the approximation and should be reported and used. As a matter of fact, if tables of the binomial distribution are available the exact tests should always be used within their range. The agreement between the exact and approximate probabilities is very good, even for small samples when the correction is applied, as students are invited to verify for various values of b and c.

There is another hypothesis that under certain circumstances probably has more meaning than the one proposed by McNemar. Perhaps the simplest way of expressing it is to state that the probability of change is constant, i.e. the same *proportion* of individuals in the two original categories will change their responses, not the same *number*. For instance, if the experimental factor applied between the pretest and a posttest has no effect, this seems to us to be in many cases a more plausible and meaningful hypothesis than that of equal change. We might add, parenthetically, that it is one of the set of hypotheses alternative to McNemar's, or the latter (of equal change) is a special one of the set of hypotheses alternative to the hypothesis of a constant probability of change. Moreover, as we shall see, the two are indistinguishable in one specific case and the statistical tests are identical.

The appropriate statistical test is not difficult to derive. Proceeding as before, we have

OBSERVED FREQUENCY	EXPECTED FREQUENCY
b	$\dfrac{(b + c)\,(a + b)}{N}$
c	$\dfrac{(b + c)\,(c + d)}{N}$

and substituting in the general formula for χ^2, we obtain

$$\chi^2_{oJ} = \frac{(ac - bd)^2}{(b + c)(a + b)(c + d)}, \text{ with 1 degree of freedom.}$$

In the particular case where $a + b = c + d$, applying the same proportion gives the same *number* of changes, i.e. the expected values of b and c become equal, and χ^2_{oJ} reduces rather simply to χ^2_{oMc}, i.e. to $\dfrac{(b - c)^2}{b + c}$.

McNemar's data‡‡ for a pair of items (the first pair in his Table 31)

‡‡ *Ibid.*, p. 201. Adapted with the permission of the publishers.

provide an interesting illustration of the tests of the two possible "null" hypotheses (equal *number* of changes versus equal *proportion*). Rearranging his tables slightly, we have

ITEM 1

I T E M 2		+	−	Total
	+	39	29	68
	−	10	22	32
	Total	49	51	100

or

ITEM 2

I T E M 1		+	−	Total
	+	39	10	49
	−	29	22	51
	Total	68	32	100

We have, for either arrangement,

$$\chi^2_{oMc} = \frac{(b-c)^2}{b+c} = \frac{(19)^2}{39} = 9.26$$

and we would reject the hypothesis of equal change in number of individuals (from + to − and − to +) on the two items. For the test of an equal proportion, we have two possible situations in this case, but under ordinary circumstances (such as the case to be considered next) only one of these would be admissible. We may ask, first, are the changes in responses from Item 2 to Item 1 proportional to the number of + and − responses on Item 2? We suspect that they might be, since of the 68 answering Item 2 correctly, 29 (or 0.426) responded incorrectly to Item 1, and of the 32 who responded incorrectly to Item 2, 10 (or 0.313) responded correctly to Item 1. We have,

$$\chi^2_{oJ} = \frac{(ac-bd)^2}{(b+c)(a+b)(c+d)} = \frac{61,504}{84,864} = 0.725$$

and accordingly we would accept the hypothesis of a constant probability of change in responses from Item 2 to Item 1. But we might, in this case, with equal justification inquire whether the changes in responses from Item 1 to Item 2 are proportional to the number of + and − responses on Item 1. On intuitive grounds, we would be inclined to answer in the negative, since only 10 of the 49, a proportion of 0.204, who got Item 1 correct had Item 2 wrong, as compared with 29 of the 51, a proportion of 0.569, who got Item 1 wrong and Item 2 correct. Applying the test we have for this situation

$$\chi^2_{oJ} = \frac{829,921}{97,461} = 8.52$$

and we would reject the hypothesis. Note that χ^2_{oMc} and χ^2_{oJ} have practically the same value in this case, since $a + b = 49$ is very nearly the same as $c + d = 51$.§§

§§ A rather interesting case occurs occasionally where $\frac{b+c}{2} > a + b$. McNemar's

The more usual situation, where the interpretation of both values of χ^2_{oJ} is more meaningful, is depicted in the responses concerning "interest" and "participation" on Item 118 of the interest inventory referred to in the preceding chapter. It will be recalled that Item 118 read, "Do work in which you become acquainted with many people." As far as "interest" versus "participation" is concerned, there is no particular reason to postulate and test the hypothesis proposed by McNemar because we are interested, not in the *number*, but in the *proportion* who change their responses. What we expected might occur was, first, that the proportion of those expressing interest who did not participate would be the same as the proportion of those expressing little interest who did participate, and, second, that the proportion of those participating who did not express an interest would be the same as the proportion of those not participating who did express an interest. For the first hypothesis,

$$\chi^2_{oJ} = \frac{\{(42)(33) - (11)(27)\}^2}{(44)(53)(60)} = 8.48$$

whereas for the second hypothesis,

$$\chi^2_{oJ} = \frac{\{(42)(11) - (33)(27)^2\}}{(44)(75)(38)} = 1.47$$

Accordingly, although somewhat to our surprise, we would reject the null hypothesis in the first case and accept it in the second.||||

As a final example of the use of these two hypotheses and the corresponding statistical tests, let us use the data given by McNemar for shifts in responses of his control group (who did not hear the radio talk designed to discourage overoptimism and hence to shift the responses from $-$ to $+$ from the pretest to the posttest, the "$-$" indicating an opinion that the war would last a year or less and the "$+$" indicating an opinion that the war would last more than a year).## The observed frequencies, for 181 soldiers, were as given in the table on the opposite page.

We have $\chi^2_{oJ} = 7.01$, so we would reject the hypothesis of a proportional change: a greater proportion changed from $-$ to $+$ than from $+$ to $-$.

---

hypothesis of equal change doesn't have much meaning in this event, because it just can't be true. In the following actual case,

12	4
36	61

, $\dfrac{b + c}{2} = 20$ whereas $a + b = 16$.

An equal change in numbers just cannot occur. But the hypothesis of a proportional change has a meaning, and would be accepted in one case and rejected in the other.

|||| We are not altogether certain of the psychological and social implications of these results for high school seniors, but it would seem that "interest-to-participation" is not the same thing as "participation-to-interest."

McNemar, *op. cit.*, p. 81. Adapted by permission of the publishers.

POSTTEST

	RESPONSE	−	+	TOTAL
PRETEST	−	52	14	66
	+	8	107	115
	Total	60	121	181

Similarly, $\chi^2_{oMc} = 1.64$, and we would accept the hypothesis of an equal change in numbers, although we do not have a proportional change.

Cochran has proposed an extension of McNemar's test to the case of more than two samples (to more than two items, for instance, on an interest inventory or a mental test).*** The statistic Q that he suggested could be used to test the null hypothesis, which reduces to χ^2_{oMc} when there are only two samples (or items), has the limiting distribution of χ^2 with $k - 1$ degrees of freedom, (where k denotes the number of samples) when the number of individuals (or sets of matched individuals), N, is large. Denoting a favorable response (e.g. a correct one for an item on a mental test) by a 1, and an unfavorable (e.g. incorrect) response by a 0, we have essentially a $k \times N$ table with 1 or 0 in each cell, as follows:†††

INDIVIDUAL (i)	VALUES OF k (j)						TOTAL
	1	2	3	4	....	k	
1	1	1	1	1	....	1	u_1
2	1	1	1	1	....	0	u_2
3	1	1	1	0	....	0	u_3
4	1	1	0	0	....	0	u_4
.	.	.	.	.	....	.	.
.	.	.	.	.	....	.	.
.	.	.	.	.	....	.	.
N	0	0	0	0	....	.	u_N
Total	T_1	T_2	T_3	T_4	....	T_k	$\Sigma u_i = \Sigma T_j$

The statistic Q is defined by Cochran in the form

$$Q = \frac{(k)(k-1)\, \Sigma(T_j - M_T)^2}{k\Sigma u_i - (\Sigma u_i^2)}$$

where $M_T = \frac{1}{k}\Sigma T_j$. As will be realized from the form of the equation, it is a statistical test of the significance of the differences among the number (or proportion) of favorable responses in the k samples.

In education and psychology, however, the alternative test which

*** W. G. Cochran, "The Comparison of Percentages in Matched Samples."

††† Those who have been concerned with item analyses for mental tests will recognize that this is equivalent to an "answer-pattern" of the responses of each individual to each item of the test.

Cochran proposed for the same hypothesis will likely prove more acceptable, since essentially the same procedure has been used in these fields since 1941. In suggesting that the analysis of variance (discussed in a later chapter) might be used to test the significance of the differences among the number of favorable responses in the k samples, Cochran seems to have been unaware of the work of Hoyt[‡‡‡] and Jackson[§§§] on similar problems that arise in mental test construction. The Q-statistic Cochran proposed be used can, in fact, be expressed in terms of the quantities used in the usual analysis of variance test and would seem to possess no inherent advantage over the latter.

Other Uses of the chi-square Distribution

The chi-square method is amazingly versatile. For example, the sum of several independent χ^2's is itself distributed as χ^2 with degrees of freedom equal to the sum of the numbers of degrees of freedom for the components. As an illustration, a die suspected of having a bias was rolled by three persons, with the results shown below:

FACE	PERSON[‖‖‖]			TOTAL
	P	M	D	
1	20	30	20	70
2	24	30	10	64
3	19	25	15	59
4	22	33	12	67
5	30	31	10	71
6	29	19	17	65
Total	144	168	84	396

Taking each person in turn, we have the following values of χ_0^2 for the test of the null hypothesis:

For P: $\chi_0^2 = 4.417$; $n = 5$; $P\{\chi^2 > \chi_0^2\} = 0.494$

For M: $\chi_0^2 = 4.714$; $n = 5$; $P\{\chi^2 > \chi_0^2\} = 0.454$

For D: $\chi_0^2 = 5.857$; $n = 5$; $P\{\chi^2 > \chi_0^2\} = 0.322$

Adding the several values of χ_0^2 and n, we have for the sum

$$\chi_0^2 = 14.988; n = 15; P\{\chi^2 > \chi_0^2\} = 0.526$$

In no case would the null hypothesis be rejected: despite the apparent irregularities, the die must be judged to be unbiased and its rolls at random.

Observe, next, that we might have used only the Total column in the analysis, obtaining

[‡‡‡] Cyril Hoyt, "Test Reliability Estimated by the Analysis of Variance," *Psychometrika*, VI (1941), 153–60.

[§§§] R. W. B. Jackson, "Note on the Relationship Between Internal Consistency and Test-Retest Estimates of the Reliability of a Test," *Psychometrika*, VII (1942), 157–64.

[‖‖‖] P denotes Peter (age 6), M denotes Michael (age 10), and D denotes the father (age not reported).

$$\chi_o^2 = 1.455; n = 5; P\{\chi^2 > \chi_o^2\} = 0.911$$

This indicates for the total a somewhat closer fit than for any of the parts. What has happened is that adding across the columns has ironed out some of the irregularities. Again, to find if the persons differ in their patterns of throws, we make a test of independence of this 6×3 table, obtaining $\chi_o^2 = 13.344$ and $n = 10$.### While differences are present, they do not lead to rejection of the hypothesis of independence. This is not an unexpected event, of course, since the first test of this section indicated that for each person separately the null hypothesis of no bias would be accepted.

We may mention, in passing, that in some cases it is possible to identify the individual degrees of freedom and to determine the contribution of each one to the total χ^2.* But such cases arise rather rarely and we need give only a reference to a discussion of the appropriate methods: in the above example, for instance, the individual degrees of freedom would have little or no meaning.

Another useful application of chi-square arises where we have a number of probabilities of errors of the first kind from independent tests of significance (based on experiments conducted by different research workers, for instance), and we wish to make a sort of composite test of the significance of the series of events. One would suspect, intuitively, that it would be a highly unlikely event in a series of random samples to obtain a set of probabilities each of which just bordered on the significance level. For example, if we observed in a series of 5 independent experiments† the probabilities 0.049, 0.052, 0.063, 0.039, and 0.046, we would soon suspect that the aggregate was significant although each of the members was not (at the 1 per cent level of significance). For such a composite test, note that we have for each probability, P, a χ^2 with 2 degrees of freedom if we take the natural logarithm‡ of that probability and multiply by -2. For the above case, we would have the following values:

P	$\chi^2 = -2 \log_e P$	n
0.049	6.032	2
0.052	5.913	2
0.063	5.529	2
0.039	6.488	2
0.046	6.158	2
Total	30.120	10

This χ_o^2 is not necessarily equal to the difference between the other two total χ_o^2, although it is very close to that value (13.344 versus 13.533) in this case.

* See, for example, A. W. Kimball, "Short-Cut Formulas for the Exact Partition of χ^2 in Contingency Tables," *Biometrics*, X, No. 4 (1954), 452–58.

† This is a not unusual situation in education and in experimental psychology, since it is frequently convenient to have students conduct a series of independent experiments.

‡ Note that $\log_e X = 2.30259 \log_{10} X$.

yielding a value $\chi_0^2 = 30.120$ with 10 degrees of freedom, and the associated probability $P(\chi^2 > \chi_0^2)$ is 0.00086. For the aggregate, therefore, we have a most significant result although none of the individual members yielded a definite rejection of the hypothesis tested.

Students should note that this test is based on the probabilities alone, not directly on the data from which these were obtained, and therefore is a non-parametric test. The final, or composite, probability relates to the chance of securing such a set of probabilities in random sampling, not to the original hypothesis or hypotheses. We are justified, however, in rejecting the original hypothesis also, if the test based on the series of probabilities proves significant.

EXERCISES

1. (a) Use the chi-square test in each of the following exercises of Chapter IV: 1, 2, 4(a), 5, 6, 7, 8, 9, 10, 11.
   (b) Explain any divergence in your two sets of results.
2. Having been "separated" from an unspecified amount of money, I secured one of the dice used in the process. In 240 rolls of the die under rigidly controlled conditions, I observed the following results:

Face	1	2	3	4	5	6	Total
Observed Frequency	60	50	36	20	44	30	240

Was I unjustly suspicious of my companion's "skill"?

3. The scores of 300 elementary school students on a "social-acceptability" scale were as follows:

Score	0	1	2	3	4	5	6	7	Total
Frequency	38	87	76	48	29	17	2	3	300

Test the goodness of fit of normal and Poisson distributions.

4. A study of 280 Indian children on three reservations in southern Ontario resulted in the following classification by intelligence:

could make this a 3 X 3 contingency table and the follow the technique on p. 142

MENTAL INDEX	RESERVATION			TOTAL
	I	II	III	
Bright	26	2	1	29
Above Average	34	16	10	60
Average	45	15	28	88
Below Average	33	25	19	77
Dull	17	3	6	26
Total	155	61	64	280

Is there any evidence of differences in intelligence in the three areas?

5. From sampling results of your own, secured by tossing coins, rolling dice, drawing numbers from a box, or from tables of random numbers, construct a chi-square distribution. Compare your empirical results with the theoretical distribution.

6. In a study of the ability of examiners to predict training success a 2×2 table was secured for each examiner. Tables for 8 examiners are given below. The problem is to test the hypothesis that the examiners do not differ among themselves with respect to their ability to predict training success.

EXAMINER	ACTUAL OUTCOME	EXAMINER'S PREDICTION Pass	Fail
1	Pass	6	2
	Fail	16	20
2	Pass	11	2
	Fail	19	5
3	Pass	7	2
	Fail	10	14
4	Pass	7	1
	Fail	8	2
5	Pass	3	1
	Fail	7	11
6	Pass	8	0
	Fail	4	12
7	Pass	5	1
	Fail	9	5
8	Pass	5	0
	Fail	9	5

CHAPTER VI

Tests of Statistical Hypotheses Expressed in Terms of Means

The statistical tests considered in the two previous chapters, based on proportions and frequencies, are appropriate when we have categorical data. In fact, they are the only types of tests that can be applied in those circumstances. Although the same tests may be, and sometimes are, used when we can measure, rather than just classify, and can assign numerical values to our observations, they are not always as efficient as those about to be considered. Where our data are continuous, and even when they are not but the classes are ordered and numerical equivalents can be assigned to them, it is frequently possible to express the general hypotheses in terms of the *mean* of the population (or of the means of two or more populations). Consequently the appropriate statistical test may be expressed in terms of the mean of a single sample or in terms of the means of two or more samples. It is the statistical tests appropriate for these situations that are to be discussed in this section. The discussion is continued and extended to the general case in the following chapter.*

The sampling model we generally use in the statistical test based on means is derived under the assumption that the parent population is normal in form, not one of the other types (e.g. Poisson or rectangular) discussed in Chapter II. But we may not know, or the hypothesis to be tested may not explicitly specify, the form of distribution of the variable in the population from which our observed results have been obtained as a sample. Any departure from normality in the parent population may greatly affect the sampling distribution of the mean when our samples are small, as will be evident from our earlier illustrations for various types of populations, although the effect may be negligible when the sample size is large. Moreover, the hypothesis to be tested may or may not completely specify the parent population (or populations), i.e. it may be a *composite* rather than a *simple* hypothesis, to use the terms defined in Chapter III. The interpretation of the results of a test of a composite hypothesis is far from a simple matter in many cases. It is for these reasons, therefore, that we have in the

---

* This division is convenient and valuable for instructional purposes although, logically, one should probably present the general case first and treat the tests of the present chapter as a special case thereof.

discussion that follows emphasized the need to examine carefully the underlying conditions of each situation and to interpret results with particular care.

For convenience of presentation and discussion, we shall consider, first, the appropriate statistical tests based on the mean of a single sample and, second, those based on the means of two samples. In each case we shall begin with the model for samples drawn from a normal population and then consider briefly the changes that need be made for samples drawn from other types of populations.

MEAN OF A SINGLE SAMPLE

In these situations, the general hypothesis is that our set of observations differ in some respect from the "ordinary" set of observed events. A teacher, for example, may believe that his class of pupils is brighter or duller, on the average, than an ordinary class. The proper way to test this hypothesis is to set up the statistical hypothesis, H_o, that the set of observations is a sample of size N drawn at random from the corresponding population, and then determine the probability of observing in repeated random sampling an event as extreme or even more extreme than that which was observed. The general hypothesis, therefore, corresponds to the set of admissible hypotheses alternative to H_o, not to H_o itself.

Population Standard Deviation Known

As a simple example, consider the case of a teacher who administers an intelligence test to his class of 33 pupils and finds a mean I.Q. of 97. Should he conclude that his class is below average in intelligence, i.e. has been selected and is other than a sample drawn at random from the general population of pupils of this age and grade? For the particular intelligence test used, the distribution of intelligence is known to be normal in form with mean $\xi_o = 100$ and standard deviation $\sigma_o = 16$. The hypothesis to be tested, H_o, is $H_o : \xi = \xi_o = 100$. The set of admissible alternative hypotheses, H, will be $H : \xi < \xi_o = 100$.

Since it is known from sampling theory that the means of samples of size $N = 33$ drawn at random from this normal population will be normally distributed about $\xi_o = 100$ with standard error $\sigma_M = \dfrac{\sigma_o}{\sqrt{N}} = \dfrac{16}{\sqrt{33}} = 2.785$,

we can make the statistical test by calculating the value of the normal deviate $z = \dfrac{M - \xi_o}{\sigma_M} = \dfrac{97 - 100}{2.785} = -1.08$ and referring to the table of areas under the normal curve. Remembering that we are interested only in the set of admissible alternative hypotheses $H : \xi < \xi_o = 100$, we find that the probability of observing in repeated random sampling an event as extreme or even more extreme than that observed, $P(z < -1.08)$, is approximately 14 in 100. Accordingly, we would accept the hypothesis H_o, and conclude that there is no valid reason to believe that the class differs from a sample drawn at random from the general population of pupils of this grade and age. The average ability of the class is not significantly below the mean for the general population, and there is no evidence of any deliberate selection of its members. As far as ability is concerned, then, it is an "ordinary" class, not an unusual one.

Obviously, we can make similar tests based on means of samples from non-normal populations, e.g. the Poisson, wherever the sampling distribution of the mean is known. But where the sampling distribution of the mean is not known, we cannot calculate the exact probability associated with the rejection of the hypothesis to be tested. The best we can do is to use an approximate solution, which in most cases consists in making the assumption that the means are normally distributed although the parent population may not be so distributed. A problem of this type arises quite frequently in research in education and psychology, where the norms of mental tests are expressed in percentile ranks. To use an actual example to illustrate the reasoning and procedure, one of the authors administered a standardized English test to two groups of students in a secondary school, namely, to 146 students enrolled in the General Course, and to 115 students enrolled in the Commercial Course. The means of the percentile ranks for these two groups were:

General Course ($N = 146$): Mean = 49.4

Commercial Course ($N = 115$): Mean = 42.8

May we conclude that the achievement of each of these groups of students is satisfactory, as compared with the group used in establishing the norms for the achievement test?

To answer this question, we determine, as in the previous case, the probability of obtaining in random sampling a result as extreme or even more extreme than that observed. Since we have a rectangular population with $n = 101$, the mean will be $\xi_o = 50$, and the standard deviation will be $\sigma_o = 29.15$. Assuming that the means of samples from this population are normally distributed about $\xi_o = 50$ with a standard error of $\dfrac{\sigma_o}{\sqrt{N}}$, which our earlier sampling results indicate will be a reasonably valid assumption, we can test the hypothesis $H_o : \xi = \xi_o = 50$ against the set of alternative hypotheses $H : \xi < \xi_o = 50$. The normal deviates and probabilities for the statistical tests are as follows:

$$\text{General Course:} \quad z = \frac{49.4 - 50}{\left(\dfrac{29.15}{\sqrt{146}}\right)} = -0.25, \; P = 0.401$$

Commercial Course: $z = \dfrac{42.8 - 50}{\left(\dfrac{29.15}{\sqrt{115}}\right)} = -2.65, P = 0.004$

We would be inclined to accept the hypothesis H_o for the General Course, therefore, and to reject it for the Commercial Course. In terms of the general hypothesis, we would conclude that the average level of achievement is not significantly below the norm for the General group but is significantly below the norm for the Commercial group.

Population Standard Deviation Unknown

In the above cases, the hypothesis to be tested specified exactly, directly or indirectly, the population from which we could assume we were sampling. This is not always so. Very often the hypothesis H_o may specify only the value of ξ_o and perhaps the form, normal or otherwise, of the population, and we may not know the value of σ_o required for the determination of the standard error of the mean. While it is true that we may use the sample standard deviation as an estimate of σ_o, students will remember that, particularly for small samples, the sample estimate may differ widely from the true value σ_o. For any particular case in the situation we have in mind we simply do not know how close our sample estimate may be to the true value (we do know that for large samples, $N > 100$, say, the difference will not be very great in any event). How, then, may we test the hypothesis H_o when the value of σ_o is unspecified?

Student's t-distribution

This was the problem that Student solved in 1908, leading to the now-famous t-distribution. He proposed that we use the statistic

$$t = \frac{M - \xi_o}{\sqrt{v/N}}$$

where v is the estimate of σ_o^2, i.e. the variance, obtained from the sample, and gave the correct solution of the distribution of this ratio for samples drawn from a normal population. The distribution function of t is

$$p(t) = \frac{\Gamma\left(\dfrac{n+1}{2}\right)}{\sqrt{n\pi}\ \Gamma\left(\dfrac{n}{2}\right)} \left(1 + \frac{t^2}{n}\right)^{-\frac{n+1}{2}}$$

where n, the number of degrees of freedom, is equal to $N-1$. As is evident from the equation for t, the distribution is always perfectly symmetrical about the point $t = 0$ (where $M = \xi_o$), and the ordinates decrease in value and approach the axis asymptotically as t approaches $\pm \infty$. We show in

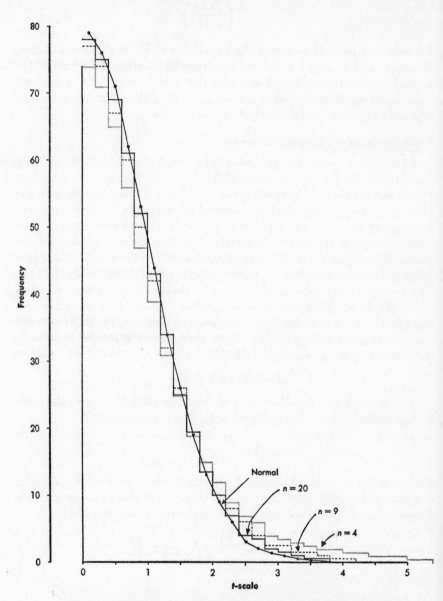

Figure VI.1. ILLUSTRATION OF THE POSITIVE HALF OF t-DISTRIBUTIONS FOR n = 4, 9, AND 20, WITH SUPERIMPOSED NORMAL DISTRIBUTION (ASSUMING SAMPLES DRAWN FROM A NORMAL DISTRIBUTION)

Figure VI.1 the histograms for the positive half of the t-distribution for $n = 4$ $(N = 5)$, $n = 9$ $(N = 10)$, and $n = 20$ $(N = 21)$ together with a superimposed frequency polygon of the normal distribution, which is the limiting form of t as n increases (for samples from a normal distribution, the t-distribution is practically indistinguishable from the normal limiting form for values of n greater than 100.[†] Observe that the t-distribution is leptokurtic, and for small samples the tail of the distribution (from which we obtain the probability of an error of the first kind) differs markedly from the normal. For $n = 4$, for instance, 5 per cent of the area lies beyond $t = 2.132$ and 1 per cent beyond $t = 3.747$, as compared with the corresponding normal deviate values of 1.645 and 2.326, respectively. Obviously, for small samples the use of the normal deviate values would give a very unsatisfactory critical region (for $n = 4$, for instance, the 1 per cent normal deviate region corresponds to a 4 per cent t-deviate region).

We have reproduced in Appendix C the table of the t-distribution prepared by Fisher and Yates. The values for the normal distribution are given in the final row of the table. Students must always remember, in using this table, that the probabilities given are for the two tails of the t-distribution, i.e. the probability in repeated random sampling from a normal population that t will exceed $\pm t_o$, where t_o is the observed value. The one-tail probabilities can easily be obtained, of course, because the t-distribution is perfectly symmetrical and one need only divide the tabled probabilities by two.

For samples drawn from a normal population, therefore, we know the sampling distribution of t, and accordingly may use the table of t to test the hypothesis H_o whenever it specifies, or we may assume, that the sample we have actually observed has been drawn from a population normal, or reasonably normal, in form. But what should we do if we have good reason to suspect that the population in question is non-normal? The answer is partly indicated by the results obtained earlier for the sampling distribution of the mean, which we observed tends very rapidly to the normal form even when the population distribution is markedly non-normal. Consequently, we would expect to find that the t-distribution yields a satisfactory approximation, and may be used to provide a valid test of the hypothesis, even for non-normal populations, particularly for samples that are not too small, say not less than 30.

As empirical support for this conclusion, we show in Table VI.1 the actual distributions of t for samples of size 10 $(n = 9)$ drawn from the binomial, Poisson, normal, and rectangular populations discussed earlier, together with the expected frequencies for the t and normal distributions.[‡]

[†] $t_{.05}$ $(n = 100) = 1.982$.
[‡] Students should be encouraged to calculate the values of t, and construct the corresponding distributions from their own data. This is the best way of gaining a full understanding of the t-distribution and of the parts played by the mean and variance in determining the values of t.

Since these are quite small samples, it will be appreciated that any departures from the model t-distribution should be very evident. As might be expected, only the distribution for the Poisson samples is unusual: it is quite skewed, owing to the fact that the means and variances are related—samples with large means tend to have large variances, and samples with small means tend to have small variances. But the relationship is far from perfect, and the effect is hardly noticeable for samples of size 50: in fact, for samples of that size the distribution of t is approximately normal with $\xi = 0$ and $\sigma = 1$.

TABLE VI.1

OBSERVED DISTRIBUTIONS OF t FOR SAMPLES OF SIZE 10
DRAWN FROM BINOMIAL, POISSON, NORMAL, AND RECTANGULAR POPULATIONS

CLASS INTERVALS (t)	OBSERVED SAMPLES FROM POPULATION				EXPECTED FREQUENCIES	
	Binomial	Poisson	Normal	Rectangular	t	Normal
5.75 to 6.24				1		
5.25 to 5.74						
4.75 to 5.24			1	1	0.1	
4.25 to 4.74					0.3	0.01
3.75 to 4.24					0.6	0.04
3.25 to 3.74			2		2	0.2
2.75 to 3.24		2	1	2	3	1.2
2.25 to 2.74	3	2	8	2	7	5
1.75 to 2.24	1	8	23	6	16	14
1.25 to 1.74	8	23	37	13	32	32
0.75 to 1.24	12	39	69	27	57	61
0.25 to 0.74	15	51	75	35	84	87
−0.25 to 0.24	24	49	86	45	96	99
−0.75 to −0.26	18	51	85	24	84	87
−1.25 to −0.76	6	30	66	22	57	61
−1.75 to −1.26	6	15	23	9	32	32
−2.25 to −1.76	6	13	11	10	16	14
−2.75 to −2.26		6	9	2	7	5
−3.25 to −2.76	1	6	3		3	1.2
−3.75 to −3.26		2	1	1	2	0.2
−4.25 to −3.76		1			0.6	0.04
−4.75 to −4.26		2			0.3	0.01
−5.25 to −4.76					0.1	
Total	100	300	500	200	500	499.9

We are now in a position to test the hypothesis concerning the mean whether or not the population from which we are sampling is normal in form. In fact, provided the distribution of values we observe does not indicate the existence of a parent population extremely asymmetrical in form, and provided, further, that our sample contains at least 30 observations, we can make the statistical test without knowledge of the exact form of the parent population and be reasonably confident that our results and the conclusions drawn therefrom will be valid. Where researchers encounter situations in which the distribution of the observations indicates the existence of a very skewed parent population, however, or the number of cases is small, the above solution will not hold. Some of the sociometric measurements in the field of psychology, for example, are essentially discontinuous in nature and indicate that the parent populations are probably of the Poisson type with m less than unity, or more likely, of the negative binomial form. In one study that a student brought to us for advice, for instance, the distribution of "social-acceptability" scores for 34 children was as follows:

Score	0	1	2	3	4	Total
Observed Frequency	25	6	3			34
Expected Frequency (Poisson, $m = 0.35$)	23.99	8.34	1.48	0.18	0.02	34.01

As a comparison with the expected frequencies (Poisson: $m = 0.35$) reveals, the observed distribution closely resembles a Poisson. However, the variance was slightly greater than the mean ($k_2 = 0.417$ and $k_1 = 0.353$), and the parent population would probably be a negative binomial rather than a Poisson. Admittedly, this was an unusual set of observations, since experience with other groups indicates that the mean social-acceptability score is generally close to unity,§ but it does indicate the need to examine the original data closely before the usual statistical tests are applied and, where the distributions are unusual in form, to use statistical tests that are independent of the form of the parent population (non-parametric tests).

Use of Student's t-distribution

As an illustration of the t-distribution, and of its limiting form—the normal, where the hypothesis to be tested specifies only the value of the population mean and not the form or the variance of the population distribution, we will consider, first, the case of a relatively small sample where the distribution of observed values was roughly symmetrical and, second, the case of a large sample where the distribution of observed values was very skewed.

In the first example, a teacher administered a standardized arithmetic test to his Grade 8 class of 33 pupils and obtained a mean of 13.84 and a variance of 25.63. May he assume that the achievement of his class is sig-

§ We could in this case determine very easily the probability of securing in repeated random sampling a mean as low or lower than 0.353, where the parent population is a Poisson with $m = 1$ (probability approximately 1 in 10,000), or a Poisson with any other specified value of m.

nificantly above the norm for the grade, which is 12 points? The hypothesis to be tested and the set of admissible alternative hypotheses are

$$H_o : \xi = \xi_o = 12 \quad \text{and} \quad H_1 : \xi > \xi_o = 12$$

The statistic, t, to be used in testing the hypothesis is

$$t = \frac{M - \xi_o}{\sqrt{v/N}}$$

whence our observed value, t_o, will be

$$t_o = \frac{13.84 - 12}{\sqrt{\dfrac{25.63}{33}}} = +2.09$$

and the corresponding probability, $P(t > t_o)$, is approximately 0.024.‖ Clearly the observed event is rather unlikely to occur when H_o is true, but the probability of its occurring is not so small that rejection of H_o is unequivocally called for. While the average achievement of the class is above the norm, the difference is not significant at the 1 per cent error-risk, although it is significant if the 5 per cent error-level were acceptable.

In the second example, the observations consisted of ratings of 396 candidates applying for admission to a teacher-training institution. The distribution was rather markedly skewed towards the upper end of the scale (i.e. the raters tended to be lenient). These particular results were obtained in an experiment designed to determine if it were possible, by giving specific instructions to the raters, to lower the average of the ratings. For this group of candidates, which did not in any known manner differ from the usual run of candidates, the mean rating was 14.28 (the range of possible ratings was from 1 to 25) and the variance was 19.58, whereas past experience in similar situations indicated that the expected mean would be 15.5.# May we conclude that the instructions affected the ratings given, and in the desired direction?

Now, if the instructions had no effect, then the means of samples of such ratings would conform to the model obtained in repeated random sampling from a population (undefined, save that we know it is markedly skewed) with mean $\xi_o = 15.5$. Accordingly, we may state the null hypothesis and the set of admissible alternative hypotheses in the form

$$H_o : \xi = \xi_o = 15.5 \quad \text{and} \quad H_1 : \xi < \xi_o = 15.5$$

The statistic t appropriate for the test of H_o will be

$$t = \frac{M - \xi_o}{\sqrt{v/N}}$$

‖ As compared with a probability of 0.0187 secured from the tables of the normal distribution. For the t-distribution, of course, we used a one-tailed test of significance, and likewise for the normal distribution.

\# The raters seemed to have been influenced, consciously or unconsciously, by the pass-mark of the institution, which was 50 per cent.

For our example, the observed value of t, t_o, is

$$t_o = \frac{14.28 - 15.5}{\sqrt{\dfrac{19.58}{396}}} = -5.49$$

From the sampling results discussed earlier, it is evident that for samples of this size ($N = 396$) the statistic t will be approximately normally distributed about 0 with a standard deviation equal to unity. The probability of observing a value of $t \leqslant -5.49$ in repeated random sampling from such a population with samples of size $N = 396$ is, therefore, approximately 2 in 100,000,000 and accordingly we would reject the hypothesis H_o in favor of H_1.** We conclude, therefore, that the instructions did have a significant effect (statistically speaking) and in the direction desired.††

Students should note that the statistical tests used in these two examples were valid only because in the first the distribution was not markedly nonnormal in form and in the second the sample was large. Consequently we could use the sampling models with reasonable confidence that the associated probabilities were fair approximations. With very small samples and for populations of unknown form but that may be markedly nonnormal, on the other hand, we must exercise considerable caution in using these sampling models and in interpreting the results (particularly the probabilities) derived therefrom.

DIFFERENCE BETWEEN MEANS OF TWO SAMPLES

By far the most common type of problem that arises in research is the one which involves the comparison of the means of *two* random samples. The reason for this is that in most researches the comparison in which we are interested is, not of a set of observed results with a predetermined standard, but of one set of observed results with another. Our problem then is to determine whether the difference, if any, between the sets of observed results is statistically significant, which when translated into statistical terms reduces to the problem of determining whether or not we can conclude that the two sets are samples drawn at random from the same population. In some cases, one group is called the *experimental* and the other the *control*, and they differ (or should differ) only in that the former has been subjected to the influence of some "experimental" factor, whereas the latter has not.

Regardless of the actual circumstances, which vary from situation to situation as we shall see, the general line of deductive and inductive rea-

** For small values of N, the probability value would, of course, be obtained from the appropriate row ($n = N - 1$) of the table of t.

†† We may add, parenthetically, that the difference, while significant, was disappointingly small, and the possibility of drastically altering the ratings in the desired direction seemed rather remote. We had hoped to attain a mean not significantly different from the theoretically optimum value of 13, but we failed to do so.

soning is as follows. If the experimental factor has an effect, then the difference between the two groups should prove to be significant; if, on the other hand, the experimental factor has little or no effect, then the difference between the two groups should prove to be not significant. This deductive reasoning is subject to two assumptions which, by the way, are seldom explicitly stated or their validity tested. First, it is assumed that no other factor of importance was operating to affect the difference between the groups; and, second, that the two groups were in fact the same *except for the experimental factor*, i.e. if it had not been applied, they would behave as if they were two samples drawn at random from the same parent population.

Now, in our research we observe a difference between the two groups and test it for significance. If it proves to be non-significant, we conclude that the two groups were samples drawn at random from the same parent population and, consequently, that the experimental factor had no effect. If, on the other hand, the difference proves to be significant, we conclude that the two groups were not samples drawn from the same parent population (i.e. that they were samples drawn from two *different* parent populations) and, consequently, that the experimental factor had an effect. Observe, however, that the above two assumptions are also involved in the chain of inductive reasoning, and that if they are not satisfied our conclusion regarding the effect of the experimental factor will be invalid. It is quite possible, for example, to obtain a non-significant difference even when the experimental factor *did* have an effect, or to obtain a significant difference when the experimental factor did not have an effect, if the two groups were different to begin with.

One of the prime purposes of the design of an experiment is to ensure that these assumptions are satisfied, and the conduct of the experiment must be such that no extraneous factors are introduced. These essential controls can be imposed in any one of a number of ways, which affects the sampling models in the sense that the model appropriate for one situation is not necessarily appropriate for another. In the illustrations that follow we will treat separately the two major types of experimental design that require different statistical tests based on the means of two samples or groups: (1) where the individuals or objects are assigned at random to the two groups, to form random groups or independent samples; and (2) where the same or equated individuals are used to form the two groups, yielding matched individuals and dependent samples.

Difficulties arise in certain situations because the hypothesis to be tested is composite, not simple. For a normal population (the simplest case), for example, a knowledge of both ξ and σ is required before the population is completely specified. Now consider the two groups or samples we have in mind: it is conceivable that the first was a sample from a normal population defined by the values ξ_1 and σ_1, and that the second was a sample from a normal population defined by ξ_2 and σ_2. But they may be samples from a common normal population defined by ξ_o and σ_o, say, in which event $\xi_1 = \xi_2 = \xi_o$ and $\sigma_1 = \sigma_2 = \sigma_o$. There will not be a common population, however, if $\xi_1 = \xi_2 = \xi_o$ but $\sigma_1 \neq \sigma_2$. The hypothesis to be tested, H_o, and the set of admissible alternative hypotheses, H_1, are usually expressed in the form

$$H_o : \xi_1 = \xi_2 = \xi_o; \qquad H_1 : \xi_1 \neq \xi_2$$

where it is assumed that $\sigma_1 = \sigma_2 = \sigma_o$. Unless this assumption is satisfied, at least within reasonable limits, the sampling model (the t-distribution) is inappropriate and the statistical test based thereon correspondingly invalid. As will be evident from the earlier discussion of the effect on the actual value of t of the values entering into the numerator and into the denominator of its equation,‡‡ acceptance or rejection of H_o will depend in part upon the equality or inequality of the σ's, not alone upon the equality or inequality of the ξ's. But this anticipates the formulation of appropriate tests for the hypothesis H_o, to which we now turn.

Differences Between Means of Two Independent Samples

Assuming for the present that the parent population is, or the two parent populations are, normal in form and that we are dealing with two independent random samples, observe that for the first sample of N_1 values of X_1, say,

$$M_1 = \frac{\Sigma X_1}{N_1}$$

$$\text{and} \quad v_1 = \frac{\Sigma(X_1 - M_1)^2}{N_1 - 1}$$

{ when this is to be used as an estimate of the universe use V_1

are unbiased estimates of ξ_1 and σ_1, respectively. Likewise, for the second sample of N_2 values of X_2, say,

$$M_2 = \frac{\Sigma X_2}{N_2}$$

$$\text{and} \quad v_2 = \frac{\Sigma(X_2 - M_2)^2}{N_2 - 1}$$

are unbiased estimates of ξ_2 and σ_2, respectively.

Consider, next, the expression §§ $(M_1 - \xi_1) - (M_2 - \xi_2)$ which may be written as $(M_1 - M_2) - (\xi_1 - \xi_2)$ or as $d - \Delta$, say, where $d = M_1 - M_2$

---

‡‡ Which gave rise, for example, to the peculiar form of distribution of t for samples of size 10 drawn from the Poisson population.

§§ The argument holds also for the other form $(M_2 - \xi_2) - (M_1 - \xi_1)$.

and $\Delta = \xi_1 - \xi_2$. Now, since both M_1 and M_2 are normally distributed, M_1 about ξ_1 with standard error $\dfrac{\sigma_1}{\sqrt{N_1}}$ and M_2 about ξ_2 with standard error $\dfrac{\sigma_2}{\sqrt{N_2}}$, the difference, $d = M_1 - M_2$, will be normally distributed about $\Delta = \xi_1 - \xi_2$ with standard error equal to $\sqrt{\dfrac{\sigma_1^2}{N_1} + \dfrac{\sigma_2^2}{N_2}}$.‖‖ Assuming that $\sigma_1 = \sigma_2 = \sigma_o$, then d will, of course, be normally distributed about Δ with standard error equal to $\sqrt{\sigma_o^2 \left(\dfrac{1}{N_1} + \dfrac{1}{N_2} \right)}$.

Now if the hypothesis to be tested is true, $H_o : \xi_1 = \xi_2 = \xi_o$, then d is normally distributed about zero, whereas if H_1 is true then d will be normally distributed about $\Delta \neq 0$. Accordingly, the test of H_o reduces to determining whether or not the observed difference, $d = M_1 - M_2$, is significantly different from zero. As in the case of the tests based on the mean of a single sample, however, we must distinguish between the situations where the population σ's are, and are not, known.

Population σ's Known

In this particular situation, the appropriate test is especially simple. Where $\sigma_1 \neq \sigma_2$, if the hypothesis to be tested, $H_o : \xi_1 = \xi_2 = \xi_o$, is true, the quantity

$$z = \frac{d}{\sqrt{\dfrac{\sigma_1^2}{N_1} + \dfrac{\sigma_2^2}{N_2}}}$$

will be normally distributed about zero with unit standard deviation. Similarly, where $\sigma_1 = \sigma_2 = \sigma_o$, if the hypothesis to be tested, $H_o : \xi_1 = \xi_2 = \xi_o$, is true, the quantity

$$z^1 = \frac{d}{\sqrt{\sigma_o^2 \left(\dfrac{1}{N_1} + \dfrac{1}{N_2} \right)}}$$

will be normally distributed about zero with unit standard deviation. Accordingly, the tables of the normal distribution may be used to determine a critical region and the probability of an error of the first kind.

Students should observe, however, that such a test is valid only when the means are normally distributed, which will be true for non-normal parent populations only when the samples are fairly large and the parent populations do not depart too much from the normal form. That "fairly large" will in most cases be surprisingly small is evident after a moment's

---

‖‖ The sums and differences of normally distributed variates are themselves normally distributed.

reflection of the nature of the sampling procedure when H_o is true. Since the samples are drawn at random, the difference between any two sample means is just as likely to be positive as negative, and more likely to be small than large (both samples are drawn from a common population, or from two populations with the same mean). In any event, therefore, we will always have a roughly symmetrical distribution for $d = M_1 - M_2$, under the conditions specified, and it will approximate very closely to the normal in form. As an empirical demonstration of the validity of this conclusion, we show in Table VI.2 the actual distribution of $d = M_1 - M_2$ for 100 consecutive pairs of the samples of size 10 drawn from the rectangular population previously described, and the expected frequencies for a normal

TABLE VI.2

DISTRIBUTION OF ACTUAL VALUES OF $d = M_1 - M_2$ FOR SAMPLES OF SIZE 10 FROM A RECTANGULAR POPULATION, AND EXPECTED FREQUENCIES FOR A NORMAL DISTRIBUTION OF SAME MEAN AND VARIANCE

CLASS INTERVALS $(d = M_1 - M_2)$	FREQUENCIES	
	Observed	Expected (Normal)
7.0 to 7.9		0.2
6.0 to 6.9	1	0.6
5.0 to 5.9	2	1.6
4.0 to 4.9	2	3.7
3.0 to 3.9	8	6.9
2.0 to 2.9	13	10.8
1.0 to 1.9	14	14.5
0.0 to 0.9	12	16.4
−1.0 to −0.1	19	15.6
−2.0 to −1.1	13	12.5
−3.0 to −2.1	8	8.5
−4.0 to −3.1	4	4.9
−5.0 to −4.1	2	2.3
−6.0 to −5.1	2	1.0
−7.0 to −6.1		0.3
−8.0 to −7.1		0.1
Total	100	99.9

distribution of the same mean and variance. We may note in passing that the mean value of d was 0.24, as compared with the expected value of 0, and the observed standard deviation of the distribution was 2.41, as compared with the expected (for $\sigma_o^2 = 33.25$, $N_1 = N_2 = 10$) value of 2.58. The agreement of observed and expected (normal) frequencies is amazingly good, considering that the samples were only of size 10.##

The situation where the population σ's, or the common σ_o, are known

Students should, as an exercise, construct similar distributions for their own sample values obtained from binomial, Poisson, or normal distributions.

occurs quite frequently in psychology and education, since most of the mental tests used are standardized and therefore the population characteristics are known. As an illustration, consider the significance of the difference between the mean achievement of students in the General and Commercial courses in secondary schools on an English test, discussed in another connection in an earlier section. We had the following values:

General Course: $N_1 = 146$; $M_1 = 49.4$
Commercial Course: $N_2 = 115$; $M_2 = 42.8$ $\sigma_o{}^2 = 850$

Accordingly, we find the observed value of desired statistic, z^1, to be

$$z_o^1 = \frac{d}{\sqrt{\sigma_o{}^2 \left(\dfrac{1}{N_1} + \dfrac{1}{N_2} \right)}} = \frac{6.6}{3.635} = 1.82$$

see p. 499

.9656 as letter w under normal curve

1.0000
.9656
.0344

and, since N_1 and N_2 are quite large, we may reasonably assume that z^1 is normally distributed about zero with unit standard deviation. From the tables of the normal distribution we find, for the set of admissible alternative hypotheses $H_1 : \xi_1 > \xi_2$,***

$$P(z^1 > z_o^1) = P(z^1 > 1.82) = 0.034$$

and we would reject the hypothesis to be tested, $H_o : \xi_1 = \xi_2 = \xi_o$, at the 5 per cent level of significance, but accept it at the 1 per cent level of significance. The observed event, if the hypothesis to be tested is true, is a somewhat unlikely one, but it is not so unlikely that an unequivocal rejection of H_o is indicated. There is evidence that the achievement of the Commercial group is significantly below that of the General, but the evidence is far from conclusive.†††

Where the circumstances are such that we cannot assume $\sigma_1 = \sigma_2 = \sigma_o$ and the values of σ_1 and σ_2 are known, the appropriate formula to use is, of course,

$$z = \frac{d}{\sqrt{\dfrac{\sigma_1{}^2}{N_1} + \dfrac{\sigma_2{}^2}{N_2}}}$$

Students will encounter such problems in practice, albeit somewhat infrequently, but the application of the test is so straightforward that we deem it unnecessary to give an illustration.

Population σ's Not Known

Consider, first, the situation where the distribution of the population is normal in form, but the value of σ_o, or of σ_1 and σ_2 where $\sigma_1 \neq \sigma_2$, is not

*** We were not interested in the other set of alternative hypotheses, namely $H_o : \xi_1 < \xi_2$.

††† This result seems to be at variance with the conclusion previously reached in regard to these two groups of students. But we have in the two situations tested hypotheses that are far from equivalent, and it is not surprising that the answers are different. All of which illustrates a rather important point in logical reasoning, viz. that the answer refers to the question asked.

known. Obviously, we cannot use the formulae of the preceding example, since the value of the denominator cannot be determined. However, if the size of the samples is large, so that the variance of k_2 in repeated random sampling will be small, a very satisfactory approximation is obtained by substituting for the unknown population variances the estimates obtained from the samples.‡‡‡ This cannot be done for small samples, of course, since as we saw in the previous chapter the sample estimates of the variance may be very different from the population values.

For small samples, we must distinguish clearly between the cases where $\sigma_1 = \sigma_2 = \sigma_o$ and $\sigma_1 \neq \sigma_2$.§§§ For the first case, for the test of the hypothesis $H_o : \xi_1 = \xi_2 = \xi_o$ knowing that $\sigma_1 = \sigma_2 = \sigma_o$, the appropriate statistic to use is

$$t = \frac{M_1 - M_2}{\sqrt{\dfrac{\Sigma (X_1 - M_1)^2 + \Sigma (X_2 - M_2)^2}{N_1 + N_2 - 2} \left(\dfrac{1}{N_1} + \dfrac{1}{N_2} \right)}}$$

which in repeated random sampling is distributed as t with $N_1 + N_2 - 2$ degrees of freedom. This extension (by R. A. Fisher) of the original t-test of Student enables us to make a valid test of the hypothesis $H_o : \xi_1 = \xi_2 = \xi_o$ in a wide variety of situations. But the restrictions on its use must be carefully noted: (1) normality of the population distribution, and (2) the assumption that $\sigma_1 = \sigma_2 = \sigma_o$. That the first restriction does not impose too severe a limitation, except for very small samples, is evident from our earlier discussion of the distribution of t for non-normal populations (note that, if the hypothesis to be tested is true, the distribution of $d = M_1 - M_2$ will be roughly symmetrical in any event and probably not too far from normal) and from the finding of M. G. Kendall that if the parent populations are symmetrical and not excessively leptokurtic or platykurtic the distribution of t is little affected.‖‖‖ But if the assumption of a common σ_o is not satisfied, the distribution of t may be greatly affected, as we shall see in the second section that follows.

Population σ's Equal

We shall illustrate the use of the above formula on the results secured by Hamel and Reif in a study of the effect of signing questionnaires (the instrument used was an employee attitude questionnaire).### The first

---

‡‡‡ Since the variance of k_2 is $2\sigma^4/N - 1$, "large" must be judged in relation to the size of σ as well as N. For N's of 500 or more, the procedure seems to yield valid results, even for fairly large σ's.

§§§ Students with a knowledge of calculus should be encouraged to read the following article: P. L. Hsu, "Contribution to the Theory of 'Student's' t-test as Applied to the Problem of Two Samples," *Statistical Research Memoirs*, Vol. II (London: Department of Statistics, University College, University of London), pp. 1–24.

‖‖‖ *The Advanced Theory of Statistics*, Vol. II, pp. 102–3.

LaVerne Hamel and Hans G. Reif, "Should Attitude Questionnaires be Signed?", *Personnel Psychology*, No. 2 (Summer, 1952).

group of employees signed their questionnaires whereas the second group did not, and the question posed was whether the difference in the average expressed attitude of the two groups was significant. The results reported were as follows:

GROUP 1   GROUP 2

$M_1 = 171.1$ $M_2 = 171.2$

$S.D._1 = 27.0$ $S.D._2 = 27.1$

$N_1 = 109$ $N_2 = 94$

where "$S.D.$" was used by the authors to denote "standard deviation"—we

will assume that the authors used the formula $S.D. = \sqrt{\dfrac{\Sigma(X - M)^2}{N}}$.

Since the sample distributions were roughly symmetrical, the random samples of a fair size, and the values of $S.D.$ approximately equal, it is evident that the usual form of t, as given above, should yield a valid test of the hypothesis $H_o : \xi_1 = \xi_2 = \xi_o$. Substituting in the above formula, we find $t_o = -0.26$, which is obviously not significantly different from zero (for 201 degrees of freedom we can use the table of the normal distribution or the last row of the table of t). Accordingly, we would accept H_o and conclude that the fact that the questionnaire was to be signed did not have an effect on the expressed attitudes of the employees.[*]

It is of some interest to note that, in this situation, the set of admissible alternative hypotheses must be $H : \xi_1 \neq \xi_2$, including $H_1 : \xi_1 < \xi_2$ and $H_2 : \xi_1 > \xi_2$, since the effect of identification might conceivably operate in either direction. The two-tailed test, i.e. use of the probabilities as tabled for t, is therefore appropriate, although it would not be if the direction of the effect were either postulated or known from previous experience.

Population σ's Unequal

Let us return to the second case, where it is either known or postulated that $\sigma_1 \neq \sigma_2$.[†] Assuming normality in the parent populations (remembering, however, that the form of the t-distribution is not greatly affected by minor departures from normality), we can make a valid test of the hypothesis $H_o : \xi_1 = \xi_2 = \xi_o$ by using the Behrens-Fisher test, for which Fisher and Yates give special tables.[‡] But this test is somewhat difficult to use,[§]

[*] Possibly because the employees were assured that the results would be treated as confidential and used for research purposes only.

[†] See next chapter for the appropriate test of significance of the difference between variances.

[‡] R. A. Fisher and F. Yates, *Statistical Tables for Biological, Agricultural, and Medical Research* (Third edition; Edinburgh: Oliver and Boyd, 1949). See also, Welch, *Biometrika*, XXXIV (1947), 28–35, and Aspin, *Biometrika*, XXXVI (1949), 290–96.

[§] The test is also somewhat controversial. For an alternative approach see, B. L.

and the approximation suggested by Cochran and Cox,‖ based on the table of the t-distribution, is quite satisfactory in the vast majority of cases (the Behrens-Fisher or Welch test should probably be applied also, at least as a check, when the samples are very small).

For the Cochran-Cox test, using the following values calculated from the samples,

$$d = M_1 - M_2$$

$$v_1 = \frac{\Sigma\,(X_1 - M_1)^2}{N_1(N_1 - 1)} \left(\text{unbiased estimate of } \frac{\sigma_1^2}{N_1}\right)$$

$$v_2 = \frac{\Sigma\,(X_2 - M_2)^2}{N_2(N_2 - 1)} \left(\text{unbiased estimate of } \frac{\sigma_2^2}{N_2}\right)$$

we calculate the value of the statistic, t_o, defined by the equation

$$t_o = \frac{d}{\sqrt{v_1 + v_2}}$$

and determine appropriate levels of significance from the usual table of t by calculating the quantity

$$t^1 = \frac{t_1 v_1 + t_2 v_2}{v_1 + v_2}$$

where t_1 is the tabled value of t for $n = N_1 - 1$ at a given level of significance and t_2 is the corresponding value of t for $n = N_2 - 1$.

It will be observed that t^1 is a weighted average, using the variance estimates as weights, of the usual tabled values of t. An interesting special case arises when $N_1 = N_2$ because in this event $t_1 = t_2 = t$, say, and the above formula reduces to $t^1 = t$ for $N - 1$, not $N_1 + N_2 - 2 = 2(N - 1)$, degrees of freedom. Accordingly, whenever $N_1 = N_2 = N$ we can use the t-table directly, but we must enter it with $n = N - 1$, not $N_1 + N_2 - 2$.# Obviously, since the region of significance for t becomes larger as n is decreased, we have in this approximate solution set up more exacting requirements for the rejection of H_o than those which apply when $\sigma_1 = \sigma_2 = \sigma_o$. The error involved, if any, is in the direction of accepting H_o somewhat more frequently than we perhaps should, but this is comforting rather than disquieting knowledge. If err we must, we are probably overly cautious. If we do reject H_o, we can reasonably be confident that our conclusion is valid.

To illustrate the use of this and the previous formula in a situation

Welch, "The Generalization of 'Student's' Problem When Different Population Variances Are Involved," *Biometrika*, XXXIV, Parts I and II (1947), 28–35.

‖ W. G. Cochran and Gertrude M. Cox, *Experimental Designs* (New York: John Wiley & Sons, 1950).

But see, for example, the paper by Hsu, previously cited, and M. G. Kendall's discussion of Welch's results (*The Advanced Theory of Statistics*, Vol. II, pp. 113–14).

where the sample standard deviations apparently differ considerably, consider the following data reported by Murray in a study of the use of different types of aeronautical charts by jet pilots.** The values reported were

CHART 1 (WAC)	CHART 2 (XJN)
$N_1 = 60$	$N_2 = 72$
$M_1 = 3.65$	$M_2 = 3.47$
$SD_1 = 1.22$	$SD_2 = 0.76$

Since no discussion of the selection of the 60 pilots for Chart 1 and the 72 pilots for Chart 2 is given by the author, we must assume that the two groups are independent (selected at random, we hope, or the interpretation of the results would be difficult).

From these reported values, we find that (using the 5 per cent level for a two-tailed test)

$$d = 0.18; \qquad N_1 = 60; \qquad N_2 = 72$$
$$v_1 = 0.02523 \qquad\qquad t_1 = 2.001$$
$$v_2 = 0.00814 \qquad\qquad t_2 = 1.994$$

whence

$$t_o = 1.0 \quad \text{and} \quad t^1 = 2.00$$

and we would accept the hypothesis H_o without question (somewhat of a victory for the experimental chart (XJN), in this instance, since in it the detail was greatly reduced).

If we had ignored the difference in the standard deviations (also in favor of the experimental chart, if significant), and applied the formula appropriate for the case $\sigma_1 = \sigma_2 = \sigma_o$, we would have secured the value $t_o = 1.03$ and, for 130 degrees of freedom, the 5 per cent level of significance (two-tailed test) the tabled value of t is 1.978. While the two tests are very nearly the same in this instance, they do differ slightly and it is clear that the Cochran-Cox test is the more stringent (for rejection of H_o). The difference is more marked for smaller samples, of course.

Difference Between Means of Two Dependent Samples (Matching)

Whereas in the previous case of independent samples the selection of individuals was designed to yield two random or independent groups, in the present case the procedure consists in using the same or equated (matched) individuals. Note how the purpose of the experimental control has changed. In the case of random groups, it is simply to ensure that any factor that may be operating will not favor one group or the other: a random assignment of the individuals ensuring a random assignment of the effect

** John E. Murray, "An Evaluation of Two Experimental Charts as Navigational Aids to Jet Pilots," *Journal of Applied Psychology*, XXXVII, No. 3 (June, 1953). Reprinted by permission of the American Psychological Association. We should point out that in the other comparisons made by Murray, the distributions appear to be markedly skewed and the validity of the usual t-test is in considerable doubt.

of such factors, if any. In the second case we endeavor to control such factors by matching or equating. Now if the circumstances are such that a large number of individuals may be used in both groups,†† thereby reducing the standard error of the difference between the means to any desired level, the random-groups method is the simplest and probably the best to use (this is frequently the case in education, since thousands of children are available in the schools). Accordingly, the matched-individuals method is normally appropriate for use only in situations where, for reasons of cost or difficulties of experimentation, small numbers of individuals must be used and where treatments are assigned by lot to the members of a pair.

In essence, matching of individuals is an alternative method of reducing the standard error of the difference between the means to any desired level, a direct control imposed through matching rather than an indirect control through increasing the size of N_1 or N_2, or both. Note that in some situations we may even use an individual as his own control, i.e. in both groups. Matching does have the advantage that, since the extraneous factors are directly controlled, the interpretation of the results is somewhat simpler. But it has the (often unsuspected) disadvantage that, unless the matching is properly done and on the proper variables, we may end up with what are no more than random groups and the supposed gain in precision of the experiment will be largely or wholly illusory. Proper matching is particularly difficult to attain in the social sciences, because so many variables normally operate, and in a manner largely unknown. Hence, in a given situation any selection of variables for matching purposes is partly guesswork and the gain in precision may be surprisingly small. Another very serious disadvantage, from the point of view of interpretation, is that, because many cases are discarded in matching, there may be considerable doubt as to what population or populations have in fact been sampled.

For experiments that use the same individuals or equated or matched individuals, such as identical twins, and where the members of each pair are assigned at random to the two groups, the statistical model to be used in testing the null hypothesis $H_o : \xi_1 = \xi_2 = \xi_o$ is particularly simple. Observe that by the design of the experiment we have ensured (assuming the equating or matching of individuals has been properly done on the proper variables) that if the hypothesis to be tested is true, i.e. that the experimental factor has no effect, the differences between the members of equated pairs of individuals‡‡ will be randomly distributed about the expected value of zero. Assuming normality in the parent population, these differences will be normally distributed about zero with a constant but (generally) unknown standard deviation, σ, say. Accordingly, if we denote by X_{i1} and

---

†† Or at least in the control group, provided we may assume $\sigma_1 = \sigma_2 = \sigma_o$.

‡‡ Or gains, if the same individuals are used and measured before and after the experiment, thus providing their own control group of matched individuals.

X_{i2} the measurements for the two matched individuals of the ith pair, and define

$$d_i = X_{i1} - X_{i2}; \qquad M_d = \frac{\Sigma d_i}{N}; \qquad \text{and} \qquad v = \frac{\Sigma(d_i - M_d)^2}{N-1}$$

where N denotes the number of matched pairs, i.e. $i = 1, 2, \ldots, N$, then

the quantity $t = \dfrac{M_d}{\sqrt{v/N}}$ will be distributed as t with degrees of freedom

$n = N - 1$. The t-distribution, therefore, provides the appropriate model for the test of the null hypothesis, $H_o : \xi_1 = \xi_2 = \xi_o$, or $H_o : \xi_d = 0$.§§

Students will observe the similarity of this equation with those of the previous section, since M_d is simply the difference between the means of the two groups. The major difference lies in the denominator, which, although this fact is not immediately obvious from the above expression for v, makes due allowance for the effort expended in matching the individuals of each

pair. That this is so becomes evident if we write the formula for $\dfrac{v}{N}$ in the form

$$\frac{v}{N} = \frac{\Sigma(X_{i1} - M_1)^2 + \Sigma(X_{i2} - M_2)^2 - 2\Sigma(X_{i1} - M_1)(X_{i2} - M_2)}{N(N-1)}$$

which in its first two terms resembles the expression in the denominator of the equation of t for random groups where $\sigma_1 = \sigma_2 = \sigma_o$. When $N_1 = N_2 = N$, say, this latter equation reduces to

$$\frac{v^1}{N} = \frac{\Sigma(X_{i1} - M_1)^2 + \Sigma(X_{i2} - M_2)^2}{N(N-1)}$$

although the number of degrees of freedom differs, being $n = N - 1$ for matched individuals and $n = 2(N - 1)$ for random groups.

Now, it is obvious from the above equations that we have both gained and lost in precision by the process of matching: "lost" in the sense that there are fewer degrees of freedom, and therefore a narrower critical region for the test of the null hypothesis, and "gained" in that if our process of

matching has been effective $\dfrac{v}{N}$ will be much smaller than $\dfrac{v^1}{N}$. Since the

quantity $\Sigma(X_{i1} - M_1)(X_{i2} - M_2)$, being the sum of products of the deviations from the means for the measures of each matched pair, will normally be positive and probably not very much smaller than the average of $\Sigma(X_{i1} - M_1)^2$ and $\Sigma(X_{i2} - M_2)^2$ when the matching process is effective, it

follows that the numerator in $\dfrac{v}{N}$ will in most cases be only a small fraction

§§ The assumptions underlying pairing can be empirically tested by plotting the N-pairs on a diagram making X_{i1} an abscissa and X_{i2} an ordinate. If the plotted points are scattered at random about a line with slope 1, and with constant variation, the assumption concerning the distribution of differences would likely be satisfied.

of the numerator in $\dfrac{v^1}{N}$. Accordingly, we would expect a very considerable net gain in precision in most experiments involving matched individuals. If this is not achieved, the fault lies in the matching process.

The above formulae (for random groups and for matched individuals) can be extended rather simply to include the case where attention is focused on gains or changes in the individual members. It will be sufficient to note that for each individual there will be, not a single measure, but an initial and final measure, which we may denote by X_{iI} and X_{iF}, respectively. But we may without loss of generality consider a new set of measures D_i, where $D_i = X_{iI} - X_{iF}$, for the individuals in each group, and we now have for the D_i's exactly the situation considered above. Thus, the above formulae for t can be used directly if we make the following substitutions:‖‖

$$X_{i1} = D_{i1} \quad \text{and} \quad X_{i2} = D_{i2}$$

As for the effect of non-normality of the parent populations on the distribution of t, the conditions and restrictions previously discussed apply to this situation also. Unless our observed distributions are markedly non-normal in form, we can with a fair degree of confidence apply the t-test and base our general conclusions on the results derived therefrom.

As a simple illustration of the use of the above formulae, let us consider the problem of determining whether the mental ages of unlike-sex fraternal twins differ significantly, putting the boys in the first group and the girls in the second. The data for a small group of 26 pairs of such twins are given in Table VI.3.## From the sums and sums of squares of the final two rows, we find

$$M_D = -\frac{124}{26} = -4.769 ; \qquad \Sigma(D_i - M_D)^2 = 12{,}736.62$$

$$M_1 = \frac{3{,}529}{26} = 135.731 ; \qquad \Sigma(X_{i1} - M_1)^2 = 8{,}753.12$$

$$M_2 = \frac{3{,}653}{26} = 140.500 ; \qquad \Sigma(X_{i2} - M_2)^2 = 13{,}004.50$$

whence, using the formula given earlier

$$\frac{v}{N} = 19.595$$

$$\text{and} \quad \frac{v^1}{N} = 33.473$$

‖‖ The formulae can be expressed in terms of the original measures, X_{i1I}, X_{i1F}, X_{i2I}, and X_{i2F}, but the algebra becomes somewhat involved and the nature of the process is obscured. We prefer to operate with the D's, at least if the number of cases is not large.

Robert W. B. Jackson, *Application of the Analysis of Variance and Covariance Method to Educational Problems*, Bulletin No. 11 (Toronto: Department of Educational Research, University of Toronto, 1940), p. 38. Students will note that observed distributions are not markedly non-normal in form.

TABLE VI.3

ILLUSTRATION OF t-TEST, MATCHED INDIVIDUALS:
MENTAL AGES OF 26 PAIRS OF UNLIKE-SEX FRATERNAL TWINS

PAIR i	MENTAL AGES Boys X_{i1}	MENTAL AGES Girls X_{i2}	D_i $(X_{i1} - X_{i2})$	PAIR i	MENTAL AGES Boys X_{i1}	MENTAL AGES Girls X_{i2}	D_i $(X_{i1} - X_{i2})$
1	97	110	−13	17	177	146	31
2	129	103	26	18	141	144	−3
3	131	139	−8	19	134	135	−1
4	151	132	19	20	120	127	−7
5	180	140	40	21	116	116	0
6	124	118	6	22	138	177	−39
7	133	142	−9	23	122	125	−3
8	158	160	−2	24	122	158	−36
9	128	145	−17	25	149	164	−15
10	140	145	−5	26	161	158	3
11	126	117	9				
12	130	136	−6	Sum	3,529	3,653	−124
13	139	205	−66				
14	130	111	19				
15	113	138	−25	Sum of Squares	487,747	526,251	13,328
16	140	162	−22				

Clearly, we have increased the precision of our experiment—in terms of the square roots of the above quantities—approximately 25 per cent by taking into account in our formula the matching of the members of each twin pair. Since for $n = N - 1 = 25$ the 1 per cent point of the t-distribution is 2.787 whereas for $n = 2(N - 1) = 50$ the 1 per cent point of the t-distribution is 2.678,*** we have obviously reaped a substantial net gain. For the above values,

$$t = \frac{M_D}{\sqrt{v/N}} = -\frac{4.769}{4.427} = -1.16$$

and $$t^1 = \frac{M_D}{\sqrt{v^{11}/N}} = -\frac{4.769}{5.786} = -0.82$$

and, although for both we would accept the hypothesis H_o, yet it is abundantly clear that in such situations the effort of matching is amply rewarded.

As a final illustration, in a situation where attention was focused on gains over a period of five months, we shall consider Koerber's data relating to gains in reading age of an experimental group (which received additional help) and a control group (which did not) of non-academic adolescent boys

*** Using a two-tailed test, since the set of admissible alternative hypotheses will comprise $\xi_D > 0$ and $\xi_D < 0$.

(19 pairs of carefully matched boys were used).††† It is assumed that treatment was assigned by lot.

The gains for the boys of each pair are shown in Table VI.4, together with the calculations necessary for the several possible statistical tests of the corresponding null hypothesis (that the additional help had no effect).

TABLE VI.4

ILLUSTRATION OF t-TEST, GAINS FOR MATCHED INDIVIDUALS:
GAINS IN READING AGE OF 19 PAIRS
OF MATCHED NON-ACADEMIC ADOLESCENT BOYS

PAIR i	GAIN		D_i $(X_{i1}-X_{i2})$	PAIR i	GAIN		D_i $(X_{i1}-X_{i2})$
	Experi- mental	Control			Experi- mental	Control	
	X_{i1}	X_{i2}			X_{i1}	X_{i2}	
1	21	0	21	13	7	1	6
2	8	−2	10	14	3	5	−2
3	17	12	5	15	11	6	5
4	17	2	15	16	8	4	4
5	3	3	0	17	20	5	15
6	14	4	10	18	7	3	4
7	11	10	1	19	5	−2	7
8	9	2	7				
9	16	−3	19	Sum	223	57	166
10	27	10	17				
11	8	0	8	Sum of Squares	3,377	515	2,222
12	11	−3	14				

From the sums and sums of squares of the final two rows of the table, we obtain

$$M_D = \frac{166}{19} = 8.737; \qquad \Sigma(D_i - M_D)^2 = 771.684$$

$$M_1 = \frac{223}{19} = 11.737; \qquad \Sigma(X_{i1} - M_1)^2 = 759.684$$

$$M_2 = \frac{57}{19} = 3.000; \qquad \Sigma(X_{i2} - M_2)^2 = 344.000$$

As in the previous illustration, we calculate

$$\frac{v}{N} = 2.2564$$

††† Walter F. Koerber, "An Evaluation of Some Methods and Procedures in the Teaching of Reading to Non-academic Adolescent Boys" (Unpublished Doctor of Pedagogy thesis, University of Toronto, 1947), p. 191.

$$\text{and} \quad \frac{v^1}{N} = 3.2271$$

The 1 per cent points of the t-distribution‡‡‡ are 2.552 for $n = N - 1 = 18$ and 2.446 for $n = 2(N - 1) = 36$. The corresponding observed values of t are

$$t = \frac{M_D}{\sqrt{v/N}} = 5.82$$

$$\text{and} \quad t^1 = \frac{M_D}{\sqrt{v^{11}/N}} = 4.86$$

and we would in each test reject the null hypothesis. Note, however, that the matching process did result in some gain in precision, and obviously must be taken into consideration in making the appropriate statistical test. Matching has also simplified the interpretation of the results, in that we know the members of each pair were as nearly equal as we could make them at the beginning of the experiment, but has at the same time rendered it difficult to determine the population to which these results do in fact relate.§§§

One unusual feature of these data, common to all like situations, is that our matching procedure was one stage removed from the measures we employ in the analysis of the results. Koerber did not, and obviously could not, match individuals directly on the observed gains but on a number of related factors (such as reading grade and intelligence). We assume in the analysis that this is equivalent, if the hypothesis to be tested is true, to matching in some fashion on gains. From the point of view of proper design, and of interpretation of the final results, it might have been advisable to attempt some form of matching directly on observed gains during an initial trial period.

Koerber was fortunate in that his process of matching did result in a gain in precision. But researchers should be aware that this will not always be the case in such situations, and that it is not impossible to find that v is *greater than or equal to* v^1, and consequently t *less than or equal to* t^1. When this occurs, the researcher must conclude, regretfully, that the matching process did *not* result in matched individuals for the variables being analyzed. In short, he has matched on independent variables and achieved no more than random groups. In this event, t^1, and not t, is the appropriate statistic to use in the test of the null hypothesis. A sound rule to follow in practice, in cases of doubt, is to calculate the values of both t and t^1, or of v and v^1, and determine what actually has happened to the data.

‡‡‡ For a one-tailed test, since the set of admissible alternative hypotheses will comprise only the positive values.

§§§ However, if the members of the respective matched pairs were allotted at random to the respective treatments, statistical inferences are valid for the experimental subjects.

We may state, however, that where pairing of individuals is effective the t-test is often more powerful than it is in the case of the two random samples. We mean by this that the null hypothesis is rejected more often when it is false since the positive correlation between the effects of the two treatments in the pairing of similar units results in a smaller variance, thus more than balancing the disadvantage in only having half as many degrees of freedom.

Another unusual feature of Koerber's data may be found in the difference in the variance for the gains in the experimental and control groups. It will be observed that

$$v_1 = \frac{\Sigma(X_{i1} - M_1)^2}{N - 1} = 42.205$$

and

$$v_2 = \frac{\Sigma(X_{i2} - M_2)^2}{N - 1} = 19.111$$

so that v_1 is more than twice as large as v_2.|||| The experimental factor has had an effect on the variance as well as on the mean.### To play it safe, we probably should in this event assume that we have random groups from populations with different variances and apply the Cochran-Cox test, discussed earlier. This is equivalent to using the value $t^1 = 4.86$, but entering the table of t with degrees of freedom $n = N - 1 = 18$. For Koerber's data, we would again reject the null hypothesis, but obviously the result in other cases may not be as convenient.

While the researcher must use his own judgment in deciding which conclusion to draw when these three possible statistical tests yield conflicting results, he should at least consider, and report if necessary, the results for each. Considering the implications of the decision, it is probably advisable to err on the side of accepting the null hypothesis even when it may possibly be false.

EXERCISES

1. Construct a t-distribution from your own sampling results. Compare your empirical results with the theoretical distribution.
2. Did the experimental factor have an effect in the following set of results?

MATCHED RATS PAIR	FINAL WEIGHT OF	
	Experimental	*Control*
1	83	87
2	81	86
3	84	90
4	80	86
5	85	90

|||| For a discussion of the corresponding statistical test of significance of the difference, see the next chapter.

This is an important experimental finding, since it indicates that the experimental method allowed greater expression of individual differences.

3. I gave my students a test in arithmetic before and after a course in statistics, and secured the following results:

Student	1	2	3	4	5	6	7	8	9	10
Before Course	9	1	4	7	0	3	3	6	6	8
Score										
After Course	3	7	2	6	1	9	7	4	2	5

What effect, if any, did the course in statistics have on achievement in arithmetic?

4. On a statistics test given to two random independent groups of students, the number of cases, sum of scores, and sum of squares of scores were as follows:

$$SD = \sqrt{\Sigma x^2 - \left(\frac{\Sigma x}{N}\right)^2 \times \frac{1}{N}}$$

$$\sqrt{286537 - \left(\frac{2342}{20}\right)^2}$$

$$\sqrt{272825}{20}$$

ITEM	GROUP PSYCHOLOGY	EDUCATION
Number	20 N_1	60 N_2
Sum of Scores	2,342 Σx	6,666 Σy
Sum of Squares of Scores	286,537 Σx^2	826,607 Σy^2

Set up and test the null hypothesis concerning ability in statistics of these two groups of students.

5. The mean A.Q. of a random sample of 30 orphan children was 92.6 and the standard deviation was 9.15. Are these orphans below average in achievement as measured by the Achievement Quotient? Test the hypothesis that the population mean is 100, but separately under two assumptions: first, that the population standard deviation is known to be 14.5 A.Q. points, and, second, that the population standard deviation is unknown. Do the probabilities of an error of the first kind differ? Why?

6. A random sample of 94 native children in Grades 7 and 8 had an average I.Q. of 85.96 and a standard deviation of 13.45 I.Q. points, whereas another sample of 78 children in the same area but of a different race had a mean I.Q. of 74.60 with a standard deviation of 15.05 I.Q. points. Test the null statistical hypothesis, and discuss the educational and other sociological implications of your findings (remembering that the obvious need not always be either the sole or the real cause).

7. Using like-sex fraternal twins (girls) in an experiment involving feeding a vitamin supplement to one member of each twin pair (the "experimental") selected at random, the results in the table on page 173 were secured:

   (a) Is there any evidence of an effect of the vitamin supplement on weight? On spelling achievement?

   (b) Did the process of random assignment result in two groups of equal mental age?

   (c) Test the significance of the difference in spelling achievement using the formula for independent samples. What effect does such an error have on the results? Why?

(e—experimental; c—control)

TWIN PAIR	MEMBER	MENTAL AGE (MONTHS)	WEIGHT	SPELLING SCORE
1	e	137	95	42
	c	113	107	36
2	e	171	99	45
	c	119	104	41
3	e	138	99	55
	c	150	107	60
4	e	191	87	60
	c	172	92	55
5	e	144	101	57
	c	188	88	67
6	e	136	100	47
	c	113	108	38
7	e	141	107	58
	c	143	109	63
8	e	141	108	54
	c	128	109	48
9	e	112	100	35
	c	121	99	42
10	e	147	93	50
	c	139	91	52
11	e	156	101	53
	c	124	98	45
12	e	118	99	35
	c	155	107	52
13	e	138	104	49
	c	111	110	44
14	e	144	96	49
	c	132	105	51
15	e	113	100	40
	c	108	100	33

8. Frequently in educational experimentation, experimental and control groups are selected so that the two groups have the same means and standard deviations on the matching variable, say X. The data in the following table were collected under this design where the pretest was the matching variable X, and the final test the experimental variable Y. Read the following reference as a source for analyzing data of this kind: Eugene Shen, "Experimental Design and Statistical Treatment in Educational Research," *Journal of Experimental Education*, VIII (1934–40), 346–53.

(a) Do you think that "balanced" grouping is a valid experimental procedure?

(b) How is the principle of randomization violated?

(c) Is there a valid error for tests of significance?

(d) Compare the method of balancing with the use of covariance of the Johnson-Neyman technique in Chapter XIII.

EXPERIMENTAL GROUP			CONTROL GROUP		
Individual	Pretest (X)	Final Test (Y)	Individual	Pretest (X)	Final Test (Y)
1	34	40	1	53	92
2	13	15	2	13	21
3	59	86	3	18	12
4	53	55	4	32	26
5	15	23	5	34	39
6	41	59	6	36	33
7	28	56	7	31	42
8	40	47	8	24	22
9	35	36	9	26	59
10	34	51	10	35	37
11	34	38	11	36	38
12	10	26	12	21	26
13	39	54	13	12	7
14	46	65	14	36	44
15	16	32	15	48	74
16	36	74	16	14	10
17	35	46	17	20	33
18	28	36	18	38	34
19	41	46	19	42	45
Sum	637	885	20	20	24
			21	66	88
Sum of Squares	24,421	46,787	22	45	60
			23	28	34
			24	25	10
Sum of Products	33,078		25	50	61
			26	41	48
			27	54	65
			28	45	88
			29	26	8
			30	31	53
			31	34	51
			Sum	1,034	1,284
			Sum of Squares	39,606	70,028
			Sum of Products	50,749	

CHAPTER VII

Tests of Statistical Hypotheses Expressed in Terms of Variances

We will consider in this chapter only the tests of statistical hypotheses expressed *directly* in terms of variances (or of standard deviations). The discussion will not include the analysis of variance technique, which appears in the next chapter, since the hypotheses tested under it are actually concerned with means and are expressed only *indirectly* in terms of variances.

In one sense this is an introductory chapter, in that it is related to tests of the validity of the assumptions underlying the application of the analysis of variance method proper to specific problems, but in another sense it is independent and stands on its own feet. It will be evident as we proceed that for many practical problems the statistical tests herein described may prove to be sufficient to meet the purpose of the researcher, and he will not need to indulge in a more complex statistical analysis. We may add, parenthetically, that the unwarranted use of a more complex statistical method is an expression by the researcher of neither virtue nor erudition.

Comparison of Sample and Population Variances

For a sample of size N drawn at random from a normal population with standard deviation σ, the quantity

$$\frac{\Sigma(X-M)^2}{\sigma^2}$$

where M denotes the sample mean and X any observed sample observation, is distributed as χ^2 with $n = N - 1$ degrees of freedom. Further, we know from the sampling results reported in Chapter II that even for non-normal populations, provided they do not depart too markedly from the normal in form, this quantity is distributed approximately as χ^2. Consequently, we may use this fact, and the fact that the sum of a number of independent values of χ^2 is itself distributed as χ^2 with degrees of freedom equal to the sum of the individual numbers of degrees of freedom, to make appropriate statistical tests of hypotheses expressed in terms of comparisons of observed and expected variances.

Single Sample

As a first example,* consider the case of the teacher who administered a standardized arithmetic test to his Grade 8 class of 33 pupils and observed a variance of 25.63, as compared with the expected variance of 35 reported by the authors of the test. May he conclude on the basis of the observed results that his class, as regards variability, may be assumed to be a sample drawn at random from the population on which the test was standardized? The hypothesis to be tested may be written

$$H_o : \sigma^2 = \sigma_o^2 = 35$$

Now the distribution of observed scores did not exhibit any marked departure from normality, and consequently the quantity

$$\frac{(32)(25.63)}{35} = 23.43$$

should be distributed as χ^2 with 32 degrees of freedom. From the table of χ^2 we find that the probability of obtaining, in repeated random sampling from the specified population, a sample variance as small or even smaller than that observed is approximately 20 in 100, so we would accept the hypothesis H_o and conclude that there is no evidence that the special drill reduced significantly the variability of the class in achievement in arithmetic.

Two or More Samples

As a second example, the following set of variances were observed by one of the authors in a study of achievement in a school subject; the expected variance for the achievement test was in each case 25.6.† Calculating for each the corresponding value of χ^2 as explained in the previous example, with in each case degrees of freedom $n = N - 1$, we find that for only three of the five classes would the hypothesis to be tested, $H_o : \sigma_1^2 = \sigma_2^2 = \sigma_3^2 = \sigma_4^2 = \sigma_5^2 = 25.6$, be rejected at the 5 per cent level of significance. The set of admissible alternative hypotheses will be of the form

CLASS	N	OBSERVED VARIANCE	χ^2	DEGREES OF FREEDOM	PROBABILITY LEVEL
1	30	14.15	16.03	29	App. .03
2	55	16.15	34.07	54	.02
3	25	12.80	12.00	24	.02
4	24	21.30	19.14	23	.30
5	32	24.71	29.92	31	.47
Total	166	—	111.16	161	.001

* Discussed in another connection in Chapter VI.

† The same procedure could be used, dividing in each χ^2 by the corresponding value of σ^2, for the case of a number of known but unequal population variances.

$H_1 : \sigma_j^2 \neq \sigma_o^2 = 25.6$. But as an over-all test, we use the values shown in the final row, viz. $\chi^2 = 111.16$ and $n = 161$. We must, therefore, reject the hypothesis tested: our set of five classes had variances significantly smaller than expected.‡ Students should note that for degrees of freedom, n, greater than 30, we may secure a reasonably satisfactory approximation by assuming that the quantity

$$\sqrt{2\chi^2} - \sqrt{2n-1}$$

is normally distributed with zero mean and unit standard deviation.

Comparison of Two Sample Variances When Population Variances Unknown

In a large number, perhaps in the majority, of situations the researcher does not know the value of the population variance or variances. Students should note, though, that where this occurs the hypotheses to be tested are not exactly the same as those just considered, although they may bear a striking resemblance to them. Although in both cases the hypotheses are expressed in terms of variances, we do not approach our data with the same question in mind. As a consequence, we do not always secure identical answers.

Independent Samples

The null hypothesis to be tested will in this case be that the two samples were drawn at random from the same population, or from two different populations having the same variance. It may be expressed in the form $H_o : \sigma_1^2 = \sigma_2^2 = \sigma^2$, where σ^2 is the common, but unknown, population variance. The set of alternative hypotheses will be $H_1 : \sigma_1^2 \neq \sigma_2^2$, although in most instances only one part or the other, i.e. either $H_1{}^1 : \sigma_1^2 > \sigma_2^2$ or $H_1{}^{11} : \sigma_1^2 < \sigma_2^2$, will be admissible. What we observe will be the two sample variances, which we may denote by v_1 and v_2, which are estimates of the unknown population variances σ_1^2 and σ_2^2, respectively, if H_1 is true, but are two independent estimates of the common variance σ^2 when H_o is true. How may we use these sample variances to provide a valid test of the null hypothesis, H_o?

Following Fisher, Snedecor proposed that we use the ratio $F = v_1/v_2$ as a test of this hypothesis.§ The outstanding advantage of using a ratio rather than a difference in this situation is that when H_o is true the ratio F is quite independent of the unknown value of the common variance σ^2.

‡ A result that was not altogether unexpected, since we suspected—on other grounds —that a selective factor was operating and would reduce the variability in these particular classes.

§ Fisher had earlier proposed use of the statistic $z = \frac{1}{2} \log_e F$. While this transformation has real advantages from a theoretical point of view, in practice it is just as satisfactory, and certainly simpler, to use F. In proposing the use of this more convenient form, Snedecor denoted the ratio by the letter F—in honor of Fisher.

Observe that when $\sigma_1^2 = \sigma_2^2$, the expected value of F in repeated random sampling will be unity. Likewise, when one of the set of alternative hypotheses is true, then the expected value of F in repeated random sampling will be different from unity: being greater than unity for $H_1{}^1$, and less than unity for $H_1{}^{11}$. Clearly, therefore, the ratio F will provide a valid test of the null hypothesis H_o, leading to the rejection of H_o in favor of the appropriate set of alternative hypotheses whenever the observed value of F differs significantly from unity.‖ But to make such a test we must know the distribution of F in repeated random sampling when H_o is true.

For simplicity and without loss of generality we can consider the distribution of F in repeated random sampling from the *same population* and, for convenience, for samples of the *same size* ($N_1 = N_2 = N$, say). This will simplify the presentation of our empirical results, since we may calculate the values of F directly from adjoining variance values secured earlier for samples of the same size. To satisfy the requirement of randomness for the several values of F, we may take each consecutive pair of variances but use each variance estimate in only one value of F. This procedure cuts in half the number of F values available from our sample results, of course, but we can recoup the loss by considering only the upper half of the F-distribution, i.e. for each pair of variances always divide the smaller into the larger. That this is a valid procedure in this situation will be evident upon consideration of the fact that the *order* of the variances, in regard to size, within each pair will be random, and it matters little for our argument whether we divide the first by the second or vice versa. Thus, our empirical distributions of F represent approximately the situation that would appear in the upper half of the distribution of F if we had twice as many pairs of variances from our samples. The values in the other half of the F distribution, for $F < 1$, can be thought of as the reciprocals of the values herein reported.#

We show in Table VII.1 the empirical distributions of F for samples of various sizes drawn from the positive binomial, Poisson, rectangular, and normal populations set out in Chapter II. Observe, first, that the variation in the values of F in repeated sampling decreases rapidly as the size of the sample is increased, which is in accord with what was discovered earlier for other types of sampling distributions, and, second, that the form of the distribution of F (at least of the half of the distribution we have shown) is surprisingly consistent and invariant, with one notable exception, no matter what the form of the original population. Attention must be drawn to the unusual curtailment of the variation of F in samples drawn from the rectangular population, perhaps especially noticeable in the case of samples of

‖ Or the value of Fisher's z differs significantly from zero.

\# From which fact we may deduce that the distribution of Fisher's z will, when the hypothesis to be tested is true, always be symmetrical about zero—a convenient property of that distribution.

TABLE VII.1

EMPIRICAL SAMPLING DISTRIBUTIONS OF F (FOR $F > 1$)
FOR SAMPLES FROM POSITIVE BINOMIAL, POISSON,
RECTANGULAR, AND NORMAL POPULATIONS

CLASS INTERVALS F	POSITIVE BINOMIAL		POISSON		RECTANGULAR		NORMAL		
	$N = 10$	$N = 20$	$N = 10$	$N = 50$	$N = 10$	$N = 50$	$N = 10$	$N = 20$	$N = 50$
1.00–1.24	13	8	34	· 10	35	17	54	40	35
1.25–1.49	10	6	25	10	25	2	64	34	11
1.50–1.74	6	5	12	6	19	1	29	21	3
1.75–1.99	7	4	23	3	8		20	14	
2.00–2.24	3	1	8	1	3		20	5	1
2.25–2.49	1	1	10		2		15	3	
2.50–2.74	2		6		2		10	3	
2.75–2.99	1		9		1		8	4	
3.00–3.24	2		4		2		5		
3.25–3.49	3		2				3		
3.50–3.74			2		1		5	1	
3.75–3.99			2						
4.00–4.24	1		1				2		
4.25–4.49			2		1		3		
4.50–4.74			5				2		
4.75–4.99			1				3		
5.00–5.49	1						4		
5.50–5.99			1		1		1		
6.00–6.49							1		
6.50–6.99			2				1		
< >									
11.50–11.99			1						
Total	50	25	150	30	100	20	250	125	50

size 50.** Supporting evidence may be found in Norton's results, as reported by Lindquist,†† which indicate that the distribution of F in repeated random sampling from various populations is affected but little by lack of symmetry and is affected by kurtosis only in the extreme cases of very flat or very peaked population distributions. Lindquist concludes that we can safely use the tables of F (which are based on the assumption of normality in the population) unless the observed data have so extreme a form of distribution that mere inspection is sufficient to reveal the fact. In some situations, of course, circumstances dictate a particular form of population

** A result which the authors viewed with considerable disbelief, at least until they remembered that unusual results for these variances were also recorded in Chapter II. Variances for samples from a rectangular population are invariably large and consequently of roughly the same order of magnitude, which means that the F-values calculated therefrom will be restricted in range.

†† E. F. Lindquist, *Design and Analysis of Experiments in Psychology and Education* (Boston: Houghton Mifflin Co., 1953), pp. 78–86.

distribution: rectangular if ranks are used, for example, and very peaked if the expected form of distribution is a negative binomial. Where these conditions prevail, we must use the tables of F with considerable caution—and with some misgivings.

The exact sampling distribution of F, and also of $z = \frac{1}{2} \log_e F$, when H_o is true is known only for independent samples from normal populations.‡‡ Tables giving the 5 per cent and 1 per cent points of the distribution have been prepared and published; the set prepared by Snedecor is reproduced in Appendix D. Complete tables of the distribution are not available and the distribution function is too difficult to evaluate to use it directly to secure expected frequencies. To obtain the expected frequencies shown in Table VII.2 we have made use of the fact that, for $N_1 = N_2 = 10$, the quantity u, where

$$u = 6.2069 \frac{\{F^{1/3} - 1\}}{\{F^{2/3} + 1\}^{1/2}}$$

is approximately normally distributed about zero with unit standard deviation.§§

TABLE VII.2

COMPARISON OF OBSERVED AND EXPECTED DISTRIBUTIONS OF F
FOR SAMPLES OF SIZE 10

CLASS INTERVALS F	POSITIVE BINOMIAL		POISSON		RECTANGULAR		NORMAL	
	Obs.	*Exp.*	*Obs.*	*Exp.*	*Obs.*	*Exp.*	*Obs.*	*Exp.*
1.00–1.49	23	22.3	59	66.4	60	44.2	118	110.6
1.50–1.99	13	12.0	35	36.0	27	24.0	49	60.0
2.00–2.49	4	6.4	18	19.3	5	12.9	35	32.1
2.50–2.99	3	3.5	15	10.6	3	7.1	18	17.7
3.00–3.49	5	2.1	6	6.2	2	4.1	8	10.3
3.50–3.99	0	1.2	4	3.7	1	2.5	5	6.2
4.00–4.49	1	0.7	3	2.3	1	1.6	5	3.9
4.50–4.99	0	0.5	6	1.5	0	1.1	5	2.6
5.00 & over	1	1.3	4	3.9	1	2.6	7	6.5
Total	50	50.0	150	149.9	100	100.1	250	249.9

Even without making χ^2-tests of goodness of fit, which students should be encouraged to do, it is clear that even for such very small samples the observed and expected frequencies agree remarkably well, with the sole excep-

‡‡ Derivation of the sampling distribution formulae is given, for example, in M. G. Kendall, *The Advanced Theory of Statistics*, Vol. II, pp. 115–18.

§§ E. Paulson, "An Approximate Normalisation of the Analysis of Variance Distribution," *Annals of Mathematical Statistics*, XIII (1942), 233. Paulson gives the general formula, not this specific illustration. This approximation is amazingly accurate, even for very small samples.

tion of the samples from the rectangular population. For this latter case, using only the recorded observed and expected frequencies, the discrepancies are statistically significant: there are too many small, and too few large, values of F in the Observed column. Accordingly, if we use in such a situation the normal-F tables in tests of significance, we will tend to accept the null hypothesis when we should in fact reject it. For samples from a rectangular population, the probability of securing a large value of F when the hypothesis to be tested is true is actually much smaller than the table of F indicates.

Students should note that the table of F is so arranged that to use it we must always calculate the observed value of F with the larger variance in the numerator (so that $F > 1$) and use for n_1 the degrees of freedom corresponding to the larger variance. Also, the probabilities of the table refer to the whole distribution of F, not just to the half of the distribution of F that we considered above. Thus the 5 per cent point, which we may denote by $F_{.05}$, is that point on the F-scale to the right, or above, which 5 per cent of the area under the curve lies, and below which 95 per cent of the area under the curve lies, and a similar interpretation holds for the 1 per cent point.

To illustrate with our observed sampling results and the 5 per cent point of the distribution, for degrees of freedom $n_1 = n_2 = 9$ we have $F_{.05} = 3.18$, which for the expected (or the observed) normal frequencies of Table VII.2 corresponds to a point beyond which lie approximately 10 per cent of the half-distribution of 250 cases, or 5 per cent of the whole distribution of 500 cases, of F. Since the reciprocal of $F_{.05} = 3.18$ is 0.31, it follows that 5 per cent of the total area of the F-distribution must lie to the left of, or below, the value of $F = 0.31$. For this particular F-distribution, therefore,

$$P\{F \geqslant 3.18/H_o\} = 0.05 \quad \text{and} \quad P\{F \leqslant 0.31/H_o\} = 0.05$$

which may also be written in the form

$$P\{0.31 \geqslant F \geqslant 3.18/H_o\} = 0.10 \quad \text{or} \quad P\{0.31 \leqslant F \leqslant 3.28/H_o\} = 0.90$$

Depending upon the way in which we define our critical region (which is determined by the set of admissible alternative hypotheses), therefore, we use either the probabilities referred to in the table of F or double those probabilities.

If we admit only the set of alternative hypotheses $H_1{}^1 : \sigma_1{}^2 > \sigma_2{}^2$, for instance, our critical region will be $F \geqslant F_{.05}$ and our region of acceptance will be $F < F_{.05}$. Here we must always accept the hypothesis when $v_1 \leqslant v_2$.‖‖

‖‖ Even so, the appearance of a very low value of F should be viewed with suspicion, since the occurrence of a value of F below $1/F_{.05}$ is just as unlikely an event as the occurrence of a value above $F_{.05}$. A *very* small F may indicate that something went wrong in the experiment, that the design was faulty, that an error was made in the calculations, or that some manipulation of the data was to blame. We will never forget the case of a student who carefully transformed all his data to standard scores and then found to his dismay that all his F-values were approximately unity!

Under other circumstances, however, we might admit both sets of alternative hypotheses. In this event our critical region will be composed of two parts, $F \geqslant F_{.05}$ and $F \leqslant \dfrac{1}{F_{.05}}$, and our region of acceptance will be $\dfrac{1}{F_{.05}} < F < F_{.05}$. But now the size of our critical region will be 10 per cent, since for this critical region the probability of an error of the first kind will be $.05 + .05 = .10$. Accordingly, when we admit only one set of alternative hypotheses (frequently called a "one-tailed test"), we may use directly the probabilities given in the table of F; when we admit both sets of alternative hypotheses (generally called a "two-tailed test"), we must double the probabilities given in the table of F. In most problems for which the F-test is appropriate, however, only one set of alternative hypotheses, viz. $H_1{}^1 : \sigma_1{}^2 > \sigma_2{}^2$, is admissible, and we may use and interpret the F-tables without adjustment.

As an illustration of the use of the F-test, we shall return to the problem encountered in the previous chapter where we wished to test a hypothesis expressed in terms of differences between means of independent samples and where the values of the population variances were unknown. For Murray's data we had

$$\text{Chart 1: } N_1 = 60; SD_1 = 1.22$$
$$\text{Chart 2: } N_2 = 72; SD_2 = 0.76$$

The hypothesis to be tested, that these are two independent samples drawn at random from populations with the same but unknown variance, may be written

$$H_o : \sigma_1{}^2 = \sigma_2{}^2 = \sigma^2$$

and the set of admissible alternative hypotheses may be expressed in the form

$$H_1 : \sigma_1{}^2 \neq \sigma_2{}^2$$

Clearly, we may use the F-distribution as the model appropriate for the test of this hypothesis, since it shows the variation to be expected in the ratio of the variances of two independent samples drawn at random from the same population. We have##

$$F = \frac{(60)(1.22)^2}{59} \bigg/ \frac{(72)(0.76)^2}{71}$$
$$= 2.58$$

and from the table of F for degrees of freedom $n_1 = 59$ and $n_2 = 71$ we observe that this value of F falls beyond the 1 per cent point. Consequently, we must reject the hypothesis H_o and conclude that the sample variances differ significantly.

Assuming that Murray calculated the values of the sample standard deviations by the usual formula.

Dependent Samples

Students and researchers should observe that we have carefully specified above that the F-distribution applies only to independent samples; it does not provide a valid test when the samples are related—e.g. when the same or equated individuals are used in an experiment. It will be remembered that in all cases where this situation arose in the previous chapters, an appropriate adjustment was made in the formulae used in the analysis. As an illustration of the corresponding adjustment for variances, consider Koerber's data on 19 pairs of matched individuals, reported in Chapter VI, for which we have:

$$N = 19$$
$$U_1 = \Sigma(X_{i1} - M_1)^2 = 759.684$$
$$U_2 = \Sigma(X_{i2} - M_2)^2 = 344.000$$
$$U_{12} = \Sigma(X_{i1} - M_1)(X_{i2} - M_2) = 166.000$$

If we apply the usual F-test, which we obviously should not since it is equivalent to ignoring the very important fact that the experimental and control groups consisted of matched boys, we would have

$$F_o = \frac{U_1}{U_2} = \frac{759.684}{344.000} = 2.21$$

for degrees of freedom $n_1 = n_2 = 18$. This observed value of F, F_o, falls just slightly beyond the point $F_{.05}$ so, since the set of admissible alternative hypotheses would be $H_1 : \sigma_1^2 > \sigma_2^2$,*** we would probably reject H_o.

To make due allowance for the effect of matching the individuals, we may calculate the quantity

$$t = \frac{(U_1 - U_2)}{\sqrt{U_1 U_2 - U_{12}^2}} \sqrt{\frac{N-2}{4}}$$

(t being distributed as Student's t with $N - 2$ degrees of freedom) and enter the table of the t-distribution with degrees of freedom $n = N - 2$.††† For the above example, the observed value of t, t_o, is

$$t_o = \frac{(759.684 - 344.000)}{\sqrt{(759.684)(344) - (166)^2}} \sqrt{\frac{17}{4}} = 1.77$$

From the table of t for 17 degrees of freedom we find that (for a one-tailed test, so we use the tabled levels of 0.1 and 0.02) the 5 per cent point is 1.740 and the 1 per cent point is 2.567, and hence we would be inclined to reject the hypothesis $H_o : \sigma_1^2 = \sigma_2^2$. The two statistical tests are roughly equivalent in this instance, because the value of U_{12} is relatively small, but they will differ markedly when U_{12} is of nearly the same magnitude as U_1 and U_2.

*** The control group would not be affected by the experimental factor.

††† Adapted from W. A. Morgan, "A Test for the Significance of the Difference between Two Variances in a Sample from a Normal Bivariate Population," *Biometrika*, XXXI, 13–19.

Comparison of Variances of k Independent Samples When Population Variances Unknown

We will consider only the case of independent samples because an appropriate test for k dependent samples has not yet been developed.‡‡‡ Strictly speaking, even the tests available for independent samples apply only to samples drawn from normal populations, but the empirical sampling results we have presented earlier indicate that the results will be valid enough for all practical purposes no matter what the form of the population distribution may be, provided only that it does not differ too markedly from the normal. Students and researchers should remember, however, that in any given situation we may have, at best, only an approximate solution and that the probability levels used will not bear too strict an interpretation.

Assume that we have k independent samples drawn from normal populations with variances σ_1^2, σ_2^2, . . . ,σ_k^2. The hypothesis to be tested, H_o, is that these are independent samples drawn at random from populations having the same, but unknown, variance, σ^2, or k independent samples drawn from the same population, and may be written

$$H_o : \sigma_1^2 = \sigma_2^2 \ldots = \sigma_k^2 = \sigma^2$$

The set of admissible alternative hypotheses is that these are independent samples drawn at random from populations of different variances, which may be expressed in the form

$$H_1 : \sigma_1^2 \neq \sigma_2^2 \neq \ldots \neq \sigma_k^2$$

Neyman and Pearson suggested, in 1931, that the appropriate statistical test of this hypothesis, H_o, was the ratio of a weighted geometric to a weighted arithmetic mean of the mean squares from which the variances were estimated, which they called the L_1 criterion.§§§ Because of the difficulty of determining the exact sampling distribution of L_1, however, various approximations have been developed and alternative tests and suggested extensions proposed.|| || || Of these, we shall present only one, by

---

‡‡‡ Except in connection with a more general test. See, for instance, D. J. Bishop, "On a Comprehensive Test for the Homogeneity of Variances and Covariances in Multivariate Problems," *Biometrika*, XXXI, 31–55.

§§§ J. Neyman and E. S. Pearson, "On the Problem of k Samples," *Bulletin de l'Académie Polonaise des Sciences et des Lettres*, Série A (1931), pp. 460–81.

|| || || See, for example, the following partial list of references:

(1935) B. L. Welch, "Some Problems in the Analysis of Regression Among k-Samples of Two Variables," *Biometrika*, XXVII: 145.

(1936) P. P. N. Nayer, "An Investigation into the Application of Neyman and Pearson's L_1 Test, with Tables of Percentage Limits," *Statistical Research Memoirs*, I: 38–51.

(1936) B. L. Welch, "Note on an Extension of the L_1 Test," *Statistical Research Memoirs*, I: 52–56.

(1937) M. S. Bartlett, "Properties of Sufficiency and Statistical Tests," *Proceedings of the Royal Society* (London), Series A, CLX: 268–73.

Bartlett: it has been selected primarily because the approximation seems to be sufficiently accurate for all practical purposes and because the test is based on the almost universally available table of χ^2. It should be noted that Bartlett's test, as is true of other variance tests in the k-sample case, is extremely sensitive to non-normal kurtosis.###

Bartlett's suggested test consists in calculating the quantity

$$M = n\log_e \left\{ \frac{\Sigma n_i S_i{}^2}{n} \right\} - \Sigma n_i \log_e S_i{}^2$$

where $S_i{}^2$ denotes the value of the variance (the unbiased estimate of $\sigma_i{}^2$) for the ith sample, n_i the associated number of degrees of freedom, $n = \Sigma n_i$, $i = 1, 2, \ldots k$, and $\log_e$ the natural (Naperian) logarithms, where $\log_e X = 2.302585 \log_{10} X$. A corrective factor, C, where

$$C = 1 + \frac{\Sigma \dfrac{1}{n_i} - \dfrac{1}{n}}{3(k - 1)}$$

is then calculated and the ratio M/C used as the statistical test. The quantity M/C is known to be approximately distributed as χ^2, when H_o is true, with degrees of freedom equal to $k - 1$.

As an empirical check on the accuracy of this approximate solution, we may apply it in the case of two samples—for which, of course, the F-test discussed earlier gives an exact solution. To simplify the calculations and the interpretation, we shall take the case where $n_1 = n_2 = f$ and $S_1{}^2 = F_{.01} S_2{}^2$, and consider two values of f: for small samples, use $f = 3$ for which $F_{.01} = 29.46$; and for large samples, use $f = 200$ for which $F_{.01} = 1.39$. Further, we may without loss of generality simplify the calculations still further by arbitrarily setting $S_2{}^2 = 1.$*

For the first case,

$$n_1 = n_2 = f = 3; \quad F_{.01} = 29.46$$

and for $n_1 = n_2 = f$, M may be written as

$$M = 2f \log_e \left(\frac{S_1{}^2 + S_2{}^2}{2} \right) - f\left(\log_e S_1{}^2 + \log_e S_2{}^2 \right)$$

(1940) H. O. Hartley, "Testing the Homogeneity of a Set of Variances," *Biometrika*, XXXI: 249–55.

(1941) W. G. Cochran, "The Distribution of the Largest of a Set of Estimated Variances as a Fraction of their Total," *Annals of Eugenics*, XI: 47–52.

(1949) G. E. P. Box, "A General Distribution Theory for a Class of Likelihood Criteria," *Biometrika*, XXXVI: 317–46.

(1950) H. O. Hartley, "The Maximum F-Ratio as a Short-cut Test for Heterogeneity of Variance," *Biometrika*, XXXVII: 308–12.

G. E. P. Box and S. L. Andersen, "Permutation Theory in the Derivation of Robust Criteria and the Study of Departures from Assumptions," *Journal of the Royal Statistical Society*, Series B, XVII (1955), 1–34.

* As an exercise in algebra, students may wish to demonstrate that for $k = 2$ the value of M is a function of $S_1{}^2/S_2{}^2$ and independent of the actual values of $S_1{}^2$ and $S_2{}^2$.

Since we set $S_2{}^2 = 1$, this expression for M reduces finally to

$$M = 2f \log_e \left(\frac{F_{.01} + 1}{2} \right) - f \log_e (F_{.01})$$

For the above example,

$$M = 6 \log_e (15.23) - 3 \log_e (29.46) = 6.1905$$

and since for $n_1 = n_2 = f$

$$\frac{\Sigma \dfrac{1}{n_i} - \dfrac{1}{n}}{3(k - 1)} = \frac{1}{2f}$$

we have

$$C = 1 + \frac{1}{2f} = 1 + \frac{1}{6} = \frac{7}{6} = 1.1666$$

and

$$\frac{M}{C} = 5.306$$

From the table of χ^2 for $k - 1 = 1$ degree of freedom, we find that $P\{\chi^2 > 5.306\} = 0.021$. The agreement is excellent, therefore, even for such small samples, since this probability corresponds to a two-tailed test in terms of F.

For the second case (large samples),

$$n_1 = n_2 = f = 200; \qquad F_{.01} = 1.39$$

and consequently

$$M = 400 \log_e (1.195) - 200 \log_e (1.39)$$
$$= 5.398$$
$$C = 1 + \frac{1}{400} = 1.0025$$

and

$$\frac{M}{C} = 5.38$$

For $\chi^2 = 5.38$ with 1 degree of freedom, the corresponding probability, $P\{\chi^2 > 5.38\}$, is approximately 0.020(4). Again the agreement is excellent, and the adequacy of Bartlett's approximation established as reasonable for all practical purposes.

Let us apply this approximation to the set of five sample variances con-

CLASS	n_i	$S_i{}^2$	$\dfrac{1}{n_i}$	$\log_e S_i{}^2$	$n_i S_i{}^2$	$n_i \log_e S_i{}^2$
1	29	14.15	0.0344828	2.64971	410.35	76.8416
2	54	16.15	0.0185185	2.78192	872.10	150.2237
3	24	12.80	0.0416667	2.54945	307.20	61.1868
4	23	21.30	0.0434783	3.05871	489.90	70.3503
5	31	24.71	0.0322581	3.20721	766.01	99.4235
Total	161	—	0.1704044	—	2,845.56	458.0259

sidered earlier, and for which we had rejected the hypothesis

$$H_o : \sigma_1^2 = \sigma_2^2 = \sigma_3^2 = \sigma_4^2 = \sigma_5^2 = \sigma_o^2 = 25.6$$

The hypothesis to be tested now will be that there is a common variance of unknown value, not necessarily equal to 25.6 as we had earlier postulated, however. The necessary calculations may be performed as shown below. Since $k = 5$ and $n = \Sigma n_i = 161$, we have

$$M = 161 \log_e (17.674) - 458.0259$$
$$= 462.41 - 458.03 = 4.38$$

$$\frac{\Sigma \dfrac{1}{n_i} - \dfrac{1}{n}}{3(k-1)} = \frac{0.1704044 - 0.0062112}{(3)(4)} = 0.01368$$

$$C = 1.01368$$

$$\frac{M}{C} = \frac{4.38}{1.01368} = 4.32$$

Since $\chi^2 = 4.32$ with 4 degrees of freedom is obviously not significant, we accept the hypothesis H_o.

As a shortcut, students should note that if $\chi^2 = M$ is not significant, we may accept the hypothesis H_o, because the adjusted value can never be larger than this first-order approximation.

Special Case of a Specified Proportional Relationship Among the k-Variances

A simple and useful extension of the F-test, and of Bartlett's test, may be derived for the test of the hypothesis of a specified proportional relationship among the variances, viz.

$$H_o : \sigma_1^2 : \sigma_2^2 : \dots : \sigma_k^2 = r_1 : r_2 : \dots : r_k$$

where the values of the r's are specified by the hypothesis, H_o, to be tested. (In the previous case, of course, all the r's were fixed at the value of unity, since the hypothesis to be tested specified a common though unknown variance. Now we test whether the samples were drawn from normal populations with variances in this specified relationship.†) The required adjustment is amazingly simple, and consists of the simple substitution of $\dfrac{S_i^2}{r_i}$ for S_i^2 (where $i = 1, 2, \dots, k$) in the formulae given earlier. As an illustration, consider the variances for classes 1 and 5, above, where we have

$$n_1 = 29, \qquad S_1^2 = 14.15$$
$$n_5 = 31, \qquad S_5^2 = 24.71$$

The hypothesis to be tested is, say,

$$H_o : \sigma_1^2 : \sigma_5^2 = r_1 : r_5 = 1 : 2$$

† This is one member of the set of alternative hypotheses for the previous case.

or that the variance in Class 5 is twice as great in Class 1. The corresponding value of F for the test, with 29 and 31 degrees of freedom, will be

$$F_o = \frac{14.15/1}{24.71/2} = \frac{28.30}{24.71} = 1.145$$

and we would accept the hypothesis H_o. In these cases we normally use a two-tailed test, since any departure from the specified proportions is admissible, although for $k = 2$ we might admit only one of the two possible sets of alternative hypotheses (for the illustrative example, that $\frac{r_5}{r_1} > 2$ *or* $\frac{r_5}{r_1} < 2$).

Use of Variances in Alternative Tests of Goodness of Fit

As Fisher suggested thirty years ago, we can under certain circumstances use variances in an alternative test which in some cases is much more sensitive than the usual chi-square test of "goodness of fit."‡ Since the test is in many respects a simple comparison of an observed variance with that expected, it resembles the statistical test considered in the first section of this chapter. In other respects, however, it is more closely akin to the basic chi-square test of goodness of fit. We will consider here only two applications of the variance test. Readers interested in other applications, including the subdivision of the corresponding degrees of freedom, will find in a recent article by Cochran a general discussion of this test and illustrations of its application to the Poisson, positive binomial, and normal distributions.§

As a first example, consider the two sets of data of Table VII.3: one is a sample from a Poisson population, and the other is a sample from a positive binomial.‖ Calculating the values of the means and variances by

TABLE VII.3

SAMPLES OF SIZE 10 FROM POISSON AND
BINOMIAL POPULATIONS

SAMPLE	OBSERVATIONS										SUM	SUM OF SQUARES
1	2	9	6	3	3	5	3	2	5	4	42	218
2	6	9	3	6	5	4	5	5	5	6	54	314

the usual formulae, we obtain

$$M_1 = 4.2 \; ; \quad (N-1)\, v_1 = 41.6 \; ; \quad N-1 = 9$$
$$M_2 = 5.4 \; ; \quad (N-1)\, v_2 = 22.4 \; ; \quad N-1 = 9$$

‡ See Chapter V.
§ W. G. Cochran, "Some Methods for Strengthening the Common χ^2 Tests."
‖ Taken from those obtained in the sampling experiments described in Chapter II.

To test whether these are samples drawn from a Poisson population, we calculate

$$\chi^2 = \sum_{i=1}^{N} \frac{(X_i - M)^2}{M} \left(\text{where } M = \frac{\Sigma X_i}{N}\right)$$

which will be distributed as χ^2 with $n = N - 1$ degrees of freedom. For the above data, we secure for the first sample a value $\chi_1^2 = \frac{41.6}{4.2} = 9.9$, and for the second sample a value $\chi_2^2 = \frac{22.4}{5.4} = 4.1$. For 9 degrees of freedom

neither χ^2 is significant, although the second may be judged suspiciously small (indicating a non-Poisson population).

To test whether these are samples drawn from a positive binomial population, $(p + q)^k$, for constant k but unknown p, we calculate

$$\chi^2 = \sum_{i=1}^{N} \frac{(X_i - M)^2}{(M)(1 - p)} \quad (p \text{ estimated from the data})$$

For the above two cases, the estimates of p are $p_1 = .42$ and $p_2 = .54$, respectively, so that for the first sample $\chi_1^2 = \frac{41.6}{(4.2)(.58)} = 17.1$, and for the second sample $\chi_2^2 = \frac{22.4}{(5.4)(.46)} = 9.0$. Since again the number of degrees of freedom is $n = N - 1 (= 9$, here), we would be inclined to reject the hypothesis in the first case (the observed variance is too large) but would accept it without question in the second.

As a matter of interest, the tests based on variances did operate properly in these cases. The first sample was in fact drawn from a Poisson population, the second from a positive binomial.

EXERCISES

1. From your sampling data, or from the data given for the samples in the text, calculate values of F and draw a histogram of the results. Superimpose a theoretical distribution of F, obtained by use of Paulson's approximation, on the histogram depicting the observed set of data. Test the goodness of fit.
2. Test the significance of the differences between the variances in questions 2, 3, 4, and 7 of Chapter VI.
3. The following data were secured in a study of five groups of subjects on a coordination test (scores were actually number of errors, and were distributed in a unimodal, symmetrical, and more or less mesokurtic form).

   What evidence is there of effect of selection on variability in performance, in light of the fact that the expected standard deviation (i.e. for the general population) was known to be 15.25?

GROUP	1	2	3	4	5
Number	135	140	153	115	138
Mean	78.83	82.96	83.42	77.41	96.67
Standard Deviation	13.90	15.71	14.75	13.85	18.31

4. The interest inventory scores of a random sample of 10 boys and of 10 girls in each of 5 home-condition levels were as shown in the following table. Is the assumption justified that these were samples drawn from populations of common variance?

BOYS HOME-CONDITION LEVEL					GIRLS HOME-CONDITION LEVEL				
Superior	Above Average	Average	Below Average	Poor	Superior	Above Average	Average	Below Average	Poor
39	71	59	87	77	43	51	78	47	60
46	23	54	65	81	64	47	84	64	71
35	66	51	45	43	80	19	41	37	50
22	56	57	64	42	48	64	66	61	50
71	71	52	53	42	35	47	53	53	59
60	43	50	72	66	53	31	53	65	75
59	42	51	68	87	45	33	53	76	64
35	41	39	64	53	83	31	39	52	54
55	78	55	74	66	74	50	45	69	85
29	71	63	79	92	62	84	50	69	43

Using the 100 values, ignoring sex and home-condition level, test for normality of distribution.

5. In a study of the variations in head width, the following observations were recorded (width was measured in centimeters).

BOYS			GIRLS		
Grade 4	Grade 5	Grade 6	Grade 4	Grade 5	Grade 6
14.1	13.7	15.4	14.2	13.6	13.6
14.5	15.5	14.6	14.7	14.4	14.8
15.2	14.3	14.6	14.2	14.2	14.1
15.0	14.9	14.3	14.5	14.1	14.7
13.9	14.8	14.3	14.1	15.6	13.9
13.4	15.0	15.1	14.0	14.1	14.6
14.7	13.6	14.5	14.3	13.7	14.2
14.4	13.7	15.1	13.9	14.0	14.6
14.8	15.3	14.2	14.2	13.6	13.6
14.1		14.8	14.4		
14.2		14.4	14.5		
13.8			13.2		
14.3			14.3		
14.2					
14.1					

Is the assumption of a common variance for the 6 subgroups satisfied? of normality?

6. Use the variance test to determine the form of distribution of the data given in Question 3 of Chapter V.

CHAPTER VIII

The Analysis of Variance

Analysis of variance is a forbidding name for what is essentially a rather simple statistical method. Moreover, it is somewhat misleading because the process involves the analysis—the division into a set of components—of the sums of squares rather than of the variance itself. Basically, the statistical test employed in the analysis of variance is the ratio of two independent estimates of a common variance, the F-ratio discussed in Chapter VII, and it may be used as a valid test whenever the hypothesis to be tested can be expressed in terms of such a ratio of variances. The fundamental requirement is that the two estimates of variance be independent; there are other assumptions involved in the use of the tables of F, as we explained in the previous chapter, but these arise through the assumptions made in the derivation of the form of the distribution of the ratio in repeated random sampling.

Historically, the development of the method (by R. A. Fisher) is related to the test of the difference between two means, and indeed the t-test of Student is only a special case of this more general method. The limitations of the t-test, and the need for its extension to a more general method, can be seen most easily in the situation where the design of the experiment calls for the comparison of the means of more than two groups. Our design might, for instance, involve three groups, each subjected to a different treatment. The null hypothesis would be expressed in the form that the three groups constituted three random samples drawn from a *common* population; the alternative hypotheses would specify that the samples were drawn from *different* populations. Assuming that the sample variances do not differ significantly and that the distributions are normal, then these hypotheses may be expressed in terms of the means of three hypothetical populations. For the null hypothesis, the population means must be equal; for the alternative hypotheses, they must be unequal. Now the t-test is appropriate only for tests of the population means in pairs; the corresponding statistical tests would not be independent of each other, nor would they provide a direct and valid test of this more general null hypothesis. But the analysis of variance technique does provide a valid test: it is a general method of analysis of data subject to the influence of a number of factors. It provides, not only a measure of the effect of each such factor (if the experiment is designed properly), but a valid statistical test of the significance of each such effect.

The analysis of variance method is amazingly versatile, in that it can be readily adapted to provide (within broad limits) an appropriate analysis of the data secured in a wide variety of types of experimental design. But we cannot hope in this chapter to illustrate the application of the method in all possible types of situations. All that we can do is present the basic principles of the method, including the assumptions that must be satisfied if the statistical tests are to yield valid results, and illustrate its application in a number of experimental situations selected to represent the simpler but fundamental types of experimental design. In short, we have attempted, not a complete exposition of the topic, but an exposition of the basic principles and applications that will permit a ready transfer of knowledge and skills to related situations.

Fundamental Principles of Analysis of Variance*

The fundamental assumptions underlying the analysis of variance method are (1) that each of N independent variates, X_i, follows the normal distribution with mean ξ_i and common, though unknown, standard deviation σ, where i varies from 1 to N, and (2) that the means ξ_i may be expressed as a linear function of S (where $S < N$), unknown parameters μ, e.g.

$$\xi_k = C_{1k}\mu_1 + C_{2k}\mu_2 + \ldots + C_{Sk}\mu_S$$

where the C's are known coefficients (in most cases, 1's or 0's). Note that the validity of the assumption of a common standard deviation must be tested before the method is used unless, perchance, it is known from previous experience (or on some other grounds) that it is valid. Moreover, the assumption that the means ξ_i may be expressed as a linear function of the unknown parameters μ should also be tested, although in practice this is difficult to do.† In some situations, e.g. where a number of chemical fertilizers are used in combination in an agricultural experiment, it may happen that the function is not linear but multiplicative and in this event we might have a linear function of $\log \xi_i$, not of ξ_i. But in the vast majority of problems the assumption of a linear function seems to be reasonable and it is unnecessary to postulate a more complex function.

Special attention must be paid to the assumption of normality of the population distribution, since the model used in testing our statistical hypotheses applies, strictly speaking, only to the normal case. The results of Pearson‡ and Norton,§ and our own results reported in the previous chapter, indicate that the model (the F-distribution) is amazingly unaffected by

---

* For a complete and mathematically rigorous discussion, see S. Kolodziejczyk, "On an Important Class of Statistical Hypotheses," *Biometrika*, XXVII (1935), 161.

† See the note by Tukey in *Biometrics*, II, No. 1 (March, 1955), 111–13.

‡ E. S. Pearson, "The Analysis of Variance in Cases of Non-normal Variation," *Biometrika*, XXIII (1931), 114.

§ See E. F. Lindquist, *Design and Analysis of Experiments in Psychology and Education*, pp. 78–90.

lack of symmetry and is affected by kurtosis only in the extreme cases of very leptokurtic or platykurtic distributions. Accordingly, we need not worry too much about the form of the parent population, provided that our sample data do not indicate the existence of an extreme form. The model is affected more by departures from a common variance, although even non-normality of distribution *and* variation in the value of σ have surprisingly little effect on the distribution of F.|| Nevertheless, the researcher must always bear in mind the fact that the tables of F, which he uses in making tests of statistical hypotheses, provide only an approximation—close though it may be—when these fundamental assumptions of normality and a common variance are not satisfied.

An implicit, and consequently unsuspected, assumption may occasion greater difficulty. As is well known, in samples from a normal population the means and variances are distributed independently, and this is basic to the analysis of variance method. Now this independence of distribution does not necessarily hold true in the case of means and variances of samples from non-normal populations, as we noted earlier for small samples from our Poisson population.# For such a population, in fact, we expect the variance to increase with any increase in the mean, whereas for a positive binomial population the variance of the binomial proportion will quite likely decrease with increase in the mean.** Anscombe has shown†† that for a Poisson variate, X, we can secure a stable variance by employing the transformation $\sqrt{X + 3/8}$, and for a binomial variate by employing the transformation, for the binomial proportion $X = \dfrac{r}{N}$, of either $\sin^{-1}\sqrt{X}$ or, preferably, $\sin^{-1}\sqrt{\dfrac{r + 3/8}{N + 3/4}}$. An added advantage of such forms of transformation is that in most cases, although not in all, the distribution becomes more nearly normal in form and, therefore, all the assumptions underlying the analysis of variance method are approximately satisfied.

With these assumptions in mind, we may return to the general theory and the expression of the hypothesis to be tested, H_o, and the set of admissible hypotheses, H. Our hypotheses are expressed in terms of the unknown parameters μ, either directly by specifying values of the μ's or indirectly by specifying the values of linear functions of the μ's. In the usual examples of the analysis of variance method, the formulation is considerably simplified by the fact that the model is determined by the design of

|| *Ibid.*

See discussion of the sampling distribution of Student's t.

** The maximum value of the variance occurs when $p = q = \frac{1}{2}$.

†† F. J. Anscombe, "The Transformation of Poisson, Binomial and Negative-binomial Data," *Biometrika*, XXXV (1948), 246. (In some cases the use of a logarithm transformation will effectively normalize the data.)

the experiment. The set of N independent variates X_i is divided into groups according to the design, and each group of values may be considered as a sample drawn from a normal population of mean ξ_i and standard deviation σ. If we have q groups, for example, there will be q values of ξ_i and our hypotheses may be expressed in terms of them. But the design of the experiment itself will quite likely impose an arrangement on the q groups, and the hypotheses must be expressed in a corresponding fashion.‡‡ For instance, if we have a threefold, e.g. $j \times k \times l$, classification of the original set of N values, with at least one member in each subclass, we have $q = j \times k \times l$ groups and, if there are two or more members in each group, a set of $j \times k \times l$ values of ξ_i (with only one member in each group, the model and the analysis are considerably simplified because of a reduction in the number of possible values of ξ_i).

We may consider any value (assuming there are at least two) in one of the subgroups, denoted by X_{jklm}, say, as made up of two parts: (1) an element common to the group, which we may denote by ξ_{jkl}, and (2) a random element, which we may denote by z_{jklm}, which is the deviation from the common group element, and we may write $X_{jklm} = \xi_{jkl} + z_{jklm}$. Thus, the values in any subclass may be thought of as a sample drawn from a normal population with mean ξ_{jkl} and standard deviation σ, the value of σ being assumed to be constant from subclass to subclass. Further, our hypotheses may be expressed in terms of the ξ_{jkl}: the quantity z_{jklm} is assumed to be normally distributed about zero mean with constant standard deviation σ.

The general case is complex, even in the expression of the hypotheses to be tested. The student cannot be expected, therefore, to plunge right into a discussion of it. We prefer to begin with simple examples, and gradually build up the theory appropriate for the more complex situations.

Case 1: One-way Classification

Here the set of observations is divided into q groups, all those in any group being similar in some defined respect but the groups being independent of each other. It matters little in this case whether or not the groups are of the same size but, as we shall see later, in more complex classifications the analysis is very difficult when the numbers are unequal in the various groups.

Let us assume, to begin with the simpler case of equal numbers in the subgroups, that the total number of observations, N, has been divided into q groups, each containing $n = \dfrac{N}{q}$ observations. Further, denote the jth ob-

‡‡ Strictly speaking, the formulation of the hypotheses precedes the design of the experiment and controls it, but it is simpler and more convenient to develop the method in this fashion. The design and the analysis cannot be separated, being part and parcel of the same process.

servation in the ith group by the quantity X_{ij}, where $i = 1, 2, \ldots, q$ and $j = 1, 2, \ldots, n$. Following the general theory outlined earlier, we may consider the set of observations in the ith group as constituting a sample drawn at random from a normal population of mean ξ_i and standard deviation σ. The values of the ξ_i may vary from group to group, but the value of σ is assumed to be constant from group to group. Also, we may write

$$X_{ij} = \xi_i + z_{ij}$$

where z_{ij} is assumed to be normally distributed with zero mean and constant standard deviation σ. The null hypothesis to be tested may be expressed as

$$H_o : \xi_1 = \xi_2 = \ldots = \xi_q = \mu_o, \text{ say,}$$

which is equivalent to the assumption that all the samples (groups) have been drawn at random from a common parent population of mean μ_o and standard deviation σ. Similarly, the set of admissible alternative hypotheses, H, may be written in the form

$$H : \xi_1 \neq \xi_2 \neq \ldots \neq \xi_q \text{ (i.e. } \xi_1 = \mu_1 \ldots \xi_q = \mu_q)$$

which is equivalent to the assumption that the samples (groups) have been drawn at random from $s \leq q$ normal parent populations with different means ξ_i but common standard deviation σ.

How may we derive an appropriate test of the hypothesis to be tested, H_o? Using the maximum likelihood approach,§§ we define the quantity

$$\chi^2 = \sum_i \sum_j (X_{ij} - \mu_i)^2 = (\sum_i \sum_j z_{ij}^2)$$

and minimize χ^2 with respect to the unknown parameters μ_i (considering them as continuous variables for the purpose); first, subject to the set of admissible alternative hypotheses, H, being true and, second, subject to the hypothesis to be tested, H_o, being true. For the minimum value of χ^2 when H is assumed to be true, which we may denote by χ_a^2 to indicate the "absolute" minimum, we obtain in the process a set of q equations of the

form $\mu_i = \dfrac{1}{n} \sum_j X_{ij} = X_{i.}$ where $X_{i.}$ denotes the mean value of X_{ij} for the observations in the ith group, and

$$\chi_a^2 = \sum_i \sum_j (X_{ij} - X_{i.})^2 = \sum_i [\sum_j (X_{ij} - X_{i.})^2]$$

Students will observe that this quantity χ_a^2 is the total, summed over i, of the sums of squares for the several groups, where for each group the sum of squares is calculated about the respective mean, and, further, that the quantity

$$\frac{\chi_a^2}{\sigma^2} = \frac{\sum_i \sum_j (X_{ij} - X_{i.})^2}{\sigma^2}$$

will be distributed as χ^2 with degrees of freedom $q(n - 1) = N - q$.

§§ For a discussion of the theory, see, for example, Palmer O. Johnson, *Statistical Methods in Research*, Chapter X, pp. 210–25,
or Robert W. B. Jackson, *Application of the Analysis of Variance and Covariance Method to Educational Problems*.

Now if H_o is assumed to be true, i.e. each of the ξ_i set equal to μ_o, the corresponding expression for χ^2 will be

$$\chi^2_{H_o} = \sum_i \sum_j (X_{ij} - \mu_o)^2$$

and its minimum value, denoted by χ^2_r to indicate that it is a "relative" minimum, may be obtained in the usual fashion. We have

$$\mu_o = \frac{1}{N} \sum_i \sum_j X_{ij} = X.. \text{ where } X.. \text{ denotes the general mean for the whole}$$

set of N values of X_{ij}, and

$$\chi^2_r = \sum_i \sum_j (X_{ij} - X..)^2$$

If H_o is in fact true, then

$$\frac{\chi^2_r}{\sigma^2} = \frac{\sum_i \sum_j (X_{ij} - X..)^2}{\sigma^2}$$

will be distributed as χ^2 with $N - 1$ degrees of freedom.

But χ^2_r and χ^2_a are not independent, and we cannot use them directly in an F-test. However, we may always write

$$X_{ij} - X.. = (X_{ij} - X_i.) + (X_i. - X..)$$

and by simple algebra, since the product term is easily shown to be equal to zero, we obtain

$$\sum_i \sum_j (X_{ij} - X..)^2 = \sum_i \sum_j (X_{ij} - X_i.)^2 + \sum_i \sum_j (X_i. - X..)^2$$

$$= \chi^2_a + \chi^2_b \text{ , say,}$$

and

$$\frac{\chi^2_b}{\sigma^2} = \frac{\sum_i \sum_j (X_i. - X..)^2}{\sigma^2}$$

will be distributed as χ^2 with $q - 1$ degrees of freedom, independently of χ^2_a. Students should note that we have in the process divided the total sum of squares, $\sum_i \sum_j (X_{ij} - X..)^2$, into two parts: $\sum_i \sum_j (X_{ij} - X_i.)^2$, which is the total of the sums of squares for each group about its respective mean, and $\sum_i \sum_j (X_i. - X..)^2$, which is the sum of squares of the group means about the general mean since

$$\sum_i \sum_j (X_i. - X..)^2 = n\sum_i (X_i. - X..)^2$$

The term "analysis of variance" has been applied to the process (which should properly be called "analysis of sums of squares") because of this simple algebraic fact that the total sum of squares can always be divided into independent parts.

Assuming H_o to be in fact true, we know from sampling theory that the group means will be distributed about the general mean with standard deviation $\sigma/\sqrt{N}$. It follows, therefore, that, if the hypothesis to be tested is true, $\dfrac{\chi^2_b}{q-1}$ and $\dfrac{\chi^2_a}{N-q}$ will be independent estimates of the common variance

σ^2 and the ratio

$$F = \frac{\chi_b^2}{q-1} \bigg/ \frac{\chi_a^2}{N-q} = \frac{N-q}{q-1} \cdot \frac{\chi_b^2}{\chi_a^2}$$

will be distributed as F in repeated random sampling with degrees of freedom $n_1 = q - 1$ and $n_2 = N - q$, and will be independent of the common standard deviation σ.

But if H_o is in fact false, and H is true, the quantity χ_b^2 will be an estimate, not of $(q - 1)\sigma^2$, but of some value greater than $(q - 1)\sigma^2$. To see why this must be so, let us denote by ξ_i. the mean of the population from which the ith group is assumed to be drawn, assuming that at least two of the ξ_i. have values that are different, and by ξ. . the mean of the several values of ξ_i., i.e. ξ. . $= \dfrac{\sum\limits_i \xi_i.}{q}$. The expected value of the quantity $n\sum\limits_{ij}(X_i. - X..)^2$ proves to be, under these conditions, larger than $(q - 1)\sigma^2$ by the quantity $n\sum\limits_i(\xi_i. - \xi..)^2$ and will provide a valid estimate of $(q - 1)\sigma^2$ only when $\xi_i. = \xi$. ., i.e. when all the population means are equal.‖‖ Since χ_a^2 is not affected by any deviation $\xi_i. - \xi$. ., it follows that when we reject H_o it will properly be in favor of H. Consequently our statistical test will operate as we desire: it provides a valid test of the hypothesis H_o, and will lead to the rejection of H_o in favor of H when H_o is in fact false and H is true.

As a simple illustration of the process in a situation where we know that all groups were in fact drawn at random from the same normal population, as required by the hypothesis to be tested, H_o, we show in Table VIII.1 the values secured in samples 117, 118, 119, and 120 (each of size 10) drawn from the normal population of numbers earlier considered.

From these totals we secure the following values,##

$$\sum_i \sum_j (X_{ij} - X..) = 8{,}162 - (548)(13.7) = 654.4$$

$$\chi_a^2 = \sum_i \sum_j (X_{ij} - X_i.)^2 = 168.1 + 174.5 + 120.4 + 124.0$$

$$= 587.0$$

$$\chi_b^2 = \sum_i \sum_j (X_i. - X..)^2 = (157)(15.7) + (125)(12.5) + (126)(12.6)$$

$$+ (140)(14.0) - (548)(13.7) = 67.4$$

Following the standard practice, first suggested by Fisher, we may present

‖‖ See, for example, M. G. Kendall, *The Advanced Theory of Statistics*, p. 181.
Students should, as an exercise, apply Bartlett's test to the $\sum\limits_j (X_{ij} - X_i.)^2$ values in order to determine whether or not the assumption of a common σ is satisfied.

TABLE VIII.1

VALUES SECURED IN FOUR SAMPLES OF SIZE 10 DRAWN FROM A
NORMAL POPULATION OF $\xi = 13$ AND $\sigma = 3.5622$

OBSERVATION j	SAMPLE NUMBER				
	117 X_{1j}	118 X_{2j}	119 X_{3j}	120 X_{4j}	
1	16	12	10	19	
2	15	21	17	15	
3	9	12	6	7	
4	25	9	15	17	
5	19	9	14	11	
6	16	6	8	15	
7	16	17	16	17	
8	11	16	15	10	
9	14	11	14	16	
10	16	12	11	13	TOTALS
$\sum\limits_{j} X_{ij}$	157	125	126	140	548
$X_{i\cdot}$	15.7	12.5	12.6	14.0	(13.7)
$\sum\limits_{j} X_{ij}^2$	2,633	1,737	1,708	2,084	8,162
$\sum\limits_{j}(X_{ij} - X_{i\cdot})^2$	168.1	174.5	120.4	124.0	587.0

these values—and others calculated therefrom—in a table of the form
shown in Table VIII.2. (In most cases the root-mean-square column is not

TABLE VIII.2

ANALYSIS OF VARIANCE TABLE: ONE-WAY CLASSIFICATION

VARIANCE CORRESPONDING TO	DEGREES OF FREEDOM	SUM OF SQUARES	MEAN SQUARE	ROOT MEAN SQUARE	F-RATIO
Among Samples	$q - 1 = 3$	$\chi_b^2 = 67.4$	22.47	4.74	1.38
Within Samples	$N - q = 36$	$\chi_a^2 = 587.0$	16.31	4.04	—
Total	$N - 1 = 39$	$\chi_r^2 = 654.4$	16.78	4.10	—

shown, but it is of peculiar interest in this particular problem.) For our test
of the hypothesis H_o, we calculate***

*** Or the quantity $F = \dfrac{\chi_a^2 / N - q}{\chi_b^2 / q - 1}$, in the rather unlikely event that the mean
square among groups is smaller than the mean square within groups.

$$F = \frac{\chi_b^2 / \; q - 1}{\chi_a^2 / N - q} = \frac{22.47}{16.31} = 1.38$$

and enter the table of F with degrees of freedom $n_1 = q - 1 = 3$ and $n_2 = N - q = 36$. Since $F_{.05} = 2.86$ and $F_{.01} = 4.38$, we accept the hypothesis H_o and conclude that the samples were drawn from a common population —which, in fact, in this case they were. The root mean squares are of interest here, since if H_o is true each of them will be an estimate of the common population standard deviation, $\sigma = 3.5622$. Although the observed values are slightly larger than the expected, we find—using the test suggested in the previous chapter dealing with comparisons of sample and population variances—that they do not depart significantly from the expected value of $\sigma = 3.5622$.

Simple applications of the analysis of variance method of this kind are extremely useful in many research problems: since they are an extension of the usual t-test of the difference between means of two independent samples to the case of q independent samples, the research worker is able to make a valid test of the corresponding wider hypothesis. It follows, of course, that the usual t-test in such situations is a special case of the F-test applied to $q = 2$ groups. In fact, in this case $F = t^2$ and either set of tables may be used. For example, for $q = 2$ and $N - q = 12$, we find that, for $n = 12$, $t_{.05} = 2.179$ and $F_{.05}$ (for $n_1 = 1$ and $n_2 = 12$) is equal to 4.75, so that within the limits of accuracy of the tabled values we have $t_{.05}^2 = F_{.05}$.

We mentioned earlier that the same form of analysis can be made even when the number of cases is not constant from group to group. As a matter of fact, even the arithmetical procedures are relatively unchanged, as the following illustration of the application of the method to a research problem reveals.††† The results, incidentally, may be of some social significance and the data were, in fact, selected not only to illustrate the statistical analysis but to give an indication of how the interpretation of the rather simple statistical results may be made in terms of a problem of ever-increasing importance in our culture. The research problem‡‡‡ was concerned with an appraisal of the competence of older and younger workers in industry: we have selected for study only the data relating to the competence of workers hired within the two years previous to the time of the study. The data are given in Table VIII.3, and the quantities required to be calculated from them are shown in the final rows of the table. From these values we calculate the following:

††† The mathematical derivation of the appropriate formulae is more complex, however, since we must allow for an unequal number, n_i, of cases in the several groups.

‡‡‡ W. H. Bowers, "An Appraisal of Worker Characteristics as Related to Age," *Journal of Applied Psychology*, XXXVI, No. 5 (October, 1952), 296–300. Adapted with permission of the American Psychological Association.

AGE GROUP	n_i	$\sum_j(X_{ij})$	$X_{i\cdot}$	$(X_{i\cdot})(\sum_j X_{ij})$	$\sum_j(X_{ij})^2$	$\sum_j(X_{ij})^2 - (X_{i\cdot})(\sum_j X_{ij})$
18–29	228	436	1.91228	833.75	2,270	1,436.25
30–44	245	587	2.39592	1,406.41	3,031	1,624.59
45–59	107	302	2.82243	852.37	1,678	825.63
60 and over	26	77	2.96154	228.04	373	144.96
Total	606	1,402	$(X.. = 2.31353)$	3,320.57	7,352	4,031.43

TABLE VIII.3

NET APPRAISALS OF COMPETENCE OF MEN WITH UNDER TWO YEARS SERVICE

NET APPRAISAL OF COMPETENCE (X_{ij})	AGE GROUP				
	18–29 (X_{1j})	30–44 (X_{2j})	45–59 (X_{3j})	60 and over (X_{4j})	
11		1			
10			2		
9			3	1	
8	1	3			
7	5	5	2		
6	7	12	8	1	
5	25	28	14	5	
4	29	40	15	4	
3	30	40	14	6	
2	32	36	15	2	
1	32	22	13	1	
0	27	21	9	5	
−1	17	20	7		
−2	16	7	3	1	
−3	3	6			
−4	2	3	1		
−5	2	1	1		TOTALS
Total	228	245	107	26	606
$\sum_j(X_{ij})$	436	587	302	77	1,402
$\sum_j(X_{ij})^2$	2,270	3,031	1,678	373	7,352

and we also have,

$$(X..)(\sum_i\sum_j X_{ij}) = (2.31353)(1,402) = 3,243.57$$

$$\sum_i\sum_j(X_{ij})^2 - (X..)(\sum_i\sum_j X_{ij}) = 7,352 - 3,243.57 = 4,108.43$$

from which we obtain the values in Table VIII.4.

TABLE VIII.4

ANALYSIS OF VARIANCE OF APPRAISALS OF COMPETENCE OF MEN

VARIANCE CORRESPONDING TO	DEGREES OF FREEDOM	SUM OF SQUARES	MEAN SQUARE	F-RATIO
Among Age-groups	3	77.00	25.667	3.83
Within Age-groups	602	4,031.43	6.697	—
Total	605	4,108.43	6.791	—

For the test of the null hypothesis

$$H_o : \xi_{1.} = \xi_{2.} = \xi_{3.} = \xi_{4.}$$

we have an observed value of $F = 3.83$ with $n_1 = 3$ and $n_2 = 602$ degrees of freedom, which is just beyond the $F_{.01}$ point so we reject the hypothesis and conclude that the differences in competence are significant. As a glance at the values of $X_{i.}$ reveals, competence (or at least this appraisal measure of it) increases steadily with age, and the industries concerned gained rather than lost through the policy of hiring older workers.

Students will remember that, strictly speaking, the F-test is valid only for normal distributions and where the variances of the several groups do not differ significantly. Observation of the distributions of Table VIII.3 is sufficient to demonstrate that the assumption of normality is reasonably well satisfied, and that the variances are not too dissimilar. But this last point is rather important from the point of view of using the combined Within Age-groups variance in the denominator of F as the best available estimate of the assumed common variance, σ^2, and the assumption should be tested. Using Bartlett's test, we find $M = 1.92$ which, for 3 degrees of freedom, is obviously not significant. Accordingly, our assumptions are reasonably well satisfied and the F-test will provide a valid test of our null hypothesis, H_o.

Case 2: Two-way Classification

In essence, this is a simple extension of the previous case of a one-way classification, differing from it only in that the set of q groups may be arranged in a two-way table. Three quite distinct situations arise in practice: we may have (1) only *one* observation in each of the q groups, (2) an equal number (>1) in each group, or (3) unequal numbers in the several groups. The analysis may be performed without difficulty in the first two situations, but awkward problems arise in the case of unequal numbers unless, perchance, the numbers are proportional for at least one classification. In most of the social sciences, unfortunately, the occurrence of unequal numbers in the subgroups is the rule rather than the exception and a satisfactory solution of the associated problems must be secured. In the discussion that follows we will consider the situations in the order enumerated above: the additional factors and problems will be introduced as the sequence unfolds.

Case 2a: Single Observation in Each Subgroup

As in the previous case, we begin with data secured in the four samples drawn at random from the normal population of numbers where the population mean was 13 and the population standard deviation was 3.5622 (see Table VIII.1). Since we know that the conditions underlying the null hypotheses to be tested were in fact satisfied, the interpretation of the results is simpler and serves as a basic model against which we may compare the results obtained in actual problems. The relevant data, together with the necessary calculations and the corresponding analysis of variance table, are shown in Table VIII.5.

The two-way classification has here been made by Sample Number and by Order of Observation (see Table VIII.5A), so that we have set up 40 subgroups (10 by 4) with one observation in each. Of course, by virtue of the manner in which the samples were drawn we would not expect either factor (*number* or *order*) to have any systematic influence on the results, but we may through the analysis determine whether this is in fact the case.

Our mathematical model has been altered by the addition of an "order" factor. Denoting by X_{ij} the jth observation, where j now refers to the *order* of observation, in the ith sample, where $i = 1, \ldots, q = 4$ and $j = 1, \ldots, n = 10$, we may in general think of X_{ij} as being a composite of a constant effect common to all samples and orders, of an effect due to the sample *number* in which it occurs, of an effect due to the *order* it occupies in the series of observations, assumed to be independent of the sample number effect, and of a random element which is independent of both sample number and order of observation. Assuming that these various component parts are additive, we may write

$$X_{ij} = \xi + \xi_i + \xi_j + z_{ij}$$

where ξ denotes the constant common effect, ξ_i the effect due to sample number, ξ_j the effect due to order of observation, and z_{ij} the random element which is assumed to be normally distributed about zero with constant standard deviation, σ. Each observation, then, is assumed to be a sample of one drawn at random from a population of mean $(\xi + \xi_i + \xi_j)$ and variance σ^2. For convenience, we shall consider ξ as the common mean of the subgroups, so that we impose the following restrictions on the ξ_i and ξ_j:

$$\sum_i \xi_i = 0 \qquad \text{and} \qquad \sum_j \xi_j = 0$$

The hypotheses we may wish to test are concerned with the values of the ξ_i and ξ_j. The hypothesis that the sample number effect is not present, is, in view of the above restriction on the ξ_i, equivalent to the hypothesis,

TABLE VIII.5

A: Values Secured in Four Samples of Size 10
Drawn from a Normal Population of
$\xi = 13$ and $\sigma = 3.5622$

ORDER OF OBSERVATION $(j = 1, \ldots, 10)$	SAMPLE NUMBER $(i = 1, \ldots, 4)$				$\sum_i X_{ij}$	$X._j$	$(\sum_i X_{ij})(X._j)$
	117 X_{1j}	118 X_{2j}	119 X_{3j}	120 X_{4j}			
1	16	12	10	19	57	14.25	812.25
2	15	21	17	15	68	17.00	1,156.00
3	9	12	6	7	34	8.50	289.00
4	25	9	15	17	66	16.50	1,089.00
5	19	9	14	11	53	13.25	702.25
6	16	6	8	15	45	11.25	506.25
7	16	17	16	17	66	16.50	1,089.00
8	11	16	15	10	52	13.00	676.00
9	14	11	14	16	55	13.75	756.25
10	16	12	11	13	52	13.00	676.00
$\sum_j X_{ij}$	157	125	126	140	548	(13.7)	7,752.00
$X_i.$	15.70	12.50	12.60	14.00	(13.7)		
$(\sum_j X_{ij})(X_i.)$	2,464.90	1,562.50	1,587.60	1,960.00	7,575.00	$(\sum_i \sum_j X_{ij}) (X..) = 7,507.60$	
$\sum_j X^2_{ij}$	2,633	1,737	1,708	2,084	8,162		

B: Analysis of Variance of the Four Samples

VARIANCE	DEGREES OF FREEDOM	SUM OF SQUARES	MEAN SQUARE	ROOT MEAN SQUARE	F-RATIO	$F._{05}$	$F._{01}$
Among Samples	3	67.40	22.47	4.74	1.77	2.96	4.60
Among Order	9	244.40	27.16	5.21	2.14	2.25	3.14
Residual	27	342.60	12.69	3.56	—	—	—
Total	39	654.40	16.78	4.10	—	—	—

H_{o1}, say,

$$H_{o1} : \xi_i = 0$$

so that, if this hypothesis be true, our fundamental equation for X_{ij} becomes $X_{ij} = \xi + \xi_j + z_{ij}$. Similarly, the hypothesis that the order-of-observation effect is not present, is under like conditions equivalent to the hypothesis, H_{o2}, say,

$$H_{o2} : \xi_j = 0$$

so that, if this hypothesis be true, our fundamental equation for X_{ij} becomes $X_{ij} = \xi + \xi_i + z_{ij}$. In like manner, that hypothesis that neither order nor number effect is present, is equivalent to the hypothesis, H_o, say,

$$H_o : \xi_i = \xi_j = 0\S\S\S$$

and, under this hypothesis, our fundamental equation for X_{ij} reduces to the simple form $X_{ij} = \xi + z_{ij}$.

Again using the maximum likelihood approach, but writing $A + B_i + C_j$ instead of $\xi + \xi_i + \xi_j$ for convenience in the process of minimizing, $\|\|\|\|$ the quantities to be operated upon will be

(a) For Absolute Minimum : $\chi^2 = \underset{i\,j}{\Sigma\Sigma}(X_{ij} - A - B_i - C_j)^2$

(b) For Hypothesis H_{o1} $\quad$: $\chi^2 = \underset{i\,j}{\Sigma\Sigma}(X_{ij} - A - C_j)^2$

(c) For Hypothesis H_{o2} $\quad$: $\chi^2 = \underset{i\,j}{\Sigma\Sigma}(X_{ij} - A - B_i)^2$

(d) For Hypothesis H_o $\quad$: $\chi^2 = \underset{i\,j}{\Sigma\Sigma}(X_{ij} - A)^2$

Denoting the absolute minimum value of χ^2 by χ_a^2, and the relative minimum values of χ^2 corresponding to the hypotheses indicated by the subscripts as χ_{ro1}^2, χ_{ro2}^2, and χ_{ro}^2, respectively, we have

$$\chi_a^2 = \underset{i\,j}{\Sigma\Sigma}(X_{ij} - X_{i.} - X_{.j} + X..)^2$$

$$\chi_{ro1}^2 = \underset{i\,j}{\Sigma\Sigma}(X_{ij} - X_{.j})^2$$

$$\chi_{ro2}^2 = \underset{i\,j}{\Sigma\Sigma}(X_{ij} - X_{i.})^2$$

$$\chi_{ro}^2 = \underset{i\,j}{\Sigma\Sigma}(X_{ij} - X..)^2$$

where

$$X_{i.} = \frac{1}{n}\underset{j}{\Sigma}X_{ij}$$

$$X_{.j} = \frac{1}{q}\underset{i}{\Sigma}X_{ij}$$

and

$$X.. = \frac{1}{qn}\underset{i\,j}{\Sigma\Sigma}X_{ij}$$

However, if we set up the following sums of squares

$$\chi_{o1}^2 = \underset{i\,j}{\Sigma\Sigma}(X_{i.} - X..)^2 = n\underset{i}{\Sigma}(X_{i.} - X..)^2$$

$$\chi_{o2}^2 = \underset{i\,j}{\Sigma\Sigma}(X._{j} - X..)^2 = q\underset{j}{\Sigma}(X_{.j} - X..)^2$$

we see that the following equations may be used in expressing the relative minimum values of χ^2,

$\S\S\S$ While this hypothesis has perhaps little immediate interest or usefulness, it becomes important under the conditions to be considered in later sections.

$\|\|\|\|$ Since we minimize subject to the restrictions on the ξ_i and ξ_j, we must use the undetermined multipliers of Lagrange. But these are always zero in this case where the number of observations in the subgroups is constant, so they may be omitted. (See Lemma in unpublished Ph.D. thesis by J. E. Hammett, University of Toronto.)

$$\chi^2_{ro1} = \chi^2_a + \chi^2_{o1}$$

$$\chi^2_{ro2} = \chi^2_a + \chi^2_{o2}$$

and $$\chi^2_{ro} = \chi^2_a + \chi^2_{o1} + \chi^2_{o2}$$

Consequently, the appropriate tests of each of the above hypotheses will be an F-ratio, as follows

(a) For $H_{o1} : F = \dfrac{\chi^2_{o1}/q - 1}{\chi^2_a/(q - 1)(n - 1)}$

(b) For $H_{o2} : F = \dfrac{\chi^2_{o2}/n - 1}{\chi^2_a/(q - 1)(n - 1)}$

(c) For $H_o : F = \dfrac{(\chi^2_{o1} + \chi^2_{o2})/q + n - 2}{\chi^2_a/(q - 1)(n - 1)}$

To simplify the calculations, we may write

$$\chi^2_{o1} = \sum_i \{(\sum_j X_{ij})(X_{i.})\} - (\sum_i \sum_j X_{ij})(X..)$$

$$\chi^2_{o2} = \sum_j \{(\sum_i X_{ij})(X_{.j})\} - (\sum_i \sum_j X_{ij})(X..)$$

and $$\chi^2_{ro} = \sum_i \sum_j (X^2_{ij}) - (\sum_i \sum_j X_{ij})(X..)$$

Students will have already observed that χ^2_{ro} is the total sum of squares about the common mean, and that the simplest way to get the value of χ^2_a is as follows:

$$\chi^2_a = \chi^2_{ro} - \chi^2_{o1} - \chi^2_{o2}$$

From the marginal values of Table VIII.5, we have

$$\chi^2_{o1} = 7,575.00 - 7,507.60 = 67.40$$

$$\chi^2_{o2} = 7,752.00 - 7,507.60 = 244.40$$

$$\chi^2_{ro} = 8,162 - 7,507.60 = 654.40$$

whence $$\chi^2_a = 654.40 - 67.40 - 244.40 = 342.60$$

We can calculate the value of χ^2_a directly, by setting up the table of residual values $z_{ij} = X_{ij} - (X_{i.} + X_{.j} - X..)$ as shown in Table VIII.6. This is not normally done, of course, because it involves a long and laborious process, but we have calculated the residual values in this instance in order to demonstrate their nature and to indicate the validity of the assumption that they are normally distributed independently of sample number and order of observation. Students will observe that these particular residuals are so distributed that it is obvious the assumptions are reasonably well satisfied.

TABLE VIII.6

TABLE OF RESIDUALS FOR FOUR SAMPLES OF SIZE 10
SHOWN IN TABLE VIII.5 $[z_{ij} = X_{ij} - (X_{i\cdot} + X_{\cdot j} - X_{\cdot\cdot})]$

ORDER OF OBSERVATION $(j = 1, \ldots, 10)$	SAMPLE NUMBER				$\sum_i z_{ij}$	$\sum z_{ij}^2$
	117	118	119	120		
	z_{1j}	z_{2j}	z_{3j}	z_{4j}		
1	−0.25	−1.05	−3.15	+4.45	0	30.89
2	−4.00	+5.20	+1.10	−2.30	0	49.54
3	−1.50	+4.70	−1.40	−1.80	0	29.54
4	+6.50	−6.30	−0.40	+0.20	0	82.14
5	+3.75	−3.05	+1.85	−2.55	0	33.29
6	+2.75	−4.05	−2.15	+3.45	0	40.49
7	−2.50	+1.70	+0.60	+0.20	0	9.54
8	−4.00	+4.20	+3.10	−3.30	0	54.14
9	−1.75	−1.55	+1.35	+1.95	0	11.09
10	+1.00	+0.20	−0.90	−0.30	0	1.94
$\sum_j z_{ij}$	0	0	0	0	0	342.60
$\sum_j z_{ij}^2$	108.50	138.60	33.90	61.60	342.60	

The results of the analysis of variance are usually set forth as shown in Table VIII.5B, except that the "root-mean-square" column is normally omitted. The four values in this column are all estimates of the common value $\sigma = 3.5622$, although only the Residual entry is free of possible effects of sample number and order of observation. The other entries have within them the additional amounts due to any systematic influences of these effects, and are in fact somewhat larger than the "pure" residual— the common and expected pattern, which is of more importance in the problems discussed in subsequent sections. The tests of the hypotheses H_{o1} and H_{o2} are shown in the table: in both cases we accept the null hypothesis and conclude that the effects of sample number and order of observation are not significant. Logically, we should test the compound hypothesis H_o first, although this is seldom if ever done, since only if H_o is rejected would we have any interest in either H_{o1} or H_{o2}. For this example, we have for the test of H_o

$$F = \frac{311.80/12}{342.60/27} = \frac{25.98}{12.69} = 2.05$$

which, for degrees of freedom $n_1 = 12$ and $n_2 = 27$, is not significant (although very nearly so at the 5 per cent level). Accordingly, it would not be necessary, here, to proceed to the tests of hypotheses H_{o1} and H_{o2}.

To turn to an actual problem in which these formulae and methods may

TABLE VIII.7A

COMPARISON OF TEST SCORES OF 26 STUDENTS IN
THREE EXAMINATIONS IN CHEMISTRY

STUDENT NUMBER (j)	TEST 1 X_{1j}	TEST 2 X_{2j}	TEST 3 X_{3j}	$\sum_i X_{ij}$	$X_{\cdot j}$	$(\sum_i X_{ij})(X_{\cdot j})$	$\sum X_{ij}^2$
1	63	71	64	198	66.000	13,068.00	13,106
2	75	62	63	200	66.667	13,333.33	13,438
3	64	55	54	173	57.667	9,976.33	10,037
4	75	71	32	178	59.333	10,561.33	11,690
5	73	67	58	198	66.000	13,068.00	13,182
6	73	62	62	197	65.667	12,936.33	13,017
7	75	70	62	207	69.000	14,283.00	14,369
8	75	70	72	217	72.333	15,696.33	15,709
9	68	60	44	172	57.333	9,861.33	10,160
10	77	66	52	195	65.000	12,675.00	12,989
11	60	60	50	170	56.667	9,633.33	9,700
12	76	78	56	210	70.000	14,700.00	14,996
13	75	79	62	216	72.000	15,552.00	15,710
14	77	70	64	211	70.333	14,840.33	14,925
15	49	50	39	138	46.000	6,348.00	6,422
16	74	62	58	194	64.667	12,545.33	12,684
17	67	55	42	164	54.667	8,965.33	9,278
18	59	66	48	173	57.667	9,976.33	10,141
19	76	62	48	186	62.000	11,532.00	11,924
20	79	73	67	219	73.000	15,987.00	16,059
21	54	53	49	156	52.000	8,112.00	8,126
22	77	69	53	199	66.333	13,200.33	13,499
23	83	84	72	239	79.667	19,040.33	19,129
24	65	51	37	153	51.000	7,803.00	8,195
25	63	52	24	139	46.333	6,440.33	7,249
26	78	67	58	203	67.667	13,736.33	13,937
$\sum_j X_{ij}$	1,830	1,685	1,390	4,905	—	313,870.95	319,671
$X_{i\cdot}$	70.385	64.808	53.462	—	62.885		
$(\sum_j X_{ij})(X_{i\cdot})$	128,803.85	109,200.96	74,311.54	312,316.35			

$$(\sum_i \sum_j X_{ij})(X_{\cdot\cdot}) = 308,449.04$$

Source, Mennow M. Gunkle, "Striving for Measurement of Individual Work in the Chemistry Laboratory," *Journal of Educational Research*, XLVI, No. 4 (December, 1952), 275–84.

be employed, we show in Table VIII.7A the scores of 26 students on three examinations in chemistry. These students comprised the experimental group in a study by Gunkle on the effect of varying laboratory procedures, but the questions in which we are for the present interested are whether these examinations differed in difficulty and the extent to which they discriminated among the students of the experimental group. The hypothesis H_{o1} is that the examinations were of equal difficulty; the hypothesis H_{o2} is

TABLE VIII.7B

ANALYSIS OF VARIANCE OF CHEMISTRY EXAMINATIONS

VARIANCE	DEGREES OF FREEDOM	SUM OF SQUARES	MEAN SQUARE	F RATIO
Among Tests	2	3,867.31	1,933.66	50.03
Among Students	25	5,421.91	216.88	5.61
Residual	50	1,932.74	38.65	—
Total	77	11,221.96	—	—

that the students did not differ in achievement, which is equivalent to the hypothesis that the examinations failed to discriminate between students; and the hypothesis H_o is that there was no effect of either examination or of student number, i.e. that the examinations were of the same level of difficulty and that the students were all of the same level in achievement.

The usual analysis of variance table is shown in Table VIII.7B. For the test of the hypothesis H_o, we have

$$F = \frac{9,289.22/27}{1,932.74/50} = 8.90$$

and, consequently, we would reject H_o. Likewise, as the F-ratios in Table VIII.7B indicate, we would reject both H_{o1} and H_{o2}, and conclude that both effects previously mentioned are present in significant amounts. It is of some interest to note, in this connection, that the more significant factor is the difference in difficulty of the examinations, its mean square being of the order of 9 times that among students. This is not the usual pattern observed in analyses of this kind, since the variation among students might be expected to be the greater, and for this case the results indicate that either the students were a selected group and differed but little in achievement or, which is a more plausible explanation, the examinations were not in fact very good and therefore failed to discriminate adequately between students of various levels of achievement (or ability).

This leads us to a consideration of the components of variance for each of the rows in Table VIII.7B.### Denoting by σ^2 the true residual variance, by σ_T^2 the true variance among the tests, and by σ_S^2 the true variance (in achievement) among students, then the expected mean squares of the several rows (for q tests and n individuals) will be

For a concise discussion of this point, see A. M. Mood, *Introduction to the Theory of Statistics* (New York: McGraw-Hill Book Company, 1950), pp. 342–49. The assumption is made that the main effects, tests and students, are random variables, equivalent to the assumption of a random sample of tests and of students. If this assumption is not justified, as it may not be for the tests, the expected mean-square—Among-Tests must be of the form $\sigma^2 + n\sum_i B_i^2$. A fairly complete discussion of the possible models of this kind is given in the next section.

VARIANCE	d.f.	EXPECTED MEAN SQUARE
Among Tests .	$q - 1$	$\sigma^2 + n\sigma_T^2$
Among Students	$n - 1$	$\sigma^2 + q\sigma_S^2$
Residual	$(q - 1)(n - 1)$	σ^2
Total	$(q)(n) - 1$	—

It will be seen that our hypotheses may be expressed in another way: if H_{o1} is true, the value of σ_T will be zero; if H_{o2} is true, the value of σ_S will be zero; and if H_o is true, then $\sigma_S = \sigma_T = 0$. From the values given in Table VIII.7B, we see that our estimates of these σ values will be as follows:

$$\text{Est. } (\sigma) = \sqrt{38.65} = 6.22$$

$$\text{Est. } (\sigma_S) = \sqrt{\frac{216.88 - 38.65}{3}} = \sqrt{59.41} = 7.71$$

$$\text{Est. } (\sigma_T) = \sqrt{\frac{1{,}933.66 - 38.65}{26}} = \sqrt{72.885} = 8.54$$

In terms of these estimates, the most significant effect is the differences among the tests; the discrimination among the students, which should be of the order of $\sigma_S = 15$, is rather poor, and as a consequence the differences between students are not much greater than the differences among the random residual elements.

Case 2b: Equal Number of Observations in Each Subgroup

In a number of research problems it is possible to design the experiment so that an equal number of cases falls in each subgroup, particularly in a two-way classification, although this may be more difficult to secure in a more complex arrangement of the experiment when the design involves more than two factors or main effects. The analysis of the results is simple when the design calls for equal numbers in each subgroup, but quite difficult when these are unequal, so that wherever possible the former type of design should be employed.

The advantages of a design of this general type, with a number of observations in each subgroup, are, first, that we may determine whether or not the main effects or factors *interact* with each other and, second, that we secure as a residual element a quantity that (subject to certain assumptions) is free of any possible effect of the factors *and* of their interaction. This is not always an unmixed blessing, as it happens, because in certain special situations the residual term (commonly called the "error" term, although it is not strictly "error") is not the appropriate one to use in the tests of our hypotheses. But this anticipates the difficulties of interpretation discussed later; these points will be dealt with fully as they appear in the sequel.

To illustrate the analysis with an actual example, we shall use the data given by Johnson and Tsao.* For our purposes, however, we shall reclassify their data as shown in Tables VIII.8 and VIII.9, despite the fact that this destroys their factorial design and as a consequence gives rise to certain difficulties of interpretation. Beginning with Table VIII.8, we see that the data (final scores) may be classified into six subgroups, on the basis of the three *grades* and two *sexes*, with nine observations in each of these. The classification used in Table VIII.9 is similar, except that we have used three scholastic groups instead of the two sexes and have nine

TABLE VIII.8

ACHIEVEMENT SCORES OF 54 BOYS AND GIRLS IN GRADES 10, 11, 12

SEX	STUDENT NUMBER	GRADE			TOTAL	MEAN
		10	11	12		
Boys	1	30	26	29		
	2	25	26	29		
	3	22	24	22		
	4	26	24	23		
	5	17	23	20		
	6	14	15	19		
	7	18	18	17		
	8	17	16	15	554	20.51852
	9	12	13	14		
	Sum	181	185	188		
	Mean	20.11111	20.55556	20.88889		
	Sum of Squares	3,927	4,007	4,166		
Girls	1	21	26	33		
	2	21	25	29		
	3	19	23	25		
	4	20	22	23		
	5	18	21	18		
	6	14	17	17		
	7	14	19	15		
	8	12	15	15	514	19.03704
	9	9	13	10		
	Sum	148	181	185		
	Mean	16.44444	20.11111	20.55556		
	Sum of Squares	2,584	3,799	4,247		
Total		329	366	373	1,068	
Mean		18.27778	20.33333	20.72222	19.77778	

* P. O. Johnson and F. Tsao, "Factorial Design and Covariance in the Study of Individual Educational Development," *Psychometrika*, X, No. 2 (1945), 133–62.

subgroups of six observations each. If we denote by X_{ijk} the kth observation in the ijth subgroup—where $i = 1, \ldots, q; j = 1, \ldots, m;$ and $k = 1, \ldots, n$—the basic model may be expressed in terms of two elements for each subgroup, a constant for that particular subgroup plus a random element, i.e.

$$X_{ijk} = \xi_{ij} + z_{ijk}$$

and there will be qm values of the ξ_{ij}, one for each subgroup. Viewed in the light of this model, we may consider the values in each of the qm subgroups as constituting a random sample drawn from a normal population of mean ξ_{ij} and standard deviation σ, this standard deviation σ being assumed to be constant from subgroup to subgroup. Thus, the values of the z_{ijk} are assumed to be normally distributed about zero with constant standard deviation σ, independent of any of the effects involved in the ξ_{ij}. This is an important point, since it determines the interpretation of σ and consequently of the test of any hypothesis concerning the ξ_{ij} that involves an estimate of σ derived from our sample values.

Rewriting the formula as follows

$$X_{ijk} = A + B_{ij} + z_{ijk}$$

where A is defined as the general mean and the restriction on the B_{ij} is that $\underset{i}{\Sigma}\underset{j}{\Sigma}\, B_{ij} = 0$, it becomes evident that for our first hypothesis we must consider that the qm values of the ξ_{ij} are equal, or that the B_{ij} are all zero, i.e.

$$H_o : \xi_{ij} = \xi \quad \text{or} \quad B_{ij} = 0$$

Only if we reject this hypothesis would it be worth considering any other hypotheses concerned with a possible classification of the ξ_{ij}. But this is clearly another instance of the analysis for a one-way classification of the data with qm groups, for which—following the procedure explained earlier—we obtain the following results for the data of Table VIII.8:[†]

VARIANCE	DEGREES OF FREEDOM	SUM OF SQUARES	MEAN SQUARE	F-RATIO
Among Subclasses	5	124.00	24.80	<1
Within Subclasses	48	1,483.33	30.90	—
Total	53	1,607.33	—	—

and we would accept this over-all hypothesis, H_o, in this instance and not proceed further with the analysis. For the data of Table VIII.9, however, we secure the following results:

[†] Students should determine whether or not the assumption of a common σ is justified, using Bartlett's test.

VARIANCE	DEGREES OF FREEDOM	SUM OF SQUARES	MEAN SQUARE	F-RATIO
Among Subclasses	8	1,136.35	142.04	13.6
Within Subclasses	45	470.98	10.47	—
Total	53	1,607.33	—	—

and we would reject the over-all hypothesis, H_o, in this case.

Students may be puzzled by the fact that, although the same set of data was used in both instances, the Within-Subclasses mean square is much smaller in the second case. This occurs because in Table VIII.8 we have included in each subgroup the differences between scholastic groups, and also a number of others, and these must inevitably be large because of the design of the experiment. Accordingly, we must in interpreting the tests of H_o bear in mind the population, or populations, to which the σ of the z_{ijk} refers. For Table VIII.8, the estimate we use refers only to differences among students—nine for each subgroup—of the same sex in the same grade. For Table VIII.9, on the other hand, the estimate we use refers only to differences among students—six for each subgroup—of the same scholastic group in the same grade. Clearly, therefore, we have in mind quite different populations in the two cases and would expect different results. But it is not always realized that this has a bearing on the test of our hypothesis H_o and the interpretation of the results: in speaking of the null hypothesis, that the $B_{ij} = 0$, we do not mean the same "zero" in both instances. In fact, what we do mean is that the B_{ij} will vary, proportionately, no more than the z_{ijk} do. Students should at this point review again the discussion of components of variance given at the end of the immediately preceding section. It is important that they appreciate now, if they have not done so earlier, that "null" as used in conjunction with "hypothesis" is a tricky adjective that requires careful definition and interpretation. It does mean "zero" in terms of certain of the components of variance, as we saw earlier, but does not mean "zero" in the absolute or ordinary sense, and the interpretation of either the acceptance or rejection of the "null" hypothesis must be made in relation to the circumstances defining the model underlying the test in each specific situation.

To complete the analysis for the data of Table VIII.9—which we need not do for the results in Table VIII.8, since we have accepted H_o—we observe that we have two main factors operating that might have given rise to the significant differences among the subgroups. These are a factor related to grades and a factor related to scholastic groups: in addition, how-

TABLE VIII.9

ACHIEVEMENT SCORES OF 54 BOYS AND GIRLS IN GRADES 10, 11, 12
CLASSIFIED ACCORDING TO SCHOLASTIC GROUP

SCHOLASTIC GROUP	STUDENT NUMBER	GRADE			TOTAL	MEAN
		10	11	12		
Good	1	30	26	29		
	2	25	26	29		
	3	22	24	22		
	4	21	26	33		
	5	21	25	29		
	6	19	23	25	455	25.27778
	Sum	138	150	167		
	Mean	23.00000	25.00000	27.83333		
	Sum of Squares	3,252	3,758	4,721		
Average	1	26	24	23		
	2	17	23	20		
	3	14	15	19		
	4	20	22	23		
	5	18	21	18		
	6	14	17	17	351	19.50000
	Sum	109	122	120		
	Mean	18.16667	20.33333	20.00000		
	Sum of Squares	2,081	2,544	2,432		
Poor	1	18	18	17		
	2	17	16	15		
	3	12	13	14		
	4	14	19	15		
	5	12	15	15		
	6	9	13	10	262	14.55556
	Sum	82	94	86		
	Mean	13.66667	15.66667	14.33333		
	Sum of Squares	1,178	1,504	1,260		
Total		329	366	373	1,068	
Mean		18.27778	20.33333	20.72222	19.77778	

ever, we must make allowance for the possible existence of what is termed an "interaction" between the two main factors. The meaning of an "interaction" is not always obvious, although if chemicals are used in the experiment—fertilizers in agriculture, or drugs in medical research—there may be a real "chemical interaction." Generally, however, such a simple ex-

THE ANALYSIS OF VARIANCE

planation is not possible, and the interaction must be interpreted in terms
of a "residual" element such as we encountered earlier.

To show the meaning of the interaction, and to illustrate the process of
calculating the sums of squares required for the complete analysis, we give
in Table VIII.10A the set of *means* from Table VIII.9.‡ Analyzing this
table of means as explained in the preceding section, i.e. considering that
it is a two-way classification with one observation in each subgroup, we
secure the analysis of variance results shown in Table VIII.10B. The
"residual" entry of this table is the "interaction" term referred to above,
and it will be observed that it is the amount of the total variation among the
nine means not accounted for by the grade factor (constant for each column)
and the scholastic group factor (constant for each row). If it is large, which
it is not in this instance, it reveals that the patterns of the means by rows
and columns in the subgroups are not in accord with the patterns of the
grade and group general means (i.e. the main effects) shown in the margins.

TABLE VIII.10

A: MEANS OF SUBCLASSES OF TABLE VIII.9

SCHOLASTIC GROUP	GRADE			TOTAL	MEAN
	10	11	12		
Good	23.00000	25.00000	27.83333	75.83333	25.27778
Average	18.16667	20.33333	20.00000	58.50000	19.50000
Poor	13.66667	15.66667	14.33333	43.66667	14.55556
Total	54.83334	61.00000	62.16666	178.00000	—
Mean	18.27778	20.33333	20.72222	—	19.77778
Sum of Squares	1,045.806	1,283.889	1,380.139	3,709.834	

B: ANALYSIS OF VARIANCE OF MEANS OF SUBCLASSES OF TABLE VIII.9

VARIANCE	DEGREES OF FREEDOM	SUM OF SQUARES	MEAN SQUARE	SUM OF SQUARES MULTIPLIED BY 6
Among Grades	2	10.351	5.1755	62.11
Among Groups	2	172.796	86.3980	1,036.78
Residual	4	6.242	1.5605	37.45
Total	8	189.389	23.6736	1,136.34

‡ At least 5 places of decimals are required, if the values for the complete analysis
are to be correct to the second place.

The complete analysis of the data is given in Table VIII.11; the top four entries coming from the last column of Table VIII.10B, where each individual sum of squares has been multiplied by 6—the constant number of observations in each of the subgroups of Table VIII.9—in order to secure comparable values throughout the table, and the final two from the previous analysis.§

TABLE VIII.11

COMPLETE ANALYSIS OF VARIANCE OF DATA OF TABLE VIII.9

VARIANCE	DEGREES OF FREEDOM	SUM OF SQUARES	MEAN SQUARE
Among Grades	2	62.11	31.06
Among Groups	2	1,036.78	518.39
Interaction: Grades × Groups	4	37.45	9.36
Total Among Subclasses	8	1,136.34	142.04
Within Subclasses	45	470.98	10.47
Total	53	1,607.32	30.33

But to interpret this table of values, and the tests of the hypotheses involved, we must set up the mathematical model underlying the analysis. We assume that any value in Table VIII.9, which we previously denoted by X_{ijk}, is expressible as the sum of a set of independent factors, viz.

$$X_{ijk} = A + B_i + C_j + I_{ij} + z_{ijk}$$

where A denotes the general mean
$\quad B_i$ denotes the grade factor
$\quad C_j$ denotes the scholastic group factor
$\quad I_{ij}$ denotes the interaction, or residual, factor of grades by scholastic
$\quad\quad$ group
$\quad z_{ijk}$ denotes a random element assumed to be normally distributed
$\quad\quad$ about zero with constant standard deviation, σ,
and $\quad i = 1, \ldots, q; j = 1, \ldots, m; k = 1, \ldots n.$
The restrictions, or conditions, on the B's, C's, and I's, are as follows:

$$\underset{i}{\Sigma}B_i = 0$$

$$\underset{j}{\Sigma}C_j = 0$$

§ Students should compute the values for a complete analysis of the data of Table VIII.8: they will find that none of the factors proves significant, as our over-all test of H_o indicated must be the case.

$$\underset{i}{\Sigma} I_{ij} = 0 \text{ for each } j \qquad \left\{ \begin{aligned} &\text{since} \underset{i}{\Sigma}\underset{j}{\Sigma} I_{ij} = 0, \text{ there are only} \\ &q + m - 1 \text{ of these restrictions,} \\ &\text{not } q + m. \end{aligned} \right\}$$

and $\qquad \underset{j}{\Sigma} I_{ij} = 0 \text{ for each } i$

The null hypotheses we wish to test may be expressed in the form, for the factors as indicated,‖

$$H_{o1} : B_1 = B_2 = \ldots B_q = 0$$
$$H_{o2} : C_1 = C_2 = \ldots C_m = 0$$
$$H_{o3} : I_{11} = \ldots = I_{qm} = 0$$

Although each of these hypotheses will be considered independently in the following discussion and the appropriate test for each derived separately, we must note that logically the test of H_{o3} is the most important and must be made first. This is so because if we accept H_{o3}, and conclude that the I_{ij} are not significant, then either H_{o1} or H_{o2}, or both, should be rejected.‖ But once H_{o3} is accepted, the appropriate tests of H_{o1} and H_{o2} should properly be based on the expression

$$X_{ijk} = A + B_i + C_j + z_{ijk}$$

with a corresponding adjustment, if necessary, for the test of H_{o1} if H_{o2} is accepted, and for the test of H_{o2} if H_{o1} is accepted. As we shall see, however, these refinements that are required by a strict application of the logic of the situation are rather frequently of little practical importance.

When we consider the contrary case, namely that H_{o3} is rejected, then the tests of H_{o1} and H_{o2} based on this model are of little or no interest.# While it may be possible to conceive of either H_{o1} or H_{o2}, or both, being accepted when H_{o3} is rejected, this would be a logically impossible situation —a significant interaction between two factors, one or both of which are nonsignificant![**] Thus, the rejection of the hypothesis H_{o3} requires the automatic rejection of both H_{o1} and H_{o2} for this model, although we may express and test rather similar hypotheses in a different fashion by using another model. But to this point we will return when we come to the discussion of the components of variance for this type of problem later in this section.

Proceeding as before, using the maximum likelihood approach, we obtain the following relative minimum values of χ^2 for the hypotheses indicated, and the absolute value of χ_a^2 as indicated:

Absolute: $\qquad \chi_a^2 = \underset{i}{\Sigma}\underset{j}{\Sigma}\underset{k}{\Sigma}(X_{ijk} - X_{ij.})^2$

‖ Assuming that the over-all hypothesis, $H_o : B_{ij} = 0$, has been rejected.
They are derived in a later section, to demonstrate the agreement with one of the components of variance models.
** A complete cross-over in the pattern of means, leading to a highly significant interaction, may lead to this apparent—although not real—effect.

H_{o3}: $$\chi^2_{ro3} = n\underset{i}{\Sigma}\underset{j}{\Sigma}(X_{ij.} - X_{i..} - X_{.j.} + X \ldots)^2 + \chi^2_a = \chi^2_{o3} + \chi^2_a$$

For the hypothesis $H_{o2} : C_j = 0$, however, we must also have $H_{o3} : I_{ij} = 0$ true but $H_{o1} : B_i = 0$ need not be true, so that the relative minimum value of χ^2 is obtained from

$$\chi^2 = \underset{i}{\Sigma}\underset{j}{\Sigma}\underset{k}{\Sigma}(X_{ijk} - A - B_i)^2$$

which is found to be

$$H_{o2} : \chi^2_{ro2} = qn\underset{j}{\Sigma}(X_{.j.} - X \ldots)^2 + \chi^2_{o3} + \chi^2_a = \chi^2_{o2} + \chi^2_{o3} + \chi^2_a$$

Likewise, for the test of $H_{o1} : B_i = 0$, we must have $H_{o3} : I_{ij} = 0$ true but $H_{o2} : C_j = 0$ need not be true, and from

$$\chi^2 = \underset{i}{\Sigma}\underset{j}{\Sigma}\underset{k}{\Sigma}(X_{ijk} - A - C_j)^2$$

we secure

$$H_{o1} : \chi^2_{ro1} = mn\underset{i}{\Sigma}(X_{i..} - X \ldots)^2 + \chi^2_{o3} + \chi^2_a = \chi^2_{o1} + \chi^2_{o3} + \chi^2_a$$

and the analysis of variance table may be written in the following form:

VARIANCE	DEGREES OF FREEDOM	SUM OF SQUARES	VALUE OF χ^2
Among Grades	$q - 1*$	$mn\underset{i}{\Sigma}(X_{i..} - X..)^2$	χ^2_{o1}
Among Groups	$m - 1*$	$qn\underset{j}{\Sigma}(X_{.j.} - X...)^2$	χ^2_{o2}
Interaction	$(q - 1)(m - 1)*$	$n\underset{i}{\Sigma}\underset{j}{\Sigma}(X_{ij.} - X_{i..} - X_{.j.} + X...)^2$	χ^2_{o3}
Within Subclasses	$qm(n - 1)$	$\underset{i}{\Sigma}\underset{j}{\Sigma}\underset{k}{\Sigma}(X_{ijk} - X_{ij.})^2$	χ^2_a
Total	$qmn - 1$	$\underset{i}{\Sigma}\underset{j}{\Sigma}\underset{k}{\Sigma}(X_{ijk} - X...)^2$	$\chi^2_a + \chi^2_{o3} + \chi^2_{o2} + \chi^2_{o1}$

* Determined by the restrictions, or conditions, on the B_i, C_j, and I_{ij}, respectively.

This gives us, therefore, the entries corresponding to those shown in Table VIII.11, save for the Total Among Subclasses row which is of no immediate interest and is readily seen to be equal to $\chi^2_{o1} + \chi^2_{o2} + \chi^2_{o3}$.

Turning now to the components of variance model and denoting the expected within subclasses variance by σ^2, the expected variance among the I_{ij} by $\sigma_I{}^2$, the expected variance among the C_j by $\sigma_C{}^2$, and the expected variance among the B_i by $\sigma_B{}^2$, it may be shown that:††

(a) the mean square $\dfrac{\chi^2_a}{qm(n - 1)}$ is an estimate of σ^2

†† See subsequent discussion of the assumptions underlying this model.

(b) the mean square $\dfrac{\chi_{o3}^2}{(q-1)(m-1)}$ is an estimate of $\sigma^2 + n\sigma_I^2$

(c) the mean square $\dfrac{\chi_{o2}^2}{m-1}$ is an estimate of $\sigma^2 + n\sigma_I^2 + qn\sigma_C^2$

and

(d) the mean square $\dfrac{\chi_{o1}^2}{q-1}$ is an estimate of $\sigma^2 + n\sigma_I^2 + mn\sigma_B^2$

The hypotheses we wish to test may be expressed in terms of these variance components, as follows:

$$H_{o1}: \sigma_B = 0$$
$$H_{o2}: \sigma_C = 0$$
$$H_{o3}: \sigma_I = 0$$

It is obvious from this model as well as from the earlier discussion, however, that the two expressions of the first two hypotheses, H_{o1} and H_{o2}, are not altogether equivalent. In fact, not unless we accept H_{o3} does the original expression of the first two hypotheses have any meaning. The first step in any such analysis, therefore, must be the test of H_{o3}, which can be made by calculating‡‡

$$F = \frac{\chi_{o3}^2 / (q-1)(m-1)}{\chi_a^2 / qm(n-1)}$$

and referring to the table of F with degrees of freedom $n_1 = (q-1)(m-1)$ and $n_2 = qm(n-1)$. For the data of Table VIII.11 we have

$$\frac{\chi_{o3}^2}{(q-1)(m-1)} = \frac{37.45}{4} = 9.36$$

and

$$\frac{\chi_a^2}{(qm)(n-1)} = \frac{470.98}{45} = 10.47$$

and we calculate

$$F^1 = \frac{10.47}{9.36} = 1.12$$

For degrees of freedom $n_1 = 45$ and $n_2 = 4$, we observe that this F-ratio is not significant and consequently we accept H_{o3} and conclude that there is no significant interaction effect present.

In any such case, where H_{o3} is accepted, the rest of the analysis presents no real difficulty. But we must realize that our basic model has been altered by the acceptance of H_{o3}, since we must now set $I_{ij} = 0$ and write

$$X_{ijk} = A + B_i + C_j + z_{ijk}$$

Students should start with this model and demonstrate that the corre-

‡‡ Or the quantity $F^1 = \dfrac{1}{F}$, in the event that $F < 1$—which is the case for our example.

sponding value of the absolute minimum χ^2 is now $\chi^2_{o3} + \chi^2_a$, that the values of χ^2_{o1} and χ^2_{o2} are unaltered, and the appropriate tests of H_{o1} and H_{o2} are:

For H_{o1}: $F = \dfrac{\chi^2_{o1}/(q-1)}{(\chi^2_{o3} + \chi^2_a)/(qmn - q - m + 1)}$; $\begin{array}{l} n_1 = q - 1 \\ n_2 = qmn - q - m + 1 \end{array}$

For H_{o2}: $F = \dfrac{\chi^2_{o2}/(m-1)}{(\chi^2_{o3} + \chi^2_a)/(qmn - q - m + 1)}$; $\begin{array}{l} n_1 = m - 1 \\ n_2 = qmn - q - m + 1 \end{array}$

with degrees of freedom as indicated. For the data of Table VIII.11, we have

$$\frac{\chi^2_{o1}}{q-1} = \frac{62.11}{2} = 31.06$$

$$\frac{\chi^2_{o2}}{m-1} = \frac{1,036.78}{2} = 518.39$$

$$\frac{\chi^2_{o3} + \chi^2_a}{qmn - q - m + 1} = \frac{508.43}{49} = 10.38$$

and our tests yield:

For H_{o1}: $\qquad F = \dfrac{31.06}{10.38} = 2.99$; $\qquad \begin{array}{l} n_1 = 2 \\ n_2 = 49 \end{array}$

For H_{o2}: $\qquad F = \dfrac{518.39}{10.38} = 49.94$; $\qquad \begin{array}{l} n_1 = 2 \\ n_2 = 49 \end{array}$

Since $F_{.05}$ is in both cases equal to 3.19, we would accept H_{o1} and reject H_{o2}. Thus the Scholastic Group factor is the only significant one in Table VIII. 11, and we could reduce the table to the following form, equivalent to writing

$$X_{ijk} = A + C_j + z_{ijk}$$

VARIANCE	DEGREES OF FREEDOM	SUM OF SQUARES	MEAN SQUARE
Among Groups	2	1,036.78	518.39
Within Groups	51	570.54	11.19
Total	53	1,607.32	30.33

In the contrary case, when H_{o3} is not accepted, we cannot proceed in this fashion. In fact, as we indicated in our earlier discussion, in this event any test of the "significance" or "existence" of the main effects or factors is somewhat pointless since we have already demonstrated the existence of a significant interaction between them. Of course, we can very easily change the model and derive a test of what appear to be equivalent hypotheses, but the interpretation of the results is not very clear. Another possibility, not a very helpful one in most situations, is to perform the analysis separately for each class in one or other of the main effects, which is equivalent to establishing a set of one-way classifications. The difficulty, of course, lies in the interpretation of the full set of separate variance analyses. Let us now explore in more detail the virtues, if any, of these two possible modes of analysis when H_{o3} is rejected.

Since there is little to be gained through a discussion of hypothetical cases, we shall immediately introduce some real data secured in an experiment conducted by one of us. For reasons that will soon be evident, the interpretation of the results of the statistical analysis proved to be far more difficult than had been anticipated; on the face of it, the study was concerned with what promised to be only a routine matter. The data were the scores made by students in each of four grades (5, 6, 7, and 8) in each of four schools (N., G.A., L., and A.B.) on an arithmetic test designed to measure achievement in the addition, subtraction, multiplication, and division of whole numbers. It was expected that the differences between grades and between schools would be large, but the appearance of a significant interaction was quite unexpected. To illustrate, we show in Part A of Table VIII.12 the scores made by five students in each of the subclasses: these students were selected at random (from an alphabetical listing) for the purpose, since we actually had unequal numbers in these subclasses and the corresponding analysis must wait until the next section. The analysis of variance of the data is shown in Part B of Table VIII.12; clearly, as the F-ratios of the last column indicate, we would reject both of the hypotheses H_o ($F = 5.92$, $n_1 = 15$, $n_2 = 64$) and H_{o3} ($F = 5.60$, $n_1 = 9$, $n_2 = 64$)—at least, if the assumptions underlying our model are satisfied. It will be remembered that the important assumption underlying the analysis is that the residual elements, the z_{ijk}'s, are normally distributed about zero with constant standard deviation, σ.

We calculated the individual values of the residuals and found that they formed a more-or-less symmetrical distribution that was obviously not markedly different from the normal,§§ but for the test of a common σ (independent of grade and school) we require the sums of squares and variances shown in Table VIII.13 (the first entry in each cell is the mean, the second the sum of squares about that mean, and the third the variance).

Inspection is sufficient to reveal that there is no clear-cut pattern, by grade or by school, in the variances, and the value of M for Bartlett's test of homogeneity of variances proves to be 9.97, which, for 15 degrees of freedom, is quite obviously not significant. Accordingly, the assumption underlying our model, namely,

$$X_{ijk} = A + B_i + C_j + I_{ij} + z_{ijk}$$

is satisfied, and the analysis shown in Table VIII.12B is, therefore, justified.

§§ This part of the assumption is nearly always satisfied, since the residuals tend to have a symmetrical distribution in any event.

TABLE VIII.12

A: ARITHMETIC SCORES OF FIVE STUDENTS IN EACH GRADE IN
EACH OF FOUR SELECTED SCHOOLS
Interaction Significant

GRADE	SCHOOL			
	N.	*G.A.*	*L.*	*A.B.*
5	110	51	56	67
	87	76	50	60
	79	43	64	50
	102	91	61	80
	73	74	43	40
6	118	93	83	127
	96	64	72	101
	104	57	60	100
	94	116	47	103
	126	84	105	126
7	82	111	102	68
	84	117	100	87
	74	91	97	69
	60	105	131	65
	70	76	89	69
8	115	79	91	90
	76	105	77	111
	85	106	98	91
	89	102	100	86
	77	92	61	74

B: ANALYSIS OF VARIANCE OF ARITHMETIC SCORES

VARIANCE	DEGREES OF FREEDOM	SUM OF SQUARES	MEAN SQUARE	F-RATIO
Among Schools	3	1,264.94	421.65	—
Among Grades	3	8,090.14	2,696.71	—
Interaction (Grades by Schools)	9	12,265.51	1,362.83	5.60
Total Among Subclasses	15	21,620.59	1,441.37	5.92
Residual	64	15,577.60 ·	243.40	—
Total	79	37,198.19	470.86	—

Students will observe that the variation among the subclass means accounts for more than 50 per cent of the total sum of squares, with the interaction term alone (with only 9 degrees of freedom) accounting for nearly one-third. Quite clearly, as we may see from the mean squares, the major

TABLE VIII.13

MEANS, SUMS OF SQUARES, AND VARIANCES OF
DATA OF TABLE VIII.12

GRADE	SCHOOL			
	N.	G.A.	L.	A.B.
5	90.2	67.0	54.8	59.4
	962.8	1,538.0	286.8	947.2
	240.7	384.5	71.7	236.8
6	107.6	82.8	73.4	111.4
	779.2	2,226.8	1,969.2	765.2
	194.8	556.7	492.3	191.3
7	74.0	100.0	103.8	71.6
	376.0	1,092.0	1,022.8	307.2
	94.0	273.0	255.7	76.8
8	88.4	96.8	85.4	90.4
	1,003.2	518.8	1,069.2	713.2
	250.8	129.7	267.3	178.3

sources of variation lie in the differences between grades and in the interaction of the two main factors, grades and schools.

Let us digress for a moment to consider the nature of this significant
interaction term, since it has a rather definite and clear-cut interpretation
in this situation. If for each column and the total for all schools, we write
the grade number corresponding to the highest mean first, and then the
others in order of size, the following pattern is secured.

	SCHOOL			TOTAL
N.	G.A.	L.	A.B.	
6	7	7	6	6
5	8	8	8	8
8	6	6	7	7
7	5	5	5	5

The interaction, then, arises through a "cross-over" in the patterns: to our
surprise, the grade-patterns differed for the several schools (and in no case,
it may be noted, did they follow the expected pattern 8, 7, 6, 5—not even
for the total of all schools). Apparently the emphasis, drill, or what have
you, on these fundamental operations varied from class to class even within
the same school (the homeroom teacher, subject to some influence by his
principal and supervisor or inspector, would determine the condition for

his class). Students may prefer a graphical presentation of these means, superimposing on the same diagram the general means of schools and grades, and should be encouraged to construct such a graph for the data of Table VIII.13.‖‖

To return to the analysis of variance table and the tests of the corresponding hypotheses, we must now consider more carefully the assumptions we may make about the B_i, C_j, and I_{ij} in the basic equation

$$X_{ijk} = A + B_i + C_j + I_{ij} + z_{ijk}$$

As Fisher recognized more than twenty years ago,## there are cases where we compare the primary effects with the residual and other cases where the appropriate comparison is primary effects with interactions (or interactions with interactions of a higher order). In the social sciences, in fact, we must recognize three distinct types of situations for the two-way classifications (and many other combinations for three or more classifications).*** Of fundamental importance, however, is the fact that the basic analysis of variance table applies to each situation, since it represents only a description of the variation and an algebraic identity that is unaffected by the assumptions about to be discussed. The question is, therefore, not how the data are to be analyzed (for which the answer is always the same), but how the results shown in the analysis of variance table are to be used in testing our hypotheses and, consequently, in statistical inference. Also, the general assumption regarding the z_{ijk} (normal population distribution with zero mean and constant standard deviation σ) remains unaltered in all situations. With these considerations in mind, therefore, we may turn to a discussion of the assumptions concerning the B's, C's, and I's of the above equation. (Normally the A is always considered to be a constant and no hypothesis concerning it is postulated, but in unusual situations we might wish to determine whether it does in fact depart significantly from some specified value. If the observations are I.Q. scores, for example, we may wish to test whether the observed general mean departs significantly from 100, or from some other specified value ξ, for which we would use the sum of squares $\sum_i \sum_j \sum_k (X \ldots - \xi)^2$ with 1 degree of freedom.)

In any given situation, each of the components (B, C, and I) must be considered either (1) as fixed constants, or (2) as random variables from corresponding (normal) populations. Which assumption is the appropriate

‖‖ Put the schools on the horizontal axis, the scale of marks on the vertical, and use different colors or symbols for the average for each grade for the within-school means.

R. A. Fisher, *The Design of Experiments* (Edinburgh: Oliver & Boyd, 1937), pp. 219–23.

*** See, for example, the following article by S. Lee Crump, "The Present Status of Variance Component Analysis," *Biometrics*, VII, No. 1 (March, 1951), 1–16. Also, T. Kelleher, H. F. Robinson, and R. E. Comstock, "Precision of Estimates of Variance Components," *Biometrics*, XIV, No. 2 (March, 1958), 69–77.

one to make will depend upon the circumstances underlying the design and conduct of the experiment, and also upon the nature of the statistical inferences to be drawn, but we can in any event set up three possibilities:

(a) all the components are fixed constants;

(b) all the components are random variables; and

(c) mixed models, where some components are fixed constants and others random variables.†††

In the example of arithmetic scores classified by schools and grades that we have just considered, must our inference concerning differences among the four schools be restricted to those four specific schools, or may we extend it to all schools in the Province of Ontario? Obviously, in the first case we have a finite population consisting of those four specific schools only; in the second case, our population—while it may still be finite—consists of all schools in Ontario having classes in each of the four grades, 5, 6, 7, and 8—in other words, our four schools constitute a random sample from the population of schools. As it happens, in this particular experiment the four schools were specifically selected for the study and could not by any stretch of the imagination be considered as a random sample of schools, so we are forced to consider the "schools" components, the B_i's, as fixed constants.

In regard to the "grades" component, on the other hand, the conditions are not as clear cut. Since each school had several classes in each grade, from which in each case one class was selected at random, we might consider the "grades" components as random variables, although in this case we would be inclined towards a decision in favor of fixed constants. If there had been only one class in each grade in each school, or if specified classes (the best, the average, or the worst, for instance) had been selected, then the "grades" components would more or less automatically have been considered as fixed constants. Even in our case, however, the population of "grades" is severely restricted; strictly speaking, we must think of it in terms of the four schools, not in terms of the "grades" in all schools.

For the "interaction" components, the selection of the appropriate model is generally determined by the decisions concerning the main effects —grades and schools, here. If both of the main components are fixed constants, for instance, the whole set of subclass means should probably be considered as of the same kind, and consequently the interaction components would also be fixed constants. If, on the other hand, either of the main components, or both, may be random variables, then it may be argued that, in the same fashion and to the same extent, the interaction

††† Eisenhart calls these Model I, Model II, and Mixed Models, respectively. See, Churchill Eisenhart, "The Assumptions Underlying the Analysis of Variance," *Biometrics*, III, No. 1 (March, 1947), 1–21. See also, Henry Scheffé, "Alternative Models for the Analysis of Variance," *Annals of Mathematical Statistics*, XXVII, No. 2 (June, 1956), 251–71.

components should be deemed random variables. The only question that arises is in connection with the assumption of independence of the B, C, and I components. The assumption of independence between the B and C components seems reasonable enough, but it is hard to see how the interaction components can be completely independent of the particular samples of the B's and C's that are chosen. That this is so in our example will be fairly clear, since once we select a particular school, B, and a particular set of classes, C, in that school (each under a homeroom teacher), the interaction components may with considerable justification be considered as fixed constants and be interpreted, not in terms of all grades (classes) in all schools in the province, but in terms of the selected classes (or grades) in the selected schools.

To illustrate what happens with actual data when we select specific schools, we show in Table VIII.14A the arithmetic scores on the achievement test considered in Table VIII.12, again selecting 5 students at random in classes selected at random from the several classes for each grade. But we have selected different schools for this example;‡‡‡ schools for which average achievement differed but little, and for each of which the pattern of means (of all pupils) by grades was of the expected form in terms of average scores of all classes in each grade, i.e. in the order of grades 8, 7, 6, 5. The results for the analysis of variance of these data are shown in Table VIII.14B, which may be compared directly, item by item, with the corresponding results shown in Table VIII.12B. Using the mean squares and calculating the F-ratio as indicated, we have the following comparisons:

VARIANCE	DEGREES OF FREEDOM	MEAN SQUARES FOR SCHOOLS IN		F-RATIO	SIGNIFICANCE
		Table VIII.12	*Table VIII.14*		
Among Schools	3	421.65	211.23	1.996	Not Significant
Among Grades	3	2,696.71	4,671.83	1.732	Not Significant
Interaction	9	1,362.83	69.58	19.587	Significant
Total Among Subclasses	15	1,441.37	1,018.36	1.415	Not Significant
Residual	64	243.40	330.32	1.357	Not Significant
Total	79	470.86	460.96	1.021	Not Significant

Observe that for each group of schools the Total variances and the Residual variances are of the same order of magnitude, as indeed are the Totals Among Subclasses, but that the distribution of the latter sums of squares among the three component parts reveals a striking difference with

‡‡‡ Twenty-one schools were used altogether in the study, all located in one municipality, and the majority of them quite large.

TABLE VIII.14

A: Arithmetic Scores of Five Students in Each Grade in Each of Four Selected Schools (Interaction Not Significant)

GRADE	SCHOOL			
	R.	S.	Q.	H.H.
5	48	55	51	51
	81	51	37	47
	14	40	67	67
	40	56	76	85
	53	78	49	72
6	62	77	88	77
	54	57	45	76
	75	83	95	69
	86	62	67	82
	77	72	81	45
7	67	92	106	89
	101	63	95	92
	96	54	63	71
	58	94	91	114
	75	107	86	75
8	107	101	120	112
	64	94	61	82
	77	100	100	85
	63	106	82	108
	123	67	84	71

B: Analysis of Variance of Arithmetic Scores

VARIANCE	DEGREES OF FREEDOM	SUM OF SQUARES	MEAN SQUARE	F-RATIO
Among Schools	3	633.70	211.23	—
Among Grades	3	14,015.50	4,671.83	—
Interaction (Grades by Schools)	9	626.20	69.58	4.75*
Total Among Subclasses	15	15,275.40	1,018.36	3.08
Residual	64	21,140.40	330.32	—
Total	79	36,415.80	460.96	—

* $\frac{1}{F}$, not F, as previously defined.

respect to the interactions. Clearly, therefore, where the two main factors, or rather their components, are forced into the "fixed constants" pattern, the interaction components may very well be forced into a similar pattern.

TABLE VIII.15

Expected Values of Mean Squares in a Two-Way Classification
Equal Numbers, Greater Than Unity, in the Subclasses

MEAN SQUARE*	MODEL I: ALL FIXED CONSTANTS	MODEL II: ALL RANDOM VARIABLES	MIXED MODELS			
			Model III: Only Schools Fixed Constants	Model IV: Only Schools and Grades Fixed Constants	Model V: Only Schools and Interactions Fixed Constants	Model VI: Only Grades and Interactions Fixed Constants
Among Schools	$\sigma^2 + \dfrac{mn}{q-1}\Sigma B_i^2$	$\sigma^2 + n\sigma_I^2 + mn\sigma_B^2$	$\sigma^2 + n\sigma_I^2 + \dfrac{mn}{q-1}\Sigma B_i^2$	$\sigma^2 + n\sigma_I^2 + \dfrac{mn}{q-1}\Sigma B_i^2$	$\sigma^2 + \dfrac{mn}{q-1}\Sigma B_i^2$	$\sigma^2 + mn\sigma_B^2$
Among Grades	$\sigma^2 + \dfrac{qn}{m-1}\Sigma C_j^2$	$\sigma^2 + n\sigma_I^2 + qn\sigma_C^2$	$\sigma^2 + n\sigma_I^2 + qn\sigma_C^2$	$\sigma^2 + n\sigma_I^2 + \dfrac{qn}{m-1}\Sigma C_j^2$	$\sigma^2 + qn\sigma_C^2$	$\sigma^2 + \dfrac{qn}{m-1}\Sigma C_j^2$
Interaction	$\sigma^2 + \dfrac{n}{(q-1)(m-1)}\underset{i}{\Sigma}\underset{j}{\Sigma}I_{ij}^2$	$\sigma^2 + n\sigma_I^2$	$\sigma^2 + n\sigma_I^2$	$\sigma^2 + n\sigma_I^2$	$\sigma^2 + \dfrac{n}{(q-1)(m-1)}\underset{i}{\Sigma}\underset{j}{\Sigma}I_{ij}^2$	$\sigma^2 + \dfrac{n}{(q-1)(m-1)}\underset{i}{\Sigma}\underset{j}{\Sigma}I_{ij}^2$
Residual	σ^2	σ^2	σ^2	σ^2	σ^2	σ^2

* For q schools; m grades; and n pupils in each subclass.

In other situations, of course, we may encounter a different set of circumstances or relations, and it is quite possible that the interaction components may be considered as random variables even if one, or both, of the main factor components are deemed to be fixed constants. For our examples, there seems to be little choice but to regard all three sets of components as fixed constants, but we will consider the other possibilities in the discussion that follows. In view of the difference it makes, as will be evident as we proceed, to the tests of the hypotheses and to the inferences drawn therefrom, it behooves the researcher to decide *before* he *designs* his experiment, as well as before he attempts to analyze and interpret his results, in which particular model he is in fact interested and concerned. In brief, it all boils down to the fact that he must determine the exact nature of the *populations* to which his results are to be referred well in advance of the design and conduct of his experiment. The choice is between fixed constants and random variables: given this decision, the design, analysis, and interpretation follow a definite pattern.

We show in Table VIII.15 what seem to be the expected values of the mean squares (the components of variance) for the various possible types of models. In the table, the appearance of the B's, C's, and I's indicate fixed-constants assumptions, whereas the appearance of σ^2-values with subscripts indicate random-variables assumptions with the subscript in each case denoting the normal population of zero mean from which it is assumed we have a random sample. Perhaps not all these types can, or do, occur in practice, e.g. models V and VI, but they do indicate the possible models or patterns that might conceivably occur. It will be noted that the residual term, σ^2, is unchanged throughout; for each model these residual components are assumed to be random variables from a normal population with zero mean and constant standard deviation σ.

Observe that for all models the test of the null hypothesis concerning the interactions, whether expressed as $H_{o3} : I_{ij} = 0$ or as $H_{o3} : \sigma_I = 0$, is made by comparing the interaction mean square with the residual mean square. For the test of the null hypothesis concerning the schools components, on the other hand, the comparison is of the schools mean square with the residual mean square in models I, V, and VI, but of the schools mean square with the interaction mean square in models II, III, and IV (and similarly for the null hypothesis concerning the grades components).

It is of some interest to note that the model underlying the usual form of the analysis of variance is really Model I (models V and VI do not differ greatly from Model I, at least as far as the tests of the hypotheses are concerned), but there is no restriction such as we applied previously that the hypothesis $H_{o3} : I_{ij}$ must be accepted *before* we can proceed with the tests of the main effects (hypotheses H_{o1} and H_{o2}). This apparent inconsistency arises through the assumption that the I's are independent of the B's and

C's, the validity or sensibleness of which we had earlier questioned. Given this assumption, and proceeding as if the I's are not zero when the B's or C's are zero, i.e. that H_{o3} is rejected, it is a matter of straightforward algebra to derive through the maximum likelihood approach the formulae required for the tests of the corresponding hypotheses.

To return to our actual examples in tables VIII.12 and VIII.14 it is our opinion that, in view of the circumstances, Model I is the only possible one that could apply. Completing the tests as indicated, therefore, always using the residual mean square in the calculation of F, we have in Table VIII.12B significant Grades and Interaction effects, but a non-significant School effect. In Table VIII.14B, we have a significant Grades effect and non-significant Schools effect, as before, but now our interaction effects are significantly smaller than the residual. This latter unusual—and theoretically impossible—result was achieved, of course, by our purposive selection of schools with a common pattern of grade means. This neatly illustrates an important point in design (after the event, here), namely, that through controls imposed on, or selection exercised in, our experiment we may secure a peculiar set of results. When this occurs, we must seek the explanation in the design or in the conduct of our experiment.

The interpretation of the tests of the hypotheses in situations where models II, III, or IV apply, is not basically different from that just considered, save that we are using a different population as a reference point in the event that the interaction components do not vanish. The first step in the analysis must be, as before, to test the hypothesis H_{o3}, which may now be written

$$H_{o3} : \sigma_I{}^2 = 0$$

and the appropriate test is the F-ratio of the interaction and residual mean squares. If H_{o3} is accepted, we combine the interaction and residual sums of squares to obtain a new residual mean square, and test the significance of the main effects by comparing the corresponding mean square with the combined residual mean square. Now if H_{o3} is rejected, *and each of the main effects mean squares is significantly greater than the original residual mean square*,§§§ then the appropriate tests of the main effects are secured by a comparison of their mean squares with the interaction mean square. As students will realize, this is equivalent to performing the analysis on the table of means, which becomes a two-way classification with one observation (mean) in each subclass. Thus we, in effect, write

$$X_{ij.} = A + B_i + C_j + I_{ij}$$

§§§ The models require that this condition hold true: if it does not—as in each of our previous examples—then any of these models is obviously inappropriate for the situation.

where the I_{ij} are assumed to be random variables normally distributed about zero mean with variance $\sigma^2 + n\sigma_I{}^2$ (note that the schools and grades components may, or may not, be random variables). But the population we now have in mind in the tests of the main effects is a population of *means*, not original scores or values as is the case when the residual mean square is used. These constitute more stringent conditions insofar as the main effects are concerned: to be judged significant, they must stand out above the interaction variation as well as above the residual variation.

There exists an important class of situations in the social sciences where models II, III, or IV are quite appropriate, namely, where the residuals refer to repeated measurements of the same individuals or objects. The residual mean square is in this situation an estimate of the errors of measurement alone, which are normally relatively small, and we are primarily interested in a comparison, not of the main effects with errors of measurement, but of the main effects with the interaction mean square which comprises errors of measurement and the other errors or variations inherent in that particular experimental design. In other words, we are interested in determining whether the main effects are of sufficient magnitude to evidence themselves over and above all sources of experimental error, not only the errors of measurement. In learning experiments, or in any experiment where several trials or measures are made under identical conditions, for example, the residual mean square is essentially a measure of errors of measurement (or of observation). These errors of measurement are particularly small, for instance, if the data are secured from physical measurements, such as measures of height or weight or measures secured from a chemical analysis of the blood or urine, and are often quite small even if mental measurements are involved (the accuracy of measurement in these cases, however, is normally much lower than that secured in physical measurement). In an example given by Goulden, of measurements of duplicate loaf volumes, for instance, the interaction mean square was 54.42 as compared with a residual (error of measurement of the laboratory technique) mean square of only 2.334.||||| Goulden concluded, quite properly, that the errors of measurement factor was so small that it did not really affect the precision of the experiment, and accordingly he used in the tests of his hypotheses the interaction mean square as the valid estimate of experimental error.

The results of any analysis of mental measurements are seldom as definite as those reported by Goulden, but even so there is seldom any doubt as to the selection of the valid estimate of experimental error (proper residual variation). We show in Table VIII.16A, for example, data secured

||||| C. H. Goulden, *Methods of Statistical Analysis* (Second edition; New York: John Wiley & Sons, Inc., 1952), pp. 90–93.

for a random sample of 10 pupils in Grade 9 on repeated measurements in three tests in arithmetic.### Since we have two measures of each pupil on each test, which we show in each subclass and may denote by X_{ij1} and X_{ij2}, the composite estimate of the errors of measurement will be secured from the following sum of squares, with 30 degrees of freedom,

$$\tfrac{1}{2} \sum_i \sum_i (X_{ij1} - X_{ij2})^2$$

The other required sums of squares are calculated as explained previously, which students should calculate as an exercise, and the complete analysis of variance is shown in Table VIII.16B.

Students will observe that the residual root mean square is approximately 3.6 score points, so that the errors of measurement constitute an

TABLE VIII.16

A: Duplicate Scores of 10 Pupils on Three Arithmetic Tests

PUPIL	TESTS					
	I		II		III	
1	30	35	22	24	27	23
2	41	45	28	26	37	36
3	25	25	22	15	27	29
4	36	30	28	32	34	38
5	36	32	26	38	32	27
6	38	41	32	34	39	49
7	31	34	24	18	28	22
8	39	34	28	30	40	50
9	35	43	30	32	37	33
10	29	31	22	20	30	28

B: Analysis of Variance of Duplicate Scores
of 10 Pupils on Three Tests

VARIANCE	DEGREES OF FREEDOM	SUM OF SQUARES	MEAN SQUARE
Among Tests	2	734.70	367.35
Among Pupils	9	1,471.01	163.45
Interaction (Tests × Pupils)	18	451.64	25.09
Total Among Subclasses	29	2,657.35	91.63
Residual (Error)	30	395.50	13.18
Total	59	3,052.85	51.74

In order to simplify the algebra and the calculation and interpretation of the analysis of variance results, we subtracted the (assumed) constant practice effect for each of the tests.

appreciable portion of the experimental error (a common characteristic of nearly all experiments involving mental measurements). In fact, the other sources of experimental error have a relatively small effect here, since the F-ratio of Interaction to Residual is only 1.903 (with degrees of freedom $n_1 = 18$ and $n_2 = 30$, this is just slightly less than $F_{.05}$). The appropriate model for this situation (reading "Tests" for "Schools" and "Pupils" for "Grades" in Table VIII.15) being Model III, it is evident that our estimate of σ_I^2 is about 5.96 $\left(= \dfrac{25.09 - 13.18}{2} \right)$ as compared with the estimated value of 13.18 for σ^2.

Small as the difference may be, in this case and in others like it, there is little doubt that the interaction mean square is the valid estimate of experimental error under such conditions and should be used, in preference to the residual mean square, in any tests of significance of the main effects (differences among Tests and among Pupils). It seems to us that the questions to be asked of the data concern the effect of the major factors in relation to experimental error, not in relation to errors of measurement alone. The individual differences among pupils, for instance, should in an experiment of this kind be greater than the interactions of pupils and tests, which will arise through both chance and the real effects of differences between the tests and of varying reactions of pupils to them. That this may affect our decisions in regard to the hypotheses H_{o1} and H_{o2} in some situations, although not in this one since both are rejected in any event, will be evident from the following F-ratios:

$$\text{For } H_{o1} : F_1 = \frac{367.35}{13.18} = 27.9$$

$$F_2 = \frac{367.35}{25.09} = 14.6$$

$$\text{For } H_{o2} : F_1 = \frac{163.45}{13.18} = 12.4$$

$$F_2 = \frac{163.45}{25.09} = 6.5$$

We must point out, however, that if the experimental situation involved only one test and the constituent elements (subtests) thereof, the appropriate model might very well be Model V. In this case, the interaction components might be considered as fixed constants and, consequently, the mean squares for the main effects would quite properly be compared with the residual mean square (involving errors of measurement only). Students are invited to endeavor to set up the arguments that would in such a situation lead to the acceptance of models similar to each of models I, II, III, IV, V, and VI, and determine how the results of the tests of H_{o1}, H_{o2}, and H_{o3}, would be interpreted for each such model (reading "Subtests" for "Schools" and "Pupils" for "Grades" in Table VIII.15, and assuming that the several subtest scores for each individual are directly comparable). The data given in Table VIII.17 may be used to illustrate the arguments and interpretation: they are real data, taken from our files relating to the study of the components of an intelligence test. While they may be far from perfect for the purpose—the results are not particularly easy to interpret— they will provide a student with a real opportunity to exercise his powers of imagination and logic, and give him some necessary practice in the arith- metic involved in the calculation of the sums of squares appearing in the usual analysis of variance tables.

TABLE VIII.17

DUPLICATE SCORES OF 10 PUPILS
ON THREE SUBTESTS OF AN INTELLIGENCE TEST

PUPIL	SUBTEST					
	I		II		III	
1	9	8	6	7	7	7
2	6	8	4	6	7	6
3	7	10	6	5	8	10
4	9	5	6	6	6	8
5	10	8	4	8	7	10
6	7	8	5	2	8	6
7	3	7	6	7	6	9
8	11	9	6	8	10	8
9	5	8	6	5	7	8
10	8	8	4	7	10	10

Case 2c: Unequal Numbers of Observations in Each Subgroup

We suggested at the beginning of the previous section that the re- searcher should, if at all possible, design his experiment so that he secures an equal number of observations in each of the subgroups or subclasses. The point of the advice will become painfully evident in this section when the student tries to struggle through the morass of arithmetic and interpre- tative difficulties that threaten to engulf him when dealing with data for which the numbers in the subclasses are unequal. Unfortunately, in the social sciences the appearance of unequal subclass numbers is the rule rather than the exception, and we will, therefore, present what seems to be the most satisfactory approximate solution of these difficulties. We make no pretence that our treatment of this case is exhaustive: that would require in itself a volume of substantial size. Researchers who encounter situations more complex than those with which we deal herein, or for which our so- lutions do not appear fully satisfactory, should consult the references given in the footnote (and also, if necessary, the references given in those articles).* A general warning may not be amiss at this point, however, namely, that in any design more complex than a two-way classification the use of unequal numbers in the subclasses may present almost unsurmountable obstacles to a satisfactory solution, both from the point of view of the arithmetic involved in the calculations and of the interpretation of the results finally secured for the analysis of variance table or tables. The latter problem, of interpretation, in complex designs is difficult enough even with equal numbers in the subclasses, as we shall see later, but it is infinitely worse if we inadvertently add the problem of a solution for unequal numbers to an already complex situation.

The basic equation with which we begin is of course the same, i.e.

$$X_{ijk} = A + B_i + C_j + I_{ij} + z_{ijk}$$

where the various components have the meanings as previously indicated. But we now have $i = 1, 2, \ldots, q; j = 1, 2, \ldots, m;$ and $k = 1, 2, \ldots, n_{ij};$ the n_{ij} representing the number of observations in the ijth subclass, and this number varying for both i and j. Using a notation similar to that used earlier in denoting the several kinds of means, we may denote the marginal total frequencies as follows:

$$n_i = \sum_j n_{ij} \quad \text{for each } i$$

$$\text{and} \quad n_j = \sum_i n_{ij} \quad \text{for each } j$$

Since the z_{ijk} are, as before, assumed to be random variables, from a normal population with zero mean and constant standard deviation σ, we must impose the usual restrictions on the B's, C's, and I_{ij}. These are, for unequal numbers,

$$\sum_i n_i B_i = 0$$

$$\sum_j n_j C_j = 0$$

$$\sum_i n_{ij} I_{ij} = 0 \quad \text{for each } j$$

$$\sum_j n_{ij} I_{ij} = 0 \quad \text{for each } i \quad \left.\begin{array}{c} q + m - 1 \text{ of these} \\ \text{are independent} \\ \text{restrictions} \end{array}\right.$$

$$\sum_i \sum_j n_{ij} I_{ij} = 0$$

For minimizing to secure the maximum likelihood solution corresponding to Model I of Table VIII.15, we write, as before,

---

* Fei Tsao, "General Solution of the Analysis of Variance and Covariance in the Case of Unequal or Disproportionate Numbers of Observations in the Subclasses," *Psychometrika*, XI, No. 2 (June, 1946), 107–28.

H. F. Smith, "Analysis of Variance with Unequal but Proportionate Numbers of Observations in the Sub-classes of a Two-Way Classification," *Biometrics*, VII, No. 1 (March, 1951), 70–74.

R. L. Anderson and T. A. Bancroft, *Statistical Theory in Research* (New York: McGraw-Hill Book Company, 1952), 278–84.

$$\chi^2 = \underset{i \; j \; k}{\Sigma\Sigma\Sigma}(X_{ijk} - A - B_i - C_j - I_{ij})^2 - 2\alpha\underset{i}{\Sigma}n_iB_i - 2\beta\underset{j}{\Sigma}n_jC_j$$

$$- 2\underset{j}{\Sigma}\gamma_j\underset{i}{\Sigma}n_{ij}I_{ij} - 2\underset{i}{\Sigma}L_i\underset{j}{\Sigma}n_{ij}I_{ij} - 2\eta\underset{i \; j}{\Sigma\Sigma}n_{ij}I_{ij}$$

where the α, β, γ_j, L_i, and η are undetermined multipliers of Lagrange, and $\underset{j}{\Sigma}\gamma_j = 0$ and $\underset{i}{\Sigma}L_i = 0$. To secure the absolute minimum value of χ^2, which we will again denote by χ_a^2, we differentiate χ^2 partially with respect to A, B_i, C_j, and I_{ij} in turn, set the resulting equations equal to zero, and solve for these quantities and the Lagrange multipliers. We find, without too much difficulty, that

$$A + B_i + C_j + I_{ij} = \frac{\underset{k}{\Sigma}X_{ijk}}{n_{ij}} = X_{ij.}$$

so that

$$\chi_a^2 = \underset{i \; j \; k}{\Sigma\Sigma\Sigma}(X_{ijk} - X_{ij.})^2$$

which, as one might expect on logical grounds, is simply the total within subclasses sum of squares.

Similarly, for the general hypothesis H_o, where

$$H_o : B_i = C_j = I_{ij} = 0$$

i.e. the hypothesis that all the subclasses are drawn from the same normal population of mean A and standard deviation σ, we obtain quite simply

$$\chi_{ro}^2 = \underset{i \; j \; k}{\Sigma\Sigma\Sigma}(X_{ijk} - X...)^2, \quad \text{where} \quad X... = \frac{\underset{i \; j \; k}{\Sigma\Sigma\Sigma}X_{ijk}}{\underset{i \; j}{\Sigma\Sigma}n_{ij}},$$

which is, of course, the total sum of squares of all the observations from the general mean. This may be written

$$\chi_{ro}^2 = \chi_a^2 + \underset{i \; j \; k}{\Sigma\Sigma\Sigma}(X_{ij.} - X...)^2 = \chi_a^2 + \chi_o^2$$

The test of H_o then becomes

$$F = \frac{\chi_o^2 \; / \; qm - 1}{\chi_a^2 \; / \; N - qm} \quad \text{where} \quad N = \underset{i \; j}{\Sigma\Sigma}n_{ij}$$

which is simply the ratio of the Among Subclasses mean square to the Within Subclasses mean square, as before.† For calculation purposes, the simplest way to write the equations for these three sums of squares is as follows:

$$\chi_{ro}^2 = \underset{i \; j \; k}{\Sigma\Sigma\Sigma}X_{ijk}^2 - (X...)(\underset{i \; j \; k}{\Sigma\Sigma\Sigma}X_{ijk})$$

† A lot of algebra can be avoided if the basic equation is written, $X_{ijk} = \xi_{ij} + z_{ijk}$, and H_o expressed in the form $H_o : \xi_{ij} = \xi$ for all i and j. The disadvantage of doing so, however, is that the meaning of H_o may not be clear.

$$\chi_o^2 = \sum_i \sum_j \{(X_{ij.})(\sum_k X_{ijk})\} - (X...)(\sum_i \sum_j \sum_k X_{ijk})$$

$$\chi_a^2 = \chi_{ro}^2 - \chi_o^2$$

which can be calculated very quickly if we set up for each subclass the sum $(\sum_k X_{ijk})$, the mean $(X_{ij.})$, and the sum of squares $(\sum_k X_{ijk}^2)$, as shown for the data given in Table VIII.18.

The data selected for illustrative purposes are scores on an intelligence test in three grades (6, 7, and 8) in each of three schools. To simplify the calculations, we selected at random from each class approximately one-quarter of the students and thereby secured the number of cases as indicated in Table VIII.18. As is usually the case in studies in education and psychology, the numbers involved in the several subclasses are unequal and not even proportionate (sometimes in education the n_{ij} are nearly proportionate to the marginal frequencies—larger schools may have larger classes, for example). For the test of the hypothesis H_o, we have the following set of values:

$N = 61$ $\qquad\qquad \sum_i \sum_j \{(X_{ij.})(\sum_k X_{ijk})\} = 66,362.662$

$\sum_i \sum_j \sum_k X_{ijk} = 1,928$ $\qquad \sum_i \sum_j \{\sum_k X_{ijk}^2 - (X_{ij.})(\sum_k X_{ijk})\} = 5,785.338$

$X... = 31.606557$

$(X...)(\sum_i \sum_j \sum_k X_{ijk}) = 60,937.443$

$\sum_i \sum_j \sum_k X_{ijk}^2 = 72,148$

$\sum_i \sum_j \sum_k X_{ijk}^2 - (X...)(\sum_i \sum_j \sum_k X_{ijk}) = 11,210.557$

VARIANCE	DEGREES OF FREEDOM	SUM OF SQUARES	MEAN SQUARE	F-RATIO
Among Subclasses	8	5,425.219	678.152	6.10
Within Subclasses	52	5,785.338	111.257	—
Total	60	11,210.557	—	

Clearly, we would reject H_o and conclude that the observed differences among the several subclasses are significant, which means that at least one of the components (schools, grades, or interaction) must be significant. Accordingly, we may proceed to the tests of the other hypotheses, concerning the B's, C's, and I's.

When we attempt the detailed analysis, either algebraically or arithmetically, we discover that if the component sums of squares are calculated

TABLE VIII.18

EXAMPLE OF UNEQUAL NUMBERS IN THE SUBCLASSES:
INTELLIGENCE TEST SCORES

GRADE	SCORES School			CALCULATIONS School		
	S.C.	Dun.	Win.	S.C.	Dun.	Win.
6	12	21	10	$n_{11} = 6$	$n_{12} = 6$	$n_{13} = 9$
	21	35	12	$\sum_k X_{11k} = 147$	$\sum_k X_{12k} = 150$	$\sum_k X_{13k} = 130$
	32	15	20	$X_{11.} = 24.50000$	$X_{12.} = 25.00000$	$X_{13.} = 14.44444$
	41	21	11	$(X_{11.})(\sum_k X_{11k}) =$	$(X_{12.})(\sum_k X_{12k}) =$	$(X_{13.})(\sum_k X_{13k}) =$
	19	15	17	$= 3,601.500$	$= 3,750.000$	$= 1,877.778$
	22	43	15	$\sum_k X_{11k}^2 = 4,135$	$\sum_k X_{12k}^2 = 4,406$	$\sum_k X_{13k}^2 = 1,992$
	.		13	$\sum_k X_{11k}^2 - (X_{11.})(\sum_k X_{11k})$	$\sum_k X_{12k}^2 - (X_{12.})(\sum_k X_{12k})$	$\sum_k X_{13k}^2 - (X_{13.})(\sum_k X_{13k})$
			12	$= 533.500$	$= 656.000$	$= 114.222$
			20			
7	47	38	39	$n_{21} = 8$	$n_{22} = 6$	$n_{23} = 7$
	42	36	50	$\sum_k X_{21k} = 291$	$\sum_k X_{22k} = 212$	$\sum_k X_{23k} = 210$
	34	20	14	$X_{21.} = 36.37500$	$X_{22.} = 35.33333$	$X_{23.} = 30.00000$
	35	33	22	$(X_{21.})(\sum_k X_{21k}) =$	$(X_{22.})(\sum_k X_{22k}) =$	$(X_{23.})(\sum_k X_{23k}) =$
	30	45	32	$= 10,585.125$	$= 7,490.667$	$= 6,300.000$
	33	40	26	$\sum_k X_{21k}^2 = 10,891$	$\sum_k X_{22k}^2 = 7,854$	$\sum_k X_{23k}^2 = 7,130$
	42		27	$\sum_k X_{21k}^2 - (X_{21.})(\sum_k X_{21k})$	$\sum_k X_{22k}^2 - (X_{22.})(\sum_k X_{22k})$	$\sum_k X_{23k}^2 - (X_{23.})(\sum_k X_{23k})$
	28			$= 305.875$	$= 363.333$	$= 830.000$
8	57	66	33	$n_{31} = 8$	$n_{32} = 5$	$n_{33} = 6$
	35	25	40	$\sum_k X_{31k} = 317$	$\sum_k X_{32k} = 223$	$\sum_k X_{33k} = 248$
	35	25	49	$X_{31.} = 39.62500$	$X_{32.} = 44.60000$	$X_{33.} = 41.33333$
	25	47	47	$(X_{31.})(\sum_k X_{31k}) =$	$(X_{32.})(\sum_k X_{32k}) =$	$(X_{33.})(\sum_k X_{33k}) =$
	36	60	32	$= 12,561.125$	$= 9,945.800$	$= 10,250.667$
	62		47	$\sum_k X_{31k}^2 = 13,793$	$\sum_k X_{32k}^2 = 11,415$	$\sum_k X_{33k}^2 = 10,532$
	40			$\sum_k X_{31k}^2 - (X_{31.})(\sum_k X_{31k})$	$\sum_k X_{32k}^2 - (X_{32.})(\sum_k X_{32k})$	$\sum_k X_{33k}^2 - (X_{33.})(\sum_k X_{33k})$
	27			$= 1,231.875$	$= 1,469.200$	$= 281.333$

in the usual fashion from the school and grade totals and means they are no longer additive. In fact, for this example the sum of squares among schools calculated in this way is 819.303, among grades is 4,634.201, and we must have a *negative* sum of squares $(= -28.285)$ for the interaction!

This being an absurd and impossible result, it is obvious that our usual method of calculation cannot be applied to such situations. There is one rather important case that is an exception: the additive property of the sums of squares holds true for the case where the subclass frequencies are proportional to the marginal totals. Since the general case of unequal numbers in the subclasses includes both proportionate and disproportionate subclass numbers, but we have only an approximate solution for the latter, we shall in what follows distinguish between these two situations.

A little algebra is sufficient to illustrate the nature of the dilemma regarding the breakdown of the total sum of squares. We may write the identity

$$(X_{ijk} - X \ldots) \equiv (X_{ijk} - X_{ij.}) + (X_{ij.} - X_{i..} - X_{.j.} + X \ldots)$$
$$+ (X_{i..} - X \ldots) + (X_{.j.} - X \ldots)$$
$$= a + b + c + d, \text{say,}$$

and consequently

$$\sum_i \sum_j \sum_k (X_{ijk} - X \ldots)^2 = \sum_i \sum_j \sum_k (a + b + c + d)^2$$

$$= \sum_i \sum_j \sum_k (a^2 + b^2 + c^2 + d^2 + 2ab + 2ac + 2ad + 2bc + 2bd + 2cd)$$

However, since $n_{ij}X_{ij.} = \sum_k X_{ijk}$, it follows that any of these sums of products involving "a" must be identically zero whether the subclass numbers be equal or unequal. Accordingly, for the general case we have

$$\sum_i \sum_j \sum_k (X_{ijk} - X \ldots)^2 = \sum_i \sum_j \sum_k (a^2 + b^2 + c^2 + d^2 + 2bc + 2bd + 2cd)$$

The remaining sums of products (i.e. the bc, bd, and cd terms) do not vanish (become equal to zero) for the general case, and consequently our sums of squares are not additive. As we shall see, they do in fact vanish for two important cases, viz. for equal and for proportionate subclass numbers. Before proceeding to this point, however, we should note that, according to our earlier definitions:

$\sum_i \sum_j \sum_k a^2$ is the Within Subclasses sum of squares;

$\sum_i \sum_j \sum_k b^2$ is the Interaction sum of squares;

$\sum_i \sum_j \sum_k c^2$ is the sum of squares for the B_i factor; and

$\sum_i \sum_j \sum_k d^2$ is the sum of squares for the C_j factor.

Let us now write out these remaining sums of products in full, so that we may observe their nature under the conditions of equal and proportionate subclass numbers. We have

$$\sum_i \sum_j \sum_k bc = \sum_i \sum_j (n_{ij})(X_{ij.} - X_{i..} - X_{.j.} + X \ldots)(X_{i..} - X \ldots)$$

$$\sum_i \sum_j \sum_k bd = \sum_i \sum_j (n_{ij})(X_{ij.} - X_{i..} - X_{.j.} + X \ldots)(X_{.j.} - X \ldots)$$

$$\sum_i \sum_j \sum_k cd = \sum_i \sum_j (n_{ij})(X_{i..} - X \ldots)(X_{.j.} - X \ldots)$$

Also, $\sum_j n_{ij} = n_i$

$$\sum_i n_{ij} = n_j$$

$$\sum_i \sum_j n_{ij} = N$$

where $i = 1, 2, \ldots, q; j = 1, 2, \ldots, m;$ and $k = 1, 2, \ldots, n_{ij};$ and

$$\sum_i n_{ij}(X_{ij.} - X_{i..} - X_{.j.} + X \ldots) = 0 \text{ for each } j$$

$$\sum_j n_{ij}(X_{ij.} - X_{i..} - X_{.j.} + X \ldots) = 0 \text{ for each } i$$

$$\sum_j n_j(X_{.j.} - X \ldots) = 0$$

$$\sum_i n_i(X_{i..} - X \ldots) = 0$$

since $n_i X_{i..} = \sum_j n_{ij} X_{ij.}$

$$n_j X_{.j.} = \sum_i n_{ij} X_{ij.}$$

$$NX \ldots = \sum_i n_i X_{i..} = \sum_i \sum_j n_{ij} X_{i..}$$

and $nX \ldots = \sum_j n_j X_{.j.} = \sum_i \sum_j n_{ij} X_{.j.}$

Consider, first, the case where $n_{ij} = n$, i.e. where the subclass numbers are equal, and $n_j = qn$, $n_i = mn$ and $N = qmn$. All of our equations are, in this event, extremely simple, and it is an easy matter to show that all the sums of products vanish and, consequently, that the sums of squares are additive, i.e.

$$\sum_i \sum_j \sum_k (X_{ijk} - X \ldots)^2 = \sum_i \sum_j \sum_k (a^2 + b^2 + c^2 + d^2)$$

For the case of proportionate subclass numbers, we may define

$$p_i = \frac{n_{ij}}{n_i}, \text{ or } n_{ij} = p_i n_i, \text{ for each } j$$

$$p_j = \frac{n_{ij}}{n_j}, \text{ or } n_{ij} = p_j n_j, \text{ for each } i$$

Now we may write

$$\sum_i \sum_j \sum_k bc = \sum_i (X_{i..} - X \ldots) \sum_j p_j n_j (X_{ij.} - X_{i..} - X_{.j.} + X \ldots) \equiv 0$$

$$\sum_i \sum_j \sum_k bd = \sum_j (X_{.j.} - X \ldots) \sum_i p_i n_i (X_{ij.} - X_{i..} - X_{.j.} + X \ldots) \equiv 0$$

and

$$\sum_i \sum_j \sum_k cd = \sum_i (X_{i..} - X \ldots) \sum_j p_j n_j (X_{.j.} - X \ldots) \equiv 0$$

In this case, also, the sums of products vanish and the sums of squares are additive.

Even for the proportionate subclass numbers, the tests of significance are relatively straightforward only if Model I (fixed constants) is assumed to be appropriate. Researchers who encounter situations involving proportionate subclass numbers where Model II or one of the Mixed Models seems to be appropriate should use the solutions proposed by Smith[‡] and Cochran.[§] For the case of unequal *and* disproportionate subclass numbers, very little has been done for any of the models other than Model I, and even for this situation the exact solution is so laborious (algebraically and arithmetically) that approximate solutions must normally be employed. A quite complete discussion of this case and of the approximate solutions for it have been given by Tsao.[‖]

Of all the possible approximate solutions (methods of fitting constants, expected subclass numbers, unweighted squares of means, and weighted squares of means), the method of unweighted squares of means is the simplest computationally and is to be preferred, partly because there is no evidence that *any* particular method is the "best" in any general or absolute sense. (The expected mean squares for the method of unweighted squares of means have been given by Crump.[#]) This method is explained below, using the data of Table VIII.18 to illustrate the calculations, and we have, in addition, included the method of expected proportionate frequencies (this case may arise frequently in education and psychology). Students will remember, of course, that in any case we would first test for homogeneity of the qm subclass variances, since this assumption must be reasonably well satisfied for any analysis.

The first step that should be taken is to determine, by employing the usual χ^2-test, whether or not the actual subclass frequencies depart significantly from the *expected* equal or proportionate subclass frequencies.[**] Our set of observed subclass frequencies were as shown on page 242. The expected frequency in each cell, for equal subclass numbers, would be $\frac{61}{9} = 6.77778$, and the expected proportionate subclass frequencies can be secured from the marginal totals, in the usual fashion employed in any $q \times m$ contingency table. For the first case we secure $\chi^2 = 2.00$ with 8

‡ H. F. Smith, "Analysis of Variance with Unequal but Proportionate Numbers of Observations in the Sub-classes of a Two-Way Classification."

§ W. G. Cochran, "Testing a Linear Relation Among Variances," *Biometrics*, VII, No. 1 (March, 1951), 17–32.

‖ Fei Tsao, "General Solution of the Analysis of Variance and Covariance in the Case of Unequal or Disproportionate Numbers of Observations in the Subclasses."

S. L. Crump, "The Estimation of Components of Variance in Multiple Classifications" (Unpublished Ph.D. Thesis, Iowa State College Library, Ames, Iowa, 1947).

** Which may in some cases be classed as "love's labor lost," since we have no other simple method of analyzing the data.

degrees of freedom, and for the second $\chi^2 = 0.985$ with 4 degrees of freedom, so that we may use either one or the other method (in practice, we would select the first wherever possible).

		SCHOOL			
		S.C.	*Dun.*	*Win.*	*Total*
G	*6*	6	6	9	21
R					
A	*7*	8	6	7	21
D					
E	*8*	8	5	6	19
		22	17	22	61

The next step for either method is to write out the table of subclass means and subclass sums of squares, as shown below (mean first, followed by sum of squares, in each cell of the table):

GRADE	SCHOOL		
	S.C.	*Dun.*	*Win.*
6	24.50000 533.500	25.00000 656.000	14.44444 114.222
7	36.37500 305.875	35.33333 363.333	30.00000 830.000
8	39.62500 1,231.875	44.60000 1,469.200	41.33333 281.333

For the case of expected equal frequencies (unweighted means), we simply analyze the table of means as if each mean were a single observation, to obtain the following results (sums of squares):

$$\text{Among Schools : } 67.037$$
$$\text{Among Grades : } 643.467$$
$$\text{Residual} \qquad : \quad 40.062$$
$$\text{Total} \qquad \quad : \ 750.566$$

To secure an equivalent within subclasses sum of squares, we must multiply each subclass sum of squares by $\dfrac{6.77778}{n_{ij}}$ and add the products.†† We obtain the Adjusted Within Subclasses Sum of Squares = 6,255.998
And multiplying each of the previous entries by 6.77778, we have

†† Or divide each by n_{ij} and multiply the sum by 6.77778.

VARIANCE	DEGREES OF FREEDOM	SUM OF SQUARES	MEAN SQUARE	F-RATIO
Among Schools	2	454.362	227.18	1.89
Among Grades	2	4,361.278	2,180.64	18.13
Interaction	4	271.531	67.88	<1
Among Subclasses	8	5,087.171	635.90	5.29
Within Subclasses	52	6,255.998	120.31	—
Total	60	11,343.169	—	—

Obviously, the only significant factor is that among grades—normally always significant in school data of this kind. However, reference back to our previous analysis shows that we have altered slightly the various sums of squares' entries, e.g.

Among Subclasses: 5,087.171 vs. 5,425.219
Within Subclasses: 6,255.998 vs. 5,785.338
Total : 11,343.169 vs. 11,210.557

so that it is clear we must interpret the results of this approximate solution (unweighted means) with some caution.

The approximate solution using expected proportionate frequencies is slightly more complicated computationally, but not greatly so. A systematic method of performing the calculations is illustrated on page 244. Operating on the adjusted subclass totals and marginal totals, remembering that the numbers are not equal, we secure the following analysis:

VARIANCE	DEGREES OF FREEDOM	SUM OF SQUARES	MEAN SQUARE	F-RATIO
Among Schools	2	477.775	238.89	2.15
Among Grades	2	4,368.565	2,184.28	19.31
Interaction	4	275.226	68.81	<1
Among Subclasses	8	5,121.566	640.20	5.66
Within Subclasses	52	5,883.831	113.13	—
Total	60	11,005.397	—	—

Although these results do not differ materially from those secured for the previous approximate method (unweighted means), they do differ enough —see, for instance, the F-ratios Among Schools—to indicate that one assumption may well yield results substantially different from the other.

Neither solution being exact, and no exact solution being available, the researcher faced with an actual problem may find himself in something of

$P_{11} = \dfrac{7.57377}{6} = 1.26230$

$\sum_k X_{11k} = 147$

$P_{11}\sum_k X_{11k} = 185.558$

$\sum_k (X_{11k} - X_{11.})^2 = 533.500$

$P_{11}\sum_k (X_{11k} - X_{11.})^2 = 673.437$

$P_{21} = \dfrac{7.57377}{8} = 0.94672$

$\sum_k X_{21k} = 291$

$P_{21}\sum_k X_{21k} = 275.496$

$\sum_k (X_{21k} - X_{21.})^2 = 305.875$

$P_{21}\sum_k (X_{21k} - X_{21.})^2 = 289.578$

$P_{31} = \dfrac{6.85246}{8} = 0.85656$

$\sum_k X_{31k} = 317$

$P_{31}\sum_k X_{31k} = 271.530$

$\sum_k (X_{31k} - X_{31.})^2 = 1,231.875$

$P_{31}\sum_k (X_{31k} - X_{31.})^2 = 1,055.175$

732.584

$P_{12} = \dfrac{5.85246}{6} = 0.97541$

$\sum_k X_{12k} = 150$

$P_{12}\sum_k X_{12k} = 146.312$

$\sum_k (X_{12k} - X_{12.})^2 = 656.000$

$P_{12}\sum_k (X_{12k} - X_{12.})^2 = 639.869$

$P_{22} = \dfrac{5.85246}{6} = 0.97541$

$\sum_k X_{22k} = 212$

$P_{22}\sum_k X_{22k} = 206.787$

$\sum_k (X_{22k} - X_{22.})^2 = 363.333$

$P_{22}\sum_k (X_{22k} - X_{22.})^2 = 354.399$

$P_{32} = \dfrac{5.29508}{5} = 1.05902$

$\sum_k X_{32k} = 223$

$P_{32}\sum_k X_{32k} = 236.161$

$\sum_k (X_{32k} - X_{32.})^2 = 1,469.200$

$P_{32}\sum_k (X_{32k} - X_{32.})^2 = 1,555.912$

589.260

Adjusted Totals

$P_{13} = \dfrac{7.57377}{9} = 0.84153$

$\sum_k X_{13k} = 130$

$P_{13}\sum_k X_{13k} = 109.399$

$\sum_k (X_{13k} - X_{13.})^2 = 114.222$

$P_{13}\sum_k (X_{13k} - X_{13.})^2 = 96.121$

$P_{23} = \dfrac{7.57377}{7} = 1.08197$

$\sum_k X_{23k} = 210$

$P_{23}\sum_k X_{23k} = 227.214$

$\sum_k (X_{23k} - X_{23.})^2 = 830.000$

$P_{23}\sum_k (X_{23k} - X_{23.})^2 = 898.035$

$P_{33} = \dfrac{6.85246}{6} = 1.14208$

$\sum_k X_{33k} = 248$

$P_{33}\sum_k X_{33k} = 283.236$

$\sum_k (X_{33k} - X_{33.})^2 = 281.333$

$P_{33}\sum_k (X_{33k} - X_{33.})^2 = 321.305$

619.849

Adjusted Totals

441.269

1,409.427

709.497

1,542.012

790.927

2,932.392

Sum = 1,941.693

Sum of Squares of Adjusted Means = 66,927.660

a quandary. He may select one approximate solution or the other, or apply both, and the only guide he has is his knowledge of the situation underlying his data. It may happen that the inequalities in the subclass numbers are of little or no importance, as often happens in educational research, and in that event the approximate solution based on unweighted means (equal expected subclass frequencies) is indicated as the proper one to employ. If, on the other hand, the inequalities in the subclass numbers are an important and essential feature of the situation, it is clear that misleading results may be obtained if they are ignored. In some of these cases, but unfortunately not in all, the distribution of subclass frequencies will reveal something approaching proportionate numbers, and the approximate solution based on proportionate expected frequencies is indicated as appropriate. All that a researcher can do is reach what seems to him to be the best solution in the light of all the evidence at hand, apply the appropriate form of analysis, and interpret the results cautiously. This is an irritating feature of research in most social sciences, but it cannot be avoided. Unlike the situation in experiments in agriculture, the appearance of unequal and disproportionate subclass frequencies is a more or less normal event and cannot be summarily dismissed as a fault in the design of the experiment.

We have neither the space nor the time to investigate here all the possible combinations of models and significant or non-significant interactions. We leave this confounding of a well-laid confusion to the reader, trusting that if he has understood the principles and applications already set forth he will be able to find some sound path out of the morass.

Case 3: Three-way and More Complex Systems of Classification

It is relatively easy to design a very complex experiment; as an example of a rather common three-way classification, the school situations previously considered would normally include a third factor—the sex of the pupils. The results for these more complex designs are not very difficult to calculate provided that equal numbers are contained in the finest subclasses, although the calculations do become horribly complicated if unequal and disproportionate subclass numbers are involved. However, the interpretation of the results is seldom simple, unless Model I is assumed to be appropriate, since interactions of various kinds must of course occur and may or may not prove to be insignificant. For a three-way classification with factors B, C, and D, for instance, the basic formula for the sth observation in the ijkth subclass is,

$$X_{ijks} = A + B_i + C_j + D_k + I_{ij} + I_{ik} + I_{jk} + I_{ijk} + z_{ijks}$$

$$\begin{pmatrix} i = 1, 2, \ldots, q \\ j = 1, 2, \ldots, m \qquad s = 1, 2, \ldots, t \\ k = 1, 2, \ldots, n \end{pmatrix}$$

where the B's, C's, and D's represent the main effects, the double-subscript I's the first-order interactions of each factor with each of the others, and the triple-subscript I the second-order interaction among the three factors. As before, the z's are assumed to be a random variable normally distributed with zero mean and constant standard deviation σ. Students should observe that, if there is only one observation in each subclass, then the s-subscript disappears and the I_{ijk} becomes the new z_{ijk}—in short, the highest-order interaction then becomes the "residual" or "error" term in the analysis of variance table.

Naturally, with four interaction terms and three main-effect terms—each of which may be either significant or non-significant—the possible types of models that can be set up (involving fixed constants and/or random variables) are many in number. But the calculation of the entries for the analysis of variance table itself is not affected by the choice of model, only the interpretation of the results is affected. We will consider only the case of equal subclass numbers in the illustration that follows, since the general pattern for the calculations can be easily extended to more complex designs.‡‡ Also, we will not treat of the case where two or more of the main factors are wholly or partially *confounded* (where the design is such that the specific effect of each factor is not completely separated from, but is entangled with, that of one or more of the others). Readers who encounter such situations will find the discussion and illustrations given by Goulden most helpful.§§

We show in Table VIII.19 some of the data reported by Johnson and Tsao (*op. cit.*, 1945) arranged in a three-way classification (grade, sex, and scholastic group) with three observations in each subclass. The first step in the analysis is again the determination of the Among Subclasses and Within Subclasses sums of squares, in order to test the general null hypothesis, H_o, concerning the subclass means. For this analysis we secure the following results:

VARIANCE	DEGREES OF FREEDOM	SUM OF SQUARES	MEAN SQUARE	F-RATIO
Among Subclasses	17	1,062.78	62.52	6.24
Within Subclasses	36	360.70	10.02	—
Total	53	1,423.48	—	—

‡‡ For the derivation of the formulae, see P. O. Johnson and Fei Tsao, "Factorial Design in the Determination of Differential Limen Values," *Psychometrika*, IX, No. 2 (June, 1944), 107–44, and "Factorial Design and Covariance in the Study of Individual Educational Development."

§§ C. H. Goulden, *Methods of Statistical Analysis*, pp. 220–56.

TABLE VIII.19

EXAMPLE OF DATA FOR A THREE-WAY CLASSIFICATION

SCHOLASTIC GROUP	GRADE 10		GRADE 11		GRADE 12	
	Male	*Female*	*Male*	*Female*	*Male*	*Female*
Good	28	16	22	22	25	29
	22	21	21	22	24	29
	19	17	21	19	19	22
Average	22	18	25	19	21	21
	14	16	18	19	17	19
	14	14	13	16	17	17
Poor	18	9	17	17	16	13
	14	7	13	12	15	14
	9	7	12	12	12	9

Since the variation among subclasses is significant, as indicated by the value $F = 6.24$, at least one of the component effects (main or interaction) must be significant.‖‖

The simplest method to be followed systematically in the calculation of the above values and of those which follow is shown in Table VIII.20. The first entry in each cell is the sum, the second the sum of squares, the third the product of the sum and the mean, and the fourth the Within Subclass sum of squares about the mean of that subclass. The marginal totals are the sums and sums of squares, as indicated, and as a check the values in the lower right-hand corner set of cells should be calculated directly. Only one more subsidiary table is required for the complete analysis. Students will, with but little difficulty, be able to prepare a similar calculation-schema for other and more complex designs.

The general correction term for the whole set of 54 values, for the general mean, is

$$\frac{(944)^2}{54} = 16,502.52$$

and we obtain directly

Total sum of squares $= 17,926 - 16,502.52 = 1,423.48$

From the sum of the subclass products of mean $\times$ sum, we have

Among Subclasses sums of squares $= 17,565.30 - 16,502.52 = 1,062.78$

and adding the final entries in each subclass we secure

Within Subclasses sum of squares $= 360.70$

Now consider the sums shown in the right-hand margin of Table VIII. 20, each based on 9 original values, as follows:

‖‖ Students should apply Bartlett's test of homogeneity of variances to the subclass sums of squares about the means.

SCHOLASTIC GROUP	MALE	FEMALE	TOTAL
Good	201	197	398
Average	161	159	320
Poor	126	100	226
Total	488	456	944

Analyzing this directly as a 2×3 table of single observations per subclass, we have:

VARIANCE	DEGREES OF FREEDOM	SUM OF SQUARES	SUM OF SQUARES / 9
Between Sexes	1	170.57	18.95
Among Scholastic Groups	2	7,417.24	824.14
Interaction	2	177.43	19.71
Total	5	7,765.24	862.80

The final column gives the adjusted sums of squares, dividing by 9, which are comparable with the quantities calculated earlier.

TABLE VIII.20

METHOD OF CALCULATING ANALYSIS OF VARIANCE VALUES

SCHOLASTIC GROUP	GRADE 10		GRADE 11		GRADE 12		TOTAL	
	Male	Female	Male	Female	Male	Female	Male	Female
Good	69 1,629 1,587.00 42.00	54 986 972.00 14.00	64 1,366 1,365.33 0.67	63 1,329 1,323.00 6.00	68 1,562 1,541.33 20.67	80 2,166 2,133.33 32.67	201 4,557	197 4,481
							398 9,038	
Average	50 876 833.33 42.67	48 776 768.00 8.00	56 1,118 1,045.33 72.67	54 978 972.00 6.00	55 1,019 1,008.33 10.67	57 1,091 1,083.00 8.00	161 3,013	159 2,845
							320 5,858	
Poor	41 601 560.33 40.67	23 179 176.33 2.67	42 602 588.00 14.00	41 577 560.33 16.67	43 625 616.33 8.67	36 446 432.00 14.00	126 1,828	100 1,202
							226 3,030	
Total	160 3,106	125 1,941	162 3,086	158 2,884	166 3,206	173 3,703	488 9,398	456 8,528
	285 5,047		320 5,970		339 6,909		944 17,926	

Next, we set up the equivalent table for the final row of Table VIII.20, where the sums are again based on 9 original observations, as follows:

GRADE	MALE	FEMALE	TOTAL
10	160	125	285
11	162	158	320
12	166	173	339
Total	488	456	944

Again, analyzing this table as a 2×3 table of single observations per subclass, we have:

VARIANCE	DEGREES OF FREEDOM	SUM OF SQUARES	SUM OF SQUARES / 9
Between Sexes	1	170.57	18.95
Among Grades	2	750.24	83.36
Interaction	2	474.43	52.71
Total	5	1,395.24	155.02

where, as before, the adjusted sums of squares of the final column are secured by dividing by 9.

Finally, construct the 3×3 table for Grades and Scholastic Groups by combining adjacent Male and Female sums in Table VIII.20, each entry being based on 6 original values, to secure:

SCHOLASTIC GROUP	GRADE 10	GRADE 11	GRADE 12	TOTAL
Good	123	127	148	398
Average	98	110	112	320
Poor	64	83	79	226
Total	285	320	339	944

Analyzing this as a 3×3 table of single observations per subclass, we have

VARIANCE	DEGREES OF FREEDOM	SUM OF SQUARES	SUM OF SQUARES / 6
Among Grades	2	500.22	83.37
Among Scholastic Groups	2	4,944.89	824.15
Interaction	4	175.78	29.30
Total	8	5,620.89	936.82

Students will undoubtedly have observed that two adjusted sums of squares (for the main effects) in each table check with the corresponding values in the other tables.

Picking up the pieces and putting them together in one table, and obtaining the missing second-order interaction value by subtraction, we have the following:

VARIANCE	DEGREES OF FREEDOM	SUM OF SQUARES	MEAN SQUARE
Between Sexes	1	18.95	18.95
Among Grades	2	83.36	41.68
Among Scholastic Groups	2	824.14	412.07
Interactions	12	136.33	11.36
Sex × Grade	2	52.71	26.36
Sex × Scholastic Groups	2	19.71	9.86
Grade × Scholastic Groups	4	29.30	7.33
Sex × Grades × Scholastic Groups	4	34.61	8.65
Among Subclasses	17	1,062.78	62.52
Within Subclasses	36	360.70	10.02
Total	53	1,423.48	—

Considering the interactions as a group, with 12 degrees of freedom, it is clear that they do not contribute significantly to the variance and might well be combined with the Within Subclasses values. Actually, in any analysis of this kind it is convenient to calculate the first three entries directly from the original table, as follows:

$$\textit{Sexes:} \quad \frac{(488)^2}{27} + \frac{(456)^2}{27} - \frac{(944)^2}{54} = 18.96$$

$$\textit{Grades:} \quad \frac{(285)^2}{18} + \frac{(320)^2}{18} + \frac{(339)^2}{18} - \frac{(944)^2}{54} = 83.37$$

$$\textit{Scholastic Groups:} \quad \frac{(398)^2}{18} + \frac{(320)^2}{18} + \frac{(226)^2}{18} - \frac{(944)^2}{54} = 824.15$$

and secure the total for the interactions by subtracting the sum of these three (926.48) from the Among Subclasses sum of squares (1,062.78). Only if the total mean square for Interactions (11.36) is significantly greater than the Within Subclasses mean square (10.02) is it worth while to complete the analysis and identify the significant interaction terms. For this particular

example, in fact, very little is lost if the whole table of variances is reduced
to the following form:

VARIANCE	DEGREES OF FREEDOM	SUM OF SQUARES	MEAN SQUARE
Among Grades	2	83.36	41.68
Among Scholastic Groups	2	824.14	412.07
Residual	49	515.98	10.53
Total	53	1,423.48	—

The only significant factors, by any form of analysis, are the differences
among grades and among scholastic groups. With only 4 degrees of freedom out of the original 53, these two factors account for approximately 64
per cent of the total sum of squares.

In conclusion, we must point out that the manner in which the tests of
the hypotheses concerning the B's, C's, D's, and I's are to be made will be
determined by the particular model accepted as appropriate. Table VIII.
21 gives the expected mean square values for the two basic types, Model I
and Model II. No doubt readers will immediately spot the numerous—
and oft seductive—possibilities for Mixed Models. Perhaps a note of warning is not amiss at this point: researchers must not view the analysis of
variance tables for complex designs as a glorious opportunity to let their
imaginations run riot in devising possible models. Although there may be
in some cases an element of doubt, in the main the circumstances underlying the design and the experiment will determine whether the main factors
and their various interactions are to be considered as fixed constants or
random variables. For the data of Table VIII.19, for example, the circumstances were such that only the z_{ijk}'s could, strictly speaking, be considered
as random variables. Reference to the description of the experiment in the
original article (*Psychometrika*, X, No. 2, 135–36), indicates that all of the
main factors and their interactions must be considered as fixed constants:
the random selection of samples would do little more than make certain the
z's could be considered as random variables.

Under Model I, it is clear that the tests of the null hypotheses concerning the B's, C's, D's, and I's, will in each case be made by comparing
the corresponding mean square with the Within Subclasses mean square,
yielding a valid test with the F-ratio if the hypothesis to be tested is true
and leading properly to a rejection of the null hypothesis when it is in fact
false. This method of analysis and interpretation has been standard practice for years, and in fact has been used—improperly—in situations where
Model I is not strictly appropriate.

For a pure Model II situation, as we can see from the values for the

TABLE VIII.21

BASIC MODELS FOR A THREE-WAY CLASSIFICATION: EXPECTED MEAN SQUARES

VARIANCE	DEGREES OF FREEDOM	EXPECTED MEAN SQUARE	
		Model I	Model II
Factor B	$q-1$	$\sigma^2 + \dfrac{tmn}{q-1}\sum_i B_i^2$	$\sigma^2 + t\sigma_{BCD}^2 + tm\sigma_{BD}^2 + tn\sigma_{BC}^2 + tmn\sigma_B^2$
Factor C	$m-1$	$\sigma^2 + \dfrac{tqn}{m-1}\sum_j C_j^2$	$\sigma^2 + t\sigma_{BCD}^2 + tq\sigma_{CD}^2 + tn\sigma_{BC}^2 + tqn\sigma_C^2$
Factor D	$n-1$	$\sigma^2 + \dfrac{tqm}{n-1}\sum_k D_k^2$	$\sigma^2 + t\sigma_{BCD}^2 + tq\sigma_{CD}^2 + tm\sigma_{BD}^2 + tqm\sigma_D^2$
$B \times C$	$(q-1)(m-1)$	$\sigma^2 + \dfrac{tn}{(q-1)(m-1)}\sum_i\sum_j I_{ij}^2$	$\sigma^2 + t\sigma_{BCD}^2 + tn\sigma_{BC}^2$
$B \times D$	$(q-1)(n-1)$	$\sigma^2 + \dfrac{tm}{(q-1)(n-1)}\sum_i\sum_k I_{ik}^2$	$\sigma^2 + t\sigma_{BCD}^2 + tm\sigma_{BD}^2$
$C \times D$	$(m-1)(n-1)$	$\sigma^2 + \dfrac{tq}{(m-1)(n-1)}\sum_j\sum_k I_{jk}^2$	$\sigma^2 + t\sigma_{BCD}^2 + tq\sigma_{CD}^2$
$B \times C \times D$	$(q-1)(m-1)(n-1)$	$\sigma^2 + \dfrac{t}{(q-1)(m-1)(n-1)}\sum_i\sum_j\sum_k I_{ijk}^2$	$\sigma^2 + t\sigma_{BCD}^2$
Within Subclasses	$qmn(t-1)$	σ^2	σ^2

expected mean squares, only for the test of the null hypothesis concerning the $B \times C \times D$ interaction is the Within Subclasses mean square the proper denominator for the F-ratio. If the $B \times C \times D$ interaction is significant, the null hypothesis for each of the first-order interactions ($B \times C$, $B \times D$, and $C \times D$) may properly be tested by comparing the corresponding mean square with the $B \times C \times D$ interaction mean square. If, on the other hand, the $B \times C \times D$ interaction is not significant, then the sums of squares for $B \times C \times D$ and Within Subclasses sums of squares may be added to secure a new residual term, and the null hypothesis for each of the first-order interactions may be tested by comparing the corresponding mean square with that for the combined residual. When we come to tests of the null hypotheses concerning the B, C, and D factors themselves, however, no simple solution is possible unless some of the first-order interactions are non-significant. For example, to test the hypothesis $\sigma_B = 0$, we can use in the denominator the $B \times D$ interaction mean square only if $\sigma_{BC} = 0$. A general solution of this problem, yielding an approximation based on the F-ratio, has been given by Cochran, but not all the associated problems have been solved and no general exact test has as yet been devised.##

In conclusion, we emphasize that the complex designs yield data that may be analyzed (arithmetically) without too much difficulty—exactly for equal and for proportionate subclass numbers, and approximately for disproportionate subclass numbers—but that the interpretation of the results so obtained is frequently far from simple and under certain circumstances impossible of an exact solution. Much more work needs to be done in the field of complex designs, along two lines: first, to determine which models are appropriate under given sets of circumstances (or at least the preparation of some sort of guide that will enable the ordinary researcher to select an appropriate model for each of his practical problems); second, to pursue the search for exact tests (or satisfactory approximations thereto, if exact tests cannot be devised) of the several null hypotheses under the conditions imposed by Model II and the various types of Mixed Models. But this is not the place to pursue the subject: we must remain content for the moment with the provision for the student of a sound basic background of the principles and practices of the statistical method known as the analysis of variance.

EXERCISES

1. If the basic assumptions seem to you to be reasonably well satisfied, analyze the data of Question 4 of Chapter VII separately for boys and girls to determine if, within each sex, the level of home-condition has an effect on expressed interests. (Use the formulae and methods for the one-way classification analysis of variance.) State the null hypothesis and set of admissible alternative hypotheses

W. G. Cochran, "Testing a Linear Relation Among Variances."

for each case, and indicate the implications of the acceptance, and of the rejection, of the null hypothesis.

2. Analyze and interpret the data of Question 6 of Chapter VII.

3. Using the means of the subgroups as single observations, do the two-way classification analysis for the data of questions 4 and 5 of Chapter VII.

4. Carry out the complete analysis (two-way classification) for the data of Question 4 of Chapter VII. Do the boys and girls differ significantly on the interest scores for the several home-condition levels? Is the interaction between sex and level significant? What does such an interaction, if present, mean?

5. Over a period of two years, the following 5 physical measurements of each of 15 individuals were secured (at six-month intervals).

INDIVIDUAL	MEASUREMENT				
	1	2	3	4	5
1	14.9	16.2	19.6	22.2	25.4
2	15.5	15.5	19.4	24.4	26.8
3	15.2	18.1	18.1	24.6	29.1
4	14.3	17.1	17.6	25.3	24.8
5	14.5	15.4	18.4	22.0	23.7
6	14.9	18.6	18.6	25.0	28.7
7	15.6	17.9	18.4	25.3	26.8
8	15.0	17.3	18.2	23.1	23.2
9	15.4	18.0	18.8	22.6	28.3
10	14.6	19.1	19.1	22.3	27.2
11	14.4	16.6	18.7	23.8	24.8
12	14.5	17.8	18.6	23.7	26.7
13	14.8	19.7	18.5	22.8	28.6
14	14.9	17.5	18.2	23.9	25.8
15	14.2	18.4	19.8	25.9	26.7

After testing the associated assumptions, determine whether significant changes occurred over the period and whether or not the group of individuals was homogeneous with respect to this physical characteristic (two-way classification with one observation per cell).

6. Do two complete analyses of variance of the data of Question 5 of Chapter VII, using the approximate methods discussed in the text. Which of the approximations seems more reasonable for this situation? What would be the meaning of an interaction here, if such existed?

7. Analyze and interpret the set of data on page 255, using the calculation-schema set out in the text (values shown are weights of children).

8. Which of the differences among the age group means in Table VIII.3 may be considered significant and which may not?

Report on the several test procedures proposed for answering the above questions and select the one you regard as most appropriate. Read the following references:

David B. Duncan, "Multiple Range and Multiple F Tests," *Biometrics*, XI (1953), 1–42.

Clyde Y. Cramer, "Extensions of Multiple Range Tests to Group Means with Unequal Number of Replications," *Biometrics*, XII (1956), 307–10. See also p. 305 Chapter X.

DATA FOR QUESTION 7

GRADE	OCCUPATION OF FATHER					
	Professional		Clerical		Laborer	
	Boys	Girls	Boys	Girls	Boys	Girls
3	21.0	26.2	25.3	26.1	27.3	31.0
	23.1	21.4	29.6	26.0	28.0	20.9
	22.3	26.7	28.7	21.8	26.2	26.0
	31.3	24.8	27.1	30.4	31.2	29.2
	24.4	22.7	27.3	28.2	28.2	25.6
4	22.0	26.1	31.5	29.3	32.5	28.5
	25.7	27.7	27.1	30.2	26.4	32.3
	33.2	27.1	31.4	26.1	26.9	28.0
	26.6	29.2	32.4	23.9	31.6	26.8
	27.5	21.2	30.6	30.3	31.0	25.3
5	28.1	29.1	36.6	28.1	25.8	37.3
	39.0	41.2	36.0	21.5	33.3	25.0
	30.7	33.7	32.9	39.6	29.4	29.9
	29.9	29.5	31.1	40.3	21.7	30.7
	31.6	33.0	42.6	24.6	35.5	26.6

CHAPTER IX

Non-Parametric Tests of Statistical Hypotheses

Most of the theory of statistical inference has been developed for samples known or assumed to have originated from populations having normal, binomial, multinomial, and other specified forms of distribution. Here the distribution function depends on one or more population parameters. The values of the parameters generally being unknown, one part of statistical inference—the theory of statistical estimation—is concerned with problems of estimating values of the unknown parameters from quantities calculated for random samples drawn or assumed to be drawn from a specified population.* The other fundamental problem of statistical inference is that of testing statistical hypotheses, i.e. of determining from the sample results whether or not a population parameter has some designated value or if certain functional relations exist among a number of parameters. This part of statistical inference is referred to as the parametric case. Many statistical procedures have been devised in order to provide test statistics and estimation statistics for the parametric case. For their efficient use, the conditions of normality of distribution and stability of variance are usually required.

There are many situations encountered where it is not possible to specify the functional form of the population distribution. The continuity of the accumulative distribution function may often be the only assumption that can reasonably be accepted. Even though this is still a somewhat restrictive assumption, it is much less restrictive than the additional ones required by the parametric statistics. It is appropriate to speak of tests of hypotheses developed for problems where it is unnecessary or impossible to specify the form of population as non-parametric or distribution-free tests.

The beginnings of non-parametric theory go back to the nineteenth century, but the most famous test was the first goodness-of-fit test, chi-square, introduced by Karl Pearson in 1900† and applied to test the fit of a theoretical distribution to observations and later extended to the problem

* Statistical estimation is discussed in Chapter X.

† Karl Pearson, "On the Criterion That a Given System of Deviations from the Probable in the Case of a Correlated System of Variables Is Such That Arises from Random Sampling," *Philosophical Magazine*, L (1900), 157–75.

of two samples in 1911.‡ However, the true beginning of the non-parametric tests as we now know them was the study by Hotelling and Pabst, in 1936, in developing the test of independence based on the rank-correlation coefficient.§

While there is now a rather extensive literature on non-parametric statistics, there does not appear to be any generally accepted definition of the field.|| Hence it is not always easy to indicate the techniques, problems, and theories that are definitely non-parametric. We shall make no attempt at an exhaustive discussion on this subject since we wish only to acquaint the reader with some of the basic theory and illustrate the uses of several non-parametric tests.

As has already been indicated there are both theoretical and practical motives for the increasing study of non-parametric problems. From a theoretical standpoint, it is important to discover procedures or methods of statistical inference which have minimum restrictions imposed by the underlying assumptions. From the practical point of view it is almost always desirable to the practitioner to make statistical operations simple and widely applicable. Let us first point out, however, that certain disadvantages may attend such uses as compared to the parametric methods, at least when the latter may be applied to the same situations.

The question may be asked: Can conclusions be drawn directly from the observations without formulating assumptions with respect to the mathematical form of the distribution? The answer is "yes," although generally speaking, conclusions drawn from distribution-free methods are weaker than those based on a specified distribution.

What course is open to the investigator, for instance, when non-normality of the population distribution is suspected (a problem frequently encountered)? The investigator may proceed to treat the data as though the parent population were in fact normal, and consider the test he applies as approximate. In many cases the approximation may be good, especially when dealing with means from large samples or where empirical evidence may be available to indicate the test applied may be quite insensitive to the assumption of normality. Moreover, the amount of information elicited by the parametric test may be greater even when the conditions are not exactly satisfied than that elicited by the less efficient non-parametric test. A second possibility is a transformation of the original data to a

‡ Karl Pearson, "On the Probability That Two Independent Distributions of Frequency Are Really Samples from the Same Population," *Biometrika*, VIII (1911), 250–54.

§ Harold Hotelling and Margaret R. Pabst, "Rank Correlation and Tests of Significance Involving No Assumption of Normality," *Annals of Mathematical Statistics*, VII (1936), 29–43.

|| Richard Savage, "Bibliography of Non-parametric Statistics and Related Topics," *Journal of the American Statistical Association*, XLVIII (1953), 844–906.

form that will satisfy the condition of normality. A third course may be that of developing a new theory for the particular distribution—a course that led, for example, to the discovery of the Poisson distribution. The fourth alternative, and the one with which this chapter is almost entirely concerned, is that provided by non-parametric tests which make few or no assumptions with respect to the form of distribution taken by the parent population. It should be noted, however, that the power and power efficiency of a statistical test cannot be determined unless some definite functional form for the underlying distribution is specified. The choice of the best non-parametric test is made intuitively in most cases. For the situation where the normal assumption holds, on the other hand, it is possible to compare directly the power efficiency of the non-parametric test with that of the corresponding normal distribution test.

Experimenters, particularly those working in fields not widely investigated, rather frequently either have no knowledge of the form of distribution with which they are working or do not have enough information to specify a normalizing function. The treatment of distribution-free methods in such cases is often based on ordered observations or *order statistics*. By order statistics is meant the arrangement of sample values in a sequence from least to highest in value. Before proceeding to the technical applications we shall describe briefly certain results in the consideration of sampling theory and functions of order statistics.

In order statistics no more restrictive assumption is required than that the cumulative distribution function of the population is continuous. The methods are applicable to both continuous and discontinuous variates though some adjustment is required in the latter case.#

The cumulative distribution function is represented by a curve, the cumulative distribution curve $[y = P(X)]$, which never decreases as it extends from 0 to 1. The ordinate of this curve gives the *area* to the left of the corresponding ordinate of the distribution curve. The graphical representations for empirical distributions, called the histogram and the cumulative frequency curve, correspond to the distribution curve and the cumulative distribution curve, respectively. The distribution of the area under the distribution (density) function between any two ordered observations is independent of the form of the distribution function. The expected area under the population density function $[f(x)]$ between two successive observations is $\dfrac{1}{n+1}$. On the average, therefore, the n ordered observations divide the area under $f(x)$ into $n + 1$ equal parts, each part having an area of $\dfrac{1}{(n+1)}$.

The cumulative distribution function (c.d.f.) of the variable X is the probability that the variable (stochastic) is less than or equal to the real number X_a, i.e., $P(X \leqq X_a) = P(X_a)$.

In the parametric case the population mean and standard deviation were used mainly as measures of position and dispersion. Other measures are used in the non-parametric case. The central position of the population is defined to be the median. Other percentage points of frequent use are the quartiles, deciles, and centiles. The distances between certain centile points are used as measures of dispersion. Thus the distance between the 75th and 25th centiles is called the interquartile range. The 90 per cent range or the $33\frac{1}{3}$ per cent range are also used.

THE TWO-SAMPLE PROBLEM

We may state the two-sample problem as follows. Let us begin with two samples A and B randomly and independently drawn. Sample A, consisting of n independent variates $X_1, X_2, \ldots, X_n$, has probability density function, p.d.f. $= f(x)$, and cumulative density function, c.d.f. $= F(x)$. Sample B, made up of m independent variates $Y_1, Y_2, \ldots, Y_m$ has p.d.f. $= g(y)$ and c.d.f. $= G(Y)$. The elements of the two samples are combined and arranged in rank order from lowest to highest values, such that $Z_1 < Z_2 < \ldots < Z_{m+n}$ where the variates $Z_1, Z_2, \ldots, Z_{m+n}$ represent the n values of the X's and the m values of the Y's from samples A and B.

The hypothesis under test is that the two populations have the same distribution: $f(x) = g(y)$. Various test-statistics are appropriate for testing the hypothesis. They fall into three main groups: those based on (1) signs of differences, (2) ranks, and (3) the randomization method.

The non-parametric tests based on signs are applicable to either matched or unmatched samples. A common application is to the type of experiment where the same individuals are measured previous and subsequent to some treatment or stimulus. The most efficient parametric test is the t-test, but the sign test is very easy to apply and uses only the information available in the signs of differences of observations. Its efficiency would be around 62 to 70 per cent depending upon the size of sample. This would mean that the sign test would require 100 paired observations to get the same information as 62 observations when the t-test is used; likewise for 70 per cent efficiency the observations would be 100 and 70, respectively. A unique use of the sign test is where the experimental data are qualitative, and therefore they cannot be measured but merely compared. There are situations also where even if measurements are made, the differences may be small but mostly in the same direction. Here the sign test would be useful as a supplementary test.

When the non-parametric tests are based on ranks, the numerical value of the observation is replaced by its rank, thereby making it independent of its p.d.f. There are situations, also, where only ranks of the observations are available. Analysis is made of the ranks without the assumption of normality required in the parametric case. The continuity assumption implies that $P(X = X_o) = 0$, and hence it is assumed that ties in rank do not occur. In practice when ties do occur, it is usual to give all the tied ranks the mean of the ranks tied for. The validity of the test is little affected if only a few ties occur.

R. A. Fisher introduced the randomization method for constructing statistical tests.** These tests are based on the principle that $n!$ (factorial n) different possible orders of n given sample values from a continuous population are equally likely when the sampling is random. Statistically stated, the condition for a sample of n observations, $X_1, X_2, \ldots, X_n$ from a population with distribution function $P(X)$ is said to be a random sample from that population if

$$P(X_1, X_2, \ldots, X_n) = P(X_1)P(X_2) \ldots, P(X_n) \ldots$$

The value of $P(X_1, X_2, \ldots, X_n)$ is independent of the permutations of the X's when this condition is satisfied. Except for very small samples, the calculations leading to the determination of whether or not an observed value of the sample point falls in a specified critical region becomes exceedingly tedious.

Tests Based on Signs of Differences

The Sign Test††

Let A and B denote two different treatments with n pairs of observations x_i and y_i. Note the sign of $d_i = x_i - y_i$. If the variables are not measurable but merely comparable, then d_i is taken as positive if A is better than B and negative when A is worse than B. If r denotes the number of times the less frequent sign occurs in the sequence $d_i (i = 1, 2, \ldots, n)$, under the hypothesis that each difference has a p.d.f. with median equal to zero, r will then be distributed according to the binomial $\left(\frac{1}{2} + \frac{1}{2}\right)^n$. It should be noted that it is not essential that each difference has the same p.d.f., an assumption necessary for the t-test, but every pair may be collected under different circumstances; thus only the sign test can be used in such a situation.

Dixon and Mood†† have tabled r for $n \leq 100$ at the 1, 5, 10, and 25 per cent points for two-tailed tests. When $n > 100$, the usual normal approximation to the binomial may be used.

We shall illustrate the use of the sign test by applying it to the results of an experiment designed to compare the outcomes of teaching high school algebra two periods per day for one semester with those for one period per day for two semesters. The individuals were paired on I.Q.'s and scores on a mathematics pretest. Treatment was assigned at random

** R. A. Fisher, *The Design of Experiments* (First edition; London: Oliver and Boyd, 1935), Section 21.

†† W. J. Dixon and A. M. Mood, "The Statistical Sign Test," *Journal of the American Statistical Association*, XLI (1946), 557–66.

to members of the pairs. A sample of 15 pairs of students had the following scores on the algebra test:

PAIR NUMBER	CONTROL y_i	EXPERIMENTAL x_i	$d_i = x_i - y_i$
1	34	33	−1
2	28	36	8
3	29	50	21
4	45	41	−4
5	26	37	11
6	27	41	14
7	24	39	15
8	15	21	6
9	15	20	5
10	27	37	10
11	23	21	−2
12	31	18	−13
13	20	29	9
14	35	38	3
15	20	27	7

If we assume for the pairs of observations x_i and y_i, that $f(x)$ and $g(y)$ are continuous, the hypothesis to be tested, H_o, is that the d_i's are distributed with a p.d.f. with median zero. The alternative hypothesis, H_1, is that the median is not zero. From Column 4, $d_i = x_i - y_i$, it is noted that the signs of d_i are: $- + + - + + + + + + - - + + +$, and $r = 4$ (number of minus signs).

The 5 per cent level of the two-tailed test can be obtained from the formula:‡‡

$[(N-1)/2] - (0.98)\sqrt{N+1}$, the integral part of which gives the level, where N is the number of pairs in the sample without zero differences.

For $N = 15$: $[(15-1)/2] - (0.98)\sqrt{16} = 7 - 0.98\ (4) = 3.08$
Accordingly, we reject the null hypothesis at the 5 per cent level if there are 3 or fewer plus (or minus) signs among the 15 differences. Since we found 4 differences that were negative, we accept the null hypothesis, H_o.

We could also calculate directly the probability of obtaining a result as extreme or even more than that observed, using the binomial expansion. Thus,

$$P(r \leq 4) = \left(\frac{1}{2}\right)^{15} + 15 \left(\frac{1}{2}\right)^{14} \left(\frac{1}{2}\right) + \frac{15.14}{2} \left(\frac{1}{2}\right)^{13} \left(\frac{1}{2}\right)^{2}$$

$$+ \frac{15.14.13}{(1)(2)(3)} \left(\frac{1}{2}\right)^{12} \left(\frac{1}{2}\right)^{3} + 15.14.13.12 \left(\frac{1}{2}\right)^{11} \left(\frac{1}{2}\right)^{4}$$

$$= \left(\frac{1}{2}\right)^{15} + (15) \left(\frac{1}{2}\right)^{15} + 105 \left(\frac{1}{2}\right)^{15} + 455 \left(\frac{1}{2}\right)^{15} + 1{,}365 \left(\frac{1}{2}\right)^{15}$$

$$= 0.0592$$

‡‡ W. J. Dixon and F. J. Massey, Jr., *Introduction to Statistical Analysis* (New York: McGraw-Hill Book Company, 1951).

At the 5 per cent level, therefore, we would accept the null hypothesis.

The Median Test

A second test based on signs is given by Mood§§ to test the null hypothesis $f(x) = g(y)$ against the alternative that $f(x) = g(y + a)$. It is not necessary in this case that the variates occur in pairs, as in the sign test, and they may in fact occur in two independent samples of size n and m. To test the null hypothesis, the procedure is to find the median, $\bar{Z}$, of the combined sample of $m + n$ variates and then count the number of x's, n_1, and the number of y's, m_1, which exceed $\bar{Z}$. Under the null hypothesis:

$E(m_1) = m/2, E(n_1) = n/2$ and the exact distribution of m_1 and n_1 is

$$g(m_1, n_1) = \frac{\binom{m}{m_1}\binom{n}{n_1}}{\binom{m+n}{a}}$$

where $a = (m + n + 1)/2$ if $m + n$ is odd and
$a = (m + n)/2$ if $m + n$ is even.

The function $g(m_1, n_1)$ is the distribution of the cell frequencies in a 2×2 contingency table with fixed marginal totals when independence exists between the classifications. Thus the χ^2-distribution with 1 degree of freedom can be used as a fairly good approximation when m and n are large. When $m \leq n \leq 10$ the distribution can be evaluated directly to obtain the exact probabilities.

The entries in the contingency table are:

	SAMPLE A	SAMPLE B
Above median	n_1	m_1
Below median	$n - n_1$	$m - m_1$

and $\chi^2 = \dfrac{[m_1(n - n_1) - n_1(m - m_1)]^2(m + n)}{(m)(n)(m_1 + n_1)(m + n - m_1 - n_1)}$

which is approximately distributed as χ^2 with 1 degree of freedom.

This test is insensitive to differences in the shape of the distribution, and is sensitive merely to the location of the median. Ties are important only when at the median of the combined distribution. An arbitrary rule, when $m + n$ is odd is to place the actual median value in the class less than the median.

§§ A. M. Mood, *Introduction to the Theory of Statistics*, p. 394.

We shall apply the median test to the data for two random samples of students in two different rooms of a public high school on whom I.Q. measures were available, to test the null hypothesis: $f(x) = g(y)$ against the alternative that $f(x) = g(y + a)$.

The intelligence quotients were:

SAMPLE A	SAMPLE B	SAMPLE A AND B IN ORDER OF MAGNITUDE
99	96	139
139	89	135
93	117	128
120	100	123
103	110	121
106	98	120
115	105	118
108	92	117
107	86	115
121	128	110
91		108
118		107
135		106
123		105
101		103
		101
		100
		99
		98
		96
		93
		92
		91
		89
		86

$\bar{Z} = 106, n = 15, m = 10$ $n_1 = 9, m_1 = 3$

	SAMPLE A	SAMPLE B	TOTAL
Above Median $\bar{Z}$	9	3	12
Below Median $\bar{Z}$	6	7	13
Total	15	10	25

$$\chi^2 = \frac{(63 - 18)^2\, 25}{(12)(13)(10)(15)} = \frac{50,625}{23,400} = 2.17$$

Referring to the χ^2-distribution, $P(\chi^2 \geqslant 2.7) > 0.05$. We would, therefore, accept the null hypothesis and conclude that $f(x) = g(y)$, or that the two samples come from the same population with respect to I.Q.'s.

Tests Based on Ranks

Wilcoxon T-test

Perhaps the two best known rank order tests in current use for testing whether two random samples come from the same population are the Wilcoxon T-test‖‖ and the Mann and Whitney U-test.## These two tests are designed to test the null hypothesis that the sample $(x_1, \ldots, x_m)$ comes from the same population as the sample $(y_1, \ldots, y_n)$ with c.d.f. $F(\xi)$, against the alternative that the c.d.f., $G(\xi)$, of $(y_1, \ldots, y_n)$ has the relation $F(\xi) > G(\xi)$. The relation between U and T is given by

$$U = mn + 1/2\,(n)(n + 1) - T$$

When the observations are given in pairs to apply the T-test, we calculate $d_i = x_i - y_i$ $(i = 1, \ldots, n)$ where x_i and y_i are the ith paired observations. We then rank the $|\,d_i\,|$ from highest to lowest in value and assign a positive or negative sign to each rank according to d_i being positive or negative. Then calculate T, which is the sum of the positive or negative ranks, whichever is less. The sum of the positive ranks should, of course, equal the sum of the negative ranks under the null hypothesis. Wilcoxon has prepared tables giving the smallest sum of the ranks for 7 through 16 replicates required for significance. It is observed that this test takes into account both sign and magnitude of differences. It may be expected, therefore, to be more powerful than the simple sign test. A study of the power of this test, or of the Mann-Whitney test, indicates that it is the most powerful of the non-parametric tests now available for detecting differences in location.

We shall apply this test to the same experimental results to which we applied the sign test on page 260, that is, to the comparison of test scores for the control and experimental group on a unit in high school algebra. We wish to test the hypothesis $f(x) = g(y)$ against the alternative that the c.d.f. $F(X) > G(Y)$. The data are given on page 265.

$T = \Sigma$ negative ranks $= -19$, and $P(T \leqq 19) < 0.02$, as found in Wilcoxon's table of the exact distribution of T.

We would reject the hypothesis and therefore conclude that $f(x) \neq g(y)$. We accept the alternative and conclude that the achievement of the experimental group is significantly larger than that of the control. Students should note how the additional information gained from ranking the differences has led to the rejection of the null hypothesis.

‖‖ Frank Wilcoxon, "Individual Comparison by Ranking Methods," *Biometrics Bulletin*, I (1945), 80–83.

H. B. Mann and D. R. Whitney, "On a Test Whether One of Two Random Variables Is Stochastically Larger Than the Other," *Annals of Mathematical Statistics*, XVIII (1947), 50–60.

EXPERIMENTAL GROUP	CONTROL GROUP	d_i	RANK OF $\pm \mid d_i \mid$
33	34	−1	−1
21	23	−2	−2
38	35	3	3
41	45	−4	−4
20	15	5	5
21	15	6	6
27	20	7	7
36	28	8	8
29	20	9	9
37	27	10	10
37	26	11	11
18	31	−13	−12
41	27	14	13
39	24	15	14
50	29	21	15

Approximate significance levels for the lower rank total may be obtained from the following formulae:

Five per cent level for lower rank total $= \dfrac{N^2 - 7N + 10}{5}$

which, for our problem, becomes $\dfrac{(15)^2 - 7(15) + 10}{5} = 26$

One per cent level for lower rank total $= \dfrac{11N^2}{60} - 2N + 5$

and, again, for our problem, this equals $\dfrac{11(15)^2}{60} - 2(15) + 5 = 16.28$

Marshall Test

The Marshall test[***] is a large sample, non-parametric test applied to group data. The basis of the test may be explained as follows. Let x and y be two random variables with continuous distribution functions, c.d.f.'s, $F(X)$ and $G(Y)$, respectively. A statistic S calculated from the sum of differences, at selected points, of the two sample c.d.f.'s is used to test the hypothesis $H_o : F(a) = G(a)$ for every a, against the alternative $H_1 : F(a) > G(a)$, or that x is stochastically larger than y.

It should be noted that the purpose of this test is the same as that of the Mann-Whitney test previously mentioned. The application of the Mann-Whitney test is very laborious for moderate or large samples, and the Marshall test considerably simplifies the calculations. It may also be pointed out that this test is less sensitive to ties in ranks. Dealing

[***] Andrew W. Marshall, "A Large Sample Test of the Hypothesis That One of Two Random Variables Is Stochastically Larger Than the Other," *Journal of the American Statistical Association*, XLVI (1951), 366–74.

TABLE IX.1

Basic Calculations for the Marshall Test Applied to Chemistry Scores for High School Students Going and Not Going to College

CHEMISTRY FINAL SCORES	$f = +$'s (going to college) (1)	$f = 0$'s (not going to college) (2)	x_i Cum. + (3)	y_i Cum. 0 (4)	Cum. + and 0 (5)	$\hat{p}_i$ [(5) ÷ 505] (6)	q_i (1 − $\hat{p}_i$) (7)	$\sum\limits_{K=i+1}^{8} q_K$ (8)
73.5-above	16	5	220	285	505	.9584	.0416	.0416
67.5-73.5	30	13	204	280	484	.8733	.1267	.1683
61.5-67.5	31	16	174	267	441	.7802	.2198	.3881
55.5-61.5	29	34	143	251	394	.6554	.3446	.7327
49.5-55.5	33	43	114	217	331	.5050	.4950	1.2277
43.5-49.5	36	46	81	174	255	.3426	.6574	1.8851
37.5-43.5	19	43	45	128	173	.2198	.7802	2.6653
31.5-37.5	15	35	26	85	111	.1208	.8792	
0 -31.5	11	50	11	50	61			
Total	$n = 220$	$m = 285$	1,018	1,737				

with large samples, the test is of particular value in analytical surveys. A preliminary report of the S-test for a special case has given a power efficiency between 0.64 and 0.94 varying with the number of class intervals used, the larger efficiency being reported for 10 class intervals.

We shall illustrate the application of this test to testing the hypothesis that the continuous cumulative distribution function of test scores on a chemistry test is the same for those senior high school students (1) who plan to attend college as for those (2) who do not plan to go to college. The alternative hypothesis is that the scores for (1) are greater than those for (2). The data were collected by Anderson (1949) in an investigation based on 56 schools chosen at random from the total number of high schools in the state of Minnesota offering chemistry.

The distribution of scores and the calculations involved for obtaining the S statistic are given in Table IX.1.

We have classified the total of 505 students into those going to college ($f = +$'s in Column 1; $n = 220$) and those not going to college ($f = 0$'s in Column 2; $m = 285$). The scores are grouped into 9 class intervals.

We secure first the test statistic S defined as:

$$S = \sum_{i=1}^{8} Z_i = \sum \left(\frac{x_i}{n} - \frac{y_i}{m} \right)$$

$$= \frac{\Sigma x_i}{220} - \frac{\Sigma y_i}{285}$$

$$= \frac{1{,}018}{220} - \frac{1{,}737}{285}$$

$$= -1.4675$$

The variance of S is:

$$\sigma_S^2 = \left(\frac{1}{n} + \frac{1}{m} \right) \left[\sum_{i=1}^{8} \hat{p}_i \hat{q}_i + 2 \sum_{i=1}^{7} \sum_{K=i+1}^{8} \hat{p}_i \hat{q}_K \right]$$

where $\dfrac{1}{n} + \dfrac{1}{m} = \dfrac{1}{220} + \dfrac{1}{285}$

$$= 0.00804$$

$$\sum_{i=1}^{8} \hat{p}_i \hat{q}_i = \sum_{i=1}^{8} \hat{p}_i (1 - \hat{p}_i) = \sum_{i=1}^{8} \hat{p}_i - \sum_{i=1}^{8} \hat{p}_i^2$$

$$= 4.4555 - 3.1547$$

$$= 1.3008$$

$$\sum_{i=1}^{7} \sum_{K=i+1}^{8} \hat{p}_i \hat{q}_K = 1.9489$$

and

$$\sigma_S^2 = (0.00804)[1.3008 + 2(1.9489)]$$
$$= 0.041797$$
$$\sigma_S = 0.2044$$
$$X = S/\sigma_S = \frac{-1.4675}{0.2044}$$
$$= -7.18$$

Assuming that X is a normal deviate of zero mean and unit standard deviation, $P(X < -7.18)$ is very small and, therefore, H_o is rejected. The variable x (scores of those going to college) is stochastically larger than the variable y (not going to college).

Test Based on Randomization Principle

The procedure to be used in applying the randomization test was laid down first by R. A. Fisher in the first edition of *The Design of Experiments* (1935). The data to which the test was applied were collected by Darwin in his study of cross- and self-pollinated plants. Fisher states (p. 52) that "it seems to have escaped recognition that the physical act of randomization, which, as has been shown, is necessary for the validity of any test of significance affords the means, in respect of any particular body of data, of examining the wider hypothesis in which no normality of distribution is implied." There were two samples of 15 observations each, with an observed difference between the totals of 314. Fisher reports the calculations showing that in just 1,726 of the 2^{15} possible partitions of the 15 pairs of observations into two paired samples of 15, a difference as large as or larger than 314 would be obtained. This gave a significance level of 5.255 per cent. This probability may be compared with a probability of 5.028 given by the t-test when adjusted for discontinuity.

Randomization tests are applicable in a wide variety of situations but, as indicated, the calculations are very laborious except for small samples.

Pitman W-test

Pitman††† has treated the two-sample problem more generally and we shall illustrate the application of his W-test. Let $X_1, X_2, \ldots, X_n$ be a random sample of n variates and $Y_1, Y_2, \ldots, Y_m$ an independent sample of m variates from populations with continuous c.d.f.'s and with means $\bar{X}$ and $\bar{Y}$, respectively. These two samples represent only one of the $(m + n)! \big/ {m!n!}$ possible separations of all the $m + n$ variates into two groups of sizes m and n that make up the pooled sample.

††† J. G. Pitman, "Significance Tests Which May Be Applied to Samples from Any Population," *Journal of the Royal Statistical Society* (B), IV (1937), 119–30.

We specify the spread of the separation as $|\bar{X} - \bar{Y}|$, but since $n\bar{X} + m\bar{Y} = (m + n)\bar{Z}$, where $\bar{Z}$ is the mean of the combined samples, the spread is also equal to

$$\frac{(m + n)\,|\,\bar{X} - \bar{Z}\,|}{m} = \frac{(m + n)\,|\,\Sigma X - n\bar{Z}\,|}{mn}$$

Since each separation is equally likely under the hypothesis $f(x) = g(y)$, each value of the spread associated with the possible individual separations has a probability equal to $1\Big/\binom{m + n}{n}$. Significance of the sample value can be determined by setting up a rejection region obtained by calculating the $k = \alpha\binom{m + n}{n}$ largest values of $|\bar{X} - \bar{Y}|$ or $|\Sigma X - n\bar{Z}|$, and noting if the sample value is one of the extreme values. Pitman has shown that the t-test is a good approximation if the sample size is at least moderately large and the distribution not too skewed.

We take as an example to which to apply the W-test, two samples taken at random from the results of an experiment dealing with the sensitivities of men and women in lifting weights changing at a constant rate. One sample gives the difference-limen values in grams for four men; the other, for five women. The values are:

F: 3.1, 3.9, 9.6, 11.2, 18.5
M: 4.5, 13.4, 14.0, 24.2

If these are two independent random samples of size m and n, with continuous density functions $f(x)$ and $g(y)$, then the hypothesis to be tested is $H_o : f(x) = g(y)$.

We calculate $n\bar{Z} = 45.6$, and the samples which give the largest separations are:

				ΣX	$\Sigma X - 45.6$
24.2	14.0	13.4	18.5	70.1	24.5
24.2	18.5	14.0	11.2	67.9	22.3
24.2	18.5	14.0	9.6	66.3	20.7
24.2	14.0	13.4	11.2	62.8	17.2
24.2	18.5	14.0	4.5	61.2	15.6
24.2	14.0	13.4	9.6	61.2	15.6
24.2	18.5	14.0	3.9	60.6	15.0
Our sample: 24.2	14.0	13.4	4.5	56.1	10.5

We accept the hypothesis that $f(x) = g(y)$, since our sample is not among the $0.05\binom{9}{4} \geqslant 6$ possible samples which make the separation the largest. We may say that there is no significant difference between the sensitivities of men and women in lifting weights increasing at a constant rate in the populations sampled.

THE k-SAMPLE PROBLEM

The k-sample problem deals with the question as to whether or not several samples could be regarded as having come from the same parent population. When the assumptions underlying the technique of the analysis of variance are warranted, this problem is solved most efficiently by this technique.‡‡‡ However, these assumptions are not a requisite condition for the non-parametric case, the continuity of the p.d.f.'s usually being the only assumption made.

The H-test

Kruskal and Wallis§§§ extended Wilcoxon's two-sample test to include k samples and adopted the analysis of variance with a single criterion of classification for use on ranked data. Given k samples or levels of a factor, it is desired to test the null hypothesis that the samples come from identical continuous populations. As with many non-parametric tests, however, little is known about the power of the test.

Let the total number of observations be $N = \sum_{i=1}^{k} n_i$. The N observations are ranked together from highest to lowest and the sum of the ranks $R_i (i = 1, 2, \ldots, k)$ computed for each of the samples. If no ties in rank occur, the statistic used to test the hypothesis that $f_1(X_1) = \ldots = f_k(X_k)$ is:

$$H = \frac{12}{N(N+1)} \sum_{i=1}^{k} \frac{R_i^2}{n_i} - 3(N+1)$$

For $n_i < 5$ and $k = 2, 3$, the significance values have been calculated and tabled. If all the n_i are large, H is distributed approximately as χ^2 with $k - 1$ degrees of freedom.

Where ties in rank occur H_t must be calculated instead of H, where

$$H_t = H(N^2 - N) \Big/ (N^2 - N - \Sigma T)$$

where $T = t^3 - t$ for each group of ties with t the number of tied observations in the group. The summation of T is over all groups of ties. Adjustments for continuity should be made in the case where the n_i's are small.

We shall apply the H-test to the null hypothesis that the three random samples of sex differences in cephalic index of three different races come from identical continuous populations. The basic data are given in Table IX.2.

‡‡‡ For the assumptions, see page 193 and also Chapter VIII.
§§§ W. H. Kruskal and W. A. Wallis, "Use of Ranks in One-Criterion Variance Analysis," *Journal of the American Statistical Association*, XLVII (1952), 583–621.

TABLE IX.2

Sex Differences in Cephalic Index with Head Length
Constant of Samples of Three Different Races
(6–19 Years of Age) — Japanese, Hawaiian, Pueblo

	J		H		P	
	Diff.	Rank	Diff.	Rank	Diff.	Rank
	4.4	33	2.9	26	1.6	13.5
	2.2	22	1.0	6.5	0.3	2
	3.7	32	1.2	9	2.0	18
	2.2	22	1.4	11.5	0.2	1
	3.6	31	2.0	18	1.9	16
	2.4	24	2.6	25	2.1	20
	2.2	22	1.0	6.5	0.6	4
	1.8	15	1.4	11.5	0.8	5
	2.0	18	1.1	8	1.3	10
	3.0	27	3.1	28	0.4	3
	1.6	13.5				
	3.2	29.5				
	3.2	29.5				*Total*
n	13		10		10	33
R	318.5		150.0		92.5	561
R^2/n	7,803.25		2,250.0		855.625	10,908.875

$$\Sigma n = N = 33 \qquad \Sigma R = \frac{(N)(N+1)}{2} = 561$$

$$H = \frac{12}{N(N+1)} \sum_{i=1}^{k} \frac{R_i^2}{n_i} - 3(N+1)$$

$$= \frac{12 \times 10,908.875}{33 \times 34} - 3(34) = 14.68$$

without mean-rank adjustment.

The adjustment for mean ranks is made as follows:

Group:	3.2	2.2	2.0	1.6	1.4	1.0
t	2	3	3	2	2	2
T	6	24	24	6	6	6

$$\Sigma T = 72; \qquad 1 - \frac{\Sigma T}{N^2 - N} = 1 - \frac{72}{1,056} = 0.9318$$

$$H_t = \frac{14.68}{0.9318} = 15.75$$

We find $H_t = 15.75$ and $P(\chi^2 \geqslant 15.75) < 0.001$ for 2 degrees of freedom. We therefore conclude that the three p.d.f.'s are not all equal, and that the samples do not come from the same continuous population.

Friedman χ_n^2-test

Friedman||||| devised an analysis of variance test based on ranks. He applied ranking methods to the double classification analysis of variance problem with a single replication in the subcells. The observation in the ith row ($i = 1, 2, \ldots, n$) and jth column ($j = 1, 2, \ldots, k$) is denoted by X_{ij} and its rank as compared with the other variates in the ith row is given by r_{ij}.

The hypothesis tested (null hypothesis) is that there are no column "effects," i.e. that the sample values within each row are from a single population with the same continuous c.d.f. This means that all possible permutations of ranks within a row have equal probability.

The two-way classification of the observations by rows and columns is:

$$X_{11}\, X_{12} \ldots X_{1k}$$
$$X_{21}\, X_{22} \ldots X_{2k}$$
$$\cdot \quad \cdot \quad \cdots \quad \cdot$$
$$\cdot \quad \cdot \quad \cdots \quad \cdot$$
$$X_{n1}\, X_{n2} \ldots X_{nk}$$

The table of ranks (by row) is:

$$r_{11}\, r_{12} \ldots r_{1k}$$
$$r_{21}\, r_{22} \ldots r_{2k}$$
$$\cdot \quad \cdot \quad \cdots \quad \cdot$$
$$\cdot \quad \cdot \quad \cdots \quad \cdot$$
$$r_{n1}\, r_{n2} \ldots r_{nk}$$

To test the hypothesis: $f_1(X_{.1}) = \ldots = f_k(X_{.k})$, one merely ranks the observations in each row and calculates the statistic:

$$\chi_r^2 = \frac{12}{nk(k + 1)} \sum_{j=1}^{k} \left(\sum_{i=1}^{n} r_{ij} \right)^2 - 3n(k + 1)$$

χ_r^2 is approximately distributed as χ^2 with $(k - 1)$ degrees of freedom. This approximation is good provided that the number of variates in the rows and columns is greater than 5. Significant points of the exact distribution of χ_r^2 are given for k equal to 3 and all n from 3 to 10, k equal to 4 and all n from 3 to 6, and k equal to 5 and n equal to 3.

The same procedure as above is used to test the hypothesis that the row classification has no effect on the variable X, except that now the columns are ranked instead of the rows and n and k are interchanged in the formula for χ_r^2.

While it is not necessary to assume that the distribution for each row or column is identical, it should be understood that the test is sensitive only to the influence of a factor in one direction. The efficiency of this test when k equals 3 and the assumptions for the analysis of variance are fulfilled has been reported as 63.7 per cent. This test is particularly useful in dealing with data when the assumptions of normality and homogeneity of variances do not hold, and when the original data are given in

||||| Milton Friedman, "The Use of Ranks to Avoid the Assumption of Normality," *Journal of the American Statistical Association*, XXXII (1937), 675–701.

the form of ranks. For an illustration of the procedures used in carrying out the test the reader is referred to Johnson.###

TESTS OF INDEPENDENCE

Tests of independence are designed to test the hypothesis that the joint c.d.f. of two random samples jointly distributed is equal to the product of the marginal c.d.f.'s. In the parametric case the problem is usually attacked by applying the product-moment correlation coefficient with the underlying assumptions of normality and homoscedasticity. In the non-parametric case the assumptions are less restrictive, being that both marginal density functions and the joint density function be continuous.

We are given n pairs of observations $(x_i\, y_i)$, where x_i is a measure of characteristic A and y_i of characteristic B. The continuous joint p.d.f. is $h(x, y)$ and the continuous marginal p.d.f.'s, $f(x)$ and $g(y)$. The hypothesis under test is: $h(x, y) = f(x)g(y)$.

We can only list a number of non-parametric tests that are available with brief descriptions of each. The references cited provide more complete information.

χ^2-test of Independence

This is probably the best known test for testing independence. It is applicable whether the variables under consideration are quantitative or categorical. The test consists in dividing the scale of the x-variable into m mutually exclusive categories $a_1, a_2, \ldots, a_m$ and the y-variable into p mutually exclusive categories $b_1, b_2, \ldots, b_p$, thus forming an m by n contingency table. The χ^2-test as a test of independence has been treated in Chapter V.

Spearman's Rank Correlation Coefficient

Of the tests of independence based on ranks, Spearman's test is the best known and most widely used.* To test the hypothesis of independence between attribute A and attribute B, given n pairs of observations X_i and Y_i, we proceed by first ranking the X's measuring attribute A denoting the rank of x_i by X_i, and the y's measuring attribute B denoting the rank y_i by Y_i. Then we calculate $\Sigma(X_i - Y_i)^2$. Olds has tabled the $\Sigma(X_i - Y_i)^2$ for $n \leq 30$. The rank correlation coefficient, r's, is given by

$$r' = 1 - \frac{6 \Sigma d_i^2}{(n^3 - n)}\, , \text{ where } d_i = (X_i - Y_i)$$

Palmer O. Johnson, *Statistical Methods in Research.*

* C. Spearman, "The Proof and Measurement of Association between Two Things," *American Journal of Psychology*, XV (1904), 72–101.

For illustration of the use of r' in testing independence the reader should refer to Chapter XI and also to Johnson.[†]

Kendall's Tau

Kendall[‡] devised a new measure of rank correlation, tau, the distribution of which is easier to find than that of Spearman's rho. While tau is somewhat more difficult to calculate, it has been extended into a partial correlation coefficient. The distribution of the partial tau, however, is not yet known, so it has only a descriptive function.

The test is performed by arranging the variates X_{ij} in rank order, thus forming the set $X_1, X_2, \ldots, X_n$ such that $X_1 < X_2 < \ldots < X_n$. Let Y_i be the rank of the y variate whose corresponding x variate has the rank X_i. Thus a new set $Y_1, Y_2, \ldots, Y_n$ is formed. Compare Y_i with every element Y_j of the set which follows it. If $Y_i > Y_j (i < j)$ let $t_{ij} = -1$ and if $Y_i < Y_j (i < j)$ let $t_{ij} = 1$. Where $i > j$ let $t_{ij} = 0$. Then tau, the test statistic is:

$$\tau = 2 \Sigma t_{ij}/n(n-1)$$

The distribution of τ is tabled for $n \leq 10$. The distribution of τ approaches normality with mean zero and variance $(2)(2n - 5)/n(n - 1)(3)$ rapidly, being almost normal for samples as small as 9.

Other Tests

Among other tests of independence are the Hoeffding D-test,[§] the Quadrant Sum Test of Olmstead and Tukey,[‖] and Pitman's Randomization Test.[#]

TEST OF RANDOMNESS

It is frequently of considerable practical and scientific importance to decide whether or not the fluctuations displayed by a series of observations are random in character or whether the existence must be assumed of some factor operating in accordance with a definite law. One general procedure in testing a statistical hypothesis has previously been considered, namely, that of working out the results which would be expected theoretically, and then comparing them with the observed results.

[†] Palmer O. Johnson, *Statistical Methods in Research.*

[‡] M. G. Kendall, "A New Measure of Rank Correlation," *Biometrika*, XXX (1938), 81–93.

[§] Wassily Hoeffding, "A Non-parametric Test of Independence," *Annals of Mathematical Statistics*, XIX (1948), 546–57.

[‖] P. S. Olmstead and J. W. Tukey, "A Corner Test of Association," *Annals of Mathematical Statistics*, XVIII (1947), 495–513.

[#] J. G. Pitman, "Significance Tests Which May Be Applied to Samples from Any Population. II. The Correlation Coefficient," *Journal of the Royal Statistical Society*, IV (1937), 225–32.

Various criteria have been developed to decide whether a series may be regarded as random or not. A series of observations which is compatible with these criteria is not necessarily a random one, but without evidence to the contrary, it is highly probable that it is so. Moreover, the failure of a series to conform to the criteria is evidence of its non-random character.

While in carrying out tests of randomness it cannot be stated exactly, in a single comprehensive statement, what all the facts of randomness are, it is possible to state what is meant by a particular non-random departure. It is then possible in testing for randomness to select from the numerous tests available, the particular test that will give the best assurance possible of detecting the type of departure from randomness with which the investigator is most concerned.

Let us assume that we have a set of observations $X_1, X_2, \ldots, X_n$ arranged in the order in which they were taken, i.e. the ith observation drawn is X_i. We wish to test whether these observations may be regarded as being in a random order. Formally, we may express the hypothesis as:

$$g(X_1, X_2, \ldots, X_n) = f(X_1) f(X_2) \ldots f(X_n)$$

where g is the joint density function and f the marginal density, both of which are assumed to be continuous.

Tests of randomness are frequently used in quality control in industry to determine if a process is under statistical control, by ascertaining whether the distribution of some product measurement is distributed randomly over a given period of time. Following Shewhart, the system of (unknown) causes corresponding to a state of statistical control is called "a constant system of chance causes," in contrast to the unknown causes of variability disturbing the state of statistical control called "assignable causes." Tests have been devised to discover lack of control and to find assignable causes and bring them under control so as to resume the state of statistical control. Such tests or tests based on other criteria may also be used to test for trends in census or economic data and the orderliness of sequence of responses of individuals in certain psychological experiments.

We will illustrate a test for randomness by applying the Mosteller Run Test, or runs above and below the median.** In this test we consider a sample of size n drawn from a population with continuous p.d.f., $f(X)$. Let the sample be $X_1, X_2, \ldots, X_n$ where the subscripts indicate the order in which the variates were drawn.

Determine X_m, the median of the sample. Compare each of the X_i with the median; if X_i is less than X_m, X_i will be replaced with an a, but if X_i is greater than X_m, X_i will be replaced with a b. If $X_i = X_m$, the value is ignored, that is, assigned neither a nor b. A sequence of letters

** Frederick Mosteller, "Note on an Application of Runs to Quality Control Charts," *Annals of Mathematical Statistics*, XII (1941), 228–32.

of the same kind is called a run. The length of the run is given by the number of like letters bounded on both ends by letters unlike those forming the sequence except when the run includes the first or last observations. A run of a's will be defined as a run "below the median," and a run of b's as a run "above the median." Denote the longest run by length k. Tables have been prepared by P. S. Olmstead giving the exact probabilities $P(R_{1k} \geqslant 1)$ as a function of k for samples of size 10, 20, 30, 40, and 50 for runs on one side (one-tailed test) or both sides (two-tailed test) of the median.††

We present below the average number of days lost per pupil according to occupation of the father (ages 6 to 18 years, grades 1 through 13, a rural sample from rural Canadian schools), which may be considered as a sample with continuous p.d.f. $= F(X)$ and variates presented in the order drawn.

(Reading across the rows):

$X_i =$ 15.1	6.6	13.2	3.9	9.4	8.7	17.0	12.6
9.0	21.1	18.7	5.5	13.9	10.3	0.3	15.5
18.4	12.3	14.2	22.5	14.3	16.9	15.7	22.3
12.5	8.2	13.7	25.3	8.9	13.2	15.3	5.2
14.4	11.2	15.4	12.5	18.1	15.0	12.6	19.1
13.8	16.9	20.7	20.1	17.3	12.7	15.9	16.8

Hypothesis: $g(X_1, X_2, \ldots, X_n) = f(X_1) f(X_2) \ldots f(X_n)$

We have $n = 48$; median, $X_m = 14.05$, and the runs may be written:
b $aaaaa$ b aa bb $aaaa$ bb a $bbbbbb$ aaa b aa b a b a b a bb a b a $bbbb$ a bb

Since the longest run is of six b's, $k = 6$; $P(k > 6) > 0.05$, using the table prepared by Olmstead. It follows from the table that runs of 6 or more b's may be expected to occur on the average with a frequency greater than 5 per cent in random arrangements, for $n \leqslant 48$. Therefore, the set of average number of days lost as recorded in the table above may be regarded as random in character.

OTHER REFERENCES AND READINGS

1. Durbin, J. "Incomplete Blocks in Ranking Experiments," *The British Journal of Psychology* (Statistical Section), IV (1951), 85–90.
2. Iyer, P. U. Krishna. "A Non-Parametric Method of Testing k-Samples," *Nature*, No. 4236 (January 6, 1951).
3. Kendall, M. G. *The Advanced Theory of Statistics*, Vol. I. London: Charles Griffin and Company, 1945.
4. Swed, F. S., and C. Eisenhart. "Tables for Testing Randomness of Grouping in a Sequence of Alternatives," *Annals of Mathematical Statistics*, XIV (1943), 66–87.
5. Wald, A., and J. Wolfowitz. "On a Test Whether Two Samples Are from the Same Population," *Annals of Mathematical Statistics*, XI (1940), 147–62.
6. Whitney, D. R. "A Bivariate Extension of the U Test," *Annals of Mathematical Statistics*, XXII (1951), 274–82.

†† *Ibid.*

EXERCISES

1. An experiment was designed to test the value of projects in the teaching of high school chemistry. The students were paired on intelligence quotients and on scores on a test of scientific method. Members of a pair were assigned by lot to one of two treatments: (1) experimental group worked on term projects in addition to the regular course work; (2) the control group studied additional material equivalent in time to that used by (1) on projects. The gains on the Anderson Chemistry Test were as follows:

PAIR	EXPERIMENTAL GROUP GAIN	CONTROL GROUP GAIN
1	33	30
2	29	33
3	29	18
4	20	16
5	33	19
6	30	25
7	15	14
8	15	19
9	21	23
10	27	12
11	26	17
12	18	14
13	16	18
14	10	9

You are to:
 (a) Set up the hypothesis to be tested, H_o
 (b) Specify the alternative hypothesis, H_1
 (c) Apply the sign test to test the hypothesis
 (d) Indicate the appropriate critical regions
 (e) Compare the result of using the sign test with
     that of using the t-test (assuming the normality assumption holds).

2. The following data were obtained from a random sample of 9 school systems in the same geographical region:

Per cent of all days lost due to medical causes in 9 different cities for the months of January and April:

JANUARY	APRIL
85.8	79.1
83.3	76.8
82.4	82.5
62.4	68.3
73.5	81.6
71.1	83.9
71.0	69.5
82.7	84.7
91.4	88.4

Apply the Median Test to test out the null hypothesis of no difference in percentage of days lost for the two months:

$$H_o : f(X) = g(y)$$
$$H_1 : f(X) = g(y + a)$$

3. Given the following data:
   Honor-Point Ratios for the freshman and sophomore years of a random sample of 23 college women who lived at home:

STUDENT NUMBER	H.P.R. FRESHMAN	H.P.R. SOPHOMORE	STUDENT NUMBER	H.P.R. FRESHMAN	H.P.R. SOPHOMORE
1	0.95	2.21	13	1.49	1.44
2	1.86	2.37	14	1.68	1.57
3	2.00	2.47	15	2.81	2.26
4	1.69	1.53	16	1.41	1.23
5	1.98	1.73	17	1.53	1.62
6	1.60	2.06	18	1.23	1.68
7	1.41	1.38	19	0.74	1.20
8	2.32	2.06	20	1.86	1.87
9	2.10	2.35	21	1.36	1.59
10	1.19	1.48	22	1.06	1.53
11	0.44	1.16	23	1.79	2.36
12	3.00	3.00			

Test the null hypothesis that the two distributions of H.P.R.'s come from the same population:

$$H_o : f_1(X) = f_2(X)$$
$$H_1 : f_1(X) > f_2(X)$$

Use the Wilcoxon T-test or the Mann-Whitney W-test.

4. Test the hypothesis that the continuous cumulative distribution function of percentile ranks on the College Aptitude Test is the same for a random sample of freshmen (entering a particular college of the University of Minnesota) with two units (years) of high school mathematics as that for a random sample of freshmen entering with three units. Use the Marshall Test.

CLASS INTERVALS IN PERCENTILE RANKS	UNITS OF HIGH SCHOOL MATHEMATICS	
	Two	Three
91–100	18	10
81–90	33	12
71–80	39	14
61–70	43	3
51–60	39	13
41–50	51	3
31–40	47	12
21–30	66	14
11–20	68	8
0–10	71	22
Total	475	111

5. Test for randomness the following set of observations giving the U.S. De-

partment of Commerce Weather Bureau, Minneapolis–St. Paul International Airport, report of daily average temperatures $\left(= \dfrac{\text{Max.} + \text{Min.}}{2} \right)$ for the month of October, 1954:

DATE	AVERAGE TEMPERATURE DEGREES FAHRENHEIT	DATE	AVERAGE TEMPERATURE DEGREES FAHRENHEIT
1	50	17	43
2	54	18	41
3	55	19	43
4	48	20	47
5	44	21	55
6	42	22	56
7	44	23	60
8	52	24	59
9	62	25	57
10	55	26	43
11	55	27	41
12	59	28	43
13	48	29	33
14	46	30	29
15	44	31	30
16	47		

6. Opinion data were obtained from a number of representative samples of the same population. On some surveys a certain question was asked and on other surveys a similar but different question was asked. In analyzing the data collected in this way, several short sequences of percentages (indicating percentage in favor of the particular issue proposed) were obtained. The table below constitutes an example. The occasions on which a question was asked were spaced over approximately the same time interval. A plus sign has been inserted between occasions when the percentage in favor increased, a minus sign, when decreased.

Test the hypothesis that these data are randomly ordered against the alternative that there is a tendency for the observations to increase the later they are taken.

QUESTION	1	2	3	4	5	6	7	NO. OF PLUS SIGNS $n+$	NO. OF MINUS SIGNS $n-$	TIMES ASKED n
1	31 − 27 + 29 + 34 + 35 + 42							4	1	6
2	24 + 26 + 28							2	0	3
3	24 + 35 − 29 + 36 + 43							3	1	5
4	21 + 31 + 35 + 36 + 47 + 54 − 44							5	1	7
Totals								14	3	21

7. A five-point rating scale was given to a group of 81 individuals before and after an experience with the object of rating. The following record was obtained:

ORIGINAL DATA (FREQUENCIES)

BEFORE	AFTER					TOTAL
	Not at all 1	A little 2	Some 3	Much 4	Very much 5	
Very much 5	2	0	3	6	11	22
Much 4	0	2	8	10	0	20
Some 3	3	5	17	3	2	30
A little 2	0	3	2	0	0	5
Not at all 1	4	0	0	0	0	4
Total	9	10	30	19	13	81

Compare the results of testing the null hypothesis by using the t-test and by the sign test or its chi-square equivalent. Specify the assumptions in each case.

8. The following ratings were obtained for a series of 6 samples of milk powder from 7 different laboratories. After testing, the laboratories were asked to rank the powders in order of quality with 1 as highest and 6 as lowest quality.

LABORATORY	POWDERS					
	A	B	C	D	E	F
1	3	6	1	2	5	4
2	1	3	4	2	5	6
3	2	3	5	1	4	6
4	3	1	5	2	6	4
5	1.5	1.5	6	4	3	5
6	3	4	5	1	2	6
7	4	1	5	2	6	3

(a) Test the null hypothesis of concordance among the rankings of the powders by the laboratories.
(b) Test the hypothesis that there are no column effects.
(c) What is the relation between the two tests applied in (a) and (b)?

9. The rankings of three students by 17 examiners are reported below:

EXAMINER	STUDENT NUMBER		
	36	23	55
1	3	1	2
2	3	2	1
3	2	1	3
4	1	2	3
5	2	1	3
6	1	2	3
7	2	1	3
8	2	1	3
9	2	1	3

(*Continued on following page*)

EXAMINER	STUDENT NUMBER		
	36	*23*	*55*
10	1	2	3
11	3	1	2
12	3	2	1
13	1	2	3
14	2	1	3
15	1	2	3
16	3	1	2
17	1	2	3

(a) Compute and test the significance of the coefficient of concordance.‡‡

(b) Calculate Spearman's rank correlation coefficient between every possible pair of judges and then average the values of the coefficients. Compare with the results in (a).

10. The following data refer to the number of mothers who had suffered any infant losses (stillbirths) previous to the birth of the child in a study of behavior problems in children. The two groups of children are specified as "Problems" and "Controls," the former representing children who had been referred by their teachers as presenting behavior problems, the latter as children who had not been so referred.

DATA ON NUMBER OF MOTHERS WITH PREVIOUS INFANT LOSSES

BIRTH ORDER	GROUP	NO. OF MOTHERS WITH		TOTAL	% LOSS
		Losses	*None*		
2	Problems	20	82	102	19.6
	Controls	10	54	64	15.6
Total		30	136	$166 = N_1$	18.1
3–4	Problems	26	41	67	38.8
	Controls	16	30	46	34.8
Total		42	71	$113 = N_2$	37.2
5+	Problems	27	22	49	55.1
	Controls	14	23	37	37.8
Total		41	45	$86 = N_3$	47.7

Examine the data separately for the 3 birth-order classes. The data then consist of three 2×2 tables. The problem is to make a combined test of significance of the difference in occurrence rates in the two sample groups: Problems and Controls. Compare the results obtained by carrying the test out in three ways:

‡‡ See, Palmer O. Johnson, *Statistical Methods in Research*, p. 174.

(a) Combine all the data into a single 2 × 2 table and then compute χ^2 (chi-square).

(b) Compute χ^2 separately for each table and add them making use of the fact that the sum of g values of χ^2 each with 1 d.f. is distributed as χ^2 with g degrees of freedom.

(c) Compute the χ values, and add them, taking account of the signs of the differences. Use the test criterion, $\dfrac{\Sigma\chi}{\sqrt{g}}$ and refer to the standard normal tables.

11. Use the H-test to test the null hypothesis that the three groups of schools classified according to the physique of the pupils come from identical continuous populations with respect to the density of population (the number of persons per acre):

Density of population in the different wards in which the schools of the group fall (Karn, 1936):

GROUP I	GROUP II		GROUP III
67.7	47.1	61.9	198.5
65.0	28.3	43.1	198.5
25.9	65.0	198.5	99.7
50.3	33.5	73.6	32.4
	73.6	73.5	50.3
	25.9	32.4	32.4
	32.4	50.3	
	198.5	24.3	

CHAPTER X

The Problem of Estimation

Up to this point we have encountered the problem of estimation in its most concrete form, i.e. in the problem of reducing data, particularly large quantities of data, into meaningful and manageable form. This reduction consisted in the replacement of the original data by a relatively few quantities adequately representing the whole. These summary values were determined so as to contain as much as possible, ideally the whole, of the relevant information that was latent in the original data. By relevant information we mean any information furnished by the data, usually the sample, which is of use in estimating the parameters or defining the properties of the population. Since the latter is the primary purpose of statistical analysis, it brings into prominence the role of statistical estimation in the object of statistical methods. Accordingly we single out for special consideration in this chapter the problems connected with statistical estimation, particularly those both of a theoretical and practical nature fundamental to a functional understanding leading to the solution of the problems of estimation.

Recalling the problems of determining the best method of reducing data, we note that the most important single factor was the form of distribution of the observations. It is also apparent that in considering the best method, say, of averaging or combining the data before him so as to elicit information on some definite issue, the investigator must be guided by the magnitude and nature of the sampling errors attendant upon different estimates. This was the genesis of the theory of estimation.

We may treat the theoretical structure underlying estimation by first presenting the three types of problems arising in the reduction of data as listed and defined by R. A. Fisher:

1. *Problems of specification* arise in the necessity of specifying the mathematical form of the distribution of the hypothetical population from which a random sample is to be regarded as drawn.

2. *Problems of estimation* involve the choice of methods of calculating statistical derivatives, called statistics, from a sample. These quantities are designed to estimate the value of one or more of the population parameters.

3. *Problems of distribution* involve the form of the sampling distribution

of the estimates or of any further statistics calculated for purposes of inference.

It should be evident that when it becomes possible to know (a) what parameters are needed to specify the population from which the sample has been drawn, (b) what is the best way to calculate estimates of these parameters from the sample, and (c) the exact distribution, in different random samples, of the derived statistics, then the theoretical basis of the treatment of any particular body of data has been completely provided.

Although problems of estimation and distribution may be profitably studied separately, it should be clearly indicated that they are closely associated in the development of statistical methods. Logically problems of distribution should have prior consideration (as has been given in Chapter II) because the investigation of the random distributions of different eligible statistics derived from samples of given size, must give direction in determining which statistic it is most productive to calculate.

The three types of problems defined may be grouped a little more broadly under just two heads: firstly, the problem of specification, secondly, the problem of statistical inference subsuming both (2) and (3) above.

These two broad categories of problems are now mainly, but not entirely, separate problems. The first calls for, in addition to a knowledge of possible mathematical models, a practical knowledge of the physical or statistical phenomenon to be represented by the theoretical probability model. This problem is not entirely independent of the second class of problem, however, because one of the functions of the latter is to check the adequacy of the specification. The more detailed the specification is, the more restricted is the inference problem, but, simultaneously, the detailed specification may be found insupportable as a representation of the data.

The two main problems of statistical inference* are (1) the problem of testing statistical hypotheses and (2) the problem of estimation. Since these problems seem to be frequently confused not only in the literature but by some authors of texts on statistical methods, we treat the two problems in different chapters. The problems of testing statistical hypotheses have been discussed in chapters III–VI and IX. As has been noted, in testing of statistical hypotheses we consider the problem of testing, on the information from a random sample, if a population parameter has a specified value, or more generally if one or more designated functional relationships occur among two or more population parameters. Both parametric and non-parametric tests of statistical hypotheses were discussed.

The theory of statistical estimation treats the problem of estimating values of the unknown parameters of distribution functions of specified

---

* We have not considered the decision problem as analogous to the inference problem. There is an essentially arbitrary character which differentiates the decision problem from the inference problem. An inference from data, although it may be uncertain, must be unique, since if arbitrary it would lack validity in any objective sense.

mathematical form from the observations in random samples. This is the parametric case. There is also the case of non-parametric estimation which deals with the estimation of properties of a distribution of unspecified form.

Having shown the broader statistical problems of which the problem of estimation is a part, we shall now proceed to describe more fully the characteristics of good estimates, the methods of estimation, and the application of principles and processes to obtain a number of estimates frequently used by the research worker.

THE CHARACTERISTICS OF GOOD STATISTICS

When the mathematical form of the distribution of the population has been specified, the problem of estimation first involves the derivation of estimates of the parameters from the observations. Certain criteria or properties provide standards which are to be looked for in "good" estimators.†

While the criteria themselves do not afford any systematic procedure of deriving estimators which comply with them, a classification of estimates may be made on the basis of properties derived from their sampling distributions. The principal criteria are:

1. consistency
2. efficiency
3. sufficiency
4. unbiasedness

The property of consistency of a statistic, or estimate, means that the estimate tends to the true or population parameter with increasing size of sample.

The criterion of efficiency is met by those estimates, which, when secured from large samples, tend to a normal distribution with a minimum standard deviation. The efficiency of a statistic represents the percentage of the total available relevant information of which it makes use. The efficiency (E) of the median as compared with the arithmetic mean in locating the normal curve is: $E = \dfrac{\sigma^2/n}{\pi\sigma^2/2n} = \dfrac{2}{\pi} = 63.66$ per cent. From this value we can deduce the correlation, in large samples, between the mean and median derived from the same sample: $r = \sqrt{E} = 0.7978$.

A statistic meets the criterion of sufficiency when it elicits all the relevant information which the sample contains on the value of the parameter. No other statistic which may be derived from the same sample can provide any additional information as to the value of the parameter. Sufficiency

† An estimate of a parameter is merely a number obtained from calculations performed on the observational values. From the procedural standpoint an estimate is a function of the observed values. Some statisticians use the word *estimator* for the function and the word *estimate* for the numerical value of the function. Others use the term *estimate* for the function and its numerical value.

is not an asymptotic property; that is, it does not call for n to be increased without limit or that the estimator be distributed normally for large n. Sufficient estimators do not exist for a considerable number of parameters.

A statistic satisfies the criterion of unbiasedness if its mathematical expectation, or the mean of the statistic taken over all possible samples of a given size, is the true value. An estimate may be positively or negatively biased according as its expectation is greater or less than the parameter value. While unbiasedness is a desirable property, it is not necessarily an indispensable one. If the magnitude of the bias is small, say, less than one-tenth of the standard deviation of the estimate, the effect of the bias on the estimate may often be negligible.

In the above discussion it is a basic condition that the sample observations have been obtained by a *random operation*. This condition in sampling from a finite population may be satisfied by using random sampling numbers and likewise in experimental designs by randomization of the experimental units. It is also assumed that the observations are statistically or *stochastically independent*, since the results may be misleading even though the observations be only slightly correlated.

We note that criteria, such as efficiency and sufficiency for determining the goodness of estimates, require knowledge of the amount of information available in a random sample relevant to the population parameter under estimation. Fisher's motive in studying the theory of information arose out of the need for quantifying the concept or the idea of treating amount of information as a metrical quantity in the theory of information.‡

It is well known that the standard deviation of two separate and similar measurements or of two similar samples is divided by $\sqrt{2}$. The variance is halved. The fact is that the reciprocal of the variance of a sample, provided the elements of the sample are independent, is proportional to the size of the sample. These considerations led Fisher to define the "amount of information" provided by an estimate normally distributed with variance V as the reciprocal of the variance, or $1/V$. It is important to note that his "amount of information" is an additive measure. Amount of information is not dimensionless, but a requirement is that it be multiplied by a quantity with the dimensions of the variance, that is, magnitude squares, thus making it independent of changes in unit of measurement.

The application of the concept of quantity of information may be illustrated in the case of variance of the mean of two combined samples. The variance of the mean of a normal sample of size n_1, is $\dfrac{\sigma^2}{n_1}$ and of another

‡ It is important that need for the quantification of information was discovered by scientists working in other fields, e.g. that of Shannon in the problem of coding information and that of Wiener in the problem of noise and messages in electrical filters.

random sample of size n_2 is $\dfrac{\sigma^2}{n_2}$. The variance of the mean of the combined

sample is $\dfrac{\sigma^2}{n_1} + \dfrac{\sigma^2}{n_2}$ or $\sigma^2\left(\dfrac{1}{n_1} + \dfrac{1}{n_2}\right)$. The variance of the estimate contains the entire information concerning the population mean and the only additive function of this variance for independent samples is the reciprocal.

In cases where the variance of the population is not known, it must be estimated from the data. In such situations the amount of information given by an observed value X relative to the unknown mean population parameter is secured from

$$\frac{n+1}{(n+3)\,s^2}$$

where s^2 is the sampling variance and n the number of degrees of freedom.

The measurement of the quantity of information plays a very important theoretical and practical part in evaluating various possible experimental and sampling designs.

METHODS OF ESTIMATION

Various methods of estimation have been proposed. Here we shall mention four: the method of maximum likelihood, the method of least squares, the method of minimum χ^2, and the method of moments.

The most important general method of estimation so far developed, at least from a theoretical standpoint, is the method of maximum likelihood. Of the optimum properties it may be said that maximum likelihood estimators are consistent, tend to normality for large samples, have minimum variance in the limit at least, and yield sufficient statistics when they exist.

We may define the likelihood function L of a random sample as

$$L(X_1, \ldots, X_n; \theta) = P\{X_1; \theta\}\, P\{X_2; \theta\} \ldots P\{X_n; \theta\} \text{ - - - (10.1)}$$

Conforming with the method of maximum likelihood, we choose as an estimator of the parameter θ, the value which maximizes L for the given sample values of $(X_1, \ldots, X_n)$. Or less mathematically, we may state that the idea of maximum likelihood is to assign to an unknown quantity, θ, that value which, if it were correct, would make the occurrence of the observed result or event more likely than any other value.

The maximum likelihood process of obtaining estimators is usually based on the methods of the calculus because the relative maximum of the likelihood function secured by differentiating $L(X_1, \ldots, X_n; \theta)$ with respect to θ and setting the derivative equal to zero is usually an absolute maximum.§

The method of least squares is carried out by taking, as estimates of

§ For applications of the maximum likelihood process see Chapter VIII, "Analysis of Variance."

the parameters, those values of the parameters that minimize the sum of squares of deviations of the observed values from their expected values based on the parameters. The most important case in statistical theory of the use of the method of least squares is that in regression equations. The regression coefficients are determined, in effect, so as to minimize the sum of squares of residuals. If the deviations are in fact normally and independently distributed, the method of least squares is contained in the method of maximum likelihood. The method of least squares is used for most purposes of experimental design.

The method of minimum χ^2 consists in testing closeness of fit of the estimates to certain parameters. The method of estimation yielding a minimum χ^2 value is called the χ^2 minimum method of estimation. The method of minimum χ^2 is used for frequency data when it is noted that n_1 of a sample of size n have the ith attribute and a law is postulated for the true proportions P_i. To estimate the parameters specified in the law, we minimize the quantity:

$$\chi^2 = \sum_i \frac{(n_i - nP_i)^2}{nP_i}$$

with respect to variations over the parameters. On theoretical grounds, no good reason is apparent for using minimum χ^2 in place of maximum likelihood. The method is asymptotically efficient and has some practical value in situations where the maximum likelihood equations are difficult to solve. The χ^2-minimum method has an advantage over all other methods in that it can be used for truncated distributions.

The oldest general method of forming estimates of the parameters of a distribution from sample values is the method of moments. In this method the sample moments are equated to the corresponding moments of the distribution which are functions of the unknown parameters. An example of this use of the method of moments is in fitting the normal curve to a series of observations. The moment coefficients often involve relatively simple calculations but their efficiency decreases when the variations among the observations depart widely from normality.

Point and Interval Estimation

The simplest form of assertion concerning the estimated parameter which can be made using the values of the observable random variables is the point estimate. The method of point estimation of a parameter consists of defining a single-valued function of the observable random variables. The function is called the point estimate or the single estimate of the parameter, say, θ. A point estimate is then the familiar kind of estimate, the number secured from computations on the observed values of the random variables.

From our discussion of methods of estimation it was observed that there are principles that can be followed in obtaining point estimates such that estimates obtained by using them possess desirable properties. However, the point estimate alone is not very informative since in this case we have a sample of one from a population whose spread or variation is unknown. We cannot tell from the single sample estimate whether it is too great or too small or how close to the true value it is likely to be. An estimate of the variance of the estimate is needed to know how close the estimate may be, e.g. a small variance implies closeness of the estimate to the true value of the sample.

The method of point estimate does not, therefore, provide a measure of the degree of confidence we may place in the estimate. Nor does point estimation take directly into account the size of the sample providing the unique estimate.

Since it is highly unlikely in many cases that a point estimate will be equal to the true value, the investigator is naturally interested in the precision of the estimate used. A useful way of expressing this precision is that of indicating the limits which, presumably, the error in the estimate could not exceed. This method of estimation is obviously different from that of point estimation. It is spoken of as the estimation by interval. Such an interval is called the confidence interval. This method defines not one, but two functions of the observable random variables. From the sample value and other ancillary information the point values of the upper and lower limits of the interval can be calculated, and then we proceed to state that this interval will include or cover the population value. From sampling theory we can calculate the number of times in repeated sampling that the statement would be correct. Thus, the proportion of cases in which the statement may be assumed to be correct furnishes a measure of the confidence that may be ascribed to our statement and is called the confidence coefficient.‖ The fundamental point is that this method of estimation is associated with a prescribed frequency or probability of correct decisions. This is not possible with any method of estimation by a fixed interval.

There are many estimation problems where an interval estimate is preferred. With a sufficiently large sample and the maximum likelihood estimate we can use normal curve methods to find such an interval. However, a more general method is needed for constructing interval estimates and we shall describe more fully the procedures by giving applications to a number of problems of different types.

‖ R. A. Fisher makes use of the terms "fiducial interval" and "fiducial probability" instead of "confidence interval" and "confidence coefficient." He restricts his results to sufficient statistics.

Problems of Interval Estimation

Problem X.1. *Estimation of the Population Mean, Variance Known*

We wish to estimate the confidence interval with a confidence coefficient of 95 per cent ($\alpha = 0.05$; $1 - \alpha = 0.95$) for the mean μ of a $N (\mu, \sigma^2)$# by use of a random sample of size n; the population variance σ^2 is known.

From sampling theory we found that the means of random samples of size n from a normal population, i.e. the $\bar{X}$'s, are normally distributed about the population mean μ with a standard deviation equal to $\dfrac{\sigma}{\sqrt{n}}$. We know, therefore, the proportion of sample means that will lie within the interval: $\mu \doteq$ some multiple of $\dfrac{\sigma}{\sqrt{n}}$.

The quantity

$$u = \frac{\bar{X} - \mu}{\sigma / \sqrt{n}} \quad \text{-------------- (10.2)}$$

is normally distributed about 0 with standard deviation 1. For our problem we choose values of u corresponding to the particular value of the confidence coefficient selected. There are an infinite number of possible limits (U_1, U_2) such that

$$P(U_1 < \mu < U_2) = 1 - \alpha \quad \text{----------- (10.3)}$$

In determining which of the possible limits (U_1, U_2) to use, we would ordinarily desire to make the confidence interval as short as possible. Limiting our consideration to unbiased estimates, asymptotically normally distributed, this interval can be made as short as possible by choosing the estimator with the smallest variance and picking the limits (U_1, U_2) so that $\alpha_1 = \alpha_2 = \dfrac{\alpha}{2}$. The maximum likelihood estimator has this desired property.

For a 95 per cent confidence coefficient

$$\alpha_1 = \alpha_2 = \frac{\alpha}{2} = 0.025$$

We may start with the relation used for determining the centiles (percentiles), say C_1 and C_2, which in our case indicate the proportion of the total number of cases below U_1 and U_2, respectively:

$$P\left\{\frac{\bar{X} - \mu}{\sigma / n}\right\} < U_1 = C_1 \quad \text{---------- (10.4)}$$

If the inequality is solved with respect to μ, we obtain

$$P\{\bar{X} - U_1\sigma/\sqrt{n} < \mu\} = C_1 \quad \text{-------- (10.5)}$$

Correspondingly, the relation

$$P\left\{U_1 < \frac{\bar{X} - \mu}{\sigma / \sqrt{n}} < U_2\right\} = C_2 - C_1$$

Read as follows: a normally distributed variate with mean, μ, and variance, σ^2.

leads to
$$P\{\bar{X} - U_2\sigma/\sqrt{n} < \mu < \bar{X} - U_1\sigma/\sqrt{n}\} = C_2 - C_1 \text{ - - - } (10.6)$$
Thus for every $M\{X\} = \mu$ the probability that the inequality
$$\bar{X} - U_2\sigma/\sqrt{n} < \mu < \bar{X} - U_1\sigma/\sqrt{n} \text{ - - - - - - } (10.7)$$
will be satisfied is $C_2 - C_1$.

If we take $C_1 = 2.5$ per cent and $C_2 = 97.5$ per cent, we obtain
$$P\{\bar{X} - 1.96\sigma/\sqrt{n} < \mu < \bar{X} + 1.96\sigma/\sqrt{n} = 95 \text{ per cent- - } (10.8)$$

The interpretation of (10.8) is that from a long series of samples of size n, drawn from a normally distributed population with parameters (μ, σ^2), we may calculate a corresponding series of intervals, i.e. $\bar{X} \pm 1.96\sigma/\sqrt{n}$ and that we may expect about 95 per cent of these intervals to include the fixed quantity, or parameter μ.

Example X.1. The following sampling experiment was carried out to illustrate the above procedure.

We took 100 random samples of 50 items each drawn from a population with $\mu = 30$; $\sigma = 10$. For samples of 50, the standard error of the mean, or standard deviation of the sampling distribution of means, $\sigma\bar{x}$, will be
$$\frac{\sigma}{\sqrt{n}} = \frac{10}{\sqrt{50}} = 1.414$$
The 95 per cent confidence limits are:
$$\bar{X} - (1.96)(1.404); \quad \bar{X} + (1.96)(1.414)$$
or
$$\bar{X} - 2.77, \bar{X} + 2.77$$
The confidence intervals for μ, calculated from the 100 samples were as follows:

25.97–31.51	27.39–32.93	28.55–34.09	28.35–33.89	27.47–33.01
27.31–33.05	25.13–30.67	27.41–32.95	27.31–32.85	26.61–32.15
*23.19–28.73	28.35–33.89	31.93–37.47	*24.31–29.85	26.37–31.91
29.29–34.83	28.37–33.91	29.23–34.77	28.65–34.19	27.21–32.75
27.85–33.39	27.53–33.07	27.61–33.15	28.31–33.85	25.53–31.07
25.93–31.47	29.31–34.85	28.53–34.07	27.29–33.33	25.95–31.49
27.53–33.07	27.49–33.03	27.31–32.85	25.97–31.51	26.23–31.77
26.83–32.37	27.15–32.69	31.73–37.27	29.61–35.15	28.05–33.59
24.93–30.47	27.01–32.55	30.23–35.77	29.25–34.79	27.87–33.41
28.27–33.81	26.43–31.97	29.15–34.69	26.91–32.45	28.83–34.37
28.11–33.65	26.79–32.33	26.05–31.59	28.49–34.03	28.75–34.29
26.03–31.57	27.13–32.67	24.81–30.35	26.15–31.69	27.81–33.35
27.53–33.07	26.69–32.23	27.89–33.43	24.99–30.53	25.65–31.19
28.93–34.47	28.01–33.55	29.93–35.47	26.81–32.35	27.55–33.09
26.19–31.73	28.81–34.35	*21.53–27.07	25.53–31.07	28.17–33.71
28.79–34.33	*24.61–30.15	24.49–30.03	25.99–31.53	28.09–33.63
27.69–33.23	26.53–32.07	26.89–32.43	26.33–31.87	29.79–35.33
30.41–35.95	25.53–31.07	28.63–34.17	25.61–31.15	29.09–34.63
28.09–33.63	28.65–34.19	26.49–32.03	26.09–31.63	29.01–34.55
29.97–35.51	27.65–33.19	26.51–32.05	*24.91–30.45	28.23–33.77

It is observed that the limits for μ vary from sample to sample as the mean $\bar{X}$ varies. If we define $\mu = 30$ as extending from 29.5 up to 30.5, it is observed that three of the intervals do not include 30, and that two do not include the complete interval of 30. This result agrees closely with theory.

In practice, we usually have only one sample from which to calculate the mean. The problem then is to calculate the position of μ from this single sample mean. The method used is to calculate the limits of μ using Equation (10.8). In this case the confidence coefficient is 95 per cent; other coefficients may of course be used.

Unless the population variance or standard deviation is known, these confidence intervals would be of little use.

Problem X.2. Estimation of Population Mean, Variance Unknown

This is the situation most often encountered in research. There are two unknown parameters, μ and σ^2. We know from previous theory that, if

$$\bar{X} = \frac{\Sigma X_i}{n} \quad \text{and} \quad s^2 = \sum \frac{(X_i - \bar{X})^2}{n - 1}$$

and $\bar{X}$ is independent of s

$$t = \frac{\bar{X} - \mu}{s/\sqrt{n}} = \frac{\sqrt{n}\,(\bar{X} - \mu)}{s}$$

is distributed as Student's t with $(n - 1)$ degrees of freedom. Here t is a function of only μ and the sample values n, $\bar{X}$, and s. We can then find numerical values of t_1 and t_2 such that

$$P\left\{ t_1 < \frac{\bar{X} - \mu}{s/\sqrt{n}} < t_2 \right\} = 1 - \alpha \quad \text{-------- (10.9)}$$

where $\alpha = 0.05, 0.01$, etc.

Since the distribution of t is symmetrical with its maximum ordinate at the center, the shortest confidence interval will be obtained by setting

$$\alpha_1 = \alpha_2 = \frac{\alpha}{2}$$

Here $t_1 = -t_2$. Since the values of t_1 and t_2 depend on n, we do not obtain unique confidence limits as in (10.1) above.

Solving the inequality of (10.9) with respect to μ gives us the confidence limits for μ:

$$P\left\{ \bar{X} - \frac{t_2 s}{\sqrt{n}} < \mu < \bar{X} + \frac{t_1 s}{\sqrt{n}} \right\} = 1 - \alpha \quad \text{----- (10.10)}$$

The confidence limits for μ given by (10.10) depend solely on the empirical quantities $\bar{X}$ and s, and on n and α.

The probability P is the probability of the interval, which is the random variable, including or covering the true value μ. If we draw the conclusion that the true mean is in the calculated interval for each sample we examine, we shall be correct on the average in $(1 - \alpha)$ of cases.

Example X.2. Set up the 95 per cent confidence limits for the population mean score on the intelligence test from the random sample of scores of 664 individuals given on p. 20.

$$\text{Mean } \bar{X} = 62.774$$
$$S = \sqrt{86.3976} = 9.295$$
$$n = 664$$
$$t_1 = -t_2 = 1.96 \text{ for } \alpha = 0.05$$

The 95 per cent confidence limits are:

$$62.774 \pm \frac{(1.96)(9.295)}{\sqrt{664}} =$$
$$62.774 \pm \frac{18.2182}{25.770} =$$
$$62.774 + 0.707 = 63.48$$
$$62.774 - 0.707 = 62.07$$
$$\text{or } (62.07, 63.48).$$

Problem X.3. Estimation of the Difference Between Two Population Means from Two Random Samples, Population Variances Known

Suppose that a random sample is drawn from each of two normally distributed populations with parameters (μ_1, σ_1^2) and (μ_2, σ_2^2), respectively, and that the two variances are known. A significant difference has been found between the two means and we wish to set up the confidence limits for the true difference, say, $\mu_1 - \mu_2 = \delta$. From the samples we have found: $d = \bar{X}_1 - \bar{X}_2$. It is known from sampling theory that d is normally distributed about δ with variance:

$$\sigma_d^2 = \frac{\sigma_1^2}{n_1} + \frac{\sigma_2^2}{n_2}$$

Then the confidence limits with confidence coefficient $1 - \alpha$ for the difference between population means may be written:

$$P\left\{d - U_2\sqrt{\frac{\sigma_1^2}{n_1} + \frac{\sigma_2^2}{n_2}} < \delta < d + U_1\sqrt{\frac{\sigma_1^2}{n_1} + \frac{\sigma_2^2}{n_2}}\right\} = 1 - \alpha$$

-------- (10.11)

If $\sigma_1^2 = \sigma_2^2 = \sigma^2$, Equation (10.11) becomes

$$P\left\{d - U_2\sqrt{\sigma^2\left(\frac{1}{n_1} + \frac{1}{n_2}\right)} < \delta < d + U_1\sqrt{\sigma^2\left(\frac{1}{n_1} + \frac{1}{n_2}\right)}\right\} = 1 - \alpha$$

---- (10.12)

Example X.3. Set up the 99 per cent confidence limits for the difference between the two population means from the mean achievements on an English test of two random samples of students, one sample of $n_1 = 146$ following a general curriculum with a mean, $\bar{X}_1 = 49.4$, the other of $n_2 = 115$ following a commercial curriculum with a mean, $\bar{X}_2 = 42.8$. The population variance is given as $\sigma^2 = 850$ (see p. 148).

The 99 per cent confidence limits are given by

$$d \pm 2.58\sqrt{\sigma^2\left(\frac{1}{n_1} + \frac{1}{n_2}\right)}$$

$$
\begin{aligned}
d &= \bar{X}_1 - \bar{X}_2 \\
&= 49.4 - 42.8 \\
&= 6.6
\end{aligned}
\qquad
\begin{aligned}
&n_1 = 146,\ n_2 = 115 \\
&\sigma^2 = 850
\end{aligned}
$$

Accordingly, the 99 per cent confidence limits for δ are:

$$6.6 \pm 2.58\sqrt{850\left(\frac{1}{146} + \frac{1}{115}\right)}$$

$$
\begin{aligned}
&= 6.6 \pm 2.58\,(3.63) \\
&= 6.6 \pm 9.37 \\
&= (15.97,\ -2.77)
\end{aligned}
$$

Problem X.4. *Estimation of the Difference Between Two Population Means from Two Random Samples, Variances Unknown*

The two-tailed confidence limits with confidence coefficient $1 - \alpha$ for the true difference δ between two means, assuming $\sigma_1{}^2 = \sigma_2{}^2 = \sigma^2$, are given by

$$d - t_\alpha S_d < \delta < d + t_\alpha S_d \qquad \text{- - - - - - - - - (10.13)}$$

where $d = \bar{X}_1 - \bar{X}_2$ and $S_d = S\sqrt{\dfrac{1}{n_1} + \dfrac{1}{n_2}}$

t_α = tabled value of t for a value of $\alpha = 0.05,\ 0.01$, etc.
and d.f. $= n_1 + n_2 - 2$;

$$S^2 = \frac{1}{n_1 + n_2 - 2}\left[\Sigma(X_{1i} - \bar{X}_{1i})^2 + \Sigma(X_{2j} - \bar{X}_{2j})^2\right]$$

Example X.4. Set up the 98 per cent confidence limits for the difference between the two population means of intelligence test scores of the two groups:

(1) Honors Graduates, and (2) Ordinary Graduates. Data from Table II.11, p. 23.

We calculate the following values:

$$
\begin{aligned}
\bar{X}_1 &= 76.875 \\
\bar{X}_2 &= 71.077 \\
d &= 5.798 \\
n_1 &= 40 \\
n_2 &= 222
\end{aligned}
\qquad
\begin{aligned}
S^2 &= \frac{51{,}710.073200}{260} \\
&= 198.884897 \\
S &= 14.103 \\
S_d &= 14.103\sqrt{\frac{1}{40} + \frac{1}{222}} = 2.423
\end{aligned}
$$

The 98 per cent confidence limits for δ are:

$$d \pm t_{\underset{(260)}{.02}}\,S_d$$

$$
\begin{aligned}
&= 5.798 \pm (2.326)(2.423) \\
&= (11.434,\ 0.162)
\end{aligned}
$$

Problem X.5. Estimation of the Population Variance from the Sample Value

It is known that $\chi^2 = \dfrac{(n-1)S^2}{\sigma^2}$ is distributed as χ^2 with $(n-1)$ degrees of freedom.

Let X_1^2 and X_2^2 be values of X^2 such that
$$P\{X_1^2 < X^2 < X_2^2\} = 1 - \alpha \qquad \text{- - - - - - -} \quad (10.14)$$
In this relation we introduce
$$X^2 = (n-1)S^2/\sigma^2$$
and solve the inequality with respect to σ_j^2.

We obtain:
$$P\left\{\frac{(n-1)S^2}{X_2^2} < \sigma^2 < \frac{(n-1)S^2}{X_1^2}\right\} = 1 - \alpha \quad \text{- - - - -}(10.15)$$

As found for t, the values of X_1^2 and X_2^2 depend on n.

Example X.5. Set up the 90 per cent confidence interval for the population variance of intelligence test scores from the sample of 664 pupils (see p. 20).

Confidence limits for σ^2:
$$\frac{(n-1)S^2}{X_2^2}, \qquad \frac{(n-1)S^2}{X_1^2},$$

or
$$\frac{\Sigma x^2}{X_2^2}, \qquad \frac{\Sigma x^2}{X_1^2}$$

$$\Sigma x^2 = 25\left[\frac{664(2{,}547) - (359)^2}{664}\right]$$
$$= 58{,}822.55275$$

$$S^2 = \frac{\Sigma x^2}{n-1}, \text{ and } (n-1)S^2 = \Sigma x^2$$

$$S^2 = \frac{1}{663}(\Sigma x^2)$$
$$= \frac{58{,}822.55275}{663}$$
$$= 88.7218$$

Since for large values of $n-1$
$$z = \sqrt{2X^2} - \sqrt{2(n-1) - 1} \text{ is distributed } N(0,1)$$
$$P\{-1.645 < z - < 1.645\} = 0.90$$
solving
$$-1.645 < \sqrt{2X^2} - \sqrt{2(663) - 1} < 1.645$$
for X^2, we may obtain X_2^2 and X_1^2 with 663 d.f.
$$_{(.05)}_{(.95)}$$
Thus:
$$-1.645 + \sqrt{2(663) - 1} < \sqrt{2X^2} < 1.645 + \sqrt{2(.663) - 1}$$
$$= 34.755 < \sqrt{2X^2} < 38.045$$

$$= 603.9550 < X^2 < 723.7110$$
$$X_2{}^2 = 723.7110; \quad X_1{}^2 = 603.9550$$

The confidence limits are then:

$$\frac{58{,}822.55275}{723.7110} = 81.2791$$

and

$$\frac{58{,}822.55275}{603.9550} = 97.39558$$

or (97.39, 81.28)

Problem X.6. Estimation of an Individual's True Score from His Obtained Score on a Test

It is assumed here that the scores a student would get on a very large number of equivalent tests are distributed normally about his true score with a standard deviation equal to the standard error of an individual score, $\sigma_x = S\sqrt{1-r}$, where S is the standard deviation of the distribution of scores and r is the reliability coefficient of the test. The upper and lower limits of the confidence interval of his true score, ξ, are

$$X \pm Z_\alpha(S\sqrt{1-r})$$

where $Z_\alpha = \dfrac{(X - \xi)}{\sigma_x}$ for a given confidence coefficient, $1 - \alpha$, which is read from the normal probability table; X is the obtained score; and σ_x is the standard error of X.

Example X.6. A student received a raw score of 24 on an intelligence test; the following values were reported for the test:

$$r(\text{reliability coeff.}) = 0.84$$
$$S_x = 9.68$$

We wish to set up the confidence interval of his true score ξ, with a confidence coefficient of 98 per cent.

We calculate

$$S_{(\text{Meas})} = S_x\sqrt{1-r}$$
$$= (9.68)(0.4)$$
$$= 3.87$$

Using a confidence coefficient of 98 per cent, the upper and lower limits of the confidence interval are, respectively:

$$24 + (2.326)(3.87) \text{ or } 24 + 9$$
$$24 - (2.326)(3.87) \text{ or } 24 - 9$$

We, therefore, conclude that the interval (15, 33) will cover the true score of this individual on this intelligence test, and we know that our statement concerning the true score ξ will be correct in 98 per cent of such cases.

Problem X.7. Confidence Interval for the Ratio of Two Population Variances Based on the Estimates of Two Independent Random Samples

The confidence interval is set up as follows:

We can obtain from the distribution of F, for a specified confidence coefficient $1 - \alpha$, the values of F for $n_1 - 1$ and $n_2 - 1$ degrees of freedom, say, F_1 and F_2 such that

$$P\{F_1 \leq F \leq F_2\} = 1 - \alpha \qquad \text{------- (10.16)}$$

Since $F = \dfrac{S_1^2/\sigma_1^2}{S_2^2/\sigma_2^2}$, the inequality can be written as:

$$\frac{S_1^2}{S_2^2} \cdot \frac{1}{F_2} \leq \frac{\sigma_1^2}{\sigma_2^2} \leq \frac{S_1^2}{S_2^2} \cdot \frac{1}{F_1} \qquad \text{------- (10.17)}$$

Therefore, the probability that the true ratio of population variances $\dfrac{\sigma_1^2}{\sigma_2^2}$ is included or covered by the random interval,

$$\frac{S_1^2}{S_2^2} \cdot \frac{1}{F_2}, \qquad \frac{S_1^2}{S_2^2} \cdot \frac{1}{F_1} \text{ is } 1 - \alpha$$

Example X.7. Set up the 98 per cent confidence interval for the ratio of the two population variances from the estimate of two independent samples. The data are from Murray's investigation (see p. 182, Chapter VII).

$$\begin{array}{cc}
\text{Chart I (WAC)} & \text{Chart 2 (XJN)} \\
n_1 = 60 & n_2 = 72 \\
M_1 = 3.65 & M_2 = 3.47 \\
S_1 = 1.22 & S_2 = 0.76
\end{array}$$

$$F_o = \frac{(60)(1.22)^2}{59} \Big/ \frac{(72)(0.76)^2}{71}$$

$$= 2.5843$$

for $F(59, 71) \sim p < 0.01$

$$P(F_1 \leq F \leq F_2) = 1 - \alpha = 0.98$$

$$\hat{S}_1^2 = \frac{60(1.22)^2}{59} \qquad \hat{S}_2^2 = \frac{72(0.76)^2}{71}$$

$$= 1.5136 \qquad\qquad = 0.5857$$

By interpolation, $\quad F_{2_{(.01)}} (59, 71) = 1.79$

$$F_{1_{(.01)}} (59, 71) = 0.5531$$

Then the confidence limits are:

$$\frac{S_1^2}{S_2^2} \cdot \frac{1}{F_1} = \frac{2.5843}{0.5531}$$

$$= 4.672$$

and

$$\frac{S_1^2}{S_2^2} \cdot \frac{1}{F_2} = \frac{2.5843}{1.79}$$

$$= 1.444$$

Problem X.8. Confidence Interval for the Ratio of Two Population Variances When the Two Samples Are Dependent or Correlated

The confidence interval is:

$$\frac{S_1^2}{S_2^2} (K - \sqrt{K^2 - 1}) \leq \frac{\sigma_1^2}{\sigma_2^2} \leq \frac{S_1^2}{S_2^2} (K + \sqrt{K^2 - 1}) \text{ --- (10.18)}$$

where $\quad K = 1 + \dfrac{2(1 - r_{12}^2)}{n - 2} t^*$

t^* is determined from the t-distribution for $n - 2$ degrees of freedom by the requirement:

$$P\{|t| \leq t^*\} = 1 - \alpha$$

An alternative formula is (see p. 183):

$$t = \frac{(U_1 - U_2)}{U_1 U_2 - U_{12}^2} \sqrt{\frac{N - 2}{4}} \qquad \text{-------- (10.19)}$$

Example X.8. Set up the 95 per cent confidence interval for the ratio of two population variances from the estimates of two dependent samples.

The data are from Koerber's investigation (see p. 183, Chapter VII).

$$N = 19, \qquad 1 - \alpha = 0.95$$

$$K = 1 + \frac{2(1 - r_{12}^2)}{n - 2} t^*$$

$$r_{12}^2 = \frac{(166.000)^2}{(759.684)(344.000)}$$

$$= 0.1054$$

$$t_{(17)}^* = 2.11$$

$$K = 1 + 2\frac{(1 - 0.1054)}{17}(2.11)$$

$$= 1.2221$$

$$\frac{S_1^2}{S_2^2} = \frac{759.684}{344.000} = 2.2084$$

$$\sqrt{K^2 - 1} = \sqrt{1.49353 - 1} = 0.702$$

$$\frac{S_1^2}{S_2^2}(K - \sqrt{K^2 - 1}) = 2.2084(1.222 - 0.702)$$

$$= 1.1484$$

$$\frac{S_1^2}{S_2^2}(K + \sqrt{K^2 - 1}) = 4.2490$$

The confidence limits are:

$$(4.249, 1.148)$$

Problem X.9. Confidence Interval for a Population Proportion or Probability

We present first the normal approximation as the basis for determining the confidence limits for a population value, or the true proportion in the population having a specified characteristic.

The confidence limits are given by

$$p \pm \left\{ U \sqrt{\frac{N - n}{N - 1}} \sqrt{\frac{pq}{n}} + \frac{1}{2n} \right\} \qquad \text{------- (10.20)}$$

where U is the normal deviate corresponding to a specified confidence coefficient, $\frac{N - n}{N - 1}$ is the correction for sampling from a finite population of size N; n is the size of sample upon which the proportion p^1 is based; p is the population value. For the unavailable p the sample estimate is substituted; likewise for $q = 1 - p$; $\frac{1}{2n}$ is the correction for continuity.

The goodness of fit of this approximation depends upon N, n, p, and U, but particularly on np, the frequency in the smaller class. As p varies from, say, 0.5 to 0.1, the smallest size of n should be 30 and 600, correspondingly.

While it is possible by analytical use of the probability terms for the hypergeometric** distribution to obtain upper and lower limits (the smallest and highest integral values) for the number in the populations falling in a given class, special prepared tables or graphs are usually employed in practice when the normal approximation does not apply or is not sufficiently accurate. Among those, the following may be indicated.

Chung and DeLury†† have constructed charts of the confidence limits of the hypergeometric function. Tables of the binomial frequency distribution give the limits for the binomial distribution; and tables prepared by Stevens and available in Fisher and Yates' Statistical Tables‡‡ (Table VIII) give limits for np.

We may also employ the following procedure: (a) We use the relationships:

$$P\{k \geqslant k_1\} = Ip(k_1, n - k_1 + 1) = \alpha; \qquad \text{- - - - - - - - - - - (10.21)}$$
$$P\{k \geqslant k_2\} = Ip(k_2, n - k_2 + 1) = 1 - \alpha. \qquad \text{- - - - - - - - (10.22)}$$

(b) If n is the sample size, and if k is taken as the number of successes recorded out of n: then k may take values $0, 1, 2, \ldots, n - 1, n$.

We may then enter Pearson's Tables of the Incomplete Beta-Function Ratio with k_1, and $n - k_1 + 1$, and obtain k_1 and k_2 values, successively $1, 2, \ldots, n - 1$, from which we can find the different values of p which satisfy the relationship (10.21, 10.22).

(c) Plot these values of p against k/n. We obtain the confidence belt by joining the points.

Example X.9. (see p. 131, Chapter IV). The observed event (using the totals for all cases of gastric disorders) was 609 male patients to 429 female patients, or an observed proportion of 0.5867 males.

Set up the 98 per cent confidence limits for the population proportion of males as based on the sample proportion 0.5867.

$$n = 1{,}038, \ p = 0.5867, \ q = 1 - p = 0.4133$$

The confidence limits for p are

$$p \pm \left\{ U\sqrt{\frac{pq}{n}} + \frac{1}{2n} \right\}$$

$$= 0.5867 \pm \left\{ 2.33\sqrt{\frac{(0.5867)(0.4133)}{1{,}030}} + \frac{1}{2(1{,}038)} \right\}$$

** Samples drawn without replacement give the hypergeometric series.

†† J. H. Chung and D. B. DeLury, *Confidence Limits for the Hypergeometric Distribution* (Toronto: University of Toronto Press, 1950).

‡‡ R. A. Fisher and F. Yates, *Statistical Tables for Biological, Agricultural, and Medical Research*, third edition.

Tables of the binomial probability distribution (Washington, D.C.: U.S. Government Printing Office, 1950).

$$= .5867 \pm \{2.33\sqrt{.000234} + .000482\}$$
$$= .5867 \pm \{.03565 + .00048\}$$
$$= .5867 \pm \{.0361\}$$
$$= .5506, .6228$$

Problem X.10. *Setting Up a Confidence Interval for Population Difference In Proportions or Percentages from the Estimated Difference Between Two Samples*

A close approximate method for large samples is given by the following relation for a 99 per cent confidence interval:§§

$$d \pm 2.58 \sqrt{\frac{P_1(100 - P_1)}{n_1} + \frac{P_2(100 - P_2)}{n_2}} \quad \text{- - - -(10.23)}$$

That this gives a conservative estimate can be noted by determining the following critical limit where the population difference, say, $\bar{d} = 0$.

Let $P_1 = 50$ and $P_2 = 50$ and X be the normal deviate corresponding to the confidence coefficient chosen.

Substituting in (10.23), we obtain:

$$d \pm X\sqrt{\frac{50 \cdot 50}{n_1} + \frac{50 \cdot 50}{n_2}}$$

$$= d \pm X\sqrt{\frac{100^2}{4n_1} + \frac{100^2}{4n_2}}$$

$$= d \pm \frac{100X}{2}\sqrt{\frac{1}{n_1} + \frac{1}{n_2}}$$

If $X = 2.58$ (for 99 per cent confidence coefficient) then the relation becomes:

$$d \pm \frac{258}{2}\sqrt{\frac{n_1 + n_2}{n_1 n_2}}$$

$$= d \pm 129\sqrt{\frac{n_1 + n_2}{n_1 n_2}} \quad \text{- - - - - - - - - - - - (10.24)}$$

which may be used as the criterion of significance at the 1 per cent level. *Example X.10.* The following data were reported by Karpinos and Grossman,‖‖ giving the prevalence of left-handedness among qualified and disqualified registrants examined at armed forces examining stations, Continental United States, 1952.

§§ S. S. Wilks, "Confidence Limits and Critical Differences Between Percentages," *Public Opinion Quarterly*, IV (1940), 91–96.

‖‖ Bernard D. Karpinos and Harold A. Grossman, "Prevalence of Left-Handedness Among Selective Service Registrants," *Human Biology*, XXV (1953), 36–49. Reprinted by permission of the Wayne State University Press.

SAMPLE 1		SAMPLE 2	
Qualified (Inducted)		Disqualified	
Total Number	Number Left-Handed	Total Number	Number Left-Handed
6,040	471	6,119	593

Set up with a 99 per cent confidence coefficient the confidence limits for the population difference between the proportions of left-handedness of the qualified and of the disqualified on the basis of the sample information (if a difference between the proportions exists).

$$P_1 = \left(\frac{471}{6,040}\right) \times 100 = 7.798 \, , 100 - P_1 = 92.202$$

$$P_2 = \left(\frac{593}{6,119}\right) \times 100 = 9.691 \, , 100 - P_2 = 90.309$$

$$\frac{P_1(100 - P_1)}{n_1} = \frac{(7.798)(92.202)}{6,040} = 0.1190$$

$$\frac{P_2(100 - P_2)}{n_2} = \frac{(9.691)(90.309)}{6,119} = 0.1430$$

$$d = 9.691 - 7.798 = 1.893$$

Confidence limits (99 per cent) are:

$$1.893 \pm 2.58 \sqrt{0.1190 + 0.1430}$$
$$= 1.893 \pm 1.321$$
$$= (3.214, 0.572)$$

**Problem X.11. Setting Up Confidence Interval
for the Population Regression Coefficient**

We may obtain confidence limits for the population value, $\beta_{Y \cdot X}$, with the aid of the t-distribution.

For the estimate, $b_{Y \cdot X}$ we know that the quantity

$$t = \frac{b - \beta}{S_b}, \qquad S_b = \frac{S_{Y \cdot X}}{\sqrt{\Sigma x^2}}, \qquad \text{d.f.} = n = N - 2$$

has a t-distribution with $N - 2$ degrees of freedom. A hypothetical value of β may be tested by the t-test, and confidence limits for β obtained. The hypothesis that there is no relation between X and the mean value of Y may be tested by setting $\beta = 0$ in the formula above. If the hypothesis is rejected the confidence interval for a confidence coefficient $1 - \alpha$ is obtained by the following inequality:

$$b_{Y \cdot X} - t_\alpha \frac{S_{Y \cdot X}}{\sqrt{\Sigma x^2}} < \beta_{Y \cdot X} < b_{Y \cdot X} + t_\alpha \frac{S_{Y \cdot X}}{\sqrt{\Sigma x^2}} \qquad \text{-- (10.25)}$$

A calculation formula for $S_{Y \cdot X}$ is

$$S_{Y \cdot X} = \sqrt{\frac{\Sigma y^2 - \frac{(xy)^2}{\Sigma x^2}}{N - 2}}$$

Example X.11. Johnson and Jackson## reported a regression coefficient, $b_{Y \cdot X}$, of 0.115 for the regression of arithmetic reasoning scores (Y) on mental age (X) obtained from a random sample of 85 girls. Set up the 98 per cent confidence limits for the population regression coefficient, $\beta_{Y \cdot X}$.

We first require the values to be inserted in the formula for $S_{Y \cdot X}$. These values were calculated from the raw data for the 85 girls as follows:

$$\Sigma y^2 = (2.78)^2(85) = 656.914000$$
$$\Sigma x^2 = (15.237)^2(85) = 19{,}734.12437$$
$$(\Sigma xy)^2 = (0.632)^2(656.914000)(19{,}734.12437)$$
$$= 5{,}177{,}981.98324$$

also

$$\Sigma xy = 85(0.632)(2.78)(15.237)$$
$$= 5{,}177{,}981.981732$$

Then

$$S_{Y \cdot X} = \sqrt{\dfrac{656.914 - \dfrac{5{,}177{,}981.982}{19{,}734.12437}}{83}}$$

$$= \sqrt{\dfrac{394.52678}{83}}$$

$$= \sqrt{4.75333}$$

$$= 2.1802$$

$$t_{\alpha_{(.02)}}(83) = 2.372$$

The 98 per cent confidence limits for $\beta_{Y \cdot X}$ are:

$$b_{Y \cdot X} \pm \frac{S_{Y \cdot X}}{\sqrt{\Sigma x^2}} t'_{(.02)}(83) = 0.115 \pm \frac{2.18}{140.478}(2.372)$$
$$= (0.152, 0.078)$$

Problem X.12. Setting Up the Confidence Interval for the Mean of All Predicted Y'_Es or $E(Y_E)$ Which Might Occur for a Specified Value of X, Say, $X = X_0$

The standard error of the estimate of the mean of all Y'_Es for a particular value of X, say X_0, is given by

$$S_{\bar{Y}_E} = \left\{ \frac{S_Y^2(1 - r^2)}{N - 2} \left[1 + \frac{(X_0 - \bar{X})^2}{S_X^2} \right] \right\}^{\frac{1}{2}} \quad \text{- - - - (10.26)}$$

where $S_{\bar{Y}_E}$ denotes the standard error of $\bar{Y}_E$, N is the number of pairs of observations, S_Y^2 is the variance of Y, r, the product moment coefficient of correlation between Y and X; S_X^2 is the variance of X.

The confidence limits of $E(Y_E)$ for a given confidence coefficient, $1 - \alpha$, then become

$$\bar{Y}_E - t_\alpha S_{\bar{Y}_E} < E(Y_E) < \bar{Y}_E + t_\alpha S_{\bar{Y}_E} \quad \text{- - - (10.27)}$$

Example X.12. Using the data from the Johnson and Jackson results, calculate the confidence limits with a confidence coefficient of 98 per cent for the mean population value (scores on the arithmetical reasoning test), that

Introduction to Statistical Methods, p. 295.

is, $E(Y_E)$ for all those individuals in the population who have mental age scores of 121, 67, and 148, respectively.

By calculations from original data (See Example X.11) we get:

$$S_{y}^2 = \frac{656.914}{84} = 7.8204$$

$$r = 0.632, \quad 1 - r^2 = 1 - 0.399424 = 0.60058$$
$$N - 2 = 83$$
$$\bar{X} = 124.06$$
$$S_X^2 = \frac{19{,}734.12437}{84} = 234.930$$

$$S_{\bar{Y}_E} = \left\{ \frac{(7.8204)(0.60058)}{83} \left[\frac{234.930 + (X_0 - 124.06)^2}{234.930} \right] \right\}^{\frac{1}{2}}$$
$$= \{(0.00024)[234.930 + (X_0 - 124.06)^2]\}^{\frac{1}{2}}$$

Confidence limits: $\qquad\qquad \bar{Y}_E = bX_0 + b\bar{X} - \bar{Y}$
$\qquad \bar{Y}_E \pm t_\alpha\, S_{\bar{Y}_E} \qquad\qquad \bar{Y}_E(121) = 8.325$
$\qquad\qquad t_\alpha(83) = 2.372 \qquad \bar{Y}_E(67) \;= 2.115$
$\qquad\qquad\qquad\qquad\qquad\qquad \bar{Y}_E(148) = 11.430$

$$\bar{Y}_E \pm 2.372\{0.00024[234.930 + (X_0 - 124.06)^2]\}^{\frac{1}{2}}$$

For $X_0 = 121$, the confidence limits are:
$$8.325 \pm 2.372\{0.00024[234.930 + (121 - 124.06)^2]\}^{\frac{1}{2}}$$
$$= 8.325 \pm 0.574$$
$$= (8.899, 7.751)$$

For $X_0 = 67$:
$$2.115 \pm 2.372\,(0.915)$$
$$= (4.285, -0.055)$$

For $X_0 = 148$:
$$11.430 \pm 2.372(0.440)$$
$$= (12.474, 10.386)$$

Problem X.13. Setting Up the Confidence Interval for Any Single Predicted Value, Y_E Predicted from a Specified Value of X, Say X_0'

The confidence interval for Y with a specified confidence coefficient from the predicted value Y_E' is given by

$$Y_E' \pm t_\alpha\, S_{Y_E'} \qquad - - - - - - - - - - - - \text{(10.28)}$$

where $Y_E' = \bar{Y} + b(X_0' - \bar{X}) = \bar{Y} + bx_0'$

$$S_{Y_E'} = \left[1 + \frac{1}{n} + \frac{(X_0' - \bar{X})^2}{\Sigma x^2} \right]^{\frac{1}{2}} S \qquad - - - - - - \text{(10.29)}$$

$$S = \sqrt{(1 - r^2)\Sigma y^2/N - 2}$$

Example X.13. Set up the 98 per cent confidence limits of Y for a single observation predicted from a single specified X value. Let the specified X values, the X_0's be 121, 67, and 148.

As from X.12 we have:

$$Y'_{E(121)} = 8.325 \qquad t_\alpha = 2.372$$
$$Y'_{E(67)} = 2.115 \qquad S = 2.180$$
$$Y'_{E(148)} = 11.430$$

$$S_{Y'_E} = 2.180 \left[1 + \frac{1}{85} + \frac{(X'_0 - \bar{X})^2}{19,734.12437} \right]^{\frac{1}{2}}$$

$$= 2.180 \left[1.01176 + \frac{(X'_0 - 124.06)^2}{19,734.12437} \right]^{\frac{1}{2}}$$

For $X'_0 = 121$, the 98 per cent confidence limits are:

$$8.325 \pm (2.372)(2.180) \left[1.01176 + \frac{(3.06)^2}{19,734.12437} \right]^{\frac{1}{2}}$$

$$= 8.325 \pm (5.1710)(1.0061)$$
$$= 8.325 \pm 5.203$$
$$= (13.528, 3.122)$$

For $X'_0 = 67$, the confidence limits are:

$$2.115 \pm (5.1710) \left[1.01176 + \frac{(67 - 124.06)^2}{19,734.12437} \right]^{\frac{1}{2}}$$

$$= 2.115 \pm 5.610$$
$$= (7.725, -3.495)$$

For $X'_0 = 148$, confidence limits are:

$$11.430 \pm (5.1710) \left[1.01176 + \frac{(148 - 124.06)^2}{19,734.12437} \right]^{\frac{1}{2}}$$

$$= 11.430 \pm 5.275$$
$$= (16.705, 6.155)$$

Problem X.14. *Confidence Interval for the Population Correlation Coefficient, ρ*

We make use of the Z-transformation to secure the confidence interval. We may first calculate[***]

$$Z = \frac{1}{2} \log_e \frac{1 + r}{1 - r}$$

Then the confidence limits may be secured for ζ for a specified confidence coefficient, $1 - \alpha$, from the relation:

$$Z - \frac{U_\alpha}{\sqrt{N - 3}} < \zeta < Z + \frac{U_\alpha}{\sqrt{N - 3}} \qquad \text{- - - - (10.30)}$$

Finally, we may read from Fisher and Yates' table the values of r, say, r_1 and r_2 corresponding to the Z-values of the limits in (10.30).

We may then write

$$P(r_1 < \rho < r_2) = 1 - \alpha \qquad \text{- - - - - - - - (10.31)}$$

Example X.14. Johnson and Jackson[†††] reported a product-moment coefficient of correlation of 0.541 between reading and arithmetic reasoning scores of a random sample of 85 girls. Set up the 99 per cent confidence limits for ρ, the population correlation coefficient.

[***] A table of Z as a function of r is to be found in R. A. Fisher and F. Yates, *Statistical Tables for Biological, Agricultural, and Medical Research,* Table VII.
[†††] Johnson and Jackson, *op. cit.,* p. 277.

The Z-transformation is:

$$Z = \tfrac{1}{2} \log_e \frac{1.541}{0.459}$$
$$= 0.606$$

$U_{(.01)} = 2.58 \; ; \qquad \sqrt{N - 3} = \sqrt{82} = 9.055$

The 99 per cent confidence limits of ζ:

$$0.606 \pm 2.58/9.055$$
$$= (0.891, 0.321)$$

The 99 per cent limits of ρ are: $(0.71, 0.31)$ and $0.31 < \rho < 0.71$.

Problem X.15. To Test Contrasts for Significance in Analysis of Variance Problems§§§

A problem frequently encountered in experimentation where a number of treatments are under test is to know what further inferences are valid about the contrasts when the analysis of variance has led to the rejection of the null hypothesis that the values of the contrasts are zero.

Scheffé‖‖‖ has developed a technique to test contrasts for significance by setting up a confidence interval:

$$C \pm G \qquad \text{- - - - - - - - - - - - - - -} \quad (10.32)$$

where $G^2 = $ Estimated variance $(C) \cdot D^2$
and $D^2 = (k - 1)F(k - 1); (f_e : \alpha)$

f_e is the number of degrees of freedom for the error component in the analysis of variance and $1 - \alpha$ is the confidence coefficient; k is the number of parameters considered in the contrast.

Example X.15. We shall illustrate by applying the technique to the contrasts specified for the data given in Table VIII.9, Achievement Scores of 54 Boys and Girls in Grades 10, 11, 12 Classified According to Scholastic Group (see p. 214).

We make the following notation and calculations:

Let $\bar{X}_{ij}$ refer to the mean of the ith scholastic group and the jth grade.

$\bar{X}_{11} = 23.00000$	$\bar{X}_{21} = 18.16667$	$\bar{X}_{31} = 13.66667$
$\bar{X}_{12} = 25.00000$	$\bar{X}_{22} = 20.33333$	$\bar{X}_{32} = 15.66667$
$\bar{X}_{13} = 27.83333$	$\bar{X}_{23} = 20.00000$	$\bar{X}_{33} = 14.33333$

Also, μ_{ij} refers to parameter value with above i and j reference. Confidence limits are to be set up for the contrast of "good" with "average" and "poor."

$$\Gamma_1 = 2\mu_{11} + 2\mu_{12} + 2\mu_{13} - \mu_{21} - \mu_{22} - \mu_{23} - \mu_{31} - \mu_{32} - \mu_{33}$$

estimated by

$$C_1 = 2\bar{X}_{11} + 2\bar{X}_{12} + 2\bar{X}_{13} - \bar{X}_{21} - \bar{X}_{22} - \bar{X}_{23} - \bar{X}_{31} - \bar{X}_{32} - \bar{X}_{33}$$

§§§ The student may return to this problem after the study of Chapter VIII, "The Analysis of Variance," and Chapter XIV, "Design and Analysis of Statistical Investigations."

‖‖‖ Henry Scheffé, "A Method for Judging All Contrasts in the Analysis of Variance," *Biometrika*, XL (1953), 87–104.

Thus the limits are

$$C_1 \pm G$$

where $G^2 = $ Est. var. $(C_1) \cdot D^2$

$$\text{Est. var. } (C_1) = S^2\left(\frac{4}{6} + \frac{4}{6} + \frac{4}{6} + \frac{1}{6} + \frac{1}{6} + \frac{1}{6} + \frac{1}{6} + \frac{1}{6} + \frac{1}{6}\right)$$
$$= 3S^2$$

$$D^2 = (k-1)F(k-1, f_e, \alpha)$$

$$k = 9 - 1 = 8 \qquad\qquad F(8, 45, 0.05) = 2.15$$
$$f_e = 45$$
$$\alpha = 0.05$$
$$S^2 = 1{,}047$$

$$D^2 = 8F(8, 45, 0.05)$$
$$= 8(2.15)$$
$$= 17.20$$

$$G_1{}^2 = 3(1{,}047)(17.20) = 540.2520$$
$$G_1 = \sqrt{540.2520} = 23.24330$$
$$C_1 = 2(23.00000) + 2(25.00000) + 2(27.83333)$$
$$\quad - 18.16667 - 20.33333 - 20.00000$$
$$\quad - 13.66667 - 15.66667 - 14.33333$$
$$= 49.49999$$

$$G_1 \pm G_1 = 49.49999 \pm 23.24330$$
$$= (72.74, 26.26)$$

The following contrasts may also be made:

1. The "average" with "good" and "poor" $(25.74, -20.74)$
2. "Good" with "poor" groups $(45.586, 18.747)$
3. "Good" with "average" $(30.75, 3.914)$
4. "Average" with "poor" $(28.25, 1.414)$
5. "Poor" with "good" and "average" $(70.24, 23.76)$

The student is invited to carry out one or more of the calculations. You may check with the interval values recorded for each contrast.

Confidence Intervals for More Than One Unknown Parameter

If the frequency distribution is a function of more than one unknown parameter, a confidence interval can be set up for one parameter if a function of the sample can be found involving one of the parameters but which is independent of the other parameters. The problem of finding such a function often involves much mathematical difficulty. As an example we may refer to the Behrens-Fisher test of significance and the setting up of fiducial limits for difference between means when the population variances are unequal or unknown.###

For an application of this test see Palmer O. Johnson, *Statistical Methods in Research*, pp. 73–75.

ESTIMATION IN THE NON-PARAMETRIC CASE

The theoretical and practical consideration just given to problems of estimation has assumed that the functional form of the basic frequency function was known and dealt with estimating its parameters.

When the distribution of the frequency function is unknown or is not of a required type, methods of statistical analysis, usually called non-parametric methods are used. The only assumption needed is that the cumulative frequency function is continuous. We dealt with the use of these methods chiefly in testing hypotheses in Chapter IX. Here we shall treat briefly the problem of estimation in the non-parametric case.

Suppose that we have a random sample of n observations $X_1, X_2, \ldots,$ $X_k, \ldots, X_n$ arranged in order of ascending magnitude. Let P_k denote the probability integral transformation of X_k. If $\dot{X}_P$ is the P-quantile (i.e. the 100 P-centile or percentile of the sampled population), then

$$\bar{P}(\dot{X}_P < X_k) = \bar{P}(P < P_k) = \frac{n!}{(k-1)!(n-k)!}\int_P^1 P^{k-1}(1-P)^{n-k}\,dP$$

$$= I_{1-p}(n-k+1, k) \quad \text{------- (10.33)}$$

where the I-function is that tabulated in the Incomplete Beta Function Table.

By definition, the probability integral corresponding to the median, $M \equiv \dot{X}_{0.5}$, is $\frac{1}{2}$. Therefore,

$$\bar{P}(M < X_k) = \bar{P}(0.5 < P_k) = I_{0.5}(n-k+1, k) \quad \text{--- (10.34)}$$

where $\bar{P}$ is used to signify the expectation in repeated sampling under the stipulated conditions.

Also, $\bar{P}(M < X_k) = \bar{P}(M > X_{n-k+1})$

Hence $\bar{P}(X_k < M < X_{n-k+1}) = 1 - 2I_{0.5}(n-k+1, k) \quad \text{-- (10.35)}$

which is the confidence interval of the population median. This states that the unknown population median will lie in the interval extending from the kth to the $(n-k+1)$-th observation in $100\,[1 - 2I_{0.5}\,(n-k+1,\,k)]$ per cent of the cases.*

Problem X.16. Setting Up the Confidence Interval of the Population Median

A confidence interval for M is readily obtained by means of the binomial distribution and from any two order statistics, say, X_r and X_s.

Thus, the probability that an observation X falls below or above M is .50 in either case. The probability that exactly i observations fall below M is

* The development is based on the work of Thompson: William R. Thompson, "On Confidence Ranges for the Median and Other Expectation Distributions for Populations of Unknown Distribution Form," *Annals of Mathematical Statistics*, VII (1936), 122–28.

$$\binom{n}{i}\left(\frac{1}{2}\right)^n$$

The probability that X_r, the rth-order observation, exceeds M is then

$$P(X_r > M) = \sum_{i=0}^{r-1} \binom{n}{i}\left(\frac{1}{2}\right)^n \quad \text{------- (10.36)}$$

Likewise

$$P(X_s < M) = \sum_{i=s}^{n} \binom{n}{i}\left(\frac{1}{2}\right)^n \quad \text{------- (10.37)}$$

Assuming $s > r$, we add (10.36) and (10.37), subtract both sides from unity, and obtain

$$P(X_r < M < X_s) = \sum_{i=r}^{s-1} \binom{n}{i}\left(\frac{1}{2}\right)^n \quad \text{--- (10.38)}$$

which is the confidence interval for M.

Thus, for a sample of 11, one possible confidence interval for the population median is

$$P(X_2 < M < X_{10}) = 1 - \frac{24}{2^{11}}$$
$$= 0.988$$

Another is

$$P(X_3 < M < X_9) = 1 - \frac{134}{2^{11}}$$
$$= 0.934$$

For moderate sample size, Nair[†] with the aid of the Incomplete Beta Function Tables prepared a Table of Confidence Intervals for the Median for values of n from 6 through 81 and for confidence coefficients of 0.95 and 0.99.

For values of n larger than 81, the normal approximation to the binomial can be used, where X, the relative deviate, is given by

$$X = \frac{(n/2) - k}{\left(\frac{\sqrt{n}}{2}\right)} = \frac{n - 2k}{\sqrt{n}} \quad \text{-------- (10.39)}$$

The corresponding value of X for a given confidence coefficient can be obtained from the normal table, and the value of k found from the relation

$$k = \frac{n - X\sqrt{n}}{2} \quad \text{----------- (10.40)}$$

For example, a 95 per cent confidence interval is obtained by counting 1.96 $n/2$ observations above and below the sample median.

Example X.16. Johnson and Jackson[‡] reported the frequency distribution

† K. R. Nair, "Table of Confidence Intervals for the Median in Samples," *Sankhya*, IV, Part 4 (1940), 551–58.
‡ *Op. cit.*, p. 39.

of chronological ages of a sample of 85 girls. Set up the 99 per cent confidence interval for the population median.

$$k = \frac{85 - 2.58\sqrt{85}}{2}$$

$$= 30.6 \text{ or the 31st item from the bottom}$$

$$n - k + 1 = 55 \text{ or the 30th item from the top}$$

The chronological ages corresponding to these ranked items are 9 years 9.7 months and 10 years 5.5 months. Accordingly the 99 per cent confidence interval for the population median is $(10 - 5.5, 9 - 9.7)$.

Confidence Interval for Any Centile

The confidence interval for any population centile may be obtained by following the procedure employed for the median. Thus if ξ_c represents the 100 centile point of the distribution, the procedure used above to secure (10.38) may be followed to secure the confidence interval of ξ_c as

$$P(X_r < \xi_c < X_s) = \sum_{i=r}^{s-1} \binom{n}{i} p^i (1 - p)^{n-i} \quad \text{- - - - (10.41)}$$

Problem X.17. To Set Up a Confidence Interval for the Difference Between the Medians of Two Populations

Mood§ has developed the techniques for obtaining exact confidence intervals for the difference between two population medians under the assumption that the distributions differ only in location. We shall outline very briefly the large-sample approximation which may be applied when n_1 and n_2 both exceed 10. Mood gives the following confidence interval when n_1 for y, and n_2 for X both exceed 10.

$$y_s' - X_r' < \text{Mdn.}_y - \text{Mdn.}_X < y_s - X_r \quad \text{- - - (10.42)}$$

where y_s is the Sth observation of the ordered sequence $y_1 \ldots y_{n_1}$ and similarly for r on X
and where

$$S = \frac{n_2}{2} + \frac{U_\alpha \sqrt{n_2}\sqrt{n_1 + n_2}}{2(\sqrt{n_1} + \sqrt{n_2})} \quad \text{- - - - - - (10.43)}$$

$$r = \frac{n_1}{2} - \frac{U_\alpha \sqrt{n_1}\sqrt{n_1 + n_2}}{2(\sqrt{n_1} + \sqrt{n_2})} \quad \text{- - - - - - (10.44)}$$

$$S' = \frac{n_2}{2} - \frac{U_\alpha \sqrt{n_2}\sqrt{n_1 + n_2}}{2(\sqrt{n_1} + \sqrt{n_2})} \quad \text{- - - - - - (10.45)}$$

$$r' = \frac{n_1}{2} + \frac{U_\alpha \sqrt{n_1}\sqrt{n_1 + n_2}}{2(\sqrt{n_1} + \sqrt{n_2})} \quad \text{- - - - - - (10.46)}$$

Example X.17. We shall illustrate the approximation by setting up the 95 per cent confidence interval for the difference between the two population

§ A. M. Mood, *Introduction to the Theory of Statistics*, pp. 295–398.

medians in chronological age from two samples of girls, n_1 of 49, n_2 of 36. The first sample is comprised of girls in the second, third, and fourth grades; the second of those in the fifth and sixth grades.||

In our problem:

$$n_1 = 49, \qquad \sqrt{n_1} = 7$$
$$n_2 = 36, \qquad \sqrt{n_2} = 6$$
$$n_1 + n_2 = 85, \qquad \sqrt{85} = 9.220$$

Thus

$$S = \frac{36}{2} + \frac{(1.96)(6)(9.220)}{2(7+6)} = 22.2$$

$$r = \frac{49}{2} - \frac{(1.96)(7)(9.220)}{2(7+6)} = 19.6$$

$$s' = 18 - 4.17 = 13.8$$

$$r' = 24.5 + 4.865 = 29.4$$

The confidence interval is given by:

$$y_{13.8} - X_{29.4} < V_2 - V_1 < y_{22.2} - X_{19.6}$$

$y_{13.8} = 10 - 4.9$ (10 years and 4.9 months of age)

$x_{29.4} = 9 - 10.1$

$y_{22.2} = 10 - 11.1$

$x_{19.6} = 9 - 4.4$

The 95 per cent confidence interval then, is

$$[(10 - 4.9) - (9 - 10.1)] < V_2 - V_1 < [(10 - 11.1) - (9 - 4.4)]$$

or

$$(0 - 6.8) < V_2 - V_1 < (1 - 6.7)$$

EXERCISES

1. To what extent do the conclusions drawn from the statistical analyses depend on the specification?
2. What conclusions can be drawn directly from the observations without making assumptions with respect to the mathematical form of the distribution?
3. An estimate of the mean P of the population furnishes also an estimate of what other parameter?
4. Contrast the method of confidence intervals with the method of estimation by a fixed interval.
5. Distinguish between confidence limits and tolerance limits.
6. What special kinds of difficulty arise when we attempt to apply the methods of interval estimation for continuous distributions to discontinuous data?
7. Interpret the efficiency of the median compared to the mean in locating the normal curve in terms of the number of observations required.
8. When would it be of interest to consider only upper or lower confidence values of a parameter instead of both values?

|| Johnson and Jackson, *op. cit.*, p. 48.

9. How is the problem of setting up the confidence interval, which is shortest on the average, related to the problem of determining best tests of hypotheses?

10. Investigate the use of double square-root paper in setting up confidence limits for a binomial sample.

Read: F. Mosteller and John W. Tukey, "The Uses and Usefulness of Probability Paper," *Journal of the American Statistical Association*, XLIV (1949), 174–212.

11. In the case of order statistics why may the centile points of the sample be regarded as estimates of the centile points of the population?

12. What method is available for estimating the cumulative distribution of the population from that of the sample?

13. Set up the 99 per cent confidence interval for the population mean on the English test of the Commercial students from the sample data given in Chapter VI, p. 148.

14. Set up with a confidence coefficient of 95 per cent the confidence interval for the population mean on the arithmetic test on the basis of the mean and variance of the sample of 33 pupils given in Chapter VI, p. 153.

15. The mean I.Q. score on the Terman-McNemar Test of Mental Ability was 118 for a random sample of 50 seventh-grade students and 110 for a random sample of 70 tenth-grade students. The norm standard deviation on this test is 16 I.Q. points. Set up the 98 per cent confidence interval for the population mean-difference in I.Q.'s on the basis of the information of the two samples from a private secondary school.

16. Set up the 90 per cent confidence intervals for the population variances of mental ages for each of the sexes of the 26 members of unlike-sex fraternal twins given in Table VI.3, p. 168.

17. Set up the 98 per cent confidence interval estimator for the ratio of the two population variances from two independent samples in an experiment by Balziak (1953). Standard deviations of scores on the laboratory performance tests were 9.14 and 6.87, for the demonstration and individual laboratory groups, respectively. The individuals assigned at random to each group were 24 in number.

18. (a) Set up the 95 per cent confidence interval estimator for the ratio of two population variances constructed from dependent samples. Lucow (1953) reported a variance of 110.58 on the pretest and a variance of 461.36 on the after-test of a chemistry test for the 18 students assigned at random to the laboratory-centered method of instruction. For the textbook-centered group the respective variances were 113.28 and 404.25 ($N = 18$). The coefficient of correlation between scores on the pre- and aftertests were 0.68 for the laboratory and 0.33 for the textbook-centered group. (b) Set up the two confidences intervals as specified. Interpret the results. (c) Test the null hypothesis on the aftertests:

$$H_o : \sigma_1{}^2 = \sigma_2{}^2 = \sigma^2$$

against the alternative

$$H_1 : \sigma_1{}^2 \neq \sigma_2{}^2$$

If H_o is rejected set up the 95 per cent confidence interval for the variance-ratio. Interpret the results.

19. In an experiment on transfer Johnson (1936) reported the following data:

$$\text{On pretest: } \bar{X}_1 = 34.079 \; ; \qquad S_{X_1}^2 = 319.891 \; ; \qquad N = 142$$
$$\text{On endtest: } \bar{X}_2 = 47.601 \; ; \qquad S_{X_2}^2 = 228.556 \; ; \qquad N = 142$$
$$r_{12} = 0.426$$

Set up the fiducial limits for the population differences in means, with a fiducial probability of 95 per cent.

20. The following data were taken from a report on Bavarian subjects:

				BRAIN WEIGHT IN GRAMS				
				Central Values				
Men	1175	1225	1275	1325	1375	1425	1475	Total
Age (yrs.) 20–49	5	36	45	50	61	49	19	265
				Central Values				
Women	1075	1125	1175	1225	1275	1325	1375	Total
Age (yrs.) 20–49	12	22	45	54	52	20	10	215

Assuming the data to be normally distributed, accurate, homogeneous, and unselected, carry out the following:

(a) Set up the 90 per cent confidence limits for the male population mean.

(b) Set up the 90 per cent confidence limits for the female population mean.

(c) Set up the 95 per cent confidence limits for the male population standard deviation.

(d) Set up the 95 per cent confidence limits for the female population standard deviation.

(e) Set up the 95 per cent confidence interval for the population difference between the means of the sexes if a significant difference exists.

(f) Set up the 95 per cent confidence interval for the ratio of the two population variances if a significant difference between variances exists.

21. Johnson and Jackson# report intelligence quotients and reading scores for a sample of 85 girls as shown on page 313.

(a) Set up the regression equation for predicting reading score (Y) from intelligence quotient (X).

(b) Test the hypothesis, $H_o : \beta_{YX} = 0$

(c) If H_o is rejected, set up the 98 per cent confidence interval for the population regression coefficient, β_{YX}.

(d) Construct the confidence limits for the mean of all $Y_E's$ or $E(Y_E)$ for the girls in the population with the following I.Q. scores: 81, 88, 100, 128.

(e) Construct the confidence limits for a single value, Y, predicted from the same I.Q. scores in (d).

(f) Plot the regression line for Y on X and the confidence bands for both $E(Y_E's)$ and (Y). What form of conic do the confidence lines form? In which conic is the curvature greater? Explain.

22. Lucow (1953) reported a product-moment coefficient of correlation, $r = -0.63$ between chronological age and scores on the Terman-McNemar Test of Mental Ability for 19 accelerated pupils assigned at random to the group using the textbook-centered method of instruction in high school chemistry.

Op. cit., p. 30.

DATA FOR QUESTION 21

NUMBER	INTELLIGENCE QUOTIENT	READING SCORE	NUMBER	INTELLIGENCE QUOTIENT	READING SCORE
1	94	12	45	83	0
2	102	8	46	117	11
3	108	10	47	91	8
4	107	4	48	91	8
5	107	7	49	106	6
6	97	3	50	80	2
7	128	7	51	80	0
8	114	6	52	94	7
9	88	5	53	102	5
10	100	10	54	95	10
11	110	11	55	115	11
12	98	2	56	121	8
13	88	8	57	120	8
14	124	14	58	108	16
15	102	7	59	106	12
16	95	5	60	107	5
17	96	6	61	104	7
18	105	9	62	102	11
19	126	7	63	104	12
20	115	11	64	99	5
21	111	9	65	125	13
22	100	6	66	95	8
23	102	7	67	103	2
24	113	7	68	108	17
25	105	6	69	114	7
26	106	4	70	96	5
27	88	4	71	94	10
28	109	9	72	108	3
29	99	3	73	101	10
30	81	3	74	104	7
31	85	8	75	101	3
32	104	14	76	99	7
33	114	6	77	126	12
34	105	1	78	96	5
35	89	13	79	87	4
36	104	7	80	94	8
37	120	10	81	89	4
38	76	2	82	102	4
39	85	4	83	104	10
40	84	7	84	97	7
41	101	8	85	85	10
42	113	13			
43	100	9			
44	100	10			

Construct the 99 per cent confidence limits for the population correlation coefficient ρ.

23. From the study of prevalence of left-handedness of men examined at the armed forces examining stations (referred to in text), 1,064 in the sample of 12,159 men examined were left-handed. Calculate by interval estimation the 0.99 confidence limits of the incidence of left-handedness in the population sampled.

24. From the data of Chapter V, p. 131, it is observed that 74 of 609 males and 14 of 429 females had gastric or duodenal ulcers. Set up the 99 per cent confidence limits for the true sex difference in proportion of incidence of this type of ulcer.

25. From the data on p. 107, Chapter IV, set up the 98 per cent confidence limits for the population difference in proportions of correct responses on the two items of a mental test.

26. Median I.Q.'s of 119 and 116 were reported, respectively, for two samples of seventh- and eighth-grade students, each of 50 students (U.H.S., 1951) on the Terman-McNemar Test of Mental Ability.

    (a) Set up with a confidence coefficient of 95 per cent the confidence interval for the population median of each of the grades. Obtain the intervals in two ways (1) by the use of Nair's Tables and (2) by the use of the Incomplete Beta-Function Ratio Tables.

    (b) Test the difference between medians of the two samples. If significant, set up the 95 per cent confidence limits for the population difference.

27. Set up the 98 per cent confidence limits for the 75th centile on the chemistry test for (a) the high school students planning to go on to college and (b) for those not planning to go on to college. Data from Table IX.1, Chapter IX, p. 266.

28. Stein reported the means and standard deviations of the intelligence quotients based on the California Test of Mental Maturity of pupils in 46 schools in the city of Winnipeg. The values for 10 schools are given below:

SCHOOL	N	M	SD
1	47	102.00	13.09
2	39	89.05	14.13
3	30	89.80	11.74
4	59	95.90	12.11
5	15	95.00	19.22
6	24	100.33	12.88
7	29	99.60	15.35
8	28	88.60	17.68
9	34	93.60	14.79
10	53	97.70	17.91

    (a) Combine the several sample means so as to obtain a single unbiased estimate of the population mean.

    (b) Combine the several sample variances so as to obtain a single unbiased estimate of the population variance.

29. Each student should bring a book by his favorite author.

    (a) The distribution of sentence length is to be found for each author and compared with those of other authors.

    (b) Calculate the constants k_1, k_2, g_1, and g_2 for each distribution. Arrange authors in ascending order of magnitude of k_1, etc. Note: Select a random sample of pages by the use of Tables of Random Numbers. Strike out blank pages, pages containing prefatory matter, titles, contents, tabular or semi-tabular matter. Take, say, a sample of 5 per cent of the number of eligible pages, and on each of the sample pages selected count, say, 10 sentences (it may be necessary to take less than 10), starting with the first complete sentence on the page and continuing until 10 have been counted.

30. Contrast a *predictive* inference with an *inverse* inference as discussed by: R. B. McHugh, "A Predictive Confidence Interval for the Validity Coefficient," *Journal of Experimental Education*, XXIV (June, 1956), 323–24. Set up the 95 per cent predictive confidence interval for r_2 on $n_2 = 115$ from the data reported by McHugh.

CHAPTER XI

Classification and Reduction of Bivariate Data

Up to this point we have been concerned, with a few exceptions, such as the discussion of matched individuals, with one variable at a time. We turn now to a systematic discussion of two or more variables and the manner in which they may vary separately and together. The new concept introduced is that of *covariation* or *correlation*, i.e. how two or more variables behave in relation to each other. We may, for instance, observe that high values of one of our variables tend to be associated with high values of a second variable, and low with low, such as occurs in studies of the *height* and *weight* of school children. Thus we find that taller children are generally heavier, and shorter children are generally lighter: at least on the average this is true, but there are notable exceptions such as tall and thin, or short and fat, children that run contrary to the general rule.

As we indicated in our first chapter, the history of the development of the statistical concepts of covariance, regression, and correlation makes fascinating reading. Not that the idea of relationship originated with the statisticians—far from it, the underlying concepts go far back to the dim history of the beginnings of the human race, even unto the savage who first related changes in weather to the waxing and waning of the moon. Indeed, most of our superstitions that have managed to survive the scientific age are based on real or fancied relationships, being the fruits of a type of statistical inference based on haphazard, incomplete, and frequently disordered sets of observations. But statisticians like Galton defined the concept precisely, systematized the observational procedures, and succeeded in devising methods of measuring the strength (or degree) of the relationship, if any, that existed. This constituted a long step forward, from a vague discussion based on general impressions to a precise description in quantitative terms. Thus, the modern researcher may reduce and describe in simple compendious expressions not only univariate data but also bivariate and multivariate data.

Students will recall that in univariate data (see Chapter II) we distinguished between various types of data and, in addition, in the calculation of the measures of the characteristics of frequency distributions we showed the methods appropriate for *ungrouped* and *grouped* data. We will follow essentially the same procedure, here, but we will begin with *grouped continuous* data because the concepts, statistics, tests of significance, and so on are more easily interpreted in this case. Later sections will, of course, deal with other types of data and various combinations of types of data.

MEASURES OF THE DEGREE OF RELATIONSHIP FOR CONTINUOUS DATA

Students will find it profitable at this juncture to review the sections of Chapter II dealing with the classification of univariate data and the construction of tables of simple and multiple classification. They will now realize that in certain of the examples given in that chapter we were dealing with two or more variables in the tables of multiple classification. We indicated at that point the procedure to be followed in tallying and in constructing a two-way frequency distribution (or *scatter diagram*, as it is sometimes called because it shows the extent to which the values of one variable "scatter" or "vary" for specified values of the other). Likewise, we indicated how percentages and other derived values may be used in summarizing and interpreting data of single and multiple classification.

As the first example, we show in Table XI.1 the two-way frequency distribution of marks made by Grade 13 students in Ontario on an external examination in French Authors and in French Composition.* We have, for convenience, used class intervals 10 score units in width for both variables—somewhat broader than we would normally use, but preferable for instructional purposes. Observe that 6,836 students wrote both examinations, that the final column at the right of the table yields the frequency distribution for French Authors marks alone, that the final row at the bottom of the table gives the frequency distribution for French Composition marks alone, and that the cell entries in the main body of the table reveal the extent or degree of association of one variable with the other. That the degree of relationship between the two variables is high is obvious: observe that students who make high marks on one examination tend also to make high marks on the other, and that low marks on one examination tend to be associated with low marks on the other examination. In fact, the largest frequency in any row or column is, in most cases, in the diagonal cell (these have been marked in the table). But there are numerous exceptions to this general rule: for instance, the 938 students who secured a mark in French Authors of 35 to 44, both inclusive, have marks on French Composition that vary from the class intervals 5–14 to 75–84. Note, however, that approximately 80 per cent of these do have French Composition marks in the three class intervals lying between 25 and 54, both inclusive.

---

* These examinations are set and marked under the direction of a Matriculation Board, and the admission requirements of the universities in Ontario are set forth, in part, in terms of them.

TABLE XI.1

Two-way Frequency Distribution of Marks on French Authors
and French Composition

FRENCH AUTHORS	FRENCH COMPOSITION									TOTAL
	5–14	15–24	25–34	35–44	45–54	55–64	65–74	75–84	85–94	
85–94							6	43	59	108
75–84					2	57	238	372	76	745
65–74				10	87	412	542	215	17	1,283
55–64			21	160	449	766	338	51	2	1,787
45–54		3	103	352	429	372	87	9		1,355
35–44	1	23	223	354	218	111	6	2		938
25–34	2	53	173	147	38	6	2			421
15–24	8	57	65	23	1	1				155
5–14	12	17	12	2	1					44
Total	23	153	597	1,048	1,225	1,725	1,219	692	154	6,836

TABLE XI.2

Means of Distributions in Columns and Arrays
of Table XI.1

FRENCH AUTHORS CLASS INTERVAL	MEAN FRENCH COMPOSITION MARK	FRENCH COMPOSITION CLASS INTERVAL	MEAN FRENCH AUTHORS MARK
85–94	84.41	85–94	81.97
75–84	75.71	75–84	75.03
65–74	66.64	65–74	67.14
55–64	57.34	55–64	58.98
45–54	49.54	45–54	52.18
35–44	41.57	35–44	44.30
25–34	34.06	25–34	36.25
15–24	26.60	15–24	25.45
5–14	21.09	5–14	16.02
Total Distribution	55.44	Total Distribution	56.23

Each row and each column of the main body of this table constitutes a
frequency distribution, and for each of these in turn we may calculate the
measures of central position, variability, skewness, and kurtosis discussed
in Chapter II. We give in Table XI.2, and illustrate graphically in Figure
XI.1, one such set, viz. the means of rows and columns, respectively, as

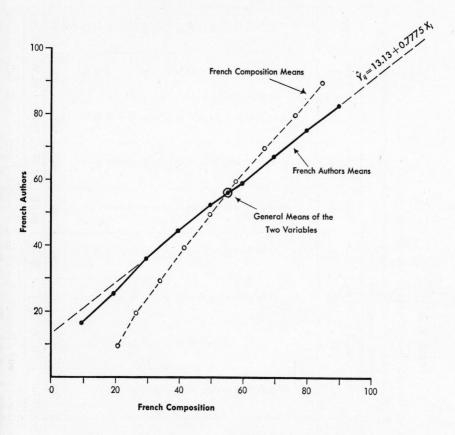

Figure XI.1. RELATIONSHIP OF MARKS IN FRENCH AUTHORS AND
COMPOSITION: PATTERNS OF MEANS

indicated. Plotting the means above the midpoints of the corresponding class intervals for the other variable yields, when the points are joined by straight lines, the two "lines" or "patterns" of means of Figure XI.1. We will return to the measures of the other characteristics as these are required in the development of the theory.

Linear Regression

Two characteristics of these row and column means should be noted by students: first, the pattern or trend is amazingly close to being a straight line (the successive increases being nearly constant); second, the means tend to be closer to the general averages (called the "general means," to distinguish them from the means for the several class intervals) than do the midpoints of the class intervals for the other variable. For example,

TABLE XI.3

Two-way Frequency Distribution of Army Alpha Scores and Age

ARMY ALPHA SCORE	CHRONOLOGICAL AGE												TOTAL
	11 and 12	13 and 14	15 and 16	17 and 18	19 to 21	22 to 24	25 to 29	30 to 34	35 to 39	40 to 44	45 to 49	50 to 54	
200–209					2								2
190–199					3								3
180–189					6		1	1		1			6
170–179				1	2	1	2	4	1	3			20
160–169			2	2	2	1	2	2	2	3	2		18
150–159			5	2	6	3	3	3	1	4	1		30
140–149			7	6	1	3	5	4	4	6	5	1	42
130–139		2	11	4	7	4	1	9	7	7	2	2	49
120–129		2	9	4	6	4	1	7	8	4	1	2	59
110–119	2	6	10	9	4	3	8	7	6	6	5	1	74
100–109	3	8	8	11	9	3	6	5	5	5	3	2	56
90–99	2	8	15	3	5	2	12	2	7	9	5	7	83
80–89	10	21	18	9	9	6	10	11	11	10	7	3	117
70–79	9	12	13	10	7	3	13	11	5	4	5	3	97
60–69	17	15	11	6	11	2	7	8	4	6	8	2	104
50–59	21	21	7	12	1	4	9	7	10	9	10	4	118
40–49	14	14	6	5	6	3	3	7	6	5	4	6	76
30–39	25	8	8	8	1	1	2	6	9	3	5	4	85
20–29	16	6	5	4		1	1	5	7	3	2	6	52
10–19	2	5	2	1			3	4	3	6	4	4	31
0–9	4	1					1	1		1		1	8
Total	125	129	137	97	88	44	90	104	96	95	69	56	1,130
Mean	51.30	67.45	90.41	95.94	101.09	91.32	89.17	88.54	83.04	91.55	78.85	82.54	82.91

From a study by H. B. Jones of the entire population of a rural community, quoted from unpublished material in the following book:
E. L. Thorndike, E. O. Bregman, J. W. Tilton, ...

for the French Authors midpoints and French Composition means we have the following pattern:†

Midpoints (French Authors)	9.5	19.5	29.5	39.5	49.5	59.5	69.5	79.5	89.5
Means (French Composition)	21.09	26.60	34.06	41.57	49.54	57.34	66.64	75.71	84.41
Difference	+11.59	+7.10	+4.56	+2.07	+0.04	−2.16	−2.86	−3.79	−5.09

It is of some interest historically that this effect—this "backward movement" to the general means—was first noted by Galton in his studies of inheritance, and he quite properly termed it a "regression" toward the racial average.‡ While we now use the term "regression" in a different sense, as indeed Galton later did also, the original effect is observable in nearly all studies of bivariate data, and an understanding of this original concept will help students to understand the theory that follows.

The term "linear regression" is applied to cases where the pattern of means is very close to a straight line. We hasten to add that the means do not always follow such a simple pattern. A rather unusual case is shown in Table XI.3—unusual not only in the pattern of means (see the bottom row of the table), but in the extent of the overlap of the Alpha score distributions for the various ages.§ In this case, for obvious reasons, we are interested mainly in the mean Alpha score for each age group, not in the mean age for each Alpha score class interval, whereas in the previous case both sets of means are of equal interest and importance. Since we will be referring to these data from time to time in subsequent discussions, we show the graph of the pattern of means in Figure XI.2. Patterns of this kind, although not generally as extreme, occur frequently in experiments concerned with learning and memory—with animals as well as with humans.

Galton, in his study of regression, was interested in prediction—of characteristics of offspring from those of their parents. From the mean heights of sons of fathers in the several height groups, for example, one can predict with fair accuracy—certainly on the average—the probable heights of sons of fathers of particular heights.‖ Likewise, from Table XI.2 or Figure XI.1, we can with considerable confidence predict for any

† The two general means being so nearly equal (55.44 vs. 56.23), the effect of any difference may be ignored here.

‡ Students may be intrigued by the implications of this effect, or of its absence, for the inheritance of physical and mental traits in humans.

§ Of some comfort to us oldsters, in that apparently not all youngsters are geniuses, nor are all oldsters morons!

‖ Recent studies indicate that, at least on this continent, the new generation will be much taller and heavier than previous generations, which requires an adjustment in any such predictions.

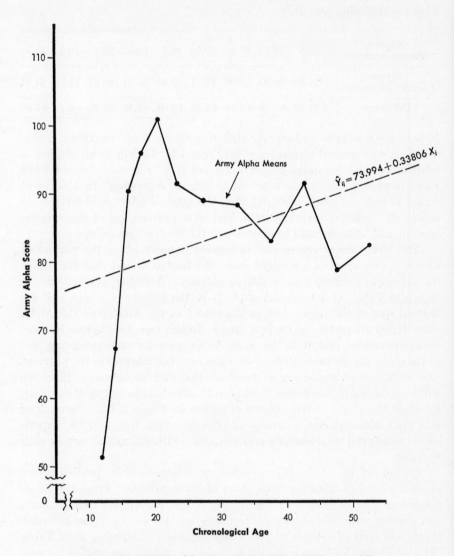

Figure XI.2. PATTERN OF MEAN ARMY ALPHA SCORES, BY AGES

individual the probable French Composition mark from the known French Authors mark, and vice versa. This process of prediction is considerably simplified, of course, if we can express the pattern of means in formula form. Where the pattern of means is linear, the appropriate formula will be of the usual linear equation form

$$\hat{Y} = a + bX$$

where $\hat{Y}$ denotes the predicted value of one variable, X the known value of the other variable, a the intercept on the Y-axis (value of Y when $X = 0$), and b the slope of the line (tangent of the angle the line makes with the X-axis), as illustrated in the following diagram:

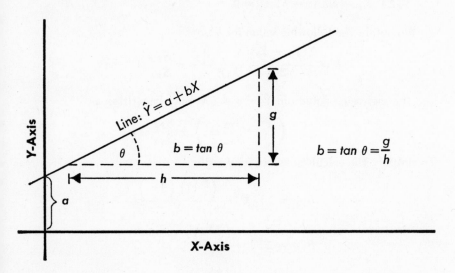

But, since there exists a very large number of possible lines, secured by varying the value of a or of b, or of both, we must select the one that seems to fit best. To do this we must define exactly what is meant by the phrase "best fit." It seems reasonable to require of the line selected that the deviations, or some function of the deviations, of the observed Y's from predicted Y's, i.e. $Y - \hat{Y}$, should be a minimum, that is, smaller than for any other possible line. To secure such a line, we apply the least squares method to determine the appropriate values of a and b.

Ungrouped Data

Let us first consider the case of ungrouped data, since the mathematics are somewhat simpler, and denote by (Y_i, X_i), where $i = 1, 2, \ldots, N$, the ith pair of our N pairs of observations. We define

$$\chi^2 = \sum_i (Y_i - \hat{Y}_i)^2 = \sum_i (Y_i - a - bX_i)^2$$

and, in much the same fashion as for the cases considered in the chapter on analysis of variance, determine those values of a and b (considering them as variables for the purpose) which minimize the value of χ^2. The line so determined we shall define as the line of "best fit." Differentiating partially with respect to a and b in turn, setting the resulting equations equal to zero and simplifying, we secure the following two equations to solve for the values of a and b.

$$a = Y. - bX.$$

$$\sum_i Y_i X_i - NaX. - b\sum_i X_i^2 = 0$$

where
$$Y. = (\sum_i Y_i)/N$$
$$X. = (\sum_i X_i)/N$$

We obtain the following value for b

$$b = \frac{\sum_i (Y_i - Y.)(X_i - X.)}{\sum_i (X_i - X.)^2} = \frac{S_{YX}}{S_{XX}}, \quad \text{say,}$$

and the regression equation, $\hat{Y} = a + bX$, may be written as

$$\hat{Y}_i = \left(Y. - \frac{S_{YX}}{S_{XX}} X.\right) + \frac{S_{YX}}{S_{XX}} X_i$$

To simplify the calculations, we may write

$$S_{YX} = \sum_i Y_i X_i - \frac{\left(\sum_i X_i\right)\left(\sum_i Y_i\right)}{N}$$

$$S_{YY} = \sum_i Y_i^2 - \frac{\left(\sum_i Y_i\right)^2}{N}$$

and
$$S_{XX} = \sum_i X_i^2 - \frac{\left(\sum_i X_i\right)^2}{N}$$

to yield the absolute minimum value, $\chi_a^2 = S_{YY} - b^2 S_{XX} = S_{YY} - \frac{S_{YX}^2}{S_{XX}}$

In order to develop tests of hypotheses concerning the values of a and b (for instance, $H_{01} : a = 0$ or $H_{02} : b = 0$, or even $H_{03} : a = 0, b = 0$) we assume that the Y_i are normally distributed with mean $a + bX_i$ and constant variance σ^2. Observe that for $H_{01} : a = 0$ we have

$$\chi^2 = \sum_i (Y_i - bX_i)^2$$

and minimizing with respect to b to obtain the relative minimum value of χ^2, we find after some algebraic manipulation that

$$\chi_{r01}^2 = \chi_a^2 + \frac{Na^2 S_{XX}}{\sum X_i^2} = \chi_a^2 + \chi_{01}^2$$

where $a = Y. - \frac{S_{YX}}{S_{XX}} X.$. The appropriate test of H_{01} is, therefore, using the analysis of variance form,

$$F = \frac{Na^2 S_{XX}}{\sum X_i^2} \bigg/ \frac{\chi_a^2}{N - 2}; \quad n_1 = 1, n_2 = N - 2 \#$$

Or $t = \sqrt{F}$ with $N - 2$ degrees of freedom.

Likewise, for the test of the hypothesis $H_{02} : b = 0$ we have for the relative minimum value of $\chi^2 = \sum_i (Y_i - a)^2$, the value

$$\chi^2_{r02} = \chi^2_a + b^2 S_{XX} = \chi^2_a + \chi^2_{02}$$

where $b = \dfrac{S_{YX}}{S_{XX}}$, and the appropriate test of H_{02} is

$$F = \frac{b^2 S_{XX}}{\chi^2_a / N - 2} ; \qquad n_1 = 1, \qquad n_2 = N - 2$$

For the test of the hypothesis $H_{03} : a = b = 0$, we have $\chi^2_{r03} = \chi^2_a + NY^2 + b^2 S_{XX} = \chi^2_a + \chi^2_{03}$ and the appropriate test of H_{03} will be

$$F = \frac{NY^2 + b^2 S_{XX}}{2} \cdot \frac{N - 2}{\chi^2_a} ; \qquad n_1 = 2, \qquad n_2 = N - 2$$

Tests of more general hypotheses may be derived in a similar fashion.** For the test of the hypothesis that a equals a specified constant a_0, for instance, we use the quantity

$$F = \frac{N(a - a_0)^2 S_{XX}}{\Sigma X_i^2} \cdot \frac{N - 2}{\chi^2_a} ; \qquad n_1 = 1, \qquad n_2 = N - 2$$

and for the test of the hypothesis that b equals a specified constant b_0, we use the quantity

$$F = \frac{(b - b_0)^2 (S_{XX})(N - 2)}{\chi^2_a} ; \qquad n_1 = 1, \qquad n_2 = N - 2$$

It is not often, however, that the researcher encounters problems in which such general hypotheses are of interest.

As an illustration of the methods of calculating and interpreting the results derived above, we show in Table XI.4 data relating to the mental ages of fraternal unlike-sex twins. Assuming linearity of regression $(\hat{Y}_i = a + bX_i)$ and normality†† and constant variance of the distribution of the Y_i about $\hat{Y}_i$, where required, we have

$$b = \frac{4,510.50}{13,004.50} = 0.346841$$

$$a = 135.73077 - (0.346841)(140.50000) = 86.99961$$

$$b^2 S_{XX} = \frac{S_{YX}^2}{S_{XX}} = \frac{(4,510.50)^2}{13,004.50} = 1,564.43$$

$$\chi^2_a = S_{YY} - \frac{S_{YX}^2}{S_{XX}} = 8,753.12 - 1,564.43 = 7,188.69$$

** For a derivation of some of these tests see, for example, A. M. Mood, *Introduction to the Theory of Statistics*, pp. 291-97.

†† Students may, as an exercise, calculate the 26 residuals $(Y_i - a - bX_i)$ and check for normality of distribution.

TABLE XI.4

ILLUSTRATION OF LINEAR REGRESSION FOR UNGROUPED CONTINUOUS DATA:
MENTAL AGES OF UNLIKE-SEX TWINS

TWIN PAIR (i)	MENTAL AGE		TWIN PAIR (i)	MENTAL AGE	
	Boys (Y_i)	Girls (X_i)		Boys (Y_i)	Girls (X_i)
1	97	110	14	130	111
2	129	103	15	113	138
3	131	139	16	140	162
4	151	132	17	177	146
5	180	140	18	141	144
6	124	118	19	134	135
7	133	142	20	120	127
8	158	160	21	116	116
9	128	145	22	138	177
10	140	145	23	122	125
11	126	117	24	122	158
12	130	136	25	149	164
13	139	205	26	161	158

$$\sum_i Y_i = 3{,}529 \qquad \sum_i X_i = 3{,}653$$

$$\sum_i Y_i^2 = 487{,}747 \qquad \sum_i X_i^2 = 526{,}251$$

$$\sum_i X_i Y_i = 500{,}335 \qquad N = 26$$

$$Y. = 135.73077 \qquad X. = 140.50000$$

$$S_{YY} = 8{,}753.12 \qquad S_{XX} = 13{,}004.50$$

$$S_{YX} = 4{,}510.50$$

$$\chi_a^2/N - 2 = 7{,}188.69/24 = 299.53$$

$$\frac{Na^2 S_{XX}}{\sum X_i^2} = \frac{(26)(86.99961)^2(13{,}004.50)}{526{,}251} = 4{,}863.05$$

$$NY^2 = \frac{\left(\sum_i Y_i\right)^2}{N} = \frac{(3{,}529)^2}{26} = 478{,}993.88$$

Whence for the test of $H_{01} : a = 0$ we calculate

$$F = \frac{4{,}863.05}{299.53} = 16.24; \qquad n_1 = 1 \quad \text{and} \quad n_2 = 24$$

and since $F_{.01}$ is 7.82 we reject H_{01} and conclude that a is significantly greater than zero. For the test of $H_{02} : b = 0$, we calculate

$$F = \frac{1{,}564.43}{299.53} = 5.22; \qquad n_1 = 1 \quad \text{and} \quad n_2 = 24$$

and, since $F_{.05} = 4.26$ and $F_{.01} = 7.82$, we would reject H_{02} at the 5 per cent level but accept it at the 1 per cent level. Similarly, for the test of the hypothesis $H_{03} : a = b = 0$, we calculate

$$F = \frac{(478{,}993.88) + (1{,}564.43)}{(2)(299.53)}$$

$$= \frac{480{,}558.31}{599.06} = 802.19; \qquad n_1 = 2 \quad \text{and} \quad n_2 = 24$$

and since $F_{.01} = 5.61$ we reject H_{03}.

It is of some interest that we may set up the quantities in an analysis of variance table, which gives the tests of H_{02} and H_{03} directly but not of H_{01}. We secure the entries in the usual fashion by writing

$$Y_i = \left\{ (Y_i - Y.) - \frac{S_{YX}}{S_{XX}}(X_i - X.) \right\} + Y. + \frac{S_{YX}}{S_{XX}}(X_i - X.)$$

whence
$$\sum_i Y_i^2 = \left(S_{YY} - \frac{S_{YX}^2}{S_{XX}} \right) + NY^2 + \frac{S_{YX}^2}{S_{XX}}$$

and we have

VARIANCE	DEGREES OF FREEDOM	SUM OF SQUARES	MEAN SQUARE
Mean	1	NY^2	NY^2
Slope	1	$\chi_{02}^2 = \dfrac{S_{YX}^2}{S_{XX}} = b^2 S_{XX}$	$b^2 S_{XX}$
Residual Deviations	$N - 2$	$S_{YY} - b^2 S_{XX} = S_{YY} - \dfrac{S_{YX}^2}{S_{XX}} = \chi_a^2$	$\dfrac{S_{YY} - b^2 S_{XX}}{N - 2}$
Total	N	$\sum Y_i^2$	—

Note, however, that the test of $H_{01} : a = 0$ (for which we have assumed $b \neq 0$) does not appear, save for the denominator $\chi_a^2/N - 2$, since its numerator χ_{01}^2 involves values other than those calculated above. For the test of $H_{03} : a = b = 0$, observe that χ_{03}^2 is the sum of the entries in the first two rows, each having 1 degree of freedom; for the test of $H_{02} : b = 0$, the value of χ_{02}^2 is given in the second row. The test of another hypothesis is indicated in the above table, to which reference was made in an earlier section, namely the hypothesis that the mean Y is zero, i.e. $H_{04} : \xi_Y = 0$. The appropriate test is

$$F = \frac{(N)(N - 2)(Y.^2)}{\chi_a^2}; \qquad n_1 = 1, n_2 = N - 2$$

Students will observe that we have considered above only the prediction of values of Y from known values of X. Normally this is all we are interested in, such as in the prediction of success at university (Y) from a knowledge of intelligence (X), but logically and mathematically we might with equal justification consider the estimation of values of X from known values of Y. The regression equation in this case may be written

$$\hat{X} = c + dY$$

where

$$c = X. - dY.$$

and

$$d = \frac{S_{XY}}{S_{YY}} = \frac{S_{YX}}{S_{YY}}$$

Students should, as an exercise, derive these formulae and the corresponding tests of the hypotheses equivalent to those considered above. As a check on the results, the corresponding formulae are most easily secured by writing X for Y and Y for X in each of the equations previously derived. We will make use of both regression equations in some of the sections that follow.‡‡

Grouped Data

For grouped data, such as those in tables XI.1 and XI.3, we can easily make a more thorough analysis and determine whether or not the regression is linear—which it obviously is not for the data of Table XI.3. A complete discussion of non-linear regression, however, will be postponed until the next chapter, because it is a special application of the theory of multiple regression. (Methods appropriate for both ungrouped and grouped data will be discussed at that time.)

To illustrate the methods applicable to grouped data, we will use the two-way frequency distribution of Table XI.1 in the first instance, and then the distribution of Table XI.3 in the discussion of the case where the regression is obviously non-linear in form. Denoting by Y_{ij} the mark on French Authors made by the ith student in the jth class interval on French Composition, where $i = 1, 2, \ldots, n_j$; n_j denotes the number of cases in the jth French Authors class interval; and $j = 1, 2, \ldots, k$ ($k = 9$, here); and denoting by $Y._j = \dfrac{\sum\limits_{i} Y_{ij}}{n_j}$ the mean French Authors mark for the jth French Composition class interval (see Table XI.2); and

‡‡ A third possible regression equation exists, although it is not of much practical value or interest. A complete discussion of the three regression lines is given, for instance, in B. H. Camp, *The Mathematical Part of Elementary Statistics* (Boston: D. C. Heath and Co., 1931), pp. 152–63. Students with some knowledge of calculus might be asked to review this discussion and report to the class on the nature and possible uses of this third regression line.

TABLE XI.5

VARIANCE	DEGREES OF FREEDOM	SUM OF SQUARES	MEAN SQUARE
Among Groups	$k - 1$	$\sum_i \sum_j (Y_{.j} - Y_{..})^2$	$\sum_j (Y_{.j} - Y_{..})^2 / k - 1$
Within Groups	$N - k$	$\sum_i \sum_j (Y_{ij} - Y_{.j})^2$	$\sum_i \sum_j (Y_{ij} - Y_{.j})^2 / N - k$
Total	$N - 1$	$\sum_i \sum_j (Y_{ij} - Y_{..})^2$	$\sum_i \sum_j (Y_{ij} - Y_{..})^2 / N - 1$

by $N = \sum_i n_j$ the total number of students (6,836 here), note that we have in general k frequency distributions or groups of Y's. Following the analysis of variance procedure of the earlier chapter, the total sum of squares of the Y's may be written as shown in Table XI.5 (assuming, as we must here, that the values in any class interval of Y are concentrated at the midpoint of that interval).

For the data of Table XI.1, we have the following numerical results:

VARIANCE	DEGREES OF FREEDOM	SUM OF SQUARES	MEAN SQUARE
Among Groups	8	1,094,525	136,815.6
Within Groups	6,827	603,372	88.38
Total	6,835	1,697,897	248.41

Up to this point no hypotheses or tests thereof have been involved, so the analysis presented is not affected by the form of the distributions or heterogeneity of variances: the equation representing the division of the total sum of squares is an algebraic identity. But generally we wish to go beyond this purely descriptive phase and test certain hypotheses. The first hypothesis we must test is obviously concerned with the differences among the group means: if these are not significant, there is no point in proceeding with the analysis—for linear or any other form of regression. For the purposes of this test, we may consider the Y's as being divided into k groups of values with an unequal number of observations, n_j, in the several groups. This, then, is the simple case of an analysis of variance for a one-way classification with unequal numbers in the subclasses. Note, however, that the statistical test involved is, strictly speaking, valid only when the distributions of Y in the several subclasses are normal with common variance.

As so often happens with data of this kind, our distributions in the subclasses at the extreme left and right of Table XI.1 are clearly not normal in form, although in the majority of the subclasses the normality assumption appears to be reasonably well satisfied. The several variances likewise indicate a departure from homogeneity in that the values for the extreme subclasses tend to be smaller, as the following table shows:

FRENCH COMPOSITION CLASS INTERVAL	DEGREES OF FREEDOM	VARIANCE OF Y (FRENCH AUTHORS)
5–14	22	69.18
15–24	152	88.74
25–34	596	111.57
35–44	1,047	104.73
45–54	1,224	91.61
55–64	1,724	88.19
65–74	1,218	79.24
75–84	691	63.15
85–94	153	48.45

Applying Bartlett's test, we obtain a value of $\chi^2 = 105$, which means that the variances are significantly different. In view of the fact that neither assumption is satisfied, we must, in applying the F-test (the only test available) to our results, interpret the findings with caution, since we will have only an approximate test. For our test of the above hypothesis, however, we have

$$F = \frac{136{,}815.6}{88.38} = 1{,}548 \; ; \qquad n_1 = 8, n_2 = 6{,}827$$

and, no matter how poor the approximation may in fact be, there is no doubt that the means do differ significantly.

Let us now introduce the linear regression equation into the analysis, algebraically in the first instance to secure a description of departures from linear regression, if any. We may always write

$$(Y_{ij} - Y..) = (Y_{ij} - Y._j) + (Y._j - a - bX_j) + (a + bX_j - Y..)$$
$$= (Y_{ij} - Y._j) + \{(Y._j - Y..) - b(X_j - X.)\}$$
$$+ b(X_j - X.)$$

where $\quad X. = \dfrac{\sum\limits_j n_j X_j}{N}, \, a = Y.. - bX. , \, \S\S$ and

$$b = \frac{\sum\limits_i \sum\limits_j (Y_{ij} - Y..)(X_j - X.)}{\sum\limits_j n_j (X_j - X.)^2} = \frac{\sum\limits_j n_j (Y._j - Y..)(X_j - X.) \, \S\S}{\sum\limits_j n_j (X_j - X.)^2}$$

since X_j is constant for all values of Y_{ij} in the jth class interval of X. The arrangement is illustrated below, showing how the distance (parallel

§§ Students should attempt the derivation of these formulae for a and b.

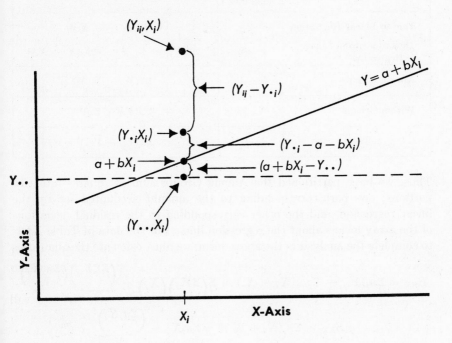

to the Y-axis) of Y_{ij} from $Y..$ is broken into three parts: $(Y_{ij} - Y._j)$ is the distance of the observation Y_{ij} from the mean $Y._j$ of that array; $(Y._j - a - bX_j)$ is the distance from the mean of the array $Y._j$ to the regression line, representing the departure of the array mean from the regression line; and $(a + bX_j - Y..)$ is the distance from the regression line to the general mean $Y..$, representing the influence of the regression since this distance must be zero if $b = 0$. Note, also, that if the deviations $(Y._j - a - bX_j)$ are large, then obviously our regression line is a poor fit to the array means.

Squaring both sides of the expression

$$(Y_{ij} - Y..) = (Y_{ij} - Y._j) + \{(Y._j - Y..) - b(X_j - X.)\} + b(X_j - X.)$$

and summing for i and j, we obtain

$$\sum_i\sum_j(Y_{ij} - Y..)^2 = \sum_i\sum_j(Y_{ij} - Y._j)^2$$
$$+ \left\{\sum_i\sum_j(Y._j - Y..)^2 - b^2\sum_j n_j(X_j - X.)^2\right\} + b^2\sum_j n_j(X_j - X.)^2$$

Accordingly, our analysis of variance table may be written in the form:

VARIANCE	DEGREES OF FREEDOM	SUM OF SQUARES
Due to Linear Regression	1	$b^2 \sum_i n_j (X_j - X.)^2$
Deviations from Linear Regression	$k - 2$	$\sum_i \sum_j (Y._j - Y..)^2 - b^2 \sum_j n_j (X_j - X.)^2$
Among Groups	$k - 1$	$\sum_i \sum_j (Y._j - Y..)^2$
Within Groups	$N - k$	$\sum_i \sum_j (Y_{ij} - Y._j)^2$
Total	$N - 1$	$\sum_i \sum_j (Y_{ij} - Y..)^2 = S_{YY}$

Thus, we have partitioned the Among Groups sum of squares into two portions: one part corresponding to the amount accounted for by the linear regression, and the other corresponding to the residual deviations of the array means about the regression line. For the data of Table XI.1, to complete the analysis in the above form, we must calculate the quantities

$$S_{YX} = \sum_j n_j (Y._j - Y..)(X_j - X.) = \sum_j \left(\sum_i Y_{ij} \right) (X_j) - \frac{\left(\sum_i \sum_j Y_{ij} \right) \left(\sum_j n_j X_j \right)}{N}$$

$$S_{XX} = \sum_j n_j (X_j - X.)^2 = \sum_j n_j X_j^2 - \frac{\left(\sum_j n_j X_j \right)^2}{N}$$

We secure the values

$$S_{YX} = 1,404,224$$
$$S_{XX} = 1,806,033$$

whence
$$b = \frac{1,404,224}{1,806,033} = 0.7775$$

Our analysis of variance table is, therefore, as follows:

VARIANCE	DEGREES OF FREEDOM	SUM OF SQUARES	MEAN SQUARE
Due to Linear Regression	1	1,091,810	1,091,810
Deviations from Linear Regression	7	2,715	387.86
Among Groups	8	1,094,525	136,815.6
Within Groups	6,827	603,372	88.38
Total	6,835	1,697,897	248.41

Practically the whole of the sum of squares among groups is accounted for by linear regression, although the deviations of the array means about the regression line, while small, are probably significant. Subject to the limitations previously discussed, we may use as an approximate test of significance of these deviations the quantity

$$F = \frac{387.86}{88.38} = 4.39$$

which, for $n_1 = 7$ and $n_2 = 6,827$, lies beyond the 1 per cent point of the F-distribution and must, therefore, be judged significant.|||| The effect, while present, is clearly not of much practical importance, since it is so small, but there is some evidence of a non-linear relation, at least at the lower end, in Figure XI.1 where the regression line

$$\hat{Y}_{ij} = a + bX_j = 13.13 + 0.7775X_j$$

has been drawn through the set of array means $(Y_{.j})$.

Students should derive and present the corresponding formulae and results for the other regression equation

$$\hat{X}_{ij} = c + dY_j$$

using the two frequency distributions, means, etc. from tables XI.1 and XI.2. They should also test the assumptions underlying the statistical tests employed and determine, at least for the approximate solution, whether the deviations from linear regression are significant for this case also. We will turn now to the data of Table XI.3, and the prediction of Army Alpha scores (Y) from a knowledge of Chronological Age (X), since these data present some unusual features and difficulties of interpretation.

We must examine first the validity of the assumptions underlying the statistical tests to be employed. Note that for the X variable, Chronological Age, no assumptions are made concerning the form of distribution or homogeneity of variance, that is for the analysis associated with the regression of Y on X. As for the assumption of normality for the distribution of the Y's in each column, inspection of the subdistributions in Table XI.3 indicates that they are reasonably symmetrical but are somewhat platykurtic. Accordingly, although the normality assumption is not completely satisfied, there is little evidence of sufficient non-normality to invalidate the statistical tests to be employed in testing for linearity of regression. With respect to the assumption of a common variance for Y in all columns (Chronological Age groups), however, we find for Bartlett's test that χ^2 is approximately 86 and, for $k = 12$, is significantly greater

|||| The test of $b = 0$ is $F = \dfrac{1,091,810}{88.38}$; $\qquad n_1 = 1$, $n_2 = 6,827$

than expected. As in the previous case, therefore, the assumption of homogeneity of variances is not satisfied (owing largely to small variances in two age groups, viz. 11–12 and 13–14). Consequently, the tests of the various hypotheses must be interpreted with considerable caution, since our Within Groups mean square is an average rather than an estimate of a common variance.

The results of the analysis are given in the following table:

VARIANCE	DEGREES OF FREEDOM	SUM OF SQUARES	MEAN SQUARE	F-RATIO
Due to Linear Regression	1	20,588	20,588	13.81
Deviations from Linear Regression	10	206,608	20,661	13.86
Among Groups	11	227,196	20,654	13.85
Within Groups	1,118	1,666,537	1,491	—
Total	1,129	1,893,733	1,677	—

(using the Within Groups mean square in each case for the denominator of the F-ratio). Even without an exact test, it is quite clear that the linear regression factor is significant (equivalent to rejection of the hypothesis that $b = 0$), and even clearer that the deviations from linear regression are significant (as a glance at Figure XI.2 will indicate must be so). It is instructive, for this case, to calculate the values for the linear regression equation. We have

$$Y.. = 82.907$$
$$X. = 26.365$$
$$S_{XX} = 180,148$$
$$S_{YX} = 60,901$$

whence
$$b = \frac{60,901}{180,148} = 0.33806; \quad a = 73.994; \quad \text{and}$$

$\hat{Y}_{ij} = 73.994 + 0.33806 X_j$. The line has been plotted and drawn in Figure XI.2. While it does pass through a sort of intermediate position with respect to the array means, it obviously does not represent an adequate formula for the prediction of Army Alpha scores from Chronological Age. Unlike the previous example, therefore, the need for a formula expressing non-linear relationship is evident. This extension will, as indicated earlier, be considered in the next chapter: we turn now to measures of the *degree* of relationship and the statistical concepts and tests associated therewith.

Measures of Degree of Relationship

The concepts of *regression* and *degree of relationship* have much in common, although the former is concerned primarily with prediction and the latter with a measure of the degree of relationship, or extent of agreement, between the two variables. In cases such as the comparison of marks on the French Authors and French Composition examinations, our interest would generally be, not in predicting marks on one paper from those on the other, but in determining the extent of the agreement between the two sets of marks. Any serious *lack* of agreement (i.e. the existence of little or no agreement between the two sets of marks) would probably lead one to question the validity or the reliability of the examinations.## In perhaps the majority of problems concerning two variables, in fact, it is degree of relationship, not regression, that is the primary concern of the researcher—from the problems concerning inheritance that Galton studied originally to the problems of the identification of factors (factor analysis begins with measures of degree of relationship) in psychology and education and of possible causes of diseases (such as cancer) in medical research.

To illustrate the concepts, consider the data of Table XI.1 and observe that the pattern of frequencies is roughly of an oval shape. Lines joining equal frequencies would, in fact, form a series of rough concentric ellipses with the major axes (in this case) running more or less through the set of diagonal cells and with relatively short minor axes. If all the values fell in the diagonal cells, the agreement between the two sets of marks (for this set of class intervals, at least) would be perfect—the ellipse pattern becoming a straight line and the two regression lines of Figure XI.1 would in that event coincide. At the other extreme, we can visualize the situation where the variation in any array is of the same order of magnitude as in the marginal distributions, the agreement between the two sets of marks being very low—in which case the ellipse pattern becomes roughly circular and the two regression lines of Figure XI.1 become perpendicular to each other and parallel to the respective axes.*** In summary, if there is no relationship between the variables, then the pattern of frequencies is circular and the two regression lines are perpendicular to each other. As the degree of relationship increases, the patterns of frequencies form ellipses with progressively shorter minor axes and the two regression lines become closer together, the ellipse becoming a straight line and the regression lines coinciding for perfect relationship or agreement. The relationship may, of course, be either positive or negative: positive, if the two variables increase and decrease in value together; negative, if one variable increases in value while the other decreases.

This discussion leads directly to the derivation of the formula for the measure of the degree of relationship, first proposed by Karl Pearson, known as the *Pearson product-moment coefficient of correlation* and generally

For detailed discussions of the means of estimating the reliability and validity of measurements see, Johnson and Jackson, *Introduction to Statistical Methods*, pp. 290–319, and Johnson, *Statistical Methods in Research*, pp. 123–47.

*** Students with training in analytic geometry will recognize that the above description may be expressed in terms of the eccentricity of an ellipse.

denoted by the symbol r. If we assume that the variable Y_i is normally distributed about a mean ξ_Y with standard deviation σ_Y, and that the variable X_i is normally distributed about a mean ξ_X with standard deviation σ_X, the bivariate normal distribution of X_i and Y_i is of the form, where $p(X_i, Y_i)$ denotes the probability distribution of X_i and Y_i,

$$p(X_i, Y_i) = \frac{1}{2\pi\sigma_X\sigma_Y\sqrt{1-\rho^2}} \exp$$

$$-\left\{\frac{1}{2(1-\rho^2)}\left[\frac{(X_i-\xi_X)^2}{\sigma_X^2} - 2\rho\frac{(X_i-\xi_X)(Y_i-\xi_Y)}{\sigma_X\sigma_Y} + \frac{(Y_i-\xi_Y)^2}{\sigma_Y^2}\right]\right\}$$

Accordingly, for samples of size N (N pairs of correlated values), the probability distribution will be

$$p(X_1 \ldots X_N, Y_1 \ldots Y_N) = \left(\frac{1}{2\pi\sigma_X\sigma_Y\sqrt{1-\rho^2}}\right)^N \exp$$

$$-\left\{\frac{1}{2(1-\rho^2)}\sum\left[\frac{(X_i-\xi_X)^2}{\sigma_X^2} - 2\rho\frac{(X_i-\xi_X)(Y_i-\xi_Y)}{\sigma_X\sigma_Y} + \frac{(Y_i-\xi_Y)^2}{\sigma_Y^2}\right]\right\}$$

To secure the maximum likelihood estimates of the unknown parameters ξ_X, ξ_Y, σ_X, σ_Y, and ρ, it is convenient to maximize $\log_e p\,(X_1 \ldots X_N, Y_1 \ldots Y_N)$ with respect to these five quantities,[†††] differentiating partially and solving the resulting equations. We secure as estimates the following five quantities:

Est. $\xi_X = \dfrac{\Sigma X_i}{N} = X.$

Est. $\xi_Y = \dfrac{\Sigma Y_i}{N} = Y.$

Est. $\sigma_X = \sqrt{\dfrac{S_{XX}}{N}} = \sqrt{\dfrac{1}{N}\left\{\Sigma X_i^2 - \dfrac{(\Sigma X_i)^2}{N}\right\}}$

Est. $\sigma_Y = \sqrt{\dfrac{S_{YY}}{N}} = \sqrt{\dfrac{1}{N}\left\{\Sigma Y_i^2 - \dfrac{(\Sigma Y_i)^2}{N}\right\}}$

Est. $\rho = \dfrac{\Sigma X_i Y_i - \dfrac{(\Sigma X_i)(\Sigma Y_i)}{N}}{\sqrt{\left\{\Sigma X_i^2 - \dfrac{(\Sigma X_i)^2}{N}\right\}\left\{\Sigma Y_i^2 - \dfrac{(\Sigma Y_i)^2}{N}\right\}}} = \dfrac{S_{YX}}{\sqrt{S_{XX}S_{YY}}} = r$

where r denotes the Pearson product-moment coefficient of correlation.[‡‡‡]

[†††] See R. W. B. Jackson and G. A. Ferguson, "Studies on the Reliability of Tests," Bulletin 12 (Toronto: Department of Educational Research, University of Toronto), Appendix A, pp. 107–12.

[‡‡‡] Interesting variations of this formula may be secured through postulating equality of the ξ's and σ's. If $\sigma_X = \sigma_Y = \sigma$, for instance, the maximum likelihood estimate of ρ proves to be

Note that the only new numerical value introduced in the formula for r is the sum of products of X_i and Y_i, i.e. $\Sigma X_i Y_i$, leading to the quantity S_{YX} used earlier in the calculation of the value of the regression coefficient. Using the formula derived earlier, we had

$$b = \frac{S_{YX}}{S_{XX}} \qquad\qquad d = \frac{S_{YX}}{S_{YY}}$$

so that, in fact,

$$b = r\frac{\sqrt{S_{YY}}}{\sqrt{S_{XX}}} \qquad \text{and} \qquad d = r\frac{\sqrt{S_{XX}}}{\sqrt{S_{YY}}}$$

and it follows that $r = \sqrt{bd}$, i.e. the geometric mean of the two regression coefficients. Observe, also, that if we define two new variables (commonly called standard measures)

$$z_{X_i} = \frac{X_i - \bar{X}}{\sqrt{\dfrac{S_{XX}}{N}}} \qquad \text{and} \qquad z_{Y_i} = \frac{Y_i - \bar{Y}}{\sqrt{\dfrac{S_{YY}}{N}}}$$

the formula for r reduces to

$$r = \frac{\sum_i z_{X_i} z_{Y_i}}{N}$$

or the arithmetic mean of the products of the variables expressed in standard measures.

This correlation coefficient, r, has the important property of being a pure number; it is independent of whatever units may be used in X and Y. Thus, it yields a measure of the degree of relationship between two variables that is directly comparable from one situation to another. It ranges in value from -1 for perfect negative relationship through 0 for no relationship (independence of the two variables), to $+1$ for perfect positive relationship.§§§

A tricky point of interpretation arises when $r = 0$, as it may or may not indicate the existence of no relationship or independence of X and Y. If the two variables are independent, then $\rho = 0$ and any estimate, r, of ρ will not be significantly different from zero. But if the estimate r is not sig-

---

$$r' = \frac{2S_{YX}}{S_{XX} + S_{YY}}$$

whereas, if $\xi_X = \xi_Y = \xi$ and $\sigma_X = \sigma_Y = \sigma$, the estimate of ρ becomes

$$r'' = \frac{2\Sigma X_i Y_i - \dfrac{(\Sigma X_i + \Sigma Y_i)^2}{2N}}{\Sigma X_i^2 + \Sigma Y_i^2 - \dfrac{(\Sigma X_i + \Sigma Y_i)^2}{2N}}$$

§§§ Students may wish to investigate the form taken by $\rho(X_i, Y_i)$ when ρ is set equal to zero (secure the product of the two independent distributions of X_i and Y_i).

nificantly different from zero, there is always the possibility that there exists a significant relationship between the two variables in some non-linear form. This means, therefore, that r is a valid estimate of the degree of relationship only if the regression of Y on X and of X on Y are linear.

This difficulty arises only when the distribution of one, or both, of the variables is non-normal. For the normal bivariate distribution we postulated in deriving the formula, the regressions are always linear and, accordingly, for this case r is always a valid estimate of the degree of relationship between the two variables. This property does not necessarily hold true for non-normal bivariate distributions; in fact, the regressions in such cases are quite apt to be non-linear, and consequently r may not always yield a valid estimate of the degree of relationship existing. However, if the regressions are in fact linear, then even for this case the estimate r secured through use of the above formula will provide a valid estimate of the degree of relationship existing between the two variables.

The calculation of the value of r for ungrouped data may be illustrated by reference to the quantities calculated at the foot of Table XI.4. Since we have $S_{YX} = 4,510.50$, $S_{YY} = 8,753.12$, and $S_{XX} = 13,004.50$, the value of r is

$$r = \frac{S_{YX}}{\sqrt{S_{XX}S_{YY}}} = \frac{4,510.50}{10,669.11} = 0.4228$$

Accordingly, the degree of relationship between the mental ages of unlike-sex twins is positive but not very high (tests of significance will be discussed in a subsequent section).

For grouped data, we could easily calculate the value of r from the formulae and values given in an earlier section, but a more systematic method of performing the calculations, and a simpler one since computation variables are introduced and used throughout, will prove useful. Moreover, we can by a simple extension calculate from the same table the quantities required for tests of linearity of regression, the significance of which for the interpretation of the correlation coefficient has already been discussed, and we may use the same quantities to calculate the values of what are termed the two *correlation ratios*. Frequently, and for good reason, the correlation ratios are termed the *coefficients of non-linear relationship*:|||||| they give measures of the *maximum* degree of relationship between the two variables. Of course, when the regressions (of Y on X and X on Y) are in fact linear, as in the case of the normal bivariate distribution, the two correlation ratios are equal, and equal in value to r. Where the regression is not linear, this equality does not hold true, but the definition and interpretation of the correlation ratios hold for any bivariate distribution.

|| || || They are related to the multiple correlation coefficient, as we shall see in the next chapter.

There are *two* correlation ratios (but only *one* correlation coefficient) for any bivariate distribution: one associated with the regression of Y on X, denoted by η_{YX}, and the other with the regression of X on Y, denoted by η_{XY}. They are defined in terms of the ratio of the sums of squares of the array means to the total sum of squares, for Y and X respectively. Using the notation examples considered earlier, we have:

$$\eta_{YX}^2 = \frac{\sum_i \sum_j (Y_{.j} - Y_{..})^2}{\sum_i \sum_j (Y_{ij} - Y_{..})^2} = \frac{\sum_j \left\{ \frac{\left(\sum_i Y_{ij} \right)^2}{\sum_i n_{ij}} \right\} - \frac{\left(\sum_i \sum_j Y_{ij} \right)^2}{N}}{\sum_i \sum_j Y_{ij}^2 - \frac{\left(\sum_i \sum_j Y_{ij} \right)^2}{N}} = \frac{S_{Y.j}}{S_{YY}}$$

$$\eta_{XY}^2 = \frac{\sum_i \sum_j (X_{i.} - X_{..})^2}{\sum_i \sum_j (X_{ij} - X_{..})^2} = \frac{\sum_j \left\{ \frac{\left(\sum_j X_{ij} \right)^2}{\sum_j n_{ij}} \right\} - \frac{\left(\sum_i \sum_j X_{ij} \right)^2}{N}}{\sum_i \sum_j X_{ij}^2 - \frac{\left(\sum_i \sum_j X_{i,j} \right)^2}{N}} = \frac{S_{X_{i.}}}{S_{XX}}$$

where $Y_{.j}$ denotes the mean value of Y for the jth class interval of X; $X_{i.}$ denotes the mean value of X for the ith class interval of Y; and n_{ij} denotes the frequency in the ijth cell. Turning to the formula for the sum of squares corresponding to the deviations from linear regression, we see that this is equal to $S_{YY}(\eta_{YX}^2 - r^2)$ for the regression of Y on X, $\hat{Y} = a + bX$; and it is equal to $S_{XX}(\eta_{XY}^2 - r^2)$ for the regression of X on Y, $\hat{X} = c + dY$.

Two deductions of considerable importance follow immediately: first, that neither η can be less than r; and, second, that if and only if $\eta = r$ is the regression linear (note that the quantity $\eta^2 - r^2$ is actually used in the test for linearity of regression derived earlier). Observe, also, that the sign of η is not fixed by definition: it is customary to use only the positive square root value to denote the degree of relationship indicated by the correlation ratio. Accordingly, η will vary between 0 and 1: having the value 0 only if each array mean is exactly equal to the general mean, and reaching the value 1 only if the Within Groups sum of squares is zero, i.e. if all the values in each array are identically equal. Observe, also, that the test of significance of differences among the array means previously considered is equivalent to the test of the hypothesis that $\eta = 0$. Considering the Y variable, for instance, the Among Groups sum of squares is $(S_{YY})(\eta_{YX}^2)$ and the Within Groups sum of squares is $(S_{YY})(1 - \eta_{YX}^2)$, so that for k groups subject to the assumptions applying previously, the quantity

$F = \dfrac{(N - k)(\eta_{YX}^2)}{(k - 1)(1 - \eta_{YX}^2)}$ will be distributed as F with degrees of freedom $n_1 = k - 1$ and $n_2 = N - k$.

We show in Table XI.6 the complete set of calculations for the data relating to marks on French Authors and French Composition (Table XI.1), and in Table XI.7 the complete set of calculations for the data of Table XI.3 (Chronological Age and Army Alpha scores), using computation variables in each case as indicated. Since the two tables are identical save in one respect, we shall discuss the calculation procedures in terms of Table XI.6 only. The point of difference—a minor, but annoying, one—is that in Table XI.7 the class intervals for Chronological Age (X) are unequal in width, and consequently the computation variable x, where $x = \dfrac{X - 27.5}{5}$, using midpoints of the class intervals and remembering that "age last birthday" is implied, is somewhat peculiar-looking and inconvenient for arithmetical purposes (the decimal points require watching!).

Since the calculation procedure is arranged systematically with a series of checks, we shall describe it in steps:

Step 1: Draw the chart as indicated, allowing seven extra rows and columns for calculated values.

Step 2: Write the cell frequencies, f_{XY}, in the center of each cell; check to make certain no errors have occurred in transcribing the values.

Step 3: Add the cell frequencies across the rows to secure the totals denoted by f_Y; add the cell frequencies down the columns to secure the totals denoted by f_X. The sum of the f_Y's must equal the total number of cases (6,836), as must the sum of the f_X's.

Step 4: Select the computation variable for Y, based on the midpoints of the Y class intervals, and write the values in the corresponding spaces of the column headed "Computation Variable y." Similarly, select the computation variable for X, based on the midpoints of the X class intervals, and write the values in the corresponding spaces in the row headed "Computation Variable x."

Step 5: Multiply (f_Y) by (y) to secure the values in the column headed $(f_Y)(y)$; check the calculations, and add the products to secure the total sum $\left(\sum_i \sum_j y_{ij} = 4{,}599 \right)$ of the y's. Multiply (f_X) by (x) to secure the values in the row headed $(f_X)(x)$; check the calculations, and add the products to secure the total sum $\left(\sum_i \sum_j x_{ij} = 4{,}062 \right)$ of the x's.

Step 6: Multiply each of the products $(f_Y)(y)$ by the corresponding value of (y) to secure the values in the column headed $(f_Y)(y^2)$; check the calculations, and add the products to secure the total sum $\left(\sum_i \sum_j y_{ij}^2 = 20{,}073 \right)$ of the y^2's. Multiply each of the products $(f_X)(x)$ by the corresponding value of (x) to secure the values in the row headed $(f_X)(x^2)$; check the calculations, and add the products to secure the total sum $\left(\sum_i \sum_j x_{ij}^2 = 20{,}474 \right)$ of the x^2's.

Step 7: Write the corresponding value of the computation variable x in the lower left-hand corner of each cell. Then, for *each row*, in turn, calculate the sum of products $(f_{XY})(x)$, with due regard to sign, and write the total in the corresponding space in the column headed $\Sigma(f_{XY})(x)$: for the first row, for example, $(2)(6) + (3)(43) + (4)(59) = 377$. Add the entries in this column (the sums of products), with due regard to sign, to secure the total $\underset{i\ j}{\Sigma\Sigma}x_{ij} = 4{,}062$: this must check with the total secured earlier, as indicated by the arrow on the table.

Step 8: Write the corresponding value of the computation variable y in the upper right-hand corner of each cell. Then, for *each column*, in turn, calculate the sum of products $(f_{XY})(y)$, with due regard to sign, and write the total in the corresponding space in the row headed $\Sigma(f_{XY})$ (y): for the first column, for instance, $(-1)(1) + (-2)(2) + (-3)(8) + (-4)(12) = -77$. Add the entries in this row (the sums of products) with due regard to sign: this must check with the total secured earlier, as indicated by the arrow on the table.

Step 9: Multiply each entry in the column headed $\Sigma(f_{XY})(x)$ by the corresponding value of y, and write the product in the corresponding space in the column headed $(y)\Sigma(f_{XY})(x)$: add these products to secure the total $\underset{i\ j}{\Sigma\Sigma}x_{ij}y_{ij} = 16{,}775$. Multiply each entry in the row headed $\Sigma(f_{XY})(y)$ by the corresponding value of x, and write the product in the corresponding space in the row headed $(x)\Sigma(f_{XY})(y)$: add these products to secure the total $\underset{i\ j}{\Sigma\Sigma}x_{ij}y_{ij} = 16{,}775$. Note that these two totals must check.

Step 10: Square each entry in the column headed $\Sigma(f_{XY})(x)$, divide by the corresponding value of f_Y, and write the quotient in the corresponding space in the column headed $\dfrac{\{\Sigma(f_{XY})(x)\}^2}{f_Y}$, e.g. $\dfrac{(377)^2}{108} = 1{,}316.01$.

Add these quotients to secure the total denoted by $\underset{i}{\Sigma}\left\{\dfrac{(\underset{j}{\Sigma}x_{ij})^2}{\underset{i}{\Sigma}n_{ij}}\right\} = 14{,}064.99$.

Check these calculations.

Step 11: Square each entry in the row headed $\Sigma(f_{XY})$ (y), divide by the corresponding value of f_X, and write the quotient in the corresponding space in the row headed $\dfrac{\{\Sigma(f_{XY})\ (y)\}^2}{f_X}$, e.g. $\dfrac{(-77)^2}{23} = 257.78$. Add these quotients to secure the total denoted by $\underset{j}{\Sigma}\left\{\dfrac{(\underset{j}{\Sigma}y_{ij})^2}{\underset{i}{\Sigma}n_{ij}}\right\} = 14{,}039.28$.

Check these calculations.

TABLE XI.6

FIRST ILLUSTRATION OF CALCULATION OF VALUES OF THE PRODUCT-MOMENT COEFFICIENT OF CORRELATION AND OF THE CORRELATION RATIOS FOR GROUPED DATA, USING DATA OF TABLE XI.1, MARKS ON FRENCH AUTHORS AND FRENCH COMPOSITION

Each interior cell lists three numbers: the top-right deviation product, the central frequency, and the bottom-left deviation value.

X → (FRENCH COMPOSITION) / Y ↓ (FRENCH AUTHORS)	5–14	15–24	25–34	35–44	45–54	55–64	65–74	75–84	85–
85–94							4 / 6 / 2	4 / 43 / 3	5 / 4
75–84					3 / 2 / 0	3 / 57 / 1	3 / 238 / 2	3 / 372 / 3	7 / 4
65–74				2 / 10 / −1	2 / 87 / 0	2 / 412 / 1	2 / 542 / 2	2 / 215 / 3	1 / 4
55–64			1 / 21 / −2	1 / 160 / −1	1 / 449 / 0	1 / 766 / 1	1 / 338 / 2	1 / 51 / 3	4
45–54		0 / 3 / −3	0 / 103 / −2	0 / 352 / −1	0 / 429 / 0	0 / 372 / 1	0 / 87 / 2	0 / 9 / 3	
35–44	−1 / 1 / −4	−1 / 23 / −3	−1 / 223 / −2	−1 / 354 / −1	−1 / 218 / 0	−1 / 111 / 1	−1 / 6 / 2	−1 / 2 / 3	
25–34	−2 / 2 / −4	−2 / 53 / −3	−2 / 173 / −2	−2 / 147 / −1	−2 / 38 / 0	−2 / 6 / 1	−2 / 2 / 2		
15–24	−3 / 8 / −4	−3 / 57 / −3	−3 / 65 / −2	−3 / 23 / −1	−3 / 1 / 0	−3 / 1 / 1			
5–14	−4 / 12 / −4	−4 / 17 / −3	−4 / 12 / −2	−4 / 2 / −1	−4 / 1 / 0				
Total f_x	23	153	597	1,048	1,225	1,725	1,219	692	1.
Computation Variable x	−4	−3	−2	−1	0	1	2	3	
$(f_x)(x)$	−92	−459	−1,194	−1,048	0	1,725	2,438	2,076	6
$(f_x)(x^2)$	368	1,377	2,388	1,048	0	1,725	4,876	6,228	2,
$\Sigma(f_{xy})(y)$	−77	−368	−791	−545	328	1,635	2,150	1,767	5
$(x)\Sigma(f_{xy})(y)$	308	1,104	1,582	545	0	1,635	4,300	5,301	2,
$\dfrac{\{\Sigma(f_{xy})(y)\}^2}{f_x}$	257.78	885.12	1,048.04	283.42	87.82	1,549.70	3,792.04	4,511.98	1,6

TABLE XI.6 Cont'd

FIRST ILLUSTRATION OF CALCULATION OF VALUES OF THE PRODUCT-MOMENT
COEFFICIENT OF CORRELATION AND OF THE CORRELATION RATIOS
FOR GROUPED DATA, USING DATA OF TABLE XI.1, MARKS ON
FRENCH AUTHORS AND FRENCH COMPOSITION (Continued)

TOTAL f_Y	COMPUTATION VARIABLE y	$(f_Y)(y)$	$(f_Y)(y^2)$	$\Sigma(f_{XY})(x)$	$(y)\Sigma(f_{XY})(x)$	$\dfrac{\{\Sigma(f_{XY})(x)\}^2}{f_Y}$
108	4	432	1,728	377	1,508	1,316.01
745	3	2,235	6,705	1,953	5,859	5,119.74
1,283	2	2,566	5,132	2,199	4,398	3,768.98
1,787	1	1,787	1,787	1,401	1,401	1,098.38
1,355	0	0	0	6	0	0.03
938	−1	−938	938	−744	744	590.12
421	−2	−842	1,684	−650	1,300	1,003.56
155	−3	−465	1,395	−355	1,065	813.06
44	−4	−176	704	−125	500	355.11
6,836	—	4,599	20,073	4,062	16,775	14,064.99
—						
4,062						
20,474						
4,599						
16,775						
14,039.28						

4,062 ←————————— Check

4,599 ←———— Check

16,775 ←———————————————— Check

CELL KEY

	y
f_{XY}	
x	

Step 12: Calculate the quantities

$$\frac{(\sum_i \sum_j y_{ij})^2}{N} = \frac{(4,599)^2}{6,836} = 3,094.03$$

$$\frac{(\sum_i \sum_j x_{ij})^2}{N} = \frac{(4,062)^2}{6,836} = 2,413.67$$

$$\frac{(\sum_i \sum_j y_{ij})(\sum_i \sum_j x_{ij})}{N} = \frac{(4,599)(4,062)}{6,836} = 2,732.76$$

from which we secure

$$S_{yy} = \sum_i \sum_j y_{ij}^2 - \frac{(\sum_i \sum_j y_{ij})^2}{N} = 20,073 - 3,094.03 = 16,978.97$$

$$S_{xx} = \sum_i \sum_j x_{ij}^2 - \frac{(\sum_i \sum_j x_{ij})^2}{N} = 20,474 - 2,413.67 = 18,060.33$$

$$S_{yx} = \sum_i \sum_j x_{ij} y_{ij} - \frac{(\sum_i \sum_j y_{ij})(\sum_i \sum_j x_{ij})}{N} = 16,775 - 2,732.76 = 14,042.24$$

$$S_{y.j} = \sum_j \left\{ \frac{(\sum_i y_{ij})^2}{\sum_i n_{ij}} \right\} - \frac{(\sum_i \sum_j y_{ij})^2}{N} = 14,039.28 - 3,094.03 = 10,945.25$$

$$S_{x_i.} = \sum_i \left\{ \frac{(\sum_j x_{ij})^2}{\sum_j n_{ij}} \right\} - \frac{(\sum_i \sum_j x_{ij})^2}{N} = 14,064.99 - 2,413.67 = 11,651.32$$

Since r and the two η's are pure numbers, being independent of the units employed as reference to their formulae reveals, we may calculate their values directly and without adjustment from the above sums of squares determined for the computation variables, y and x, only. We have

$$r = \frac{S_{yx}}{\sqrt{S_{yy}S_{xx}}} = \frac{14,042.24}{\sqrt{(16,978.97)(18,060.33)}} = 0.801895; \qquad r^2 = 0.643036$$

$$\eta_{YX}^2 = \frac{S_{y.j}}{S_{yy}} = \frac{10,945.25}{16,978.97} = 0.644636; \qquad \eta_{YX} = 0.802892$$

$$\eta_{XY}^2 = \frac{S_{x_i.}}{S_{xx}} = \frac{11,651.32}{18,060.33} = 0.645133; \qquad \eta_{XY} = 0.803202$$

The value of r is so nearly equal to that of η_{YX} and of η_{XY} that it is obvious the regression is very nearly linear. However, there does exist in each case a statistically significant departure from linearity. For the regression of Y on X, $\hat{Y} = a + bX$, we have

$$F = \frac{(6,827)(\eta_{YX}^2 - r^2)}{(7)(1 - \eta_{YX}^2)} = 4.39 \qquad \begin{array}{l} n_1 = 7 \\ n_2 = 6,827 \end{array}$$

and for the regression of X on Y, $\hat{X} = c + dY$, we have

$$F = \frac{(6,827)(\eta_{XY}^2 - r^2)}{(7)(1 - \eta_{XY}^2)} = 5.76 \qquad \begin{array}{l} n_1 = 7 \\ n_2 = 6,827 \end{array}$$

both of which are greater than the 1 per cent point of the F-distribution, and consequently the departures from linearity, though small, are significant.

For the data of Table XI.7, following the same procedure, we have

$$S_{yy} = \sum_i \sum_j y_{ij}^2 - \frac{(\sum_i \sum_j y_{ij})^2}{N} = 19,736 - 798.67 = 18,937.33$$

$$S_{xx} = \sum_i \sum_j x_{ij}^2 - \frac{(\sum_i \sum_j x_{ij})^2}{N} = 7,264.20 - 58.27 = 7,205.93$$

$$S_{yx} = \sum_i \sum_j x_{ij} y_{ij} - \frac{(\sum_i \sum_j y_{ij})(\sum_i \sum_j x_{ij})}{N} = 1,002.3 + 215.73 = 1,218.03$$

$$S_{y.j} = \sum_j \left\{ \frac{(\sum_i y_{ij})^2}{\sum_i n_{ij}} \right\} - \frac{(\sum_i \sum_j y_{ij})^2}{N} = 3,070.63 - 798.67 = 2,271.96$$

$$S_{x_i.} = \sum_i \left\{ \frac{(\sum_j x_{ij})^2}{\sum_j n_{ij}} \right\} - \frac{(\sum_i \sum_j x_{ij})^2}{N} = 257.36 - 58.27 = 199.09$$

$$r = \frac{S_{yx}}{\sqrt{S_{yy}S_{xx}}} = \frac{1,218.03}{\sqrt{(18,937.33)(7,205.93)}} = 0.104269$$

$$\eta_{YX}^2 = \frac{S_{y.j}}{S_{yy}} = \frac{2,271.96}{18,937.33} = 0.119973; \qquad \eta_{YX} = 0.346371$$

$$\eta_{XY}^2 = \frac{S_{x_i.}}{S_{xx}} = \frac{199.09}{7,205.93} = 0.0276286; \qquad \eta_{XY} = 0.166219$$

In this case, η_{YX} is considerably greater than either r or η_{XY}. For the tests of linearity of regression we have, for the regression of Y on X,

$$F = \frac{(1,118)(\eta_{YX}^2 - r^2)}{(10)(1 - \eta_{YX}^2)} = 13.86; \qquad \begin{array}{l} n_1 = 10 \\ n_2 = 1,118 \end{array}$$

and for the regression of X on Y

$$F = \frac{(1,118)(\eta_{XY}^2 - r^2)}{(19)(1 - \eta_{XY}^2)} = 1.006 \qquad \begin{array}{l} n_1 = 19 \\ n_2 = 1,118 \end{array}$$

Each cell shows the y computation-variable value (top), the frequency (middle), and the x computation-variable value (bottom).

Y \\ X (CHRONOLOGICAL AGE)	11 & 12	13 & 14	15 & 16	17 & 18	19–21	22–24	25–29	30–34	35–39
200–209					13 2 −1.4				
190–199						12 1 −.8	12 1 0	12 1 1	
180–189				11 1 −1.9	11 3 −1.4				11 1 2
170–179				10 2 −1.9	10 6 −1.4		10 2 0	10 4 1	10 2 2
160–169			9 2 −2.3	9 2 −1.9	9 2 −1.4	9 1 −.8	9 2 0	9 2 1	
150–159			8 5 −2.3	8 6 −1.9	8 2 −1.4	8 3 −.8	8 3 0	8 3 1	8 1 2
140–149			7 7 −2.3	7 4 −1.9	7 6 −1.4		7 5 0	7 4 1	7 4 2
130–139		6 2 −2.7	6 11 −2.3	6 4 −1.9	6 1 −1.4	6 3 −.8	6 1 0	6 9 1	6 7 2
120–129		5 2 −2.7	5 9 −2.3	5 9 −1.9	5 7 −1.4	5 4 −.8	5 1 0	5 7 1	5 8 2
110–119	4 2 −3.1	4 6 −2.7	4 10 −2.3	4 11 −1.9	4 6 −1.4	4 4 −.8	4 8 0	4 7 1	4 6 2
100–109	3 3 −3.1	3 8 −2.7	3 8 −2.3	3 3 −1.9	3 4 −1.4	3 3 −.8	3 6 0	3 5 1	3 5 2
90–99	2 2 −3.1	2 8 −2.7	2 15 −2.3	2 9 −1.9	2 9 −1.4	2 3 −.8	2 12 0	2 2 1	2 7 2
80–89	1 10 −3.1	1 21 −2.7	1 18 −2.3	1 10 −1.9	1 5 −1.4	1 2 −.8	1 10 0	1 11 1	1 11 2
70–79	0 9 −3.1	0 12 −2.7	0 13 −2.3	0 6 −1.9	0 9 −1.4	0 6 −.8	0 13 0	0 11 1	0 5 2
60–69	−1 17 −3.1	−1 15 −2.7	−1 11 −2.3	−1 12 −1.9	−1 7 −1.4	−1 3 −.8	−1 7 0	−1 8 1	−1 4 2
50–59	−2 21 −3.1	−2 21 −2.7	−2 7 −2.3	−2 5 −1.9	−2 11 −1.4	−2 2 −.8	−2 9 0	−2 7 1	−2 10 2
40–49	−3 14 −3.1	−3 14 −2.7	−3 6 −2.3	−3 8 −1.9	−3 1 −1.4	−3 4 −.8	−3 3 0	−3 7 1	−3 6 2
30–39	−4 25 −3.1	−4 8 −2.7	−4 8 −2.3	−4 4 −1.9	−4 6 −1.4	−4 3 −.8	−4 2 0	−4 6 1	−4 9 2
20–29	−5 16 −3.1	−5 6 −2.7	−5 5 −2.3	−5 1 −1.9	−5 1 −1.4	−5 1 −.8	−5 1 0	−5 5 1	−5 7 2
10–19	−6 2 −3.1	−6 5 −2.7	−6 2 −2.3			−6 1 −.8	−6 3 0	−6 4 1	−6 3 2
0–9	−7 4 −3.1	−7 1 −2.7					−7 1 0	−7 1 1	
Total f_X	125	129	137	97	88	44	90	104	96
Computation Variable x	−3.1	−2.7	−2.3	−1.9	−1.4	−.8	0	1	2
$(f_X)(x)$	−387.5	−348.3	−315.1	−184.3	−123.2	−35.2	0	104	192
$(f_X)(x^2)$	1,201.25	940.41	724.73	350.17	172.48	28.16	0	104	384
$\Sigma(f_{XY})(y)$	−290	−91	218	208	234	74	132	146	82
$(x)\Sigma(f_{XY})(y)$	899.0	245.7	−501.4	−395.2	−327.6	−59.2	0	146	164
$\dfrac{\{\Sigma(f_{XY})(y)\}^2}{f_X}$	672.80	64.19	346.89	446.02	622.23	124.45	193.60	204.96	70.04

ARMY ALPHA SCORE (row variable Y)

SECOND ILLUSTRATION OF CALCULATION OF VALUES OF THE PRODUCT-MOMENT
COEFFICIENT OF CORRELATION AND OF THE CORRELATION RATIOS FOR GROUPED DATA,
USING DATA OF TABLE XI.3, CHRONOLOGICAL AGE AND ARMY ALPHA SCORES

| CHRONOLOGICAL AGE | | | TOTAL f_Y | COMPUTATION VARIABLE y | $(f_Y)(y)$ | $(f_Y)(y^2)$ | $\Sigma(f_{XY})(x)$ | $(y)\Sigma(f_{XY})(x)$ | $\dfrac{\{\Sigma(f_{XY})(x)\}^2}{f_Y}$ |
40-44	45-49	50-54							
			2	13	26	338	−2.8	−36.4	3.92
			3	12	36	432	.2	2.4	.01
1 (x=3)			6	11	66	726	−1.1	−12.1	.20
3 (x=3)		1 (x=5)	20	10	200	2,000	9.8	98.0	4.80
3 (x=3)	2 (x=4)	2 (x=5)	18	9	162	1,458	17.0	153.0	16.06
4 (x=3)	1 (x=4)	2 (x=5)	30	8	240	1,920	2.9	23.2	.28
6 (x=3)	5 (x=4)	1 (x=5)	42	7	294	2,058	22.9	160.3	12.49
7 (x=3)	2 (x=4)	2 (x=5)	49	6	294	1,764	19.9	119.4	8.08
4 (x=3)	1 (x=4)	7 (x=5)	59	5	295	1,475	17.8	89.0	5.37
6 (x=3)	5 (x=4)	3 (x=5)	74	4	296	1,184	−5.9	−23.6	.47
5 (x=3)	3 (x=4)	3 (x=5)	56	3	168	504	−6.0	−18.0	.64
9 (x=3)	5 (x=4)	2 (x=5)	83	2	166	332	−21.4	−42.8	5.52
10 (x=3)	7 (x=4)	2 (x=5)	117	1	117	117	−55.7	−55.7	26.52
4 (x=3)	5 (x=4)	4 (x=5)	97	0	0	0	−46.0	0	21.81
6 (x=3)	8 (x=4)	6 (x=5)	104	−1	−104	104	−57.5	57.5	31.79
9 (x=3)	10 (x=4)	6 (x=5)	118	−2	−236	472	−40.4	80.8	13.83
5 (x=3)	4 (x=4)	4 (x=5)	76	−3	−228	684	−44.8	134.4	26.41
3 (x=3)	5 (x=4)	6 (x=5)	85	−4	−340	1,360	−52.9	211.6	32.92
3 (x=3)	2 (x=4)	4 (x=5)	52	−5	−260	1,300	−25.4	127.0	12.41
6 (x=3)	4 (x=4)	1 (x=5)	31	−6	−186	1,116	23.9	−143.4	18.43
1 (x=3)			8	−7	−56	392	−11.1	77.7	15.40
95	69	56	1,130	—	950	19,736	−256.6	1,002.3	257.36
3	4	5	—						
285	276	280	−256.6 ← Check						
855	1,104	1,400	7,264.20						
162	30	45	950 ← Check						
486	120	225	1,002.3 ← Check						
276.25	13.04	36.16	3,070.63						

Check (→ $\Sigma(f_{XY})(x)$)
Check (→ $(f_Y)(y)$)
Check (→ $(y)\Sigma(f_{XY})(x)$)

TABLE XI.7

CELL KEY

	y
	f_{XY}
x	

Accordingly, the departures from linearity are significant in the first case (regression of Army Alpha score on Chronological Age), but are not significant in the second (regression of Chronological Age on Army Alpha score). Students will, of course, remember in the interpretation of these results that the basic assumptions are far from being satisfied and that the tests we have employed are approximate only.

Tests of Hypotheses Concerning the Correlation Coefficient

As in all the previous cases where tests of statistical hypotheses were involved, the first problem that must be solved is the derivation of the form of distribution of the statistic or measure used (r, here) in repeated random sampling. For the normal bivariate distribution we have been considering, the solution (empirical) for the case where the population value, ρ, is zero was first given by Student in 1906.### The general solution for any value of ρ was given by R. A. Fisher in 1915.* For non-normal populations, the general exact solution is not known, but empirical studies, such as those by E. S. Pearson,† indicate that the distribution of r in repeated random sampling is affected surprisingly little by even marked departures from normality. Accordingly, as we have so often suggested previously in like situations, we may with considerable justification use the proposed statistical tests even if we know, or suspect, that the parent populations differ somewhat from the normal in form. True, the solution will be only an approximation, but the evidence available indicates that, if caution is used in interpreting the results, the approximation will be satisfactory enough for all practical purposes.

Very complete and extremely useful tables of the distribution of the product-moment coefficient of correlation for the normal bivariate distribution have been prepared by David,‡ giving both the areas and ordinates of the distribution for values of ρ from 0.0 to 0.9 and for values of N (size of the sample) from 3 to 400. We show in Figure XI.3 the sampling distribution of r (using David's tables) for samples of size 10, for normal bivariate populations with $\rho = 0$, $\rho = 0.5$, and $\rho = 0.9$. Note that in no case is the distribution of r normal in form, although it is always symmetrical for $\rho = 0$, and is indeed quite skewed even for moderate values of ρ. The distributions tend very slowly to normality even for relatively large samples ($N = 500$, say), and it is probably unwise—as well as being unnecessary—ever to assume normality of the distribution of r. The lack of necessity is due to a simple transformation proposed by R. A. Fisher§ that gives amaz-

Biometrika, VI (1906), 302–10.
* *Biometrika*, X (1915), 507–21.
† *Biometrika*, XXI (1929), 356–60.
‡ F. N. David, *Tables of the Ordinates and Probability Integral of the Distribution of the Correlation Coefficient in Small Samples* (Cambridge, Eng.: Cambridge University Press, 1938).
§ *Metron*, I, iv(1921), 1–30.

ingly accurate results, using the normal distribution tables, over the whole range of ρ and r. If we define

$$z' = \frac{1}{2} \log e \left(\frac{1 + r}{1 - r}\right) \qquad \xi = \frac{1}{2} \log e \left(\frac{1 + \rho}{1 - \rho}\right)$$

then z' is approximately normally distributed, and for any value of ρ the kurtosis is of order $\frac{2}{N}$ and the skewness is zero for $\rho = 0$ and of order $\frac{2}{N^3}$ for $\rho \neq 0$. The most useful of the set of approximations is that which assumes z' is normally distributed about a mean of $\xi + \frac{\rho}{2(N - 1)}$ with variance $\frac{1}{N - 3}$; it is sufficiently accurate for all practical purposes for samples even as small as $N = 10$.

To illustrate the type of results obtained in random sampling, we show below the set of 50 values of r secured by correlating pairs of adjacent random samples of size 10 from the normal population considered in Chapter II. Since in calculating the value of r for each pair of samples we used the order of appearance of the individual values to determine the value of $(X_i) (Y_i)$, the situation corresponds to that of sampling from a normal bivariate distribution for which $\rho = 0$.|| The values secured were: .59, .52, .46, .43, .40, .38, .35, .33, .32, .30, .29, .24, .23, .20, .20, .20, .19, .17, .16, .09, .09, .08, .02, .02, .00, $-.02$, $-.04$, $-.05$, $-.05$, $-.08$, $-.11$, $-.13$, $-.13$, $-.13$, $-.13$, $-.18$, $-.22$, $-.24$, $-.26$, $-.26$, $-.29$, $-.32$, $-.32$, $-.35$, $-.36$, $-.38$, $-.39$, $-.48$, $-.54$, $-.70$.
Note the extreme range of values ($+.59$ to $-.70$) that occurs in even this limited set of 50 cases.

Hypotheses for Single Samples

1. Test of the Hypothesis $H_o : \rho = 0$. This is the simplest and possibly the most useful of the tests. Assuming normality of the parent bivariate population, as we shall do for each of the cases which follow, it is known that the quantity

$$t = \frac{r\sqrt{N - 2}}{\sqrt{1 - r^2}}$$

is distributed as Student's t with $n = N - 2$ degrees of freedom when the hypothesis $H_o : \rho = 0$ is true. Likewise, from Fisher's transformation the quantity

$$z' = \frac{1}{2} \log e \left\{\frac{1 + r}{1 - r}\right\}$$

|| Students should be encouraged to calculate similar sets of values of r for the other populations considered in Chapter II.

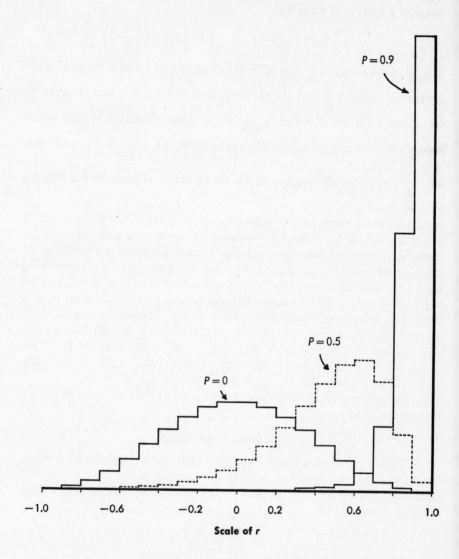

Figure XI.3. ILLUSTRATION OF DISTRIBUTION OF THE COEFFICIENT OF CORRELATION (SAMPLES OF SIZE 10; $\rho = 0$, $\rho = 0.5$, AND $\rho = 0.9$)

will be approximately normally distributed about a mean of zero with

standard deviation $\dfrac{1}{\sqrt{N-3}}$ when $H_o : \rho = 0$ is true. Thus we may use

either the exact t-test or the approximate z' test for this hypothesis. That the approximation is exceedingly good may be demonstrated by the following example: let $N = 10$ and $r = 0.5$. We have

$$t = \frac{(.5)\sqrt{8}}{\sqrt{.75}} = 1.633, \text{ with } N - 2 = 8 \text{ degrees of freedom}$$

and, from the table of t, $\rho\{t \geqslant 1.633\} \doteq 0.0745$. Using the transformation we have

$$z' = \frac{1}{2} \log e \left(\frac{1.5}{.5} \right) = 0.5493, \qquad \frac{1}{\sqrt{N-3}} = \frac{1}{\sqrt{7}} = 0.3780$$

so that our normal deviate is $z = 1.453$ and, from the tables of the normal distribution, $\rho\{z \geqslant 1.453\} \doteq 0.0731$. Even for samples as small as this, therefore, Fisher's approximation gives amazingly accurate results. However, there is no need to employ an approximation in such cases where the equally simple but exact test (i.e. the t-test) is available.

Students will have observed that in the above example we used the set of admissible alternative hypotheses defined by $H : \rho > 0$, or a one-tailed test. Very often, however, the set of admissible alternative hypotheses will be $H : \rho \neq 0$ (i.e. $0 < \rho < 0$), in which event the two-tailed test would have been used and the above probabilities doubled. For this example, of course, we would in both cases accept the null hypothesis and conclude that ρ was not different from zero.

2. Test of the Hypothesis $H_o : \rho = \rho_o \neq 0$. Researchers encounter problems of this kind in comparative studies or in any study where either theory or experience determines an expected value for the degree of relationship. For example, the degree of relationship between scores on an achievement test in English Composition and marks at the end of a course in Freshman English for 54 students proved to be $r = 0.225$. Is this value significantly lower than the expected value of 0.40, determined by widespread experience? The hypothesis to be tested is $H_o : \rho = 0.40$, and the set of admissible alternative hypotheses is $H : \rho < 0.40$. From David's tables we find that, if H_o is true, then $\rho\{r \leqslant 0.225\} \doteq 0.089$; accordingly, we would accept the hypothesis tested, and conclude that the observed value was not significantly below the expected.

Using Fisher's logarithmic transformation, we have

$$z' = \frac{1}{2} \log e \left\{ \frac{1.225}{0.775} \right\} = 0.22903$$

$$\zeta = \frac{1}{2} \log e \left\{ \frac{1.40}{0.60} \right\} = 0.42358$$

so that we may assume z' is normally distributed about a mean of $\zeta + \dfrac{\rho}{2(N-1)} = 0.4274$ with standard deviation equal to $\dfrac{1}{\sqrt{N-3}} = \dfrac{1}{\sqrt{51}} = 0.1400$. The corresponding normal deviate is

$$z = \frac{0.2290 - 0.4274}{0.1400} = -\frac{0.1984}{0.1400} = -1.417$$

and from the tables of the normal distribution we find that

$$\rho\{z \leqslant -1.417\} \doteq 0.078$$

This agreement of the approximate with the exact test (using David's tables) is fair but far from perfect. However, the z' approximation is probably good enough for most practical purposes provided N is not small and ρ not too close to unity.

Hypotheses for Two Samples: Differences between Correlation Coefficients

1. Independent Samples: Test of the Hypothesis $H_o : \rho_1 = \rho_2 = \rho$. In these cases the samples from which the observed correlation coefficients are obtained are independent, and the hypothesis to be tested is that for the normal bivariate populations from which the samples are assumed to be drawn the value of ρ has the same, although unknown, value, so that we may write $H_o : \rho_1 = \rho_2 = \rho$. The set of admissible alternative hypotheses will in nearly all cases be $H : \rho_1 \neq \rho_2$, so that a two-tailed test is normally employed. (A one-tailed test would, of course, be used if we specify that $\rho_1 > \rho_2$ or $\rho_1 < \rho_2$.)

No exact test of this hypothesis is known, and we must perforce use Fisher's transformation which will yield values of z' that are practically independent of the unknown value of ρ. Denoting by r_1 the correlation coefficient for the first sample of N_1 cases, and by r_2 the correlation coefficient for the second sample of N_2 cases, then the quantity

$$z = \frac{z_1' - z_2'}{\sqrt{\dfrac{1}{N_1 - 3} + \dfrac{1}{N_2 - 3}}}$$

where
$$z_1' = \frac{1}{2} \log e \left(\frac{1 + r_1}{1 - r_1} \right)$$

and
$$z_2' = \frac{1}{2} \log e \left(\frac{1 + r_2}{1 - r_2} \right)$$

will, if the hypothesis to be tested is true, be approximately normally distributed about zero with unit standard deviation.

As an illustration, the following results were secured in a study of the relationship between two variables in two independent samples of high school students:

$$N_1 = 30 \qquad N_2 = 33$$
$$r_1 = 0.352 \qquad r_2 = 0.534$$

Using the formulae given above, we have

$$z_1' = \frac{1}{2} \log e \left\{ \frac{1.352}{0.648} \right\} = \frac{1}{2} \log e(2.0864) = 0.36772$$

$$z_2' = \frac{1}{2} \log e \left\{ \frac{1.534}{0.466} \right\} = \frac{1}{2} \log e(3.2918) = 0.59587$$

$$z = \frac{0.36772 - 0.59587}{\sqrt{\frac{1}{27} + \frac{1}{30}}} = -\frac{0.22815}{0.2653} = -0.86$$

From the tables of the normal distribution we find that

$$\rho\{ - 0.86 \geqslant z \geqslant 0.86 \} = 0.39$$

Accordingly, we would accept the hypothesis $H_o : \rho_1 = \rho_2 = \rho$ and conclude that the two observed correlation coefficients do not differ significantly. (Note that the probability would be halved for a one-tailed test.)

2. Dependent Samples: Test of the Hypothesis $H_o : \rho_1 = \rho_2 = \rho$. The statistical problem in this situation is the same as that of the previous example, save in one important respect: both correlation coefficients have been calculated from data for a single sample of objects or individuals. This is a rather common type of situation in the social sciences, because it is usual to make a number of measurements of the same sample of individuals and calculate correlation coefficients for pairs of variables. For example, in a study of the predictive value of two objective tests in science, which we may denote by X_1 and X_2, the correlation coefficients of each with two school examinations, denoted by X_3 and X_4, were calculated, and likewise the correlation coefficients between the two objective tests and between the two school examinations. The number of students used was 128, each of whom completed the four tests. The values secured, using subscripts to denote the variables concerned, were as follows:

$$r_{13} = 0.438 \qquad r_{23} = 0.485$$
$$r_{14} = 0.593 \qquad r_{24} = 0.362$$

and, for the two objective tests, $r_{12} = 0.514$, while for the two school examinations, $r_{34} = 0.336$.

Researchers will observe that there are really two problems here, not just one. The first involves a comparison of two coefficients of correlation where one subscript is common: for example, the difference between r_{14} and r_{24} is a measure of the comparative predictive value of the two objective tests in terms of one school examination. The second involves a comparison of two coefficients of correlation with no subscripts in common: for example, the difference between r_{12} and r_{34} is a measure of the difference in agreement of the two objective tests and the two school examinations with each other. Unfortunately, there is no completely satisfactory statistical test of the null hypothesis for either case, and the test suggested below based on Fisher's z' transformation is an approximation about the validity of which very little is known. But these statistical tests must serve until better are devised, and they will probably be satisfactory enough for most purposes if the results derived therefrom are interpreted with proper caution and reserve.

For the first case, the null hypothesis to be tested may be written without loss of generality as $H_o: \rho_{14} = \rho_{24}$, and the set of admissible alternative hypotheses will in most instances be $H: \rho_{14} \neq \rho_{24}$. The test of this hypothesis proposed by Hotelling# is exact, but must be interpreted in terms of subpopulations of samples for which the variables X_1 and X_2 take exactly the same values as those found in the observed sample, subject to the assumption that the variable X_4 is normally distributed for each set of values of X_1 and X_2 with common variance and with linear regressions of X_4 on X_1 and on X_2. The implications of these restrictions for any practical problem and for the interpretation of its solution are not very clear. The test proposed involves calculating the quantity

$$t = \frac{(r_{14} - r_{24})\sqrt{(N-3)(1+r_{12})}}{\sqrt{2(1 - r_{12}^2 - r_{14}^2 - r_{24}^2 + 2r_{12}r_{14}r_{24})}}$$

which, under the conditions specified above, is distributed as t with $N-3$ degrees of freedom. For the example referred to above, $r_{14} = 0.593$, $r_{24} = 0.362$, $r_{12} = 0.514$, and $N = 128$. Substituting in the formula, we have

$$t_o = \frac{(.231)\sqrt{(125)(1.514)}}{\sqrt{2\{1 - (.514)^2 - (.593)^2 - (.362)^2 + 2(.514)(.593)(.362)\}}}$$

$$= \frac{(.231)(13.757)}{\sqrt{2\{.4738\}}} = \frac{3.178}{.9734} = 3.26$$

which, for degrees of freedom $n = 125$, is between the 1 per cent and 0.1 per cent points of the tabled t-distribution. Accordingly, we would reject the hypothesis $H_o: \rho_{14} = \rho_{24}$ and conclude that, for the observed set of values of X_1 and X_2 at least, the predictive power of the objective tests differs for the variable X_4.

As an alternative test for this first case, McNemar** proposed that we use Fisher's transformation, i.e. calculate

Annals of Mathematical Statistics, XI (1940), 271–83.
** Q. McNemar, *Psychological Statistics*, pp. 124–25.

$$z'_{14} = \frac{1}{2} \log e \left\{ \frac{1 + r_{14}}{1 - r_{14}} \right\}$$

and
$$z'_{24} = \frac{1}{2} \log e \left\{ \frac{1 + r_{24}}{1 - r_{24}} \right\}$$

and use as our estimate the standard error of the difference between the z''s, the quantity

$$S_{D_{z'}} = \sqrt{\frac{2}{N - 3} (1 - r)}$$

where

$$r = r_{12} - \frac{r_{14} r_{24} (1 - r_{12}^2 - r_{14}^2 - r_{24}^2 + 2 r_{12} r_{14} r_{24})}{2 (1 - r_{14}^2)(1 - r_{24}^2)}$$

For our example we have

$$z'_{14} = \frac{1}{2} \log e \left(\frac{1.593}{.407} \right) = 0.68223$$

$$z'_{24} = \frac{1}{2} \log e \left(\frac{1.362}{.638} \right) = 0.37923$$

$$r = 0.514 - \frac{(.593)(.362)(.4738)}{2(1 - .593^2)(1 - .362^2)}$$

$$= 0.514 - \frac{0.1017}{1.1268} = 0.514 - 0.090 = 0.424$$

and
$$S_{D_{z'}} = \sqrt{\frac{2(0.576)}{125}} = 0.0960$$

Accordingly, the normal deviate for our test of significance is

$$z_o = \frac{0.303}{0.0960} = 3.16$$

and from the tables of the normal distribution we find that

$$\rho \{ |z| \geqslant z_o \} = 0.0016$$

and we would again reject the hypothesis $H_o : \rho_{14} = \rho_{24}$. The agreement between the results of these two methods is surprisingly good, at least in this case and in others that we have encountered. McNemar's test appears to be less restrictive in its interpretation and may prove to be more useful when more is known about the validity of the assumption regarding the value of r to be used.

For the second case, with no subscripts in common, the null hypothesis is $H_o : \rho_{12} = \rho_{34}$, and the only test that seems to be known is the one proposed by McNemar, where we use for the estimate of r, in the standard error of the difference of the z''s, the quantity

$$r = \frac{1}{2(1 - r_{12}^2)(1 - r_{34}^2)} [(r_{13} - r_{12}r_{23})(r_{24} - r_{23}r_{34}) + (r_{14} - r_{13}r_{34})(r_{23} - r_{12}r_{13})$$
$$+ (r_{13} - r_{14}r_{34})(r_{24} - r_{12}r_{14}) + (r_{14} - r_{12}r_{24})(r_{23} - r_{14}r_{34})]$$

For our example, we have

$$z_{12}' = \frac{1}{2} \log e \left\{ \frac{1 + r_{12}}{1 - r_{12}} \right\} = \frac{1}{2} \log e \left\{ \frac{1.514}{0.486} \right\} = 0.56812$$

$$z_{34}' = \frac{1}{2} \log e \left\{ \frac{1 + r_{34}}{1 - r_{34}} \right\} = \frac{1}{2} \log e \left\{ \frac{1.336}{0.664} \right\} = 0.34957$$

$$r = \frac{1}{(2)(.7358)(.8871)} [(.1887)(.1990) + (.4458)(.2599) + (.2388)(.0572)$$
$$+ (.4069)(.3624)]$$

$$= \frac{0.3149}{1.305} = 0.2413$$

whence $\qquad S_{D_{z'}} = \sqrt{\frac{(2)(.7587)}{125}} = 0.1102$

Our normal deviate is, therefore, $z_o = \dfrac{0.2413}{0.1102} = 2.19$, and from the tables

of the normal distribution we find that $\rho\{|z| \geqslant z_o\} = 0.029$. Accordingly, we would accept the null hypothesis at the 1 per cent level, but reject it at the 5 per cent level. In view of our lack of knowledge of the accuracy of this approximate test, however, we would probably be inclined to accept H_o, since its unequivocal rejection is not indicated.

Hypotheses for k Samples: Differences Among Correlation Coefficients

The only situation for which even an approximate test is available is where the samples are independent. The hypothesis to be tested may be expressed in the form, with ρ_i denoting the correlation in the normal bivariate population from which the ith sample was drawn,

$$H_o : \rho_1 = \rho_2 = \ldots = \rho_k = \rho_o$$

and the set of admissible alternative hypotheses will be that the ρ's are not all equal to ρ_o. As in the earlier sections, we must distinguish between two cases: (1) the case where $\rho_o = 0$; and (2) the case where $\rho_o \neq 0$. In either case, the test is based on Fisher's z' transformation and the basic assumption is that when H_o is true z_i', where for the ith sample $z_i' = \frac{1}{2} \log e \left(\frac{1 + r_i}{1 - r_i} \right)$, is normally distributed about a common mean for all values of i, and with variance $\dfrac{1}{N_i - 3}$.

Case 1: $H_o : \rho_1 = \rho_2 = \ldots = \rho_k = 0$

If this hypothesis is true, then the quantity

$$\chi^2 = \sum_{i=1}^{k} (N_i - 3)(z_i'^2)$$

will be distributed as χ^2 with degrees of freedom $n = k$.

Case 2: $H_o : \rho_1 = \rho_2 = \ldots = \rho_k = \rho_o \, (\neq 0)$

If this hypothesis is true, then the quantity

$$\chi^2 = \sum_{i=1}^{k}(N_i - 3)(z_i' - z_.')^2$$

where

$$z_.' = \frac{\sum\limits_{i=1}^{k}(N_i - 3)(z_i')}{\sum\limits_{i=1}^{k}(N_i - 3)} \dagger\dagger$$

will be distributed as χ^2 with $n = k - 1$ degrees of freedom.

In a study of prediction of university success, the following set of correlation coefficients were obtained for six departments:

N_i	r_i
83	0.257
132	0.363
31	0.349
57	0.228
34	0.529
33	0.401

The values required for the tests of the above hypotheses may be calculated as follows:

DEPART- MENT	N_i	$N_i - 3$	r_i	z_i'	$(N_i - 3)z_i'$	$(N_i - 3)(z_i'^2)$	$(N_i - 3)(z_i' - z_.')^2$
1	83	80	0.257	0.26290	21.0320	5.529	0.632
2	132	129	0.363	0.38033	49.0626	18.660	0.105
3	31	28	0.349	0.36430	10.2004	3.716	0.004
4	57	54	0.228	0.23209	12.5329	2.909	0.773
5	34	31	0.529	0.58876	18.2516	10.746	1.741
6	33	30	0.401	0.42484	12.7452	5.415	0.160
Total	370	352	--	--	123.8247[a]	46.975	3.415[b]

[a]Whence $z_.' = 0.35177$.
[b]Equals $46.975 - (352)(z_.'^2)$.

For the test of the hypothesis $H_o : \rho_1 = \rho_2 = \ldots = \rho_6 = 0$, we have $\chi^2 = 46.975$ with $n = 6$ degrees of freedom, and we would reject the null hypothesis. Apparently the correlation coefficients as a set, although not

†† If the hypothesis is accepted, this weighted average z' value may be used to secure an estimate of the unknown value of the common population parameter ρ (using antilogs).

necessarily individually, indicate the existence of a significant degree of relationship between the predicting variables and university success.

For the test of the hypothesis $H_o : \rho_1 = \rho_2 = \ldots = \rho_6 = \rho_o \neq 0$, we have $\chi^2 = 3.414$ with $n = 5$ degrees of freedom, and we would accept the hypothesis tested. The result indicates that the differences among the correlation coefficients are not significant. To secure an estimate of the common although unknown value, ρ_o, we solve the following equation for ρ_o:

$$\frac{1}{2} \log e \left(\frac{1 + \rho_o}{1 - \rho_o} \right) = 0.35177$$

whence $\rho_o = 0.338$. Students will observe that the unweighted mean value of the r's is 0.355, and the weighted mean value of the r's is 0.336. However, although the estimates do not differ very much in this instance, in other cases they do and for theoretical reasons the estimate based on z'_i is to be preferred. One advantage is that the average z'_i may be considered as if it were a value of z' with variance equal to $\dfrac{1}{\overset{k}{\underset{i=1}{\Sigma}} (N_i - 3)}$, and

the usual tests of significance may be applied to such average values. In our problem, for example, the value $z'_i = 0.35177$ may be considered equivalent to a single value z' based on $352 + 3 = 355$ pairs of observations. For a test of the hypothesis that the common ρ is zero, for instance, we may calculate

$$z = \frac{z'_i}{\sqrt{\dfrac{1}{\overset{k}{\underset{i=1}{\Sigma}} (N_i - 3)}}} = \frac{0.35177}{\sqrt{\dfrac{1}{352}}} = 6.60$$

and refer to the tables of the normal distribution. The hypothesis $H_o : \rho = 0$ would, of course, be rejected, as we found by the previous test.

MEASURES OF THE DEGREE OF RELATIONSHIP FOR OTHER TYPES OF VARIATION‡‡

Students will remember that at the beginning of this chapter we excluded from consideration any variation other than continuous, and also any combination of continuous with discontinuous or categorical data. In actual practice, however, a researcher rather frequently encounters data that may in whole or in part be other than continuous, yet desire to measure the degree of relationship that may appear to exist or to test hypotheses that are, or may be, expressed in terms of degree of relationship. These specific problems will now be considered; in some cases, a form of analysis other than that based on the concept of relationship is indicated.

‡‡ See also Chapter IX.

Categorical Data

Where both variables are categorical in nature, being neither quantitatively measurable nor orderable, the test of independence based on χ^2 (see Chapter V) is used to determine whether or not they are associated. When the null hypothesis (of independence) is rejected, the researcher frequently wishes to measure and express numerically the degree of relationship between the two variables. For this purpose and under these circumstances, the contingency coefficient, C, where

$$C = \sqrt{\frac{\chi^2}{\chi^2 + N}} \qquad \text{(only the positive root is used)}$$

proposed by Pearson in 1901§§ is the most satisfactory measure available. The minimum value of C is zero, which for finite N can occur only when $\chi^2 = 0$ and this is a very unlikely event as reference to the sampling distribution of χ^2 will demonstrate. The maximum value of C depends, unfortunately, upon the number of categories: for a symmetrical table of k categories for both variables, its maximum value is $\sqrt{\dfrac{k-1}{k}}$. For $k = 2$, for example, the maximum value of C is 0.707, not unity, and even for $k = 10$ the maximum value is only 0.949. Accordingly, values of C are comparable only for contingency tables of the same size (number of categories), which is an inconvenient limitation. To overcome this difficulty, we may divide C by its maximum value (interpolated for nonsymmetrical tables), or we may use the coefficient, T, proposed by Tschuprow (for a t by k contingency table), where

$$T = \sqrt{\frac{\chi^2}{N\sqrt{(t-1)(k-1)}}}$$

The quantity T has the maximum value of unity when $t = k$, but may not attain unity when $t \neq k$, and values of T and C are not comparable. Probably Pearson's C, despite its obvious shortcomings, is the best measure to use, but it cannot be interpreted as a product-moment coefficient of correlation, or even as a rough estimate thereof. It is something quite different, although it is a measure of the association of the two variables.

As an illustration, consider the data, presented earlier, relating to the skill and adjustment of 180 West Indian technicians (Table II.5), for which we have $t = 4$, $k = 3$, $N = 180$, and $\chi^2 = 99.61$. For these data we have

$$C = \sqrt{\frac{99.61}{99.61 + 180}} = \sqrt{\frac{99.61}{279.61}} = 0.597$$

§§ *Philosophical Transactions*, A, CXCV (1901), 1–47.

which, when corrected for its maximum value of approximately 0.841, becomes

$$C_c = \frac{C}{\text{Max } C} = \frac{0.597}{0.841} = 0.71$$

indicating a high degree of relationship between the two variables. Note that Tschuprow's coefficient, T, for the same data is

$$T = \sqrt{\frac{99.61}{(180)\sqrt{(3)(2)}}} = \sqrt{\frac{99.61}{440.91}} = 0.475$$

from which it is obvious that T is comparable in magnitude with neither C nor C_c.

Students should observe that where one variable is categorized but the other is not (being either a discontinuous or a continuous variable) the methods of this section may be used, and used in fact with any table of data for which χ^2 would normally be employed as a test of independence. This is true because we can always arrange ordered data, discontinuous or continuous, into whatever system of categories we deem expedient or desirable. What is frequently overlooked, however, is that this is not always the most efficient procedure to employ. As an illustration, consider the data of Table II.4, essentially a mixture of categorical (attitude) and continuous (really discontinuous, being test scores) variation. The general hypothesis is that the attitude of a worker toward the Taft-Hartley Law depends upon the amount of information he possesses about that law, from which the general null hypothesis is that amount of information has no effect on attitude. We now have a choice of methods, depending upon the manner in which we translate the set of general hypotheses to statistical hypotheses: if expressed in the form that the two variables are independent, we would use the χ^2-test of independence; if expressed in terms of equality of mean scores on the information test for the three Attitude groups, we would use analysis of variance.|||| Students should, as an exercise, analyze these data in the two ways indicated: combining the scores 12 and 13, and also 2 and 3, to secure a 3 × 10 contingency table, but analyzing the data without such grouping for the analysis of variance, as a type of single classification with three groups of unequal size to secure the Among Attitude Groups and Within Attitude Groups sums of squares and mean squares. At the same time, they may specify and test the assumptions underlying the two procedures—from which it will be evident to them that one method admits of a much more general application than the other does.

|||| Students interested in the relationship between correlation and analysis of variance, in the form of *intraclass correlation,* should read the relevant chapter ("Intraclass Correlations and the Analysis of Variance") in *Statistical Methods for Research Workers,* by R. A. Fisher.

Of course, we can always apply the method of this section when both variables are continuous, i.e. even in cases where the Pearson product-moment coefficient of correlation is the best measure of the degree of relationship. This is not a wise thing to do, however, since the two measures are not equivalent and nothing can be gained through use of the poorer method. Consider, for instance, the data of Table XI.6, for which we have $r = 0.802$. Combining the class intervals by groups of three to secure a 3×3 contingency table, we find for these data:

$$\chi^2 = 4,458.62; \qquad n = 6,836$$

$$\text{whence} \qquad C = 0.628 \qquad \text{and} \qquad C_c = 0.77$$

Tschuprow's coefficient, T, on the other hand, proves to be equal to

$$T = 0.571$$

Quite clearly, T and C are not comparable with each other nor with r, and should not be used in situations where r (or η) is applicable. However, if the conditions required for the use of the correlation coefficient or correlation ratio are not satisfied, so much so that it is evident that neither will yield a satisfactory measure of the degree of relationship, it would be appropriate to use the contingency coefficient as a measure. Under the circumstances, it would be the only method that could be employed.

Ranked Data

In very many problems, particularly in personnel work in industry, we cannot secure quantitative measures for certain factors—e.g. in an assessment of leadership ability—but we can arrange the individuals in order, thereby securing for each individual a number indicating his *rank* in the group. Our measures, then, consist of a set of ordinal numbers, with 1 for the individual ranked first and so on to N for the individual ranked last in a group of N individuals.

Before proceeding to the methods appropriate for such data, a word of warning is not amiss. Researchers are rather inclined to apply ranking procedures uncritically, without first determining whether in fact the material or objects can be ranked. Unless there is an inherent order, the appropriate method of analysis is, not by a forced system of ranks, but through the use of categories, which are more general in that no ordering of the classes is required. If, on the other hand, it is possible with a little extra effort to secure measures on a variate scale (continuous or discontinuous data, such as scores), or such measures have been secured, it is a mistake to use ranks, although it is always possible to transform to ranks. The relationship will be more clearly defined with quantitative measures than with ranks, both magnitude and order being considered, and nothing can be gained—in fact, something may be lost—by using ranks.

Consider, for example, the following ranks## assigned by two judges to ten characteristics of good leaders (arranged, for convenience, by ranks of the first judge):

CHARACTERISTIC	RANKS ASSIGNED		DIFFERENCE IN RANKS (D)	D^2
	Judge 1	*Judge 2*		
A	1	9	−8	64
B	2	3	−1	1
C	3	4	−1	1
D	4	8	−4	16
E	5	1	4	16
F	6	7	−1	1
G	7	5	2	4
H	8	2	6	36
I	9	10	−1	1
J	10	6	4	16
		Total	16 − 16 = 0	156

Is there evidence of agreement between the two sets of ranks? The *rank-difference coefficient of correlation, R,* originally suggested by Spearman*** in 1904, is defined as

$$R = 1 - \frac{6\Sigma D^2}{(N)(N^2 - 1)}$$

where N denotes the number of objects ranked and D the difference between the ranks for any particular object. The calculation procedure is indicated in the final two columns above: note that, as a check, $\Sigma D = 0$. For this case

$$R = 1 - \frac{(6)(156)}{(10)(99)} = 1 - \frac{936}{990} = 0.055$$

Since R can take values from −1, for perfect disagreement in ranks, through 0, for no agreement in ranks, to +1, for perfect agreement in ranks, it is obvious from the value of R—or from the table of ranks, for that matter—that there is little agreement between the two judges.†††

To test the null hypothesis of no agreement, Kendall has given tables

---

In the case of ties in ranks, the average of the corresponding ordinal numbers is used for each of the objects so tied in position.

*** *American Journal of Psychology,* XV (1904), 72–101. The formula is a direct derivation, for ranks, from the usual product-moment coefficient formula.

††† For the above 10 characteristics, perfect disagreement would be

Judge 1: 1, 2, 3, 4, 5, 6, 7, 8, 9, 10
Judge 2: 10, 9, 8, 7, 6, 5, 4, 3, 2, 1 $(R = -1)$

and perfect agreement would be

Judge 1: 1, 2, 3, 4, 5, 6, 7, 8, 9, 10
Judge 2: 1, 2, 3, 4, 5, 6, 7, 8, 9, 10 $(R = +1)$

for $N \leqslant 8$.‡‡‡ For larger values of N, we may use as an approximation

$$t = \frac{R\sqrt{N-2}}{\sqrt{1-R^2}}$$

which is approximately distributed as Student's t with $N-2$ degrees of freedom. For values of $N \leqslant 25$, a correction for continuity may be made by calculating

$$X = 1 - \frac{\Sigma D^2}{\frac{1}{6}(N)(N^2 - 1) + 1}$$

and

$$t' = \frac{X\sqrt{N-2}}{\sqrt{1-X^2}}$$

which again is approximately distributed as Student's t with $N-2$ degrees of freedom. For our example, we have

$$t = \frac{(.055)\sqrt{8}}{\sqrt{.945}} = \frac{.1556}{.972} = 0.160$$

$$X = 1 - \frac{156}{166} = 0.060$$

$$t' = \frac{(.060)\sqrt{8}}{\sqrt{.940}} = \frac{.1697}{.970} = 0.175$$

and for either value we would, of course, accept the null hypothesis and conclude that there is no agreement between the ranks assigned by the two judges.

For an alternative measure—*Tau*, proposed by Kendall, and the coefficient of concordance proposed by the same author for the case of m rankings (e.g. if 3 or more judges had been used)—students should refer to the corresponding sections of Chapter IX, above.

Tetrachoric Correlation Coefficient

This correlation coefficient, unlike those just considered, is essentially an estimate of the population value of the Pearson product-moment coefficient of correlation, but is derived from a 2×2 table. The assumptions underlying its use are that both of the variables are continuous and the 2×2 table represents a normal bivariate distribution divided into four quadrants. Karl Pearson suggested it in 1901,§§§ but it has a very limited value. Normally, we have variate values and may calculate the value of the correlation coefficient, r, and certainly nothing would be gained by regrouping the data into a 2×2 table. In other cases, but in

‡‡‡ M. G. Kendall, *The Advanced Theory of Statistics*, Vol. I, p. 397.
§§§ *Philosophical Transactions*, A, CXCV (1901), 1–47.

very few, the researcher may have been given, or may have collected, data only in the form of a 2×2 table and may have good reason to believe that the underlying variation is continuous and normal for both variables. Only if these conditions are reasonably well satisfied, however, is the use of the tetrachoric correlation coefficient justified. In all other cases, including doubtful cases, the researcher would be well advised to use the methods described above that are appropriate for categorical data.

As an illustration, let us turn again to the data of Table XI.6, for which the conditions are reasonably well satisfied and the value of the product-moment coefficient of correlation is known to be 0.802. Setting up four quadrants with the dividing line at 55 for each variable, we secure the following fourfold frequency table:

FRENCH AUTHORS	FRENCH COMPOSITION		TOTAL
	Under 55	*55 and above*	
55 and above	729	3,194	3,923
Under 55	2,317	596	2,913
Total	3,046	3,790	6,836

In general, using letters to denote the frequencies, we have a contingency table of the type‖‖‖

a	b	$a + b$
c	d	$c + d$
$a + c$	$b + d$	N

Where the pairs of marginal frequencies are equal, or nearly so, i.e. $a + b = c + d$ and $a + c = b + d$, equivalent to a division at or near the median, the tetrachoric correlation coefficient, r_T, is given approximately by the equation

$$r_T = \sin \left[\{90°\} \left\{ \frac{(b + c) - (a + d)}{N} \right\} \right]$$

which for our example yields

$$r_T = \sin \left[\{90°\} \left\{ \frac{4,186}{6,836} \right\} \right] = \sin 55°7' = 0.820$$

as compared with the observed value of $r = 0.802$. Where the marginal

‖‖‖ Obviously, we could use as a measure of the degree of relationship either the contingency coefficient $C = \sqrt{\dfrac{\chi^2}{\chi^2 + N}}$, or the phi coefficient $\phi = \sqrt{\dfrac{\chi^2}{N}}$, for any table of this kind.

frequencies are not equal, however, the appropriate formula becomes

$$r_T = \cos\left[\{180°\}\left\{\frac{\sqrt{ad}}{\sqrt{bc} + \sqrt{ad}}\right\}\right]$$

which for our example yields

$$r_T = \cos\left[\{180°\}\left\{\frac{\sqrt{(729)(596)}}{\sqrt{(3,194)(2,317)} + \sqrt{(729)(596)}}\right\}\right]$$

$$= \cos 35°6' = 0.818$$

The agreement is good in this case, as it generally is for large samples, but this is not always true. For very small samples, and for any sample for which one of the marginal totals (e.g. $a + c$) is small in proportion to the total number of cases, r_T may be a very poor estimate of the population value ρ and have little or no meaning.

We do not advocate the use of tetrachoric correlation, but we do recognize that in some situations—by accident or design, or through force of circumstances—it may be necessary to calculate and use the tetrachoric correlation coefficient. It must always be used and interpreted with extreme caution, and full recognition paid to the fact that it may in any given situation yield a very poor estimate of the population value ρ. Moreover, it is practically impossible to devise satisfactory tests of hypotheses expressed in terms of r_T.

Biserial Correlation Coefficients

This is, again, a situation where our data are in a form that does not permit of the application of the standard formulae for estimating the degree of relationship between two variables. The common pattern is that one variable is on a continuous scale but the other is a dichotomy, i.e. only two values (or classes or categories) could be or have been used. The resulting table of data looks like a $2 \times k$ contingency table, and may in fact be analyzed as such. Actually, there are two types of situations that may occur: first, the "scale" underlying the dichotomy may be truly discontinuous or categorical, of which a common example is classification by sex; second, the "scale" underlying the dichotomy may in fact be continuous and we have, for convenience or by accident, divided it into two parts only. For the first case the appropriate measure is the *point biserial coefficient of correlation*, denoted by r_{pb}; for the second case the appropriate measure is the *biserial coefficient of correlation*, denoted by r_{bis}. Students and researchers must examine any given situation carefully to determine its type, since the two coefficients are not necessarily equivalent. As a general rule, in the majority of cases the point

Students may be interested in the original discussion by Karl Pearson, *Biometrika*, VII (1909), 96–105.

biserial coefficient is the better one to use, unless it is known or can be demonstrated beyond reasonable doubt that the dichotomized variable does in fact have a continuous scale.

One major advantage of the point biserial coefficient is that it is a product-moment coefficient of correlation and can be used with, and under the same conditions as, the usual product-moment coefficient. In tests of significance based upon it, however, the additional assumption is made that in each of the two categories the continuous variable is normally distributed with a common variance. (No assumption is made concerning the dichotomized variable.) Accordingly, any test of significance of r_{pb} is equivalent to the t-test of the significance of the difference between the means of two independent samples (see Chapter VI), and may most easily be made in that form.

The biserial coefficient, r_{bis}, is subject to much more restrictive conditions. Basically, it is an estimate of the population value ρ of a normal bivariate distribution and can be used and interpreted only in light of those conditions. Unfortunately, it can take values greater than unity, since its range is theoretically unlimited, and, taking into account all its limitations, is at best a rather unsatisfactory measure. But it is the only coefficient that can properly be used in the situation for which it was designed, although even so it should not be used for small samples.

Point Biserial Correlation Coefficient

As an illustration, consider the data of Table II.4, relating to information about and attitude toward the Taft-Hartley Law, arranged in two groups for attitude—those With Opinion and those Without Opinion, as shown below. Here we have what may be considered as a continuous variable for the information test scores, and roughly normally distributed, but a true dichotomy for the other variable. The problem is to secure a measure of the degree of relationship between the two variables, information possessed and holding or not-holding an opinion.*

Performing the calculations as indicated, we have

$$Y_{1.} = 8.103$$
$$Y_{0.} = 7.128$$
$$V_Y = \frac{72,262 - \dfrac{(8,512)^2}{N}}{N - 1} = 5.2145$$

and
$$r_{pb} = \frac{Y_{1.} - Y_{0.}}{\sqrt{V_Y}} \sqrt{\frac{N_1 N_0}{N(N - 1)}}^{\dagger} = \frac{0.9749}{2.2835}(0.4525) = 0.193$$

* Students may apply the usual tests of significance for variability and means.
† Derived from the usual product-moment formula where X can take only the value 1 for With Opinion and 0 for No Opinion. Students may also be interested in

INFORMATION TEST SCORE (Y)	ATTITUDE		TOTAL
	With Opinion (1)	*No Opinion (0)*	
13	5	1	6
12	24	4	28
11	88	17	105
10	113	31	144
9	137	40	177
8	117	49	166
7	99	37	136
6	83	45	128
5	58	48	106
4	33	27	60
3	17	11	28
2	2	2	4
Total	776 (N_1)	312 (N_0)	1,088 (N)
Sum	6,288	2,224	8,512
Mean	8.1031 ($Y_1.$)	7.1282 ($Y_0.$)	7.824 ($Y.$)
Sum of Squares	54,812	17,450	72,262

There is a positive relationship between the two variables, as might be expected, but it is surprisingly small: note the complete overlapping of the two distributions, although the means differ slightly. To test the null hypothesis of no relationship, using r_{pb} rather than the difference in the means, we may use the quantity

$$t = \frac{r_{pb} \sqrt{N-2}}{\sqrt{1 - r_{pb}^2}}$$

which is distributed as t with $N - 2$ degrees of freedom. For our example we have

$$t = \frac{(0.193)(32.95)}{0.9812} = 6.48$$

and we conclude that the relationship is significantly greater than zero.

Biserial Correlation Coefficient

To illustrate the calculation of this coefficient of correlation we shall again use the data of Table XI.6, since for these data the assumptions are reasonably well satisfied, using a dividing point of 55 on French Composition.

---

variations of the formula in which $Y.$ and either $Y_1.$ or $Y_0.$, but not both, are used (useful when a number of such coefficients are to be calculated from the same data, as in item analysis in test construction).

FRENCH AUTHORS (Y)	COMPUTATION VARIABLE (y)	FRENCH COMPOSITION $X_1(<55)$	$X_2(\geqslant 55)$	TOTAL
85–94	4		108	108
75–84	3	2	743	745
65–74	2	97	1,186	1,283
55–64	1	630	1,157	1,787
45–54	0	887	468	1,355
35–44	−1	819	119	938
25–34	−2	413	8	421
15–24	−3	154	1	155
5–14	−4	44		44
Total		3,046	3,790	6,836
Sum		−1,453	6,052	4,599
Mean		−0.4770	1.5968	0.6728
Sum of Squares		5,597	14,476	20,073

From these values we have, for the computation variable y,

$$y_1. = -0.4770$$
$$y_2. = 1.5968$$
$$V_y = 2.4841 \qquad \sqrt{V_y} = 1.5761$$
$$q = \frac{3,046}{6,836} = 0.4456; \qquad p = \frac{3,790}{6,836} = 0.5544$$

If we denote by o the ordinate of the assumed normal distribution of X at the point of dichotomy, which may be read directly from any table of the normal distribution giving both areas and ordinates, the formula for r_{bis} may be written

$$r_{bis} = \frac{y_2. - y_1.}{\sqrt{V_y}} \cdot \frac{pq}{o}$$

For our example, since the proportionate area up to the point of dichotomy is $p = 0.5544$, the corresponding normal deviate is 0.1368, and, from Pearson's tables,‡ we have

$$o = 0.3952$$

whence
$$r_{bis} = \frac{1.5968 - (-.4770)}{1.5761} \cdot \frac{(.4456)(.5544)}{.3952}$$

$$= \frac{.5123}{.6229} = 0.822$$

as compared with the product-moment coefficient of correlation $r = 0.802$.

‡ *Tables for Statisticians and Biometricians, Part 1,* Table II: Area and Ordinates in Terms of Abscissa.

Little can be done with r_{bis} with respect to tests of hypotheses, since the sampling distribution is unknown. Adding to this the fact that r_{bis} is seldom a very good estimate of ρ, the population value, unless the sample is very large and the point of division is close to the median, it will be appreciated that r_{bis} is a coefficient of doubtful value. It should perhaps be used only as a last resort, although a recent study by Tate§ gives a transformation of r_{bis} that should overcome some of the difficulties in regard to tests of significance. As in the case of so many of these approximate methods, including those discussed above and others too numerous to mention, the researcher should design his experiment so that it is not necessary to use approximations.

EXERCISES

1. Derive the corresponding formulae, and state and test the hypotheses, as suggested at the top of page 325 of the text. Read the relevant sections of the reference given in the footnote on the same page.
2. Derive and present the corresponding formulae and results for the regression of X on Y, as suggested on page 333 of the text. Test the assumptions underlying the statistical tests employed.
3. Using the data of Table XI.3, check the calculation of the values of a and b for the prediction of Army Alpha scores from Chronological Age. Check also the entries in the corresponding analysis of variance table on page 334 of the text.
4. By regrouping the class intervals in pairs for both variables in Table XI.7 beginning at the lower end in each case, and putting the final three Army Alpha score groups together, recalculate the values of the correlation coefficient and correlation ratios, using suitable computation variables.
5. The author of a study of teaching success observed a correlation of 0.164 between the scores on a general information test and marks assigned for teaching. Was he justified in concluding that the two variables were unrelated?
6. To be acceptable for Air Force selection purposes, it was determined that no mental test would be used unless the correlation between the scores on it and subsequent flying success was 0.50. A recommended mental test was tried out on a group of 45 cadets, yielding a correlation of 0.42; should the mental test be included in the selection battery?
7. For one class of 58 students in Sociology the correlation between high school record and class mark proved to be 0.43; for a class of 27 students in Psychology, on the other hand, the corresponding correlation coefficient was 0.32. Was high school record an equally good predictor in the two cases?
8. Rearranging subscripts as required, test the following hypotheses for the coefficients of correlation given in the text on page 353.

$$\text{(a)} \quad H_o : \rho_{13} = \rho_{23} \quad \text{(b)} \quad H_o : \rho_{23} = \rho_{14}$$

Interpret your findings.

§ R. F. Tate, "The Biserial and Point Correlation Coefficients" (Durham, N.C.: Office of Naval Research Project NR042031, Institute of Mathematical Statistics, University of North Carolina).

9. For five classes in a secondary school, the correlation coefficients between intelligence and high school grades were as follows:

Class	1	2	3	4	5
Number	36	29	34	32	37
r	.1456	.0092	.3432	.7953	.1434

Test the hypotheses of (a) a common $\rho = 0$, and (b) a common $\rho \neq 0$.

10. Complete the exercises suggested on page 360 of the text (χ^2-test of independence and analysis of variance for data relating to Taft-Hartley Law).

CHAPTER XII

Classification and Reduction of Multivariate Data

Consideration of univariate and bivariate data leads rather naturally to the discussion of multivariate data, since in only very few problems is the researcher restricted to one or even two variables. As a general rule, in fact, any phenomenon under observation is, or may be, affected by the influence of numerous factors, and these factors may be related among themselves—sometimes operating in the same direction, sometimes in opposition. One of the tasks of the researcher is to identify and describe these relationships and inter-relationships, and the purpose of the present chapter is to present a general method designed to achieve this purpose.

Students should note that the content of this chapter consists only of what is called the methods of partial and multiple regression and correlation, this being the logical sequence of the methods discussed in the earlier chapters. Further, and more specific, methods used in the analysis of multivariate data will be considered in the following chapter. It is of some interest to note that the theory of partial and multiple regression and correlation for normal variates was given by Karl Pearson in 1896,* and for other variates (assuming only linearity of regression) by G. U. Yule in 1897.† The exact sampling distribution (for samples from a normal population) of the partial correlation coefficient was given by Fisher in 1924‡ and of the multiple correlation coefficient in 1928.§ The special methods of the succeeding chapter are, however, of more recent origin.

Partial and Multiple Regression

The general problem of partial and multiple regression can be illustrated most simply in terms of prediction of the values of one variable from a knowledge of the values of k other variables. As an example, consider the problem of predicting the success of students in the first year of the Faculty of Applied Science and Engineering at the University of Toronto, using for purposes of prediction the marks obtained by each student (on examinations held at the end of the final year in secondary school) in five

---

* *Philosophical Transactions*, A, CLXXXVII, 253–318.

† *Proceedings of the Royal Society*, LX, 477–89; and *Journal of the Royal Statistical Society*, LX, 812–54.

‡ *Metron*, III, 329.

§ *Proceedings of the Royal Society*, A, CXXI, 654.

subjects, namely, Algebra, Geometry, Trigonometry, Physics, and Chemistry. Using the following notation, where the subscript "i" denotes the ith student,

N = Number of Students = 1,008

Y_i denotes the first-year University mark

X_{1i} denotes the mark on the Algebra examination

X_{2i} denotes the mark on the Geometry examination

X_{3i} denotes the mark on the Trigonometry examination

X_{4i} denotes the mark on the Physics examination

X_{5i} denotes the mark on the Chemistry examination

then the general problem is to find the "best" combination of the marks on $X_1, \ldots, X_5$ to predict Y. Assuming that a linear relation is adequate in the situation,‖ we may write

$$\hat{Y}_i = \alpha + \beta_1 X_{1i} + \beta_2 X_{2i} + \beta_3 X_{3i} + \beta_4 X_{4i} + \beta_5 X_{5i}$$

where $\hat{Y}_i$ denotes the predicted value of Y_i, and α and the β's denote quantities to be estimated so as to yield the 'best" linear relation. Using the theory of least squares, as in the earlier cases, the values to be used for α and the β's will be those for which the quantity

$$\chi^2 = \sum_i (Y_i - \hat{Y}_i)^2 = \sum_i (Y_i - \alpha - \beta_1 X_{1i} - \beta_2 X_{2i} - \beta_3 X_{3i} - \beta_4 X_{4i} - \beta_5 X_{5i})^2$$

is a minimum, thus defining exactly the meaning of the "best" linear relation.# Students will observe that the form of distribution of the Y- and X-values has not been stipulated: the only restriction is that the linear form for the relation hold. Additional assumptions will be made, or restrictions imposed, however, when we come to the problem of tests of significance of the results secured by the process.

In order to secure the appropriate estimates of α and the β's, which we may denote by a and b's, it is necessary to differentiate the expression for χ^2 partially with respect to α and each of the β's in turn. Particular note should be made of the fact that this is *partial* differentiation, each of the remaining quantities being considered as a constant for the purpose, since this has important implications for the interpretation of the results. First, the Y and X values are considered as constants, so that strictly speaking the solution applies only to the set of values observed. This restriction is not serious if we can consider the set of Y and X's as a random sample; on the other hand, it has very serious consequences if we attempt to apply the regression equation secured in one situation to a completely different situ-

‖ The case of non-linear relationship will be considered later in this chapter, as a special application of the general theory.

The extension to the general case of k predictor variables is obvious.

ation.** Second, holding the values of the other β's constant when differentiating partially with respect to one of them makes the estimates, in effect, *partial* regression coefficients, i.e. the regression coefficient that would be secured if all the other variables (X's) were held constant or their effects *partialled out*. This does not apply to α because, as we shall see, it can be expressed in terms of the β's. The reason why the inclusion, for example, of one variable that has a high degree of relationship with one or more of the other variables has such an effect on the partial regression coefficients can be properly understood only in light of the process by which the values are secured.

The process of securing the least squares estimates can be simplified considerably by first differentiating

$$\chi^2 = \sum_i (Y_i - \alpha - \beta_1 X_{1i} - \beta_2 X_{2i} - \beta_3 X_{3i} - \beta_4 X_{4i} - \beta_5 X_{5i})^2$$

partially with respect to α, setting the resulting equation equal to zero, from which we obtain

$$\alpha = Y. - \beta_1 X_1. - \beta_2 X_2. - \beta_3 X_3. - \beta_4 X_4. - \beta_5 X_5.$$

where

$$Y. = \frac{\sum_i Y_i}{N}$$

$$X_j. = \frac{\sum_i X_{ji}}{N}$$

Defining a new set of variables as follows:

$$y_i = Y_i - Y.$$
$$x_{ji} = X_{ji} - X_j.$$

we note that χ^2 may be written as

$$\chi^2 = \sum_i (y_i - \beta_1 x_{1i} - \beta_2 x_{2i} - \beta_3 x_{3i} - \beta_4 x_{4i} - \beta_5 x_{5i})^2$$

Differentiating this partially with respect to each of the β's in turn, setting the resulting equation equal to zero and simplifying, we secure the following set of equations to solve for the β's, where the general expression S_{uv} has the following definition

$$S_{uv} = \sum_i u_i v_i \ (= S_{vu})$$

being a sum of squares when $u = v$, and a sum of products when $u \neq v$,

$$\beta_1 S_{x_1 x_1} + \beta_2 S_{x_1 x_2} + \beta_3 S_{x_1 x_3} + \beta_4 S_{x_1 x_4} + \beta_5 S_{x_1 x_5} = S_{yx_1}$$

** This difficulty arose rather frequently in personnel selection for the armed forces during the last war, whenever the vagaries of the authorities resulted in a substantial change in the nature and type of recruits to be screened.

$$\beta_1 S_{x_2 x_1} + \beta_2 S_{x_2 x_2} + \beta_3 S_{x_2 x_3} + \beta_4 S_{x_2 x_4} + \beta_5 S_{x_2 x_5} = S_{yx_2}$$
$$\beta_1 S_{x_3 x_1} + \beta_2 S_{x_3 x_2} + \beta_3 S_{x_3 x_3} + \beta_4 S_{x_3 x_4} + \beta_5 S_{x_3 x_5} = S_{yx_3}$$
$$\beta_1 S_{x_4 x_1} + \beta_2 S_{x_4 x_2} + \beta_3 S_{x_4 x_3} + \beta_4 S_{x_4 x_4} + \beta_5 S_{x_4 x_5} = S_{yx_4}$$
$$\beta_1 S_{x_5 x_1} + \beta_2 S_{x_5 x_2} + \beta_3 S_{x_5 x_3} + \beta_4 S_{x_5 x_4} + \beta_5 S_{x_5 x_5} = S_{yx_5}$$

Students will observe that the solution, i.e. the estimates of the β's, is determined by the values of the sums of squares and sums of products. To simplify the work, however, it is convenient to transform the equations by dividing both sides of each by $\sqrt{S_{yy}}$ and also by $\sqrt{S_{x_j x_j}}$, where $j = 1$ to 5 depending upon the order of the equation, assuming that none of the variances is zero. Let us also define

$$B_j = \frac{\beta_j \sqrt{S_{x_j x_j}}}{\sqrt{S_{yy}}}$$

so that

$$\beta_j = \frac{\sqrt{S_{yy}}}{\sqrt{S_{x_j x_j}}} \cdot B_j$$

and we may write the above set of equations in terms of product-moment coefficients of correlation,†† r, as follows

$$B_1 \quad + B_2 r_{12} + B_3 r_{13} + B_4 r_{14} + B_5 r_{15} = r_{y1}$$
$$B_1 r_{12} + B_2 \quad + B_3 r_{23} + B_4 r_{24} + B_5 r_{25} = r_{y2}$$
$$B_1 r_{13} + B_2 r_{23} + B_3 \quad + B_4 r_{34} + B_5 r_{35} = r_{y3}$$
$$B_1 r_{14} + B_2 r_{24} + B_3 r_{34} + B_4 \quad + B_5 r_{45} = r_{y4}$$
$$B_1 r_{15} + B_2 r_{25} + B_3 r_{35} + B_4 r_{45} + B_5 \quad = r_{y5}$$

where

$$r_{yj} = \frac{S_{yx_j}}{\sqrt{S_{yy} S_{x_j x_j}}}$$

$(j = 1 - 5)$

and

$$r_{jk} = \frac{S_{x_j x_k}}{\sqrt{S_{x_j x_j} S_{x_k x_k}}} \qquad \left(\begin{matrix} r_{jj} = r_{kk} = 1 \\ r_{jk} = r_{kj} \end{matrix} \right)$$

$j,k = 1 - 5$

This set of simultaneous equations, or the earlier set, can be solved by any of the usual methods—by determinants or by substitution—but it is convenient for three or more predictor variables (X's) to use a systematic procedure with automatic checks on the accuracy of the calculations. Moreover, the method about to be described has the additional advantage that it gives directly Fisher's set of auxiliary statistics, commonly denoted by g's, which may be used to give the regression equations for several criterion variables, to test for the significance of the partial regression coefficients, the significance of the difference between any two of these coefficients, and in the calculation of the appropriate values when one (or more) of the predictor variables is omitted (its regression coefficient, for

†† Of any kind, provided only that each be in fact a product-moment coefficient (such as point biserial, but not biserial).

instance, being found to be not significantly different from zero). We shall illustrate the method by applying it to the problem of prediction of university success, for which the formulae given above were derived. Students should observe that, in using this method, a substantial error may be introduced in the process of calculation unless the values of the correlation coefficients are originally calculated to at least five places of decimal, and preferably six if six or more predictor variables are involved.

The correlation coefficients found in the above study were as follows:

VARIABLE	PREDICTOR VARIABLE				
	X_1	X_2	X_3	X_4	X_5
Y	.50941	.53423	.47757	.53392	.47696
X_1	—	.54422	.54949	.48484	.47548
X_2		—	.53159	.49962	.47988
X_3			—	.45238	.40233
X_4				—	.52213

The means and sums of squares were

$$Y. = 59.05; \quad X_1. = 70.96; \quad X_2. = 71.33; \quad X_3. = 74.64;$$
$$X_4. = 69.70; \quad X_5. = 70.24$$
$$S_{yy} = 190,902; \quad S_{x_1x_1} = 155,905; \quad S_{x_2x_2} = 153,165;$$
$$S_{x_3x_3} = 147,539; \quad S_{x_4x_4} = 140,235; \quad S_{x_5x_5} = 140,775$$

Since the necessary calculations are performed in a series of stages, some of them rather far removed from the original problem, the following discussion will be arranged in a sequence of stages with various steps within each stage, where necessary.

Stage 1: Calculation of Auxiliary g-statistics

This stage consists essentially in the solution of the sets of equations with the B's for the following set of arbitrary r_{yj} values

Y^i	Y^{ii}	Y^{iii}	Y^{iv}	Y^v
1	0	0	0	0
0	1	0	0	0
0	0	1	0	0
0	0	0	1	0
0	0	0	0	1

The following procedure, however, gives the complete set in one systematic series of calculations. (Students will soon note shortcuts that we have not discussed here.)

Step 1: Prepare the calculation table, as shown (Table XII.1), with a sufficient number of rows and columns (determined by the number of predictor variables used).

Step 2: Write the correlation coefficients in the top line of the corre-

TABLE XII.1

CALCULATION OF AUXILIARY g-STATISTICS IN MULTIPLE REGRESSION

VARIABLE	X_1	X_2	X_3	X_4	X_5	Y^i	CHECK COLUMN
X_1	1.00000 1.00000	.54422 .54422	.54949 .54949	.48484 .48484	.47548 .47548	1.00000 1.00000 −.32957	4.0540(4.0540(
X_2	−.54422	1.00000 .70382	.53159 .23255	.49962 .23576	.47988 .22111	0 −.54422 .07756	3.0553 .8490((.84909
X_3	−.54949	−.33041	1.00000 .62122	.45238 .10807	.40233 .06800	0 −.36967 +.09540	2.9357 .4276 (.42762
X_4	−.48484	−.33497	−.17396	1.00000 .66716	.52213 .20570	0 −.23823 +.04885	2.9589 .6346 (.63463
X_5	−.47548	−.31416	−.10946	−.30832	1.00000 .63359	0 −.19059 +.05560	2.8798 .4430 (.44300
Y^i	−1.00000	+.77324	+.59507	+.35708	+.30081	.18482	
Check Row	−4.05403 (−3.05403)	−1.20632 (−.20630)	−.68834 (+.31165)	−.95124 (+.04876)	−.69919 (+.30081)		
Y^{ii}	0	−1.42082	+.53187	+.41593	+.30373	.18482	
Check Row	−3.05403 (−2.05403)	−3.40037 (−2.40036)	−.75155 (+.24845)	−.89239 (+.10761)	−.69629 (+.30373)		
Y^{iii}	0	0	−1.60974	+.26075	+.08810	.18482	
Check Row	−3.05403 (−2.05403)	−1.97955 (−.97954)	−2.89316 (−1.89316)	−1.04757 (−.04757)	−.91190 (+.08810)		
Y^{iv}	0	0	0	−1.49889	+.48662	.18482	
Check Row	−3.05403 (−2.05403)	−1.97955 (−.97954)	−1.28343 (−.28342)	−2.80721 (−1.80721)	−.51338 (+.48662)		
Y^v	0	0	0	0	−1.57831	.18482	
Check Row	−3.05403 (−2.05403)	−1.97955 (−.97954)	−1.28343 (−.28342)	−1.30832 (−.30832)	−2.57831 (−1.57831)		

TABLE XII.1

CALCULATION OF AUXILIARY g-STATISTICS IN MULTIPLE REGRESSION

Y^{ii}	CHECK COLUMN	Y^{iii}	CHECK COLUMN	Y^{iv}	CHECK COLUMN	Y^{v}	CHECK COLUMN
0	3.05403	0	3.05403	0	3.05403	0	3.05403
0	3.05403	0	3.05403	0	3.05403	0	3.05403
+.07756		+.09540		+.04885		+.05560	
1.00000	4.05531	0	3.05531	0	3.05531	0	3.05531
1.00000	2.39325	0	1.39325	0	1.39325	0	1.39325
−.32721	(2.39324)	+.08179	(1.39324)	+.05956	(1.39324)	+.05614	(1.39324)
0	2.93579	1.00000	3.93579	0	2.93579	0	2.93579
−.33041	.46688	1.00000	1.79729	0	.79729	0	.79729
+.08179	(.46688)	−.30680	(1.79729)	+.04317	(.79729)	+.01628	(.79729)
0	2.95897	0	2.95897	1.00000	3.95897	0	2.95897
−.27749	.59537	−.17396	.69890	1.00000	1.87286	0	.87286
+.05956	(.59537)	+.04317	(.69890)	−.30476	(1.87286)	+.08994	(.87286)
0	2.87982	0	2.87982	0	2.87982	1.00000	3.87982
−.19244	.44116	−.05582	.57777	−.30832	.32527	1.00000	1.63359
+.05614	(.44115)	+.01628	(.57777)	+.08994	(.32527)	−.29170	(1.63359)

TABLE OF g_{ij}

j \ i	1	2	3	4	5	r_{yi}
1	1.7832	−.4197	−.5162	−.2643	−.3008	.50941
2	−.4197	1.7704	−.4425	−.3223	−.3038	.53423
3	−.5162	−.4425	1.6600	−.2336	−.0881	.47757
4	−.2643	−.3223	−.2336	1.6490	−.4866	.53392
5	−.3008	−.3038	−.0881	−.4866	1.5783	.47696

B_i	+.1531	+.2037	+.1267	+.2300	+.1354

$\sqrt{Sx_ix_i}$	394.85	391.36	384.11	374.48	375.20

$\sqrt{S_{yy}} = 436.92$

b_i	+.1694	+.2274	+.1441	+.2683	+.1577

sponding spaces, including the set of arbitrary values of the r_{yj}'s, as indicated. Check the entries.

Step 3: Calculate the entries in the top line of each space in each check column; for the jth row this is the sum $r_{j1} + r_{j2} + r_{j3} + r_{j4} + r_{j5} + r_{yj}$ (using the appropriate value of r_{yj} for that specific check column); check the addition carefully. For example, for the second row and Y^{ii}, we have

$.54422 + 1.00000 + .53159 + .49962 + .47988 + 1.00000 = 4.05531.$

(Students will observe that once the entries for the Y^i check column have been calculated, the remaining entries are easily determined from them.)

Step 4: In the second line of each space in the first row, write again the value in the first line of that space. Check the entries.

Step 5: In the column headed X_1, write below the diagonal cell double line the entry in the corresponding space of the second line of the first row, with the sign changed, as indicated. Check the entries, by addition, noting that the sum of the values below the diagonal cell double line must differ by unity from the first entry in each check row. For example, for the check row for Y^{iii},

$(-.54422) + (-.54949) + (-.48484) + (-.47548) + 0$
$$= -2.05403 = -3.05403 + 1.00000.$$

Step 6: Calculate the entries in the second line of each space, including check columns, of the second row as follows, beginning with the diagonal cell value:

$$1.00000 + (.54422)(-.54422) = .70382$$
$$.53159 + (.54949)(-.54422) = .23255$$
$$.49962 + (.48484)(-.54422) = .23576$$
$$\text{etc.}$$

Observe that in each space in this row the entry in the top line has added to it the product of $(-.54422)$ by the value in the second line of the space immediately above. Accordingly, the single entry under the double line in the column headed X_1 is used throughout to obtain the new values for this row.

As a check, the sum of the entries in the second line of this row, beginning with the diagonal cell value of 0.70382, must check with the value in the corresponding check column. For example, for Y^{ii} we have

$(.70382) + (.23255) + (.23576) + (.22111) + (1.00000)$
$$= 2.39324(\text{cf. } 2.39325).$$

Step 7: Calculate the entries below the diagonal cell of the column headed X_2 as follows: multiply the entry in the second line of the corresponding space in the second row by the reciprocal of the diagonal cell value, and change the sign. For example,

$$- (.23255)\left(\frac{1}{.70382}\right) = -.33041$$

$$- (.23576)\left(\frac{1}{.70382}\right) = -.33497$$

etc.

Check by addition, as in Step 5, for the check rows.

Step 8: Calculate the entries in the second line of each space of the third row as follows, beginning with the diagonal cell value:

$1.00000 + (-.54949)(.54949) + (-.33041)(.23255) = .62122$

$.45238 + (-.54949)(.48484) + (-.33041)(.23576) = .10807$

etc.

Observe that in each space in this row the entry in the top line has added to it the product of $(-.54949)$ times the entry in the second line of the first row (above the space), plus the product of $(-.33041)$ times the entry in the second line of the second row (above the space), and that this is done throughout all spaces in the row.

Check by addition, as in Step 6, for the check columns.

Step 9: Calculate the entries below the diagonal cell of the column headed X_3 as follows: multiply the entry in the second line of the corresponding space in the third row by the reciprocal of the diagonal cell value, and change the sign. For example,

$$-(.10807)\left(\frac{1}{.62122}\right) = -.17396$$

etc.

Check by addition, as in Step 7, for the check rows.

Step 10: Calculate the entries in the second line of each space of the fourth row as follows, beginning with the diagonal cell value:

$1.00000 + (-.48484)(.48484) + (-.33497)(.23576)$
$\qquad\qquad\qquad\qquad + (-.17396)(.10807) = .66716$

The other entries are calculated as previously explained, using the three multipliers in this case.

Check by addition, as in Step 8, for the check columns.

Step 11: Calculate the entries below the diagonal cell in the column headed X_4 by multiplying by the reciprocal of the diagonal cell value and changing the sign, e.g.

$$-(.20570)\left(\frac{1}{.66716}\right) = -.30832$$

Check by addition, as in Step 9, for the check rows.

Step 12: Calculate the entries in the second line of each space of the fifth row as follows, beginning with the diagonal cell value:

$1.00000 + (-.47548)(.47548) + (-.31416)(.22111)$
$\qquad\qquad\qquad + (-.10946)(.06800) + (-.30832)(.20570) = .63359$

The other entries are calculated as usual, using the four multipliers in this case.

Check by addition, as in Step 10, for the check columns.

Step 13: Calculate the entries below the diagonal cell in the column headed X_5 by multiplying by the reciprocal of the diagonal cell value and changing the sign, e.g.

$$-(-.19059)\left(\frac{1}{.63359}\right) = +.30081$$

Check for the check rows as usual, noting that it is more or less automatic for this set of values.

Step 14: Multiply the five diagonal cell values, and write the product in the $Y^i Y^i$ diagonal cell.

$$(1.00000)(.70382)(.62122)(.66716)(.63359) = .18482$$

Check this multiplication by calculating again.

Step 15: Calculation of third line entries in Y^i column

$(.18482)(.30081) = +.05560$

$(.18482)(.35708) + (.05560)(-.30832) = +.04885$

$(.18482)(.59507) + (.05560)(-.10946) + (.04885)(-.17396)$
$$= +.09540$$

$(.18482)(.77324) + (.05560)(-.31416) + (.04885)(-.33497)$
$$+ (.09540)(-.33041) = +.07756$$

$(.18482)(-1.00000) + (.05560)(-.47548) + (.04885)(-.48484)$
$$+ (.09540)(-.54949) + (.07968)(-.54422) = -.32957$$

This final calculation should be checked; all the remaining calculations may be checked with each other in pairs in the other Y columns.

Step 16: Repeat Step 15 for each of the other Y columns, using in each the corresponding Y row (not the Y^i row that was used above). Check the calculations by noting that pairs of entries can be found, symmetrically placed, that agree exactly.

Step 17: Calculate the values in the g_{ij} table by multiplying the entry in the third line of the corresponding space of the Y column by the reciprocal of 0.18482 (using this as a constant multiplier) and changing the sign. For example,

$$g_{11} = (-.32957)(-1)\left(\frac{1}{.18482}\right) = 1.7832$$

$$g_{12} = (.07756)(-1)\left(\frac{1}{.18482}\right) = -.4197$$

$$g_{13} = (.09540)(-1)\left(\frac{1}{.18482}\right) = -.5162$$

and so on. Note that the table of g_{ij} is symmetrical, which provides a check on all the calculations except for the diagonal cell values $(i = j)$. These latter must be checked by recalculating.

Stage 2: Calculation of Values of B's

Since we may write

$$B_i = \sum_{j=1}^{5} (g_{ij})(r_{yj}) \qquad i = 1, 2, \ldots, 5$$

the simplest way to calculate the B values is to add the two subsidiary tables shown attached to the table of g_{ij} in Table XII.1. The r_{yj} are used as a set of multipliers for each column, yielding the values of the B_i shown. The calculations should be checked, by recalculating the value of each B_i.

Stage 3: Calculation of Estimates of β's

If we denote by b_i the least squares estimate of β_i, we have from the earlier formula

$$b_i = \frac{\sqrt{S_{yy}}}{\sqrt{S_{x_i x_i}}} \cdot B_i$$

To systematize the calculations, thereby helping to avoid the possibility of a gross error, we may proceed as shown in the final two auxiliary rows attached to the table of g_{ij}, writing down the required values of the S's and performing all the calculations at one time.

Stage 4: Regression Equation in Raw Score Form

In addition to the values of the b's, we require the value of the estimate, a, of the quantity α. This may be secured from the equation

$$a = Y. - b_1 X_1. - b_2 X_2. - b_3 X_3. - b_4 X_4. - b_5 X_5.$$

which for our example is

$$a = 59.05 - (.1694)(70.96) - (.2274)(71.33)$$
$$- (.1441)(74.64) - (.2683)(69.70) - (.1577)(70.24)$$
$$= -9.72$$

Accordingly, the regression equation is

$$\hat{Y}_i = .1694 X_{1i} + .2274 X_{2i} + .1441 X_{3i} + .2683 X_{4i}$$
$$+ .1577 X_{5i} - 9.72$$

and an individual with the following scores on the five examinations: $X_{1i} = 71$, $X_{2i} = 72$, $X_{3i} = 75$, $X_{4i} = 70$, and $X_{5i} = 70$, would have a predicted university score of

$$\hat{Y}_i = (.1694)(71) + (.2274)(72) + (.1441)(75) + (.2683)(70)$$
$$+ (.1577)(70) - 9.72 = 59.31$$

Stage 5: Calculation of Multiple Correlation Coefficient

The multiple correlation coefficient, generally denoted by R, is the usual product-moment coefficient calculated for the two variables Y_i and $\hat{Y}_i$. It therefore gives a very good measure of the correspondence between actual and predicted marks (for the group of students concerned) and, consequently, of the accuracy with which predictions may be made. Although one may actually calculate the value of $\hat{Y}_i$ for each student and calculate the correlation coefficient directly, there is no need to expend all this effort. It may be shown that

$$R^2 = \sum_i B_i r_{yi}$$

which for our example proves to be

$$R^2 = .4347$$

whence

$$R = .6593$$

as compared with the highest correlation coefficient of 0.5342 for the second variable alone (X_2).

This indicates a disappointing feature of the multiple regression method, namely that the increase in agreement between actual and predicted values is almost never proportional to the number of variables used. In the above example, for instance, we used in another context six additional predictor variables (making eleven all told) but the value of R increased only slightly, to $R = 0.6886$ in fact, and certainly not enough to warrant the extra labor involved in the use of all the variables. A rather simple method of illustrating the gain, if any, in prediction secured may be found in the use of the analysis of variance, similar to the procedure followed in the previous chapter in connection with linear regression of two variables. We may always divide the sum of squares for Y as shown below, where m denotes the number of predictor variables employed (associated with R):

VARIANCE	SUM OF SQUARES	DEGREES OF FREEDOM
Due to Regression	$R^2 S_{yy}$	m
Residual Deviation	$(1 - R^2)S_{yy}$	$N - m - 1$
Total	S_{yy}	$N - 1$

For the 11 predictor variables, $m = 11$, we have

VARIANCE	DEGREES OF FREEDOM	SUM OF SQUARES	MEAN SQUARE
Due to Regression	11	90,520	8,229.1
Residual Deviation	996	100,382	100.8
Total	1,007	190,902	189.6

and it will be seen that the residual deviation sum of squares, the deviations about the regression plane or $\sum (Y - \hat{Y})^2$, is little more than half the total sum of squares of Y.

For the five predictor variables alone, we would have a sum of squares due to regression equal to $(.4347)(190,902) = 82,985$, and the analysis of variance table can be set up to show the effect of the additional six variables, as follows:

VARIANCE	DEGREES OF FREEDOM	SUM OF SQUARES	MEAN SQUARE
Due to Regression	11	90,520	8,229.1
(i) 5 Variables	5	82,985	16,597.0
(ii) Remainder	6	7,535	1,255.8
Residual Deviation	996	100,382	100.8
Total	1,007	190,902	189.6

Obviously, the addition of six more variables accounts for a relatively small proportion of the total variance: the "remainder" term, above, with 6 degrees of freedom shows the effect of adding these additional predictor variables to the multiple regression equation composed of the original five. Students must note that this "remainder" sum of squares is not the amount that would have been obtained had the six additional variables been used by themselves. It is, however, the *additional* variation due to regression when these six predictor variables are added to the original five.

The advantage of setting up these analysis of variance tables is twofold. First, as we have seen, they provide a *description* of the accuracy with which prediction can be made. For the 11 predictor variables, for instance, the total variation of the criterion variable, Y, has been reduced from 190,902 to 100,382, and the predictions can be made with a considerable degree of confidence. The agreement between the observed values, Y, and the predicted values, $\hat{Y}$, is far from perfect, of course, since the residual deviations constitute more than 50 per cent of the total Y variation. Students will note that only if $R = 1$ will the residual deviations be zero; for low values of R, on the other hand, the residual deviations will be of the same order of magnitude as the total variation. Second, the analysis of variance table provides a test of significance of the multiple correlation coefficient, R; this test is valid, for the hypothesis $H_o: R = 0$, provided the usual assumptions underlying the analysis of variance are satisfied. The statistical test is performed by calculating the quantity

$$F = \frac{(R^2)(N - m - 1)}{(1 - R^2)(m)}$$

which is distributed as F, exactly or approximately depending on the extent to which the assumptions are satisfied, with degrees of freedom $n_1 = m$ and $n_2 = N - m - 1$. For the 11 predictor variables, we have

$$F = \frac{8,229.1}{100.8} = 81.6 ; \qquad n_1 = 11 \\ n_2 = 996$$

which is obviously significant and requires the rejection of the null hypothesis $H_o: R = 0$. Likewise, for the test of significance of the effect of adding the six additional predictor variables, we may calculate the quantity

$$F = \frac{1,255.8}{100.8} = 12.5$$

which, for degrees of freedom $n_1 = 6$ and $n_2 = 996$, must be judged significant. Consequently, we may conclude that adding the six predictor variables to the original team of five resulted in an improvement that, while small, was significant.

Stage 6: Tests of Significance of Partial Regression Coefficients

The interpretation of the tests of significance of partial regression coefficients is severely restricted by the assumptions made. We assume, in the first place, that Y will be normally distributed about a mean $\hat{Y}$ for each particular combination of $X_1, X_2, \ldots, X_m$, and with constant standard deviation. In most cases this assumption is reasonably well satisfied, and minor departures from normality of distribution or from constancy of standard deviation are probably not too serious. More serious is the restriction or assumption that generalization can only be made for values of the predictor variables, X, exactly the same as those observed in the sample for which the regression coefficients were calculated. We can, therefore, interpret the partial regression coefficients only in terms of these *fixed values of the predictor variables* or, which amounts to the same thing, in terms of sets of samples in which only these specific X values occur. As we mentioned earlier, to apply the results secured for one set of X's to another, and possibly different, set may not be justified and is in any event a risky procedure. In practice we may have to do just that, but the researcher must be aware of the possibility of securing results that are altogether untrustworthy and invalid.

Subject to these restrictions or limitations, we may apply tests of significance to the partial regression coefficients. The tests are quite simple when expressed in terms of the B's (frequently called the *standard* partial regression coefficients); they are not simple for the b's, since these involve also the S_{yy} and S_{xx} terms. If we denote by $\hat{B}_i$ the unknown population value of which B_i is the least squares estimate and by S_{Res} the quantity

$$S_{Res} = \sqrt{\frac{1 - R^2}{N - m - 1}}$$

(cf. the Residual Deviation Mean Square of the earlier tables) then the quantity

$$t = \frac{B_i - \hat{B}_i}{S_{Res}\sqrt{g_{ii}}}$$

will be distributed as Student's t with $N - m - 1$ degrees of freedom. For our example of five predictor variables,

$$N = 1,008; \quad m = 5; \quad R^2 = 0.4347$$

whence
$$S_{Res} = \sqrt{\frac{0.5653}{1,002}} = 0.02375$$

The hypothetical value, $\hat{B}_i$, specified by the hypothesis to be tested is used, whether or not this is zero. For the test of the null hypothesis, $H_o : \hat{B}_i = 0$, for each of our five standard partial regression coefficients in turn, we have

$$t_1 = \frac{B_1 - \hat{B}_1}{S_{Res} \sqrt{g_{11}}} = \frac{0.1531 - 0}{(0.02375) \sqrt{1.7832}} = 4.83$$

$$t_2 = \frac{B_2 - \hat{B}_2}{S_{Res} \sqrt{g_{22}}} = \frac{0.2037 - 0}{(0.02375) \sqrt{1.7704}} = 6.45$$

$$t_3 = \frac{B_3 - \hat{B}_3}{S_{Res} \sqrt{g_{33}}} = \frac{0.1267 - 0}{(0.02375) \sqrt{1.6600}} = 4.14$$

$$t_4 = \frac{B_4 - \hat{B}_4}{S_{Res} \sqrt{g_{44}}} = \frac{0.2300 - 0}{(0.02375) \sqrt{1.6490}} = 7.54$$

$$t_5 = \frac{B_5 - \hat{B}_5}{S_{Res} \sqrt{g_{55}}} = \frac{0.1354 - 0}{(0.02375) \sqrt{1.5783}} = 4.54$$

For degrees of freedom equal to 1,002, each of these t's is significant, and consequently we reject the null hypothesis for each B.

A similar type of test, not normally of importance, involves the comparison of two standard partial regression coefficients.‡‡ In the present case, for example, it may be of some interest to determine whether the difference between B_4 (Physics) and B_5 (Chemistry) is significant. The corresponding null hypothesis is

$$H_o : \hat{B}_4 = \hat{B}_5$$

The appropriate statistic is

$$t = \frac{B_4 - B_5}{S_{Res} \sqrt{g_{44} - 2g_{45} + g_{55}}}$$

which is distributed as t, when H_o is true, with degrees of freedom $N - m - 1$. For our example,

$$t = \frac{.2300 - .1354}{(.02375) \sqrt{1.6490 + (2)(.4866) + 1.5783}}$$

$$= \frac{.0946}{.04868} = 1.94$$

‡‡ This can be extended to the sum or the difference, or any linear function, of two or more regression coefficients.

which, for 1,002 degrees of freedom, is slightly larger than the 5 per cent of t (using a two-tailed test) and hence not significant. For the set of admissible alternative hypotheses $H_1 : \hat{B}_4 > \hat{B}_5$, however, the difference would be significant at the 5 per cent level but not at the 1 per cent level. In both cases we would be inclined to accept the null hypothesis, since the difference, while indicative of superiority of Physics over Chemistry for predictive purposes, is not great enough to permit of an unequivocal conclusion in favor of the former.

Stage 7: Omission of One (or More) of the Predictor Variables

One of the greatest advantages of Fisher's set of auxiliary g-statistics is that one or more of the predictor variables can be omitted and the new set of partial regression coefficients calculated with relatively little labor.§§ In practice, a researcher may desire to omit one or more variables from the multiple regression analysis for any one of a number of reasons: for example, to see what effect such omission has on certain of the remaining coefficients; for theoretical reasons, when interest may be centered in a particular set of predictor variables; or where the tests of significance discussed in the preceding stage indicate that one of the standard partial regression coefficients is not significantly different from zero. In the illustration used earlier, we will consider the omission of the third predictor variable (Trigonometry) because the question was raised whether the university admission requirements should include two or three mathematics papers, and this is the poorest of the three. Of course, the t-test of the previous stage does reveal that this variable makes a significant contribution to the team of predictors and should be retained, but if the net effect of omitting it is not too great the resulting simplification of the admission procedures might justify the step.

The effect of omitting a variable may be determined immediately by noting that R^2 will be reduced by the amount

$$\frac{B_i^2}{g_{ii}}$$

For our example, $B_3 = 0.1267$ and $g_{33} = 1.6600$, so the amount by which R^2 is reduced will be

$$\frac{(.1267)}{1.6600} = 0.00967$$

and for the remaining four predictor variables we will have a new multiple correlation coefficient of $R^1 = 0.6519$. This is, of course, not much smaller than the former value (0.6593), and it will be immediately realized that, as statisticians, we can probably go this far in meeting the desires of adminis-

§§ This is not true of the other methods of calculating these coefficients. In fact, if these other methods are used one must begin anew when it is desired to omit variables. Where only two or three predictor variables are used, however, this is not so serious a matter.

trators for the streamlining of their operations. Nevertheless, the statistician would in such case be duty bound to point out that the loss, while small, is statistically significant.

A somewhat similar problem arises when we wish to replace the actual B's by theoretical values, a situation that will inevitably arise when, for practical reasons, we wish to round off the obtained coefficients and use simpler values. Where this is done for any B_i, using B_i^1 as the new value, the decrement for R^2 will be

$$\frac{(B_i - B_i^1)^2}{g_{ii}}$$

As an illustration, consider the following set of theoretical values of the B's:

$B_1 = 0.2;$ $B_2 = 0.2;$ $B_3 = 0.1;$ $B_4 = 0.2;$ $B_5 = 0.1$

The individual decrements will be:
For

$$B_1 : \frac{(.1531 - .2)^2}{1.7832} = .00123$$

$$B_2 : \frac{(.2037 - .2)^2}{1.7704} = .00001$$

$$B_3 : \frac{(.1267 - .1)^2}{1.6600} = .00043$$

$$B_4 : \frac{(.2300 - .2)^2}{1.6490} = .00055$$

$$B_5 : \frac{(.1354 - .1)^2}{1.5783} = .00079$$

and the total decrement in R^2 will be 0.00301, resulting in a new multiple correlation coefficient of $R^{11} = 0.6571$. The multiple correlation coefficient is reduced surprisingly little: it is, in fact, amazingly invariant to even substantial changes (except for sign) in the values of the standard partial regression coefficients.|||

Let us now return to the procedure to be followed when one of the predictor variables is to be omitted and new standard partial regression coefficients calculated. Basically, the procedure consists in calculating a new set of g's from those already secured, i.e. the calculation of the set of g's that would have been obtained if in the original solution we had used only the $m - 1$ variables we now desire to retain. Students will realize, of course, that the omission of two or more variables can be accomplished in a series of steps, omitting one variable after the other, in turn, until the desired number have been dropped.

The general formula for the calculation of the new set of g's, denoted by g^1, is as follows:

||| A point to which we will refer later in the section on approximate multiple regression weights.

$$g^1_{ij} = g_{ij} - \frac{g_{ik}g_{jk}}{g_{kk}}$$

where the subscript k denotes the particular predictor variable to be omitted, and i and j can take all values, save k, from 1 to m. For our case $k = 3$, and our new set of g's will be for all values of i and j for the numbers 1, 2, 4, and 5. We have

$$g^1_{11} = g_{11} - \frac{g_{13}g_{13}}{g_{33}} = 1.7832 - \frac{(-.5162)^2}{1.6600} = 1.6227$$

$$g^1_{12} = g_{12} - \frac{g_{13}g_{23}}{g_{33}} = -.4197 - \frac{(-.5162)(-.4425)}{1.6600} = -.5573$$

$$g^1_{14} = g_{14} - \frac{g_{13}g_{43}}{g_{33}} = -.2643 - \frac{(-.5162)(-.2336)}{1.6600} = -.3369$$

$$g^1_{15} = g_{15} - \frac{g_{13}g_{53}}{g_{33}} = -.3008 - \frac{(-.5162)(-.0881)}{1.6600} = -.3282$$

$$g^1_{22} = g_{22} - \frac{g_{23}g_{23}}{g_{33}} = 1.7704 - \frac{(-.4425)^2}{1.6600} = 1.6524$$

$$g^1_{24} = g_{24} - \frac{g_{23}g_{43}}{g_{33}} = -.3223 - \frac{(-.4425)(-.2336)}{1.6600} = -.3846$$

$$g^1_{25} = g_{25} - \frac{g_{23}g_{53}}{g_{33}} = -.3038 - \frac{(-.4425)(-.0881)}{1.6600} = -.3273$$

$$g^1_{44} = g_{44} - \frac{g_{43}g_{43}}{g_{33}} = 1.6490 - \frac{(-.2336)^2}{1.6600} = 1.6161$$

$$g^1_{45} = g_{45} - \frac{g_{43}g_{53}}{g_{33}} = -.4866 - \frac{(-.2336)(-.0881)}{1.6600} = -.4990$$

$$g^1_{55} = g_{55} - \frac{g_{53}g_{53}}{g_{33}} = 1.5783 - \frac{(-.0881)^2}{1.6600} = 1.5736$$

TABLE OF g^1_{ij}

j \ i	1	2	4	5	r_{yi}
1	1.6227	−.5573	−.3369	−.3282	.50941
2	−.5573	1.6524	−.3846	−.3273	.53423
4	−.3369	−.3846	1.6161	−.4990	.53393
5	−.3282	−.3273	−.4990	1.5736	.47696
B^1_i	+.1925	+.2374	+.2478	+.1421	

$$R^2 = .4250$$

$$R = .6519$$

The values of the B_i^1's, of the b_i^1's, and of R^2 can be calculated as in the earlier illustration: we show in the table of g_{ij}^1 the calculation of the B's and R^2. As an additional check, one already being provided in the two values of R, the values of the B_i^1's may be calculated directly from the formula

$$B_i^1 = B_i - \frac{g_{i3}}{g_{33}} B_3 \qquad \text{(for } i = 1, 2, 4, \text{ and } 5\text{)}$$

In some situations, in fact, where the main interest lies in the B_i^1 and R, a researcher would calculate the B_i^1 directly and calculate the g_{ij}^1 only if required. As in the case of the g_{ij}^1, of course, the new values of the remaining B_i can be determined by eliminating one variable at a time, thus omitting two or more by doing each in turn through application of the same formula. In either event, of course, the values of the corresponding b's and $\hat{Y}$ can be secured as illustrated earlier.

Stage 8: Use of the g_{ij} With Another Criterion Variable

In very many prediction problems we have two or more *criterion* variables, i.e. variables it is desired to predict, associated with the same set of marks or scores of the predictor variables. In the example used previously, for instance, the criterion variable, Y, was the average mark secured in courses. But we also had the average mark secured in practical work, e.g. in laboratory assignments, the average mark on which we may denote by L_i for the ith student. The correlations of each of the predictor variables with L were as follows:

$$r_{L1} = .4016$$
$$r_{L2} = .4241$$
$$r_{L3} = .4211$$
$$r_{L4} = .4418$$
$$r_{L5} = .3717$$

We may now use the same set of g_{ij} (see Table XII.1) to determine the B's and R for this new criterion variable, as shown below.

Quite clearly the prediction in this case will be much less accurate than in the former, and the predictor variables vary in usefulness in the two situations. Students should, as an exercise, apply the various statistical tests discussed in earlier sections, and various types of analysis, and work through the procedure of omitting the first and fifth predictor variables. We need not devote time and space to a repetition of methods already covered, particularly since an application of the methods will be of more value to students if actually carried through on their own.##

Efforts aimed at avoiding the admittedly heavy arithmetical labor of multiple regression techniques have led to the development of *approximate* methods. The major, and serious, disadvantage of these approximations is that tests of significance cannot

CALCULATIONS FOR SECOND CRITERION VARIABLE
Table of g_{ij} and r_{Lj}

j \\ i	1	2	3	4	5	r_{Lj}
1	1.7832	−.4197	−.5162	−.2643	−.3008	.4016
2	−.4197	1.7704	−.4425	−.3223	−.3038	.4241
3	−.5162	−.4425	1.6600	−.2336	−.0881	.4211
4	−.2643	−.3223	−.2336	1.6490	−.4866	.4418
5	−.3008	−.3038	−.0881	−.4866	1.5783	.3717

B_i	+.0922	+.1406	+.1681	+.2065	+.0849

$$R^2 = .2902 \qquad R = .5387$$

Partial Correlation

It is convenient at this juncture to discuss briefly the related concepts and methods of *partial correlation,* although these are not generally of the same interest and usefulness as multiple regression methods. The origin of the method is to be found, like so much else in correlation and regression theory, in the interest of Galton, Karl Pearson, Yule, and others in the measurement of the strength of heredity. The method devised is, of course, of general application and not restricted to problems of heredity. The problem in which these early workers were interested was that of determining the degree of relationship between two variables when the influence or effect of one or more other variables, related to these two, is *held constant* or *partialled out.* Researchers in the social sciences, especially in psychology and education, will recognize this as a common problem that upon occasion is of considerable importance. In education, for example, it is well known that the relationship between two variables—such as achievement in two school subjects—arises in part because both are related to intelligence. Accordingly, to determine the intrinsic relationship between the two variables it is common practice to partial out the effect of intelligence (and of whatever other variables the researcher may deem to be of importance in the particular situation).

To illustrate the arguments and development, let us consider the case of three variables,

---

validly be applied to the results therefrom. Students interested in this phase of the theory may find the following paper of some value:

R. W. B. Jackson, "Approximate Multiple Regression Weights," *Journal of Experimental Education,* XI (1943), 221–25. Recent developments in machine calculations, however, may make such approximate solutions of little practical value.

$$X_1, \; X_2, \text{ and } X_3$$

for which it is desired to determine the partial correlation coefficient between X_1 and X_2 with the effect of X_3, if any, held constant. If we denote by r_{jk} the usual product-moment coefficient of correlation between two variables X_j and X_k and by $r_{jk \cdot m}$ the desired partial correlation coefficient between these two variables with the influence of a third, X_m, where $m \neq j \neq k$, then the general basic formula for $r_{jk \cdot m}$ may be written

$$r_{jk \cdot m} = \frac{r_{jk} - r_{jm} r_{km}}{\sqrt{(1 - r_{jm}^2)(1 - r_{km}^2)}}$$

which for our case becomes

$$r_{12.3} = \frac{r_{12} - r_{13} r_{23}}{\sqrt{(1 - r_{13}^2)(1 - r_{23}^2)}}$$

To use actual data as an illustration, let us return to the university success prediction problem earlier considered, but now let X_1 denote the university mark, X_2 the mark in Geometry, and X_3 the mark in Trigonometry. What will be the degree of relationship between university and Geometry marks if the influence of Trigonometry (or achievement in Trigonometry) is held constant? We had the following set of values (see Table XII.1):

$$r_{12} = .53423$$
$$r_{13} = .47757$$
$$r_{23} = .53159$$

so that

$$r_{12.3} = \frac{.53423 - (.47757)(.53159)}{\sqrt{\{1 - (.47757)^2\}\{1 - (.53159)^2\}}}$$

$$= .3767$$

which is considerably lower than the original value of r_{12}. Students should note that unless a reasonably large number of figures are carried throughout the calculations the accuracy of the final result will be seriously affected. With values less than unity, as the correlation coefficients must always be, multiplication, squaring, and taking the square root may introduce a substantial discrepancy in the calculations unless a fair number of significant figures are retained.

Two or more variables may be eliminated in a similar manner, although considerably more laboriously since the amount of labor increases rapidly as the number of variables to be partialled out increases. For example, to eliminate also the effect of a fourth variable, X_4, we must first calculate

$$r_{12.3}; \quad r_{14.3}; \quad \text{and} \quad r_{24.3}$$

whence

$$r_{12.34} = \frac{r_{12.3} - r_{14.3} \, r_{24.3}}{\sqrt{\{1 - (r_{14.3})^2\}\{1 - (r_{24.3})^2\}}}$$

or, alternatively, calculate

$$r_{12.4}; \quad r_{13.4}; \quad \text{and} \quad r_{23.4}$$

whence
$$r_{12.34} = \frac{r_{12.4} - r_{13.4}\, r_{23.4}}{\sqrt{\{1 - (r_{13.4})^2\}\, \{1 - (r_{23.4})^2\}}}$$

Using Algebra as the fourth variable, for instance, we would have

$$r_{12} = .53423 \qquad r_{14} = .50941$$
$$r_{13} = .47757 \qquad r_{24} = .54422$$
$$r_{23} = .53159 \qquad r_{34} = .54949$$

From these the required values of the first-order partial coefficients will be

$$r_{12.3} = .3767 \qquad\quad r_{12.4} = .3560$$
$$r_{14.3} = .3365 \quad or \quad r_{13.4} = .2749$$
$$r_{24.3} = .3563 \qquad\quad r_{23.4} = .3318$$

whence
$$r_{12.34} = \frac{.3767 - (.3365)(.3563)}{\sqrt{\{1 - (.3365)^2\}\, \{1 - (.3563)^2\}}} = .292$$

$$or \quad = \frac{.3560 - (.2749)(.3318)}{\sqrt{\{1 - (.2749)^2\}\, \{1 - (.3318)^2\}}} = .292$$

The degree of relationship between university and Geometry marks is, therefore, reduced from 0.53423 to 0.292 when achievement in Algebra and Trigonometry is held constant, i.e. for students of the same achievement level in these two high school subjects.

This leads to the question of tests of significance of partial correlation coefficients, since a researcher will naturally wish to know whether or not the reduced degree of relationship is significantly different from zero. Subject to the normality assumption for the restricted bivariate distribution of X_i and X_j, but not required for the variables eliminated, to be discussed below, and of the usual assumption of linearity of all associated regressions when the results are to be interpreted, the appropriate test of significance for the null hypothesis (that in the population, restricted, to which the partial coefficient applies, the degree of relationship is zero) is equivalent to that applied earlier to the usual product-moment coefficient of correlation, the only adjustment being a reduction in the degrees of freedom of unity for each variable partialled out. For our example, since $N = 1,008$, for the partial correlation coefficient

$$r_{12.3} = .3767$$

we calculate the quantity

$$t = \frac{r\sqrt{N-3}}{\sqrt{1-r^2}} = \frac{.3767\sqrt{1,005}}{\sqrt{.8581}} = 12.9$$

which will be distributed as Student's t with degrees of freedom

$1,008 - 3 = 1,005$. We would, of course, reject the null hypothesis, as we would for $r_{12.34} = 0.292$ since we have

$$t = \frac{.292\sqrt{1,004}}{\sqrt{.915}} = 9.7, \text{ with } n = 1,004 \text{ degrees of freedom.}$$

Probably the best way to gain an understanding of partial correlation coefficients and of the assumptions underlying their use is to consider them in terms of an ordinary product-moment correlation between variables that are deviations from fitted regression lines. For simplicity of presentation we shall consider below the case where only one variable is eliminated or partialled out; the extension to more complex situations is obvious. For our three variables X_1, X_2, and X_3, we may write the regression equations (assuming that the regression is in fact linear) for X_1 and for X_2 in terms of X_3, as follows:

$$\hat{X}_1 = a + b X_3 = X_1. + b(X_3 - X_3.)$$
$$\hat{X}_2 = c + d X_3 = X_2. + d(X_3 - X_3.)$$

where X_j. denotes the mean for the variable X_j.

Now define two new variables,

$$X_1^1 = X_1 - \hat{X}_1 = (X_1 - X_1.) - b(X_3 - X_3.)$$
$$X_2^1 = X_2 - \hat{X}_2 = (X_2 - X_2.) - d(X_3 - X_3.)$$

so that these two new variables are the deviations about the regression lines and, assuming linearity of regression, will be independent of X_3—the influence of X_3 having been removed or held constant by the process. If we now calculate the product-moment coefficient of correlation between X_1^1 and X_2^1 the value secured is that of the partial correlation coefficient $r_{12.3}$. Assuming that the regression between these two variables is linear, this will measure adequately the degree of relationship between them. If the two variables are normally distributed, the regression will be linear and the tests of significance discussed above may be applied. Note that the eliminated variable, or variables, need not be normally distributed; the test of significance will not depend upon the form of distribution of any variable that is partialled out or held constant.

Students will observe from the formulae for the partial correlation coefficients that the procedure may result in either a decrease or increase in value, even no change under certain conditions, and even a change from a positive to a negative (or vice versa) relationship under other conditions. As another interesting sidelight, note that since no partial coefficient can be numerically greater than 1, this fact can be used to set up a *consistency condition* on the coefficients entering into the formula. For three variables, for instance,

$$1 - r_{12}^2 - r_{13}^2 - r_{23}^2 + 2r_{12}r_{13}r_{23} > 0$$

is the consistency condition imposed upon r_{12}, r_{13}, and r_{23} by virtue of the fact that none of the possible partials can be greater than 1.***

Finally, it should be remembered that random errors in the variables partialled out will introduce systematic errors in the results. For three variables, for instance, of which X_3 is partialled out, random errors in X_3 would tend to reduce numerically both r_{13} and r_{23}, even resulting, in the extreme case, in the appearance of an apparent positive partial correlation $r_{12.3}$ that should be zero.

Non-Linear Regression

Students will remember that in the previous chapter, where linear regression was discussed, it was found that the deviations from linear regression were significant for some examples, indicating that some form of curvilinear regression was required to describe adequately the observed relationship between the two variables. The correlation ratio was also introduced as a measure of such curvilinear relationship. Reference to Figure XI.2 will indicate a common situation where the pattern of means (average Army Alpha scores for different age groups) is obviously curvilinear in nature. The purpose of this section is to present illustrations of the general method of calculating the appropriate regression formulae for such cases of non-linear regression.

Basically, the methods for non-linear regression are nothing more than a special application of the general theory of multiple regression discussed in earlier sections of the present chapter. This will become evident as we proceed. We present in the pages that follow two quite different situations, however, to each of which has been applied an adaptation of the general theory peculiarly suited for an analysis under the specific conditions pertaining. The first, and probably more general, situation is the one found in the usual two-way frequency distribution (see Tables XI.1 and XI.3) where one or other regression is not linear, the class intervals for the predictor variable are not necessarily equal, and the number of cases in the several class intervals (of X, and of Y for each X) is not necessarily equal, not even approximately so. The second type of situation is one encountered frequently in laboratory experiments in psychology, where a fixed number of measurements is made (often under varying conditions) of each member of a group of individuals. In the latter situation, owing largely to the fact that the number of observations per cell is constant (generally unity, although the observations may be made in duplicate or triplicate) and that

*** For a further discussion of this point, see, for example, G. Udny Yule, *An Introduction to the Theory of Statistics*, pp. 250-51.

the intervals for the predictor variable are of equal width, a simpler and more detailed analysis using orthogonal polynomials can be used.

Fitting a Polynominal to Two-Way Frequency Distribution (Unequal Y-Frequencies)

We have presented herein only the case of one predictor variable and the sum of components of powers of that variable. Students will realize, of course, that two or more predictor variables could also be used and different functions considered, such as logarithms, sines, or cosines. The method is quite general and little difficulty should be experienced in adapting it to meet the requirements of any specific situation. We may note, in passing, that the researcher must use his judgment in the selection of a type—or types—of functions to use. For perhaps the majority of situations the simple polynomial form we use as an illustration will suffice. The only guides a researcher has are the pattern of observed means and a knowledge of the shapes of various types of theoretical curves.

Ignoring subscripts for the moment, the general formula for the polynomial may be written

$$f(X) = a + bX + cX^2 + dX^3 + \ldots + wX^k$$

where the $b, c, d, \ldots, w$ are the partial regression coefficients earlier considered, and X the predictor variable. Note that the only real difference between this formula and the common multiple regression formula is that the additional variables, beyond the first, are powers of the first, not completely different variables: our first variable is X, the second X^2, the third X^3, and so on. A word of warning will not be amiss at this point: since these are *partial* regression coefficients, they will change if we add or omit one of the predictors (a variable or a term in the polynomial). Students—and researchers—are apt to overlook this point: the regression coefficients for the cubic (third power), using $\hat{Y}$ to denote the variable *predicted*,

$$\hat{Y} = a + bX + cX^2 + dX^3$$

will not necessarily be the same (nor will $\hat{Y}$) as for the quadratic

$$\hat{Y}' = a' + b'X + c'X^2$$

as the primes for the latter indicate.

As an illustration, let us return to the data of Table XI.7, which shows the two-way distribution for Army Alpha Scores and Chronological Age and part of the calculations necessary for fitting a polynomial to the peculiar pattern of Army Alpha Score means. For convenience, we will use the same computation variable values as given in that table—y for Army Alpha mid-points and x for Chronological Age mid-points.††† Al-

††† The transformation to the original values is relatively simple and may be left to the students to perform as an exercise.

TABLE XII.2

ILLUSTRATION OF FITTING OF CUBIC POLYNOMIAL
Data of Table XI.7

(1)	(2)	(3) = (1)(2)	(4) = (1)(3)	(5) = (1)(4)	(6)	(7) = (1)(6)	(8) = (1)(7)	(9) = (1)(8)	(10) = (1)(9)	(11) = (1)(10)	(12) = (1)(11)
x_j	$\sum_i y_{ij}$	$x_j\sum_i y_{ij}$	$x_j^2\sum_i y_{ij}$	$x_j^3\sum_i y_{ij}$	f_x	$f_x x$	$f_x x^2$	$f_x x^3$	$f_x x^4$	$f_x x^5$	$f_x x^6$
-3.1	-290	899.0	-2,786.90	8,639.39	125	-387.5	1,201.25	-3,723.88	11,544.01	-35,786.44	110,937.96
-2.7	-91	245.7	-663.39	1,791.15	129	-348.3	940.41	-2,539.11	6,855.59	-18,510.09	49,977.24
-2.3	218	-501.4	1,153.22	-2,652.41	137	-315.1	724.73	-1,666.88	3,833.82	-8,817.79	20,280.92
-1.9	208	-395.2	750.88	-1,426.67	97	-184.3	350.17	-665.32	1,264.11	-2,401.82	4,563.45
-1.4	234	-327.6	458.64	-642.10	88	-123.2	172.48	-241.47	338.06	-473.29	662.60
-0.8	74	-59.2	47.36	-37.89	44	-35.2	28.16	-22.53	18.02	-14.42	11.53
0	132	0	0	0	90	0	0	0	0	0	0
1	146	146	146	146	104	104	104	104	104	104	104
2	82	164	328	656	96	192	384	768	1,536	3,072	6,144
3	162	486	1,458	4,374	95	285	855	2,565	7,695	23,085	69,255
4	30	120	480	1,920	69	276	1,104	4,416	17,664	70,656	282,624
5	45	225	1,125	5,625	56	280	1,400	7,000	35,000	175,000	875,000
Total	950	1,002.3	2,496.81	18,392.47	1,130	-256.6	7,264.20	5,993.81	85,852.61	205,913.15	1,419,560.70
	$\sum_i\sum_j y_{ij}$	$\sum_j x_j\sum_i y_{ij}$	$\sum_j x_j^2\sum_i y_{ij}$	$\sum_j x_j^3\sum_i y_{ij}$	N	$\sum_i\sum_j x_j$	$\sum_i\sum_j x_j^2$	$\sum_i\sum_j x_j^3$	$\sum_i\sum_j x_j^4$	$\sum_i\sum_j x_j^5$	$\sum_i\sum_j x_j^6$

though the pattern of means is somewhat peculiar, inspection indicates that an equation of the third power

$$\hat{y} = a + bx + cx^2 + dx^3$$

should provide a reasonably satisfactory fit (the appropriate test will be applied at a later stage). Using i to denote the varying values of y within each array, j, of x, we may write the general equation in the form

$$\hat{y}_{ij} = a + bx_j + cx_j^2 + dx_j^3$$

Again applying the theory of least squares, we secure estimates of a, b, c, and d by minimizing the quantity

$$\chi^2 = \sum_i \sum_j (y_{ij} - a - bx_j - cx_j^2 - dx_j^3)^2$$

Differentiating partially with respect to a, b, c, and d in turn, setting the equation equal to zero and simplifying, we secure the following set of four simultaneous equations to solve for the values of a, b, c, and d, where N denotes the total number of cases.

$$aN + b\sum_i\sum_j x_j + c\sum_i\sum_j x_j^2 + d\sum_i\sum_j x_j^3 = \sum_i\sum_j y_{ij}$$

$$a\sum_i\sum_j x_j + b\sum_i\sum_j x_j^2 + c\sum_i\sum_j x_j^3 + d\sum_i\sum_j x_j^4 = \sum_j x_j\sum_i y_{ij}$$

$$a\sum_i\sum_j x_j^2 + b\sum_i\sum_j x_j^3 + c\sum_i\sum_j x_j^4 + d\sum_i\sum_j x_j^5 = \sum_j x_j^2\sum_i y_{ij}$$

$$a\sum_i\sum_j x_j^3 + b\sum_i\sum_j x_j^4 + c\sum_i\sum_j x_j^5 + d\sum_i\sum_j x_j^6 = \sum_j x_j^3\sum_i y_{ij}$$

As will be seen, this involves calculation of the sums of the powers of x up to the sixth and also the sums of products of y with powers of x up to the third. Although this may seem at first sight to be complex and difficult, the calculations are surprisingly simple and easy if arranged as shown in Table XII.2. Comparison with the values in the rows at the bottom of Table XI.7 will reveal, in fact, that the entries for columns 1, 2, 3, 6, 7, and 8 may be copied directly therefrom. The remaining entries in each row are obtained, as indicated at the top of each column, by multiplying successively by the corresponding value of x_j: the entries in Column 4, for example, are secured by multiplying those in Column 3 by those in Column 1. After checking all the calculations, the total of each column is obtained (and checked), yielding the following numerical values in our set of simultaneous equations (writing all values, rounded off where necessary, to the first decimal for convenience in subsequent calculations):

$$a(1{,}130.0) + b(-256.6) + c(7{,}264.2) + d(5{,}993.8) = 950.0$$
$$a(-256.6) + b(7{,}264.2) + c(5{,}993.8) + d(85{,}852.6) = 1{,}002.3$$
$$a(7{,}264.2) + b(5{,}993.8) + c(85{,}852.6) + d(205{,}913.2) = 2{,}496.8$$
$$a(5{,}993.8) + b(85{,}852.6) + c(205{,}913.2) + d(1{,}419{,}560.7) = 18{,}392.5$$

Although the values of a, b, c, and d may be secured as explained earlier in this chapter, for our present purposes the ordinary Doolittle solution shown and explained in Table XII.3 is preferable. From it the values required for descriptive purposes and for tests of significance can be obtained directly. The basic analysis of variance table is as follows, showing the Among Arrays and Within Arrays sums of squares and mean squares for our computation variable y:

VARIANCE	DEGREES OF FREEDOM	SUM OF SQUARES	MEAN SQUARE
Among Arrays	11	2,271.96	206.54
Within Arrays	1,118	16,665.37	14.906
Total	1,129	18,937.33	—

The sum of squares due to fitting a straight line equation of the form $\hat{y}_1 = a_1 + b_1 x$ is given by $(2,5) \times (5,6)^2 = (7,205.93)(.169032)^2 = 205.89$ where (c,r) denotes the entry in the cth column and rth row of Table XII.3. The sum of squares corresponding to the quadratic $y_2 = a_2 + b_2 x + c_2 x^2$ will be $205.89 + (3,10) \times (5,11)^2 = 205.89 + (31,047.4)(-.157895)^2 = 205.89 + 774.04 = 979.93$. Similarly, for the cubic equation $y_3 = a_3 + b_3 x + c_3 x^2 + d_3 x^3$ we have the sum of squares $979.93 + (4,16) \times (5,17)^2 = (151,648.5) (.068803)^2 = 979.93 + 717.88 = 1,697.81$. The effects of the several stages of fitting polynomials of higher orders can be seen from the following analysis of variance table, where the above values are entered as indicated.
Steps
1. Write in the values in rows 1, 3, 7, and 12 from the set of simultaneous equations.
2. Divide each entry in Row 1 by (1,130.0) to get entries in Row 2.
3. Multiply entries in Row 1 by $(-.227080)$, change sign, and write in Row 4 of same column.
4. Add entries in rows 3 and 4 to get entries in Row 5, in each column.
5. Divide entries in Row 5 by (7,205.93) to get entries in Row 6.
6. Multiply entries of same column in Row 1 by (6.428496), change sign, and enter in Row 8.
7. Multiply entries of same column in Row 5 by (1.060703), change sign, and enter in Row 9.
8. Add, in each column, entries in rows 7, 8, and 9, to get entry of Row 10.
9. Divide entries in Row 10 by (31,047.4) to get entries in Row 11.
10. Multiply entries of Row 1, columns 4 and 5, by (5.304248), change sign, and enter in Row 13.
11. Multiply entries of Row 5, columns 4 and 5, by (12.10305), change sign, and enter in Row 14.
12. Multiply entries of Row 10, columns 4 and 5, by (2.411613), change sign, and enter in Row 15.
13. Add, in each column, entries in rows 12, 13, 14, and 15, to get entries in Row 16.

TABLE XII.3

Solution of Simultaneous Equations for Cubic Polynomial
Data of Table XII.2

Row	Column 1	2	3	4	5
1	1,130.0	−256.6	7,264.2	5,993.8	950.0
2	1.000000	−.227080	6.428496	5.304248	0.840708
3		7,264.2	5,993.8	85,852.6	1,002.3
4		−58.2687	+1,649.55	+1,361.07	+215.726
5		7,205.93	7,643.35	87,213.7	1,218.03
6		1.000000	1.060703	12.10305	.169032
7			85,852.6	205,913.2	2,496.8
8			−46,697.9	−38,531.1	−6,107.07
9			−8,107.3	−92,507.8	−1,291.97
10			31,047.4	74,874.3	−4,902.24
11			1.000000	2.411613	−.157895
12				1,419,560.7	18,392.5
13				−31,792.6	−5,039.04
14				−1,055,551.8	−14,741.88
15				−180,567.8	+11,822.31
16				151,648.5	10,433.89
17				1.000000	.068803
18				d=0.068803	.068803
19			c=−.323821	−.165926	−.157895
20		b=−.320216	.343478	−.832726	.169032
21	a=2.484727	−.072715	2.081682	−.364948	.840708
	(a)	(b)	(c)	(d)	

14. Divide entries in Row 16 by (151,648.5) to get entries of Row 17.
15. Rows 18–21, Column 5: copy entries of Column 5, rows 17, 11, 6, and 2, respectively.
16. Row 18, Column 4: $d = (.068803)\ (1.000000) = +.068803$.
17. Row 19, Column 4: $-(.068803)\ (2.411613) = -.165926$;
Column 3: $c = (-.165926) + (-.157895) = -.323821$.
18. Row 20, Column 4: $-\ (.068803)\ (12.10305) = -.832726$;
Column 3: $-\ (-.323821)\ (1.060703) = +.343478$;
Column 2: $b = (.343478) + (-.832726) + (.169032)$
$= -.320216$.
19. Row 21, Column 4: $-\ (.068803)\ (5.304248) = -.364948$;
Column 3: $-\ (-.323821)\ (6.428496) = +\ 2.081682$;
Column 2: $-\ (-.320216)\ (-.227080) = -.072715$;
Column 1: a = (sum of 4 entries in row) = 2.484727.
20. Check by substitution in original equations.

Subject to the assumptions underlying the analysis of variance being

VARIANCE	DEGREES OF FREEDOM	SUM OF SQUARES	MEAN SQUARE
Linear Regression	1	205.89	205.89
Additional for Quadratic	1	774.04	774.04
Additional for Cubic	1	717.88	717.88
Total for Regression	3	1,697.81	565.94
Deviations from Regression	8	574.15	71.77
Total Among Arrays	11	2,271.96	206.54
Within Arrays	1,118	16,665.37	14.906
Total	1,129	18,937.33	—

satisfied, which they are fairly well for this example, we see that each of our coefficients (linear, quadratic, and cubic) is significantly greater than zero (tested against the Within Arrays Mean Square). Unfortunately, our deviations from regression are also significant, which indicates that at least one more term should have been used in the polynomial, i.e. at least a quartic polynomial $\hat{y}_4 = a_4 + b_4x + c_4x^2 + d_4x^3 + e_4x^4$ should have been fitted. Students should, as an exercise, add this term: the simplest way of doing so is to insert the corresponding column between columns 4 and 5 in Table XII.3, and a new set of rows between 17 and 18, which will leave these basic calculations unaltered and yield the additional sum of squares for the quartic.‡‡‡ They should also convince themselves, arithmetically or algebraically, that to delete the term of highest order (but not any of the others) requires only a deletion of the corresponding column and rows from the basic table (Table XII.3).

It may be of some interest in this situation to show both the pattern of means and the regression equation values $\hat{y} = 2.485 - .320x - .324x^2 + .0688x^3$, rounding off the coefficients for convenience. The actual and predicted (from the cubic equation) values for each x-array are shown below. Students should, as an exercise, plot these two sets of values and compare the actual and theoretical patterns. They will find it necessary, however, to calculate a number of additional values from the equation in order to be able to draw the theoretical pattern with any degree of accuracy.

From inspection it can be seen that the fit, while fair, is far from perfect —as, indeed, the test of significance of the deviations from regression indicated. Students should also, in order to learn not to extrapolate too far beyond their observed data, calculate the theoretical values from the equation for values of x corresponding to the age group 3 and 4 and to the age group 75 to 79. It often happens with polynomial prediction, even for the

‡‡‡ An exasperating feature of fitting polynomials is that the researcher can only estimate the number of terms required from the shape of the pattern of means. It often happens, as it did with us in this case, that the estimate is short and additional terms must then be fitted.

VALUE OF x_i	ACTUAL MEAN y VALUE	VALUE OF $\hat{y}$ FROM CUBIC EQUATION
−3.1	−2.320	−1.686
−2.7	−0.705	−0.367
−2.3	1.591	0.670
−1.9	2.144	1.452
−1.4	2.659	2.109
−0.8	1.682	2.498
0	1.467	2.485
1	1.404	1.910
2	0.854	1.099
3	1.705	0.467
4	0.435	0.424
5	0.804	1.385

linear case for that matter, that these extrapolated values turn out to be utterly ridiculous—a salutary illustration of the fact that the fitted regression equation may only fit the set of observed data to which it was in fact fitted.

Fitting Orthogonal Polynomials (Y Values of Equal Weight; Equal X Intervals)

In problems of this type, as we intimated earlier, interest is focused more on the use of regression as a part of the analysis of variance technique than in the calculation of the regression formula itself.§§§ The latter may, of course, be obtained also, if desired. As an illustration, we have selected part of the results of a learning experiment conducted by three students enrolled in the Honors Psychology course in the University of Toronto.|| || || The data are typical of those secured in a large number of types of psychological experiments, although in most cases additional variables are introduced and consequently the analysis is often more complicated than that herein presented. In the part of the experiment with which we are concerned, 10 students were involved as subjects and each student had 10 trials of learning a letter-digit substitution key, using a one-minute letter-digit substitution test, and the amount of learning was defined as the number of correct substitutions on each trial. The scores obtained by each of the 10 students on each of the 10 trials are shown in the main body of Table XII.4: the other values in the table will be discussed as we come to them in the development of the analysis.

The first step in the analysis is the preparation of the basic analysis of variance table shown below:

§§§ For a useful extension see, David A. Grant, "Analysis of Variance Tests in the Analysis and Comparison of Curves," *Psychological Bulletin*, LIII, No. 2 (1956), 141–54, and C. R. Rao, "Some Statistical Methods for Comparison of Growth Curves," *Biometrics* (March, 1958), 1–17.

|| || Rupert Brook, Gordon Edwards, and Hume Foxton, "Interference in the Retention of Letter-Digit Associations as a Function of Interpolated Learning" (unpublished term work, Course 351, University of Toronto).

TABLE XII.4

Illustration of Use of Orthogonal Polynomials
Learning Experiment Data

STUDENT	TRIAL 1	2	3	4	5	6	7	8	9	10	TOTAL	SUM OF SQUARES	REGRESSION COMPONENT Linear	Quadratic	INDIVIDUAL RESIDUALS Total Sum of Squares	Regression Components	Residual
1	26	31	30	33	35	45	43	48	36	36	363	13,621	255	−120	444.1	306.1	138.0
2	29	36	36	40	42	37	41	43	45	44	393	15,657	231	− 38	212.1	172.6	39.5
3	30	38	38	39	40	43	49	42	50	45	414	17,448	272	− 50	308.4	243.1	65.3
4	23	30	37	33	32	34	32	32	33	38	324	10,648	130	− 36	150.4	61.0	89.4
5	24	32	34	44	44	36	49	50	44	38	405	17,065	387	− 99	662.5	528.1	134.4
6	36	34	40	40	43	44	43	43	47	47	417	17,553	215	− 20	164.1	143.1	21.0
7	34	38	36	41	39	44	44	46	49	48	419	17,791	267	− 3	234.9	216.1	18.8
8	27	32	32	35	37	40	37	39	42	45	366	13,650	276	− 15	254.4	232.5	21.9
9	24	28	29	33	26	35	34	37	33	28	307	9,589	123	− 77	164.1	90.8	73.3
10	38	37	38	42	39	40	49	49	45	51	428	18,570	250	+ 22	251.6	193.1	58.5
Total	291	336	350	380	377	398	421	429	424	430	3,836	151,592	2,406	−436	2,846.6	2,186.5	660.1
Sum of Squares	8,723	11,402	12,370	14,594	14,485	15,992	18,067	18,697	18,334	18,928	151,592						

VARIANCE	DEGREES OF FREEDOM	SUM OF SQUARES	MEAN SQUARE	*F*-RATIO
Among Trials	9	1,947.84	216.4	19.5
Among Students	9	1,596.44	177.4	16.0
Residual	81	898.76	11.10	—
Total	99	4,443.04	—	

Differences among trials and among students account for a large part of the total sum of squares, both effects clearly being significant.### We may, therefore, proceed with the analysis and, since it was a learning experiment, focus attention on the nature of the learning, for this purpose fitting a polynomial to the means of the 10 trials.

The simplest way of doing this is to use the system of orthogonal polynomials devised by R. A. Fisher, since the sums of squares due to regression can be calculated directly and for each degree of freedom at each stage of fitting. Unlike the method used in the previous example, there is no need to solve a new set of simultaneous equations each time a new variable is added. Basically, this consists in the transformation of our X values to a new set of variables, which Fisher denotes by ξ, which can be done very simply when the X values are at equal intervals and can be represented by a series of natural numbers (directly in our case, since the trials are numbered from 1 to 10, and there are 10 values of Y for each X). Instead of fitting the usual polynomial

$$\hat{Y} = a + bx + cx^2 + dx^3 + \ldots$$

we fit the polynomial

$$\hat{Y} = A + B\xi_1 + C\xi_2 + D\xi_3 + \ldots$$

where ξ_1 is a function of the first degree (linear) in X, ξ_2 is a function of the second degree (quadratic) in X, and so on. These functions are determined in such a way that

$$\Sigma\xi_1 = \Sigma\xi_2 = \Sigma\xi_3 = \ldots = 0$$

$$\Sigma\xi_1\xi_2 = \Sigma\xi_1\xi_3 = \Sigma\xi_2\xi_3 = \ldots = 0$$

Fisher has given the general formulae for these functions,* but it is more convenient to use the numerical values given by Fisher and Yates.† These

As a matter of interest, we may note that in this experiment neither trials nor students could, strictly speaking, be considered as random variables. Any generalization of the results is, therefore, severely restricted.

* R. A. Fisher, *Statistical Methods for Research Workers* (Fourth Edition; Edinburgh: Oliver and Boyd, 1932), pp. 134–36.

† R. A. Fisher and F. Yates, *Statistical Tables for Biological, Agricultural, and Medical Research*, Table XXIII, pp. 54–60.

are available for all ξ's from ξ_1 to ξ_5 and for all N from 3 to 52 (N is the number of values of X, which is 10 for our example). We shall use these tabled numerical values and all five values of ξ in our example, i.e. use an equation of the form

$$Y = A + B\xi_1 + C\xi_2 + D\xi_3 + E\xi_4 + F\xi_5$$

It may easily be shown, minimizing in the usual fashion and using the above properties of the ξ's, that

$$A = \frac{\Sigma Y}{N} ; \qquad B = \frac{\Sigma \xi_1 Y}{\Sigma \xi_1^2} ; \qquad C = \frac{\Sigma \xi_2 Y}{\Sigma \xi_2^2}$$

$$D = \frac{\Sigma \xi_3 Y}{\Sigma \xi_3^2} ; \qquad E = \frac{\Sigma \xi_4 Y}{\Sigma \xi_4^2} ; \qquad F = \frac{\Sigma \xi_5 Y}{\Sigma \xi_5^2}$$

and, further, that the sum of squares in the analysis of variance corresponding to C, say, will be

$$(C)(\Sigma \xi_2 Y) = \frac{\{\Sigma \xi_2 Y\}^2}{\Sigma \xi_2^2}$$

It follows, therefore, that we can obtain the sums of squares for regression for each degree of freedom at each stage of fitting, since these amounts are additive. We will have, for instance, the following sums of squares:

Linear Regression: $B\Sigma\xi_1 Y$

Quadratic Regression: $B\Sigma\xi_1 Y + C\Sigma\xi_2 Y$

Cubic Regression: $B\Sigma\xi_1 Y + C\Sigma\xi_2 Y + D\Sigma\xi_3 Y$

Quartic Regression: $B\Sigma\xi_1 Y + C\Sigma\xi_2 Y + D\Sigma\xi_3 Y + E\Sigma\xi_4 Y$

Quintic Regression: $B\Sigma\xi_1 Y + C\Sigma\xi_2 Y + D\Sigma\xi_3 Y + E\Sigma\xi_4 Y + F\Sigma \xi_5 Y$

The numerical values required for our calculations are as follows:

ξ	VALUE OF X										SUM OF SQUARES OF CO-EFFICIENTS
	1	*2*	*3*	*4*	*5*	*6*	*7*	*8*	*9*	*10*	
ξ_1	-9	-7	-5	-3	-1	1	3	5	7	9	330
ξ_2	6	2	-1	-3	-4	-4	-3	-1	2	6	132
ξ_3	-42	14	35	31	12	-12	-31	-35	-14	42	8,580
ξ_4	18	-22	-17	3	18	18	3	-17	-22	18	2,860
ξ_5	-6	14	-1	-11	-6	6	11	1	-14	6	780
Total Y	291	336	350	380	377	398	421	429	424	430	$\Sigma Y = 3,836$

In the bottom row of the table we have written the total values of Y corresponding to each X (the means could have been used, multiplying by 10 later). Multiplying these totals for Y by the coefficients in each row in turn, squaring the total, and dividing by the sum of squares shown in the last column multiplied by 10, we secure the following set of values:

$$\text{Linear Term:} \quad \frac{(+2,406)^2}{3,300} = 1,754.19$$

$$\text{Quadratic Term:} \quad \frac{(-436)^2}{1,320} = 144.01$$

$$\text{Cubic Term:} \quad \frac{(+318)^2}{85,800} = 1.18$$

$$\text{Quartic Term:} \quad \frac{(-632)^2}{28,600} = 13.97$$

$$\text{Quintic Term:} \quad \frac{(+258)^2}{7,800} = 8.53$$

Putting these values together with the original analysis of variance table, we have the following results:

VARIANCE	DEGREES OF FREEDOM	SUM OF SQUARES	MEAN SQUARE
Regression			
Linear	1	1,754.19	1,754.19
Quadratic	1	144.01	144.01
Cubic	1	1.18	1.18
Quartic	1	13.97	13.97
Quintic	1	8.53	8.53
Deviations	4	25.96	6.49
Among Trials	9	1,947.84	216.4
Among Students	9	1,596.44	177.4
Residual	81	898.76	11.10
Total	99	4,443.04	—

Comparing each of the Regression terms with the Residual, we see that only the linear and quadratic are significant so that we may write the top entries, for Regression, as follows:

COMPONENT	DEGREES OF FREEDOM	SUM OF SQUARES	MEAN SQUARE
Linear Component	1	1,754.19	1,754.19
Quadratic Component	1	144.01	144.01
Deviations from Regression	7	49.64	7.09

Actually, the fit is so good that the deviations from regression are somewhat smaller than the residual, although not significantly so.

We are now in a position to extend the analysis to an investigation of the possible differences in patterns for the 10 individuals, the first part of which is equivalent to the determination of the interaction effect, if any, between students and each of the polynomial components (linear and quadratic only). Applying the same coefficients to each student's scores in turn, we obtain the values shown in the two columns headed Regression Component to the right of the main part of Table XII.4. As students will undoubtedly realize, this amounts to fitting a quadratic polynomial to the scores for each student. The sum of squares of the 10 linear components, $(255)^2 + (231)^2 + \ldots + (123)^2 + (250)^2$ is equal to 630,358. Dividing this sum by 330 and subtracting 1,754.19 from the quotient, we have:

$$\text{Linear Component by Students} = \frac{630,358}{330} - 1,754.19 = 155.99$$

which has 9 degrees of freedom. Proceeding in exactly the same way with the 10 quadratic components, but dividing by 132 and subtracting 144.01 from the quotient, we have:

$$\text{Quadratic Component by Students} = \frac{36,488}{132} - 144.01 = 132.41$$

which again has 9 degrees of freedom. The analysis of variance table may now be written in the form:

VARIANCE		DEGREES OF FREEDOM	SUM OF SQUARES	MEAN SQUARE
Among Trials		9	1,947.84	216.4
Parts	Linear Component	1	1,754.19	1,754.2
	Quadratic Component	1	144.01	144.0
	Regression Deviations	7	49.64	7.09
Among Individuals		9	1,596.44	177.4
Residual		81	898.76	11.10
Parts	Linear by Students	9	155.99	17.33
	Quadratic by Students	9	132.41	14.71
	Remainder	63	610.36	9.69
Total		99	4,443.04	—

Neither of these interaction components is significant, although the Linear X Students mean square yields an F-ratio of $F = \dfrac{17.33}{9.69} = 1.79$ which is large enough to indicate that if more students had been used a significant interaction would have been obtained (i.e. the pattern of scores, the learning curve, differs from individual to individual). The final summary of the results, putting all non-significant sums of squares into a composite residual, would be as follows:

VARIANCE	DEGREES OF FREEDOM	SUM OF SQUARES	MEAN SQUARE
Among Trials			
Linear Component	1	1,754.19	1,754.2
Quadratic Component	1	144.01	144.0
Among Individuals	9	1,596.44	177.4
Residual	88	948.40	10.78
Total	99	4,443.04	—

As a matter of interest, and to indicate the form of analysis appropriate if the interactions of the regression components and students had been significant, we show in the last subtable to the right of Table XII.4 under the heading Individual Residuals the residuals by individual students. Each of these has 7 degrees of freedom, since a linear and a quadratic component have been fitted for each student. For the first student, for example, the Total Sum of Squares will be

$$13,621 - \frac{(363)^2}{10} = 444.1$$

the Regression Components will be

$$\frac{(255)^2}{330} + \frac{(120)^2}{132} = 306.1$$

yielding a residual (residual deviations from regression) for that student of
$$444.1 - 306.1 = 138.0$$

The total of these residuals must, of course, be equal to the sum of the two entries in the second preceding table, as follows:

ITEM	DEGREES OF FREEDOM	SUM OF SQUARES
Regression Deviations	7	49.64
Remainder	63	610.36
Sum	70	660.00

(within limits of the accuracy with which the 10 residual values have been calculated). The several entries are as shown below on page 408. Students will observe, comparing the regression components with the residual mean square for each student with 1 and 7 degrees of freedom, that the learning patterns vary somewhat from student to student. For the fourth and ninth students, for instance, neither regression component is significant. This supports the indication given by the interaction terms of an earlier analysis, in that if more students had been used in the experiment the differences between regressions might have proved significant.

STUDENT	LINEAR COMPONENT	QUADRATIC COMPONENT	RESIDUAL DEVIATIONS		
			Sum of Squares	Degrees of Freedom	Mean Square
1	197.05	109.09	138.0	7	19.7
2	161.70	10.94	39.5	7	5.6
3	224.19	18.94	65.3	7	9.3
4	51.21	9.82	89.4	7	12.8
5	453.84	74.25	134.4	7	19.2
6	140.08	3.03	21.0	7	3.0
7	216.03	0.07	18.8	7	2.7
8	230.84	1.70	21.9	7	3.1
9	45.85	44.91	73.3	7	10.5
10	189.39	3.67	58.5	7	8.4

Students should, as an exercise, make a test of homogeneity of variance, using the method explained in an earlier chapter, to determine whether the students differ significantly in (a) total variance and (b) residual variance.

EXERCISES

1. In a study of prediction of reading achievement, the following results were secured:

VARIABLE	MEAN	STANDARD DEVIATION	CORRELATION COEFFICIENTS		
			Mental Age	Reading Readiness	Reading Achievement
Chronological Age	79.5	3.82	−.0726	.1278	−.1691
Mental Age	85.4	10.63	—	.5932	.5214
Reading Readiness	92.6	16.81	—	—	.5563
Reading Achievement	2.8	.51	—	—	—

    (a) Calculate the multiple regression equation for predicting Reading Achievement from a knowledge of Chronological Age, Mental Age, and Reading Readiness.
    (b) Recalculate the equation omitting the Chronological Age variable.
    (c) For each of (a) and (b) make the appropriate tests of significance of the regression coefficients and calculate the value of the multiple correlation coefficient.
    (d) Is it worth while retaining Chronological Age as a predictor variable?
    (e) What is the relationship between Reading Readiness and Reading Achievement when the effect of Mental Age is partialled out?
2. Fit a polynomial of the second order to the data of Table XI.1, using French Composition as the predictor variable. Is there any evidence of a need to fit a polynomial of higher order?

3. Complete the exercise suggested in the text by computing a quartic polynomial for the data of Table XII.2.

4. For the data of Table XII.4, omit the scores for the first three trials (since these were partly of the nature of practice trials) and recalculate the values given in the text for the complete data.

CHAPTER XIII

Special Applications of Multivariate Analysis

Special applications of multivariate analysis are numerous and varied, and we make no pretense to give a complete discussion of all of them in this chapter. We have, however, selected for presentation and illustration a few of the major and fundamental concepts and methods. Given an understanding of these basic concepts, the student should be able, without undue difficulty, to understand and use properly any other special application that may be required by the peculiar circumstances of the problem in which he is interested.

It is of some importance, as well as of interest, to note that in certain respects these special applications represent a culmination or fusion of the methods earlier discussed. They employ, either in sequence or together, the methods appropriate for univariate analysis and those for multivariate analysis, reducing very often to a combination, in some form, of analysis of variance and multiple regression concepts and methods.

THE ANALYSIS OF COVARIANCE

Basically, the analysis of covariance is an extension of the methods of analysis of variance to two or more variables. As the name implies, and as one might expect since covariation is involved whenever two or more variables are considered together, the analysis consists of a subdivision of the covariance, not the variance. Actually, the situation is analogous to that which occurs in the analysis of variance: in the one case the sum of squares of the variable is subdivided into its constituent elements, in the other the sum of products of two (or more) variables is similarly subdivided.

The method may be used for either of two quite different purposes. For descriptive purposes, it leads directly (subject to certain assumptions) to the calculation and comparison of regression coefficients and/or correlation coefficients for each element of the classificatory system (or in the design of the experiment). Important as this purpose or function may be, the second purpose—a simple extension of the first, essentially—is of paramount importance in experimental work. This is the statistical control through elimination of possible effects, using regression methods, of factors or variables that are measurable but which it is inadvisable, inconvenient, or impossible to control directly in the design of the experiment. The meaning of this second purpose and the reasons underlying it will become evident as we proceed. We will begin with a simple example of an analysis where the purpose is largely, if not entirely, descriptive, and introduce the additional functions or purposes in subsequent examples.

The basic data for our first example are given in Table XIII.1: observe that we have, in order to simplify the process, selected five boys and five girls in each of grades 6, 7, and 8; and for each pupil we show two values, the Intelligence Quotient (X) and Achievement Score (Y). Also, in view of the various models discussed in Chapter VIII, we should note that no attempt was made to secure a truly random sample of boys or girls in each grade. While not deliberately selected in terms of X or Y, the values certainly do not constitute a random sample but were not in any way from matched individuals.

From these original data we calculate the quantities shown in Table XIII.2A. Students will realize that the only new feature of the analysis to this point is that in the last column we have shown the sum of products (ΣXY) for each group of five boys and girls. Otherwise we proceed exactly as for the usual analysis of variance, at least for X and Y separately.

TABLE XIII.1

BASIC DATA FOR EXAMPLE OF ANALYSIS OF VARIANCE AND COVARIANCE:
INTELLIGENCE QUOTIENTS AND ACHIEVEMENT SCORES OF
FIVE BOYS AND GIRLS IN EACH OF GRADES 6, 7, AND 8

GRADE	6				7				8			
Sex	Boys		Girls		Boys		Girls		Boys		Girls	
Variable	I.Q. (X)	Ach. (Y)	I.Q. (X)	Ach. (Y)	I.Q. (X)	Ach. (Y)	I.Q. (X)	Ach. (Y)	I.Q. (X)	Ach. (Y)	I.Q. (X)	Ach. (Y)
Student 1	96	58	81	36	110	62	122	65	108	51	118	59
2	115	65	136	62	111	72	111	71	115	68	134	77
3	111	62	86	49	101	73	97	66	96	49	111	62
4	100	38	109	73	91	67	122	70	100	40	108	58
5	89	54	128	77	127	70	106	64	121	79	132	82

For convenience, it is probably worth while to calculate the set of subsidiary values shown in Table XIII.2B: these are secured from the sums as indicated. For the Grand Total row of Table XIII.2A we also have for the squares and product:

$$\frac{(3,292)^2}{30} = 361,242.13$$

$$\frac{(3,292)(1,879)}{30} = 206,188.93$$

$$\frac{(1,879)^2}{30} = 117,688.03$$

From the Grand Total row of Table XIII.2A, the set of values just

TABLE XIII.2A

Sums, Sums of Squares, and Sums of Products of Data of Table XIII.1

GRADE	SEX	ΣX	ΣY	ΣX^2	ΣY^2	ΣXY
6	Boys	511	277	52,683	15,793	28,531
	Girls	540	297	60,718	18,799	33,375
7	Boys	540	344	59,032	23,746	37,172
	Girls	558	336	62,734	22,618	37,537
8	Boys	540	287	58,746	17,467	31,591
	Girls	603	338	73,289	23,342	41,250
Grand Total		3,292	1,879	367,202	121,765	209,456

TABLE XIII.2B

Subsidiary Values Calculated From Sums of Table XIII.2A

GRADE	SEX	$(\Sigma X)^2/5$	$(\Sigma Y)^2/5$	$\dfrac{(\Sigma X)(\Sigma Y)}{5}$
6	Boys	52,224.2	15,345.8	28,309.4
	Girls	58,320.0	17,641.8	32,076.0
7	Boys	58,320.0	23,667.2	37,152.0
	Girls	62,272.8	22,579.2	37,497.6
8	Boys	58,320.0	16,473.8	30,996.0
	Girls	72,721.8	22,848.8	40,762.8
Total		362,178.8	118,556.6	206,793.8

calculated, and the Total row of Table XIII.2B, we may calculate the usual first set of values as if Table XIII.1 were in fact a simple one-way classification. The results are given in Table XIII.3; they are obtained as follows:

(1) *Between Classes*
Sum of Squares for $X = 362,178.80 - 361,242.13 = 936.67$
Sum of Squares for $Y = 118,556.60 - 117,688.03 = 868.57$
Sum of Products $= 206,793.80 - 206,188.93 = 604.87$

(2) *Within Classes*
Sum of Squares for $X = 367,202 - 362,178.80 = 5,023.20$
Sum of Squares for $Y = 121,765 - 118,556.60 = 3,208.40$
Sum of Products $= 209,456 - 206,793.80 = 2,662.20$

(3) *Total*
Sum of Squares for $X = 367,202 - 361,242.13 = 5,959.87$
Sum of Squares for $Y = 121,765 - 117,688.03 = 4,076.97$
Sum of Products $= 209,456 - 206,188.93 = 3,267.07$

To complete the analysis for the two-way classification (sex by grade), we may for convenience rewrite the sums of Table XIII.2A—the amounts shown under ΣX and ΣY—in the following way:

GRADE	SEX				TOTAL	
	Boys		Girls			
	X	Y	X	Y	X	Y
6	511	277	540	297	1,051	574
7	540	344	558	336	1,098	680
8	540	287	603	338	1,143	625
Total	1,591	908	1,701	971	3,292	1,879

Operating on these sums, for the present, as if they were in fact original values, we secure the results shown in Table XIII.4. The entries are calculated as follows:

(1) *Between Sexes*

Sum of Squares for $X = \dfrac{(1,591)^2}{3} + \dfrac{(1,701)^2}{3} - \dfrac{(3,292)^2}{6} = 2{,}016.67$

Sum of Squares for $Y = \dfrac{(908)^2}{3} + \dfrac{(971)^2}{3} - \dfrac{(1,879)^2}{6} = 661.50$

Sum of Products $= \dfrac{(1,591)(908)}{3} + \dfrac{(1,701)(971)}{3} - \dfrac{(3,292)(1,879)}{6}$
$$= 1{,}155.00$$

(2) *Among Grades*

Sum of Squares for $X = \dfrac{(1,051)^2}{2} + \dfrac{(1,098)^2}{2} + \dfrac{(1,143)^2}{2} - \dfrac{(3,292)^2}{6}$
$$= 2{,}116.33$$

Sum of Squares for $Y = \dfrac{(574)^2}{2} + \dfrac{(680)^2}{2} + \dfrac{(625)^2}{2} - \dfrac{(1,879)^2}{6}$
$$= 2{,}810.33$$

Sum of Products $= \dfrac{(1,051)(574)}{2} + \dfrac{(1,098)(680)}{2} + \dfrac{(1,143)(625)}{2}$
$$- \dfrac{(3,292)(1,879)}{6} = 1{,}199.83$$

(3) *Total*

Sum of Squares for $X = (511)^2 + (540)^2 + \ldots + (603)^2$
$$- \dfrac{(3,292)^2}{6} = 4{,}683.33$$

Sum of Squares for $Y = (277)^2 + (344)^2 + \ldots + (338)^2$
$$- \dfrac{(1,879)^2}{6} = 4{,}342.83$$

Sum of Products $= (511)(277) + \ldots + (603)(338)$
$$- \dfrac{(3,292)(1,879)}{6} = 3{,}024.33$$

(4) *Residual*

Values secured most easily by subtraction within each column.

TABLE XIII.3

ANALYSIS OF VARIANCE AND COVARIANCE OF DATA OF TABLE XIII.1:
ONE-WAY CLASSIFICATION

SOURCE OF VARIATION	DEGREES OF FREEDOM	SUM OF SQUARES		SUM OF PRODUCTS XY
		X	Y	
Between Classes	5	936.67	868.57	604.87
Within Classes	24	5,023.20	3,208.40	2,662.20
Total	29	5,959.87	4,076.97	3,267.07

These values are, of course, based on the sums of the original values (five original values summed in each case) and must be correspondingly reduced to yield entries comparable to those of Table XIII.3. As students will have no doubt anticipated, for example, the Total row of Table XIII.4, when each entry is divided by 5, gives the Between Classes entries of Table XIII.3. Accordingly, we may set up the complete analysis of variance and covariance table for the data of Table XIII.1 as shown in Table XIII.5. The values of Table XIII.4 are divided by 5 throughout before being transferred, we have now called the Residual of Table XIII.4 the Interaction of Sex and Grade, and the Within Classes of Table XIII.3 now becomes the Residual.

It is of particular interest and importance to note that the results given in Table XIII.5 are based simply on an algebraic breakdown of both the sums of squares and the products. No assumption has been, or need be, made concerning form of distribution, linearity of regression, and so on, to set up these entries. We worked the example through in this way for another reason also: namely, to demonstrate the parallelism (from the arithmetical point of view) between the analyses of squares and of products that yields the full set of entries for the analysis of covariance and the double analysis of variance. Students should experience no difficulty, consequently, in performing such analyses for three-way and more complex tables of classification, since they have earlier learned the necessary procedures (see Chapter VIII) in another connection.

TABLE XIII.4

ANALYSIS OF VARIANCE AND COVARIANCE OF SUMS OF TABLE XIII.2A

SOURCE OF VARIATION	DEGREES OF FREEDOM	SUM OF SQUARES		SUM OF PRODUCTS
		X	Y	
Between Sexes	1	2,016.67	661.50	1,155.00
Among Grades	2	2,116.33	2,810.33	1,199.83
Residual	2	550.33	871.00	669.50
Total	5	4,683.33	4,342.83	3,024.33

TABLE XIII.5

COMPLETE ANALYSIS OF VARIANCE AND COVARIANCE OF TABLE XIII.1

SOURCE OF VARIATION	DEGREES OF FREEDOM	SUM OF SQUARES		SUM OF PRODUCTS
		X	Y	
Between Sexes	1	403.33	132.30	231.00
Among Grades	2	423.27	562.07	239.97
Interaction of Sex and Grade	2	110.07	174.20	133.90
Total Among Classes	5	936.67	868.57	604.87
Residual	24	5,023.20	3,208.40	2,662.20
Total	29	5,959.87	4,076.97	3,267.07

But the analysis of the covariance, unlike that of the variance, does not admit of a ready interpretation in the form shown in Table XIII.5. This will occasion no surprise, of course, since in the previous chapters on measures of relationship we used the covariance values only in order to calculate therefrom regression or correlation coefficients.   Observe that for each row of Table XIII.5 we may, subject to the assumptions to be discussed presently, calculate the following regression and correlation coefficients (using only the values within that row):

SOURCE OF VARIATION	REGRESSION COEFFICIENTS		CORRELATION COEFFICIENT
	Y on X	X on Y	
Between Sexes	0.573	1.746	1.000
Among Grades	0.567	0.427	0.492
Interaction of Sex and Grade	1.216	0.769	0.967
Total Among Classes	0.646	0.696	0.671
Residual	0.530	0.830	0.663
Total	0.548	0.801	0.663

The entries in the first row, for Between Sexes with 1 degree of freedom, are not of much interest or utility: students may, as an exercise in algebra, prove to their own satisfaction that for any case of two pairs of values of X and Y the product-moment correlation coefficient—save for the trivial case where $X_1 - X_2 = Y_1 - Y_2 = 0$ —must be unity.*

As for assumptions, the calculation of the correlation or the regression coefficients implies the assumption that the corresponding regressions are in fact linear in form.   Additional assumptions are made for the Total

* Since a straight line can always be drawn exactly through any two points.

Among Classes and Residual rows, at least in the use and interpretation of the values so secured, since each is based on a sum of components and has a meaning only if it can be demonstrated that there does exist a common relationship—save for deviations arising through sampling errors—in all the parts. The Residual component of Table XIII.5, for example, is made up of the following six parts, each with 4 degrees of freedom, corresponding to the classes set out originally in Table XIII.1. These are obtained, in the usual fashion, from the entries for each class given in tables XIII.2A and XIII.2B, and are as shown in Table XIII.6.

TABLE XIII.6

COMPONENTS OF RESIDUAL OF TABLE XIII.5
(from Tables XIII.2A and XIII.2B)

GRADE	SEX	DEGREES OF FREEDOM	SUM OF SQUARES		SUM OF PRODUCTS	REGRESSION COEFFICIENT (Y ON X)
			X	Y		
6	Boys	4	458.8	447.2	221.6	0.483
	Girls	4	2,398.0	1,157.2	1,299.0	0.542
7	Boys	4	712.0	78.8	20.0	0.028
	Girls	4	461.2	38.8	39.4	0.085
8	Boys	4	426.0	993.2	595.0	1.397
	Girls	4	567.2	493.2	487.2	0.859
Total		24	5,023.2	3,208.4	2,662.2	0.530

Apart altogether from the question of linearity of regression within each of these classes, an assumption that inspection of the data of Table XIII.1 reveals to be reasonably well satisfied,† it is evident that there is a need to test for homogeneity of variance for both X and Y before the values are pooled in the Residual of the analysis of variance table. This we may leave as an exercise for the student to perform, using Bartlett's test as explained in an earlier chapter, since our main interest here is in the equality of the regression coefficients themselves.

Using the subscript j to denote the class, $j = 1, 2, \ldots, 6$, and the subscript i to denote a value within a class, $i = 1, 2, \ldots, 5$, we have the 30 pairs of values (Y_{ji}, X_{ji}). Assume that for each class there is a linear relation of the form

$$Y_{ji} = \alpha_j + \beta_j X_{ji}$$

and, further, that Y_{ji} is normally distributed about $\alpha_j + \beta_j X_{ji}$ with standard deviation σ_j. For sampling theory purposes the values of X are

---

† Students should as an exercise, and to aid in the interpretation of the results that follow, plot the pairs of points for these 30 students, preferably using a different color for the five points in each of the six classes.

regarded as fixed, or selected in advance without error.‡ Denoting the means of the jth class by $Y_{j.}$ and $X_{j.}$, we may define

$$S_{XX_j} = \sum_i (X_{ji} - X_{j.})^2$$

$$S_{YY_j} = \sum_i (Y_{ji} - Y_{j.})^2$$

$$S_{XY_j} = \sum_i (X_{ji} - X_{j.})(Y_{ji} - Y_{j.})$$

then, from the theory of linear regression, the best estimate of $f_j \sigma_j^2$, denoted by S_j^2, where f_j denotes the number of degrees of freedom, will be for each j

$$S_j^2 = S_{YY_j} - \frac{S_{XY_j}^2}{S_{XX_j}}$$

the best estimate of β_j, denoted by b_j, and of α_j, denoted by a_j, will be

$$b_j = \frac{S_{XY_j}}{S_{XX_j}} \quad \text{and} \quad a_j = Y_{j.} - b_j X_{j.}$$

Now any tests of hypotheses concerning the β_j and α_j are based on the assumption, or hypothesis, that the k values of σ_j are equal, so that we must first test the hypothesis

$$H_1 : \sigma_1 = \sigma_2 = \ldots = \sigma_j = \sigma$$

The six estimates of $f_j \sigma_j^2$, the S_j^2, are as follows, calculated from the data of Table XIII.6 as indicated by the formula for S_j^2:

j	S_{YY_j}	$\dfrac{S_{XY_j}^2}{S_{XX_j}}$	S_j^2	DEGREES OF FREEDOM f_j
1	447.20	107.03	340.17	3
2	1,157.20	703.67	453.53	3
3	78.80	0.56	78.24	3
4	38.80	3.37	35.43	3
5	993.20	831.04	162.16	3
6	493.20	418.48	74.72	3
Total	3,208.40	2,064.15	1,144.25	18

Applying Bartlett's test (see Chapter VII) to the values of the S_j^2/f_j, we have

$$M = 20.518$$
$$C = 1.1296$$

whence the quantity $\dfrac{M}{C} = \dfrac{20.518}{1.1296} = 18.16$ will be approximately distributed as χ^2 with $k - 1 = 5$ degrees of freedom. Now for this number of

‡ The assumptions are similar, save for interchange of X and Y, for tests of the regression coefficients of X on Y.

degrees of freedom the value of $\chi^2_{.01}$ is 15.086 and of $\chi^2_{.001}$ is 20.517, so that we should, strictly speaking, reject the hypothesis $H_1 = \sigma_1 = \sigma_2 = \ldots = \sigma_j = \sigma$ and stop the analysis at this point. The groups (samples) differ in their residual deviations and this basic inequality renders invalid subsequent tests of homogeneity or equality. For illustrative purposes, however, particularly since the value of $\dfrac{M}{C}$ is not extremely large (beyond $\chi^2_{.001}$), we shall proceed with the analysis as if, in fact, H_1 had not been rejected.§

The next hypothesis in the sequence to be tested relates to the regression coefficients β_j, and may be expressed in the form
$$H_2 : \beta_1 = \beta_2 = \ldots = \beta_j = \beta$$
or, in words, that the slopes of the population regression lines are all equal to a common value β. (The individual values of the b's given in Table XIII.6 indicate that this hypothesis may not be accepted.) Students should observe that in testing this hypothesis it is assumed that H_1 has been accepted, but no assumption or restriction is applied to the α_j. Now if H_2 is true, the best estimate of the common β will be given by
$$b_R = \frac{S_{XYR}}{S_{XXR}}$$
where $S_{XYR} = \Sigma S_{XY_j}$ and $S_{XXR} = \Sigma S_{XX_j}$, and consequently the best estimate of the (assumed) common $f\sigma^2$, denoted by S_R^2 where f denotes the number of degrees of freedom, will be
$$S_R^2 = S_{YYR} - \frac{(S_{XYR})^2}{S_{XXR}}$$
where $S_{YYR} = \Sigma S_{YY_j}$ and f is now $N - k - 1$. Therefore, if H_2 is true the quantity
$$F = \frac{N - 2k}{k - 1} \cdot \frac{S_R^2 - \Sigma S_j^2}{\Sigma S_j^2}$$
will be distributed as Snedecor's F with degrees of freedom $n_1 = k - 1$ and $n_2 = N - 2k$. For our particular example, we have
$$S_{YYR} = 3{,}208.40, \ S_{XYR} = 2{,}662.20, \ S_{XXR} = 5{,}023.20$$
whence
$$S_R^2 = 3{,}208.40 - \frac{(2{,}662.20)^2}{5{,}023.20} = 1{,}797.48$$
and $\qquad \Sigma S_j^2 = 1{,}144.25$
so that, for $N = 30$ and $k = 6$,
$$F = \frac{18}{5} \cdot \frac{653.23}{1{,}144.25} = 2.055$$
which, for $n_1 = 5$ and $n_2 = 18$, is less than $F_{.05}$ and consequently we would

§ The data used are real, not fictitious, and these inconvenient situations are very likely to arise in practice!

accept H_2.∥ We may, therefore, in subsequent analyses use the pooled estimate of the common β, and need not retain and use the estimates of the k values of β_j. Note, however, that if H_2 is rejected, then the analysis must be stopped at that point.

The next hypothesis to be tested in the series is concerned with the α_j, being that there is a common value, α. The hypothesis may be written

$$H_3 : \alpha_1 = \alpha_2 = \ldots = \alpha_j = \alpha$$

but the test about to be discussed assumes that both H_1 and H_2 are true (so that these two hypotheses must be first tested and accepted). Students should note that if H_2 and H_3 are true we have a single regression line for the k groups, since

$$Y_{ji} = \alpha_j + \beta_j X_{ji}$$

now becomes

$$Y_{ji} = \alpha + \beta X_{ji}$$

and all the individual regression lines prove to have the same slopes and the same intercepts on the Y-axis. If H_3 is rejected, then obviously we will have a number of parallel regression lines, i.e. not all coincide.

Now if H_3 is true there will be no significant difference among the adjusted Y group means, i.e. among the $Y_{j.} - b_R X_{j.}$. Consequently, defining the sums of squares and products of the Total row of Table XIII.5 (i.e. for all classes thrown into one total class) by the symbols S_{XXT}, S_{YYT}, and S_{XYT}, respectively, and by $S_T{}^2$ the quantity

$$S_T{}^2 = S_{YYT} - \frac{(S_{XYT})^2}{S_{XXT}}$$

we see that the quantity

$$F = \frac{N - k - 1}{k - 1} \cdot \frac{S_T{}^2 - S_R{}^2}{S_R{}^2}$$

will be distributed as F with $n_1 = k - 1$ and $n_2 = N - k - 1$ degrees of freedom. For our example, $N = 30$, $k = 6$, $S_R{}^2 = 1{,}797.48$, $S_{YYT} = 4{,}076.97$, $S_{XXT} = 5{,}959.87$, and $S_{XYT} = 3{,}267.07$. Accordingly,

$$S_T{}^2 = 4{,}076.97 - \frac{(3{,}267.07)^2}{5{,}959.87} = 2{,}286.03$$

and

$$F = \frac{23}{5} \cdot \frac{488.55}{1{,}797.48} = 1.25$$

and since $F_{.01} = 3.94$ for $n_1 = 5$ and $n_2 = 23$, we would accept H_3. We may, therefore, use a single regression line for all these classes, of common

∥ To test the hypothesis, a special case, that the common $\beta = 0$, we note that the quantity

$$F = \frac{N - k - 1}{1} \cdot \frac{S_{XYR}^2}{S_{XXR} S_{YYR} - S_{XYR}^2}$$

is distributed as Snedecor's F with $n_1 = 1$ and $n_2 = N - k - 1$ degrees of freedom. For our case $F = 18.05$ and we would reject this hypothesis. If the hypothesis is accepted, then the analysis would be stopped at this point.

slope and intercept. Indeed, a glance at the graph (which it was earlier suggested students should construct), would indicate that this was a likely possibility.

All of the calculations and tests made to this point, save those for the test of H_1 relating to a common σ, can be neatly summarized as shown in Table XIII.7. The natural extension to the several parts of the Total Among Classes of Table XIII.5 will be considered next, and then the use of the analysis of covariance method in statistical control in experimental studies.

TABLE XIII.7

Summary of Analysis of Within Classes Regression Components
among k Classes (Regression of Y on X)

SOURCE OF VARIATION	DEGREES OF FREEDOM	SUM OF SQUARES Formula	For Example	D.F. FOR EXAMPLE
Deviations about regression lines within classes	$N - 2k$	$\Sigma_j S_j^2 = \Sigma_j \left\{ S_{YY_j} - \dfrac{S_{XY_j}^2}{S_{XX_j}} \right\}$	1,144.25	18
Deviations about within classes regression lines of common slope β	$N - k - 1$	$S_R^2 = \Sigma_j S_{YY_j} - \dfrac{(\Sigma_j S_{XY_j})^2}{\Sigma S_{XX_j}}$	1,797.48	23
Deviations of within classes regression coefficients about common slope β	$k - 1$	$S_R^2 - \Sigma_j S_j^2$	653.23	5
Deviations about common regression line (common α and β)	$N - 2$	$S_T^2 = S_{YYT} - \dfrac{(S_{XYT})^2}{S_{XXT}}$	2,286.03	28
Deviations of classes α_j about common α	$k - 1$	$S_T^2 - S_R^2$	488.55	5

Let us turn now to the Among Classes section of Table XIII.5 and the analysis of the Class means related thereto. Analyzing each row in turn, using the subscripts S, G, I, and C to denote values corresponding to Sexes, Grades, Interaction, and Total Among Classes, respectively, we secure the values shown in Table XIII.8. Since we will require it for tests of significance, we show in the first row the value of S_R^2 with $N - k - 1$ degrees of freedom from Table XIII.7 for which the mean square is $\dfrac{1,797.48}{23} = 78.15$. The first hypothesis is related to the several possible regression coefficients for the Class means (of Y). Since there are three possible values (β_S for Sex, β_G for Grades, and β_I for Interaction) the hypothesis of a common Among Classes regression coefficient, which we may denote by β_C, may be expressed in the form

$$H_4 : \beta_S = \beta_G = \beta_I \ (= \beta_C)$$

The appropriate test of this hypothesis may be made by calculating the quantity

$$F = \frac{N - k - 1}{2} \cdot \frac{\dfrac{S_{XYS}^2}{S_{XXS}} + \dfrac{S_{XYG}^2}{S_{XXG}} + \dfrac{S_{XYI}^2}{S_{XXI}} - \dfrac{S_{XYC}^2}{S_{XXC}}}{S_R{}^2}$$

which, if H_4 is true, will be distributed as F with $n_1 = 2$ and $n_2 = N - k - 1$ degrees of freedom. For our example,

$$F = \frac{23}{2} \cdot \frac{40.64}{1{,}797.48} = \frac{20.32}{78.15} = 0.26$$

and since this is less than unity we would accept H_4.# We may, therefore, proceed with the analysis on the basis of a common Among Classes regression slope (students may, by plotting the Class means in different colors on the graph mentioned earlier, observe that this seems reasonable).

The next hypothesis concerns the difference between the common Among Classes regression coefficient, β_C, and the common Within Classes regression coefficient, β, which may be expressed as

$$H_5 : \beta_C = \beta$$

The appropriate test of this hypothesis will be to calculate the quantity

$$F = \frac{N - k - 1}{1} \cdot \frac{\dfrac{S_{XYC}^2}{S_{XXC}} + \dfrac{S_{XYR}^2}{S_{XXR}} - \dfrac{S_{XYT}^2}{S_{XXT}}}{S_R{}^2}$$

which, if H_5 be true, is distributed as Snedecor's F with degrees of freedom $n_1 = 1$ and $n_2 = N - k - 1$. For our example we have

$$F = \frac{10.58}{78.15}$$

and since this is less than unity (but not significantly small, as $\dfrac{1}{F} = 7.39$ and for $n_1 = 23$ and $n_2 = 1$ the value of $F_{.05}$ is approximately 249) we would accept the hypothesis H_5. Accordingly we would use as an estimate of the common regression coefficient, β_T, the value

$$b_T = \frac{3{,}267.07}{5{,}959.87} = 0.548 \, .$$

A test of linearity of regression for the Class means is given by calculating the quantity

$$F = \frac{N - k - 1}{k - 2} \cdot \frac{S_{YYC} - \dfrac{S_{XYC}^2}{S_{XXC}}}{S_R{}^2}$$

F is not significantly small, since the value of $\dfrac{1}{F} = 3.85$ and for $n_1 = 23$ and $n_2 = 2$ the value of $F_{.05}$ is approximately 19.45.

TABLE XIII.8

SUMMARY OF ANALYSIS OF AMONG CLASSES REGRESSION COMPONENTS
FOR TWO-WAY CLASSIFICATION (Regression of Y on X)

SOURCE OF VARIATION	DEGREES OF FREEDOM		SUM OF SQUARES	
	Formula	*For Example*	*Formula*	*For Example*
Deviations about Within Classes regression lines of common slope β	$N-k-1$	23	$S_R^2 = \sum_j S_{YY_j} - \dfrac{(\sum_j S_{XY_j})^2}{\sum_j S_{XX_j}}$	1,797.48
Between Sexes: Regression component	1	1	$\dfrac{S_{XYS}^2}{S_{XXS}}$	132.30
Deviations about regression line for Sex	0	0	$S_{YYS} - \dfrac{S_{XYS}^2}{S_{XXS}}$	0
Among Grades (m grades): Regression component	1	1	S_{XYG}^2/S_{XXG}	136.05
Deviations about regression line for Grades	$m-2$	1	$S_{YYG} - \dfrac{S_{XYG}^2}{S_{XXG}}$	426.02
Interaction: Regression component	1	1	S_{XYI}^2/S_{XXI}	162.89
Deviations about regression line for Interaction	$m-2$	1	$S_{YYI} - \dfrac{S_{XYI}^2}{S_{XXI}}$	11.31
Total Among Classes: Regression component	1	1	S_{XYC}^2/S_{XXC}	390.60
Deviations of class means about common Among Classes regression	$k-2$	4	$S_{YYC} - \dfrac{S_{XYC}^2}{S_{XXC}}$	477.97
Deviations of Section regression coefficients about common Among Classes regression coefficient	2	2	$\dfrac{S_{XYS}^2}{S_{XXS}} + \dfrac{S_{XYG}^2}{S_{XXG}} + \dfrac{S_{XYI}^2}{S_{XXI}} - \dfrac{S_{XYC}^2}{S_{XXC}}$	40.64
Regression component for Within Classes regression line of common slope β	1	1	$\dfrac{S_{XYR}^2}{S_{XXR}} = \dfrac{(\sum_j S_{XY_j})^2}{\sum_j S_{XX_j}}$	1,410.92
Regression component for Total (all classes combined)	1	1	$\dfrac{S_{XYT}^2}{S_{XXT}}$	1,790.94
Difference between Among Classes regression coefficient and common Within Classes regression coefficient	1	1	$\dfrac{S_{XYC}^2}{S_{XXC}} + \dfrac{S_{XYR}^2}{S_{XXR}} - \dfrac{S_{XYT}^2}{S_{XXT}}$	10.58

which, if the regression is in fact linear, will be distributed as F with degrees of freedom $n_1 = k - 2$ and $n_2 = N - k - 1$. For this particular example,

$$F = \frac{23}{4} \cdot \frac{477.97}{1,797.48} = 1.53$$

which, for $n_1 = 4$ and $n_2 = 23$, is considerably less than $F_{.05} = 2.80$, and we may conclude that linear regression will suffice.

The value of using covariance methods to introduce a statistical control in an experiment can be most clearly seen by a comparison of the original and reduced Residual sum of squares and mean square for Y. Note from Table XIII.5 that the Residual mean square for Y, without taking into account the relationship of achievement with intelligence, is

$$\frac{3,208.40}{24} = 133.68$$

whereas at the sacrifice of 1 degree of freedom the reduced mean square for Y becomes

$$\frac{S_R^2}{23} = 78.15$$

which represents a considerable reduction in the experimental error (at very little extra cost, it may be added, since this additional information about the subjects can generally be easily secured).

The test of the significance of the adjusted Y means, i.e. after allowance has been made for the effect of the relationship between intelligence and achievement here, using the common Within Classes regression coefficient for the adjustment, may be performed most simply as explained above for the test of H_3. However, the adjustment can be shown directly as given in Table XIII.9: the effect of differences in the X (Intelligence) means being eliminated by use of the adjustment $b_R(X_j. - X..)$. The adjusted Y means will therefore be of the form

$$Y_j. - b_C(X_j. - X..)$$

so that a "dampening" effect (for b_R positive) is introduced—the Y_j. are reduced where X_j. is greater than $X..$ and increased where X_j. is less than $X...$ The sum of squares of these reduced means about the general Y mean, with 5 degrees of freedom, will be equal to $S_T^2 - S_R^2$ of Table XIII.7 divided by 5 (the number of observations entering into the calculation of each Y_j.). Students will note that in the calculations the values $X.. = 109.733$ and $b_R = 0.52998$ have been used. The results do not check exactly, of course, but are fairly close.

We have not given the mathematical derivation of the statistical tests discussed above, nor of the analysis of covariance breakdown of the sums of products. These may be developed, however, along the lines we set out in some detail in Chapter VIII, "The Analysis of Variance," using only the new concept of linear regression as an additional feature. It will be obvious also, and we need not illustrate the process here, that what we have done above for one control variable, X, may easily be extended to two or more variables through the use of multiple regression concepts and

TABLE XIII.9

ADJUSTMENT OF Y CLASS MEANS FOR DIFFERENCES IN X MEANS,
USING COMMON WITHIN CLASSES REGRESSION COEFFICIENT

j	$Y_{j.}$	$X_{j.}$	$X_{j.} - X_{..}$	$-b_R(X_{j.} - X_{..})$	$Y_{j.} - b_R(X_{j.} - X_{..})$
1	55.4	102.2	$-$ 7.533	$+3.9923$	59.3923
2	59.4	108.0	$-$ 1.733	$+ .9185$	60.3185
3	68.8	108.0	$-$ 1.733	$+ .9185$	69.7185
4	67.2	111.6	$+$ 1.867	$- .9895$	66.2105
5	57.4	108.0	$-$ 1.733	$+ .9185$	58.3185
6	67.6	120.6	$+10.867$	-5.7593	61.8407
Total	375.8	658.4	—	—	375.7990

techniques. Readers interested in the derivation of the formulae, in the extension to more complex designs, and in the general case for large numbers of observations, should consult the references given in the footnote below.**

COMPARISON OF TWO GROUPS:
REGRESSION MATCHING AND THE JOHNSON-NEYMAN METHOD

In experimental work in education and psychology, probably the most common and most important design involves the comparison of results for two groups. Very often one group is subjected to an experimental treatment, so that it constitutes the "experimental" group, whereas the other is not, and consequently forms a "control" group or basis upon which the effect of the experimental treatment (e.g. a new teaching method or some extra instructional aid) may be judged.†† *Other things being equal*, the difference between the results for the two groups will be a valid measure of the effect of the experimental treatment. It matters little from the statistical point of view, of course, whether the second group is or is not itself subjected to another experimental treatment: the analysis in any event involves a comparison of the results for the two groups. This type of problem was considered earlier, in Chapter VI, in connection with the *t*-test of the significance of the difference between the means of two groups. The difficulty encountered there, and which generally arises in any experiment, is that the qualification "other things being equal" does not, and normally cannot, hold true—at least when human beings are involved in the experiment. One method used to overcome this diffi-

** Palmer O. Johnson and Fei Tsao, "Factorial Design and Covariance in the Study of Individual Educational Development."

Fei Tsao, "General Solution of the Analysis of Variance and Covariance in the Case of Unequal or Disproportionate Numbers of Observations in the Subclasses."

Harold Gulliksen and S. S. Wilks, "Regression Tests for Several Samples," *Psychometrika*, No. 2 (June, 1950), 91–114.

†† Assignment to experimental and control groups should be at random.

culty is that of matching (on those variables deemed related to or which might conceivably affect the variable to be used in the comparison) an individual in the experimental group with one in the control group. This is done individual by individual, in an attempt to secure in one group the exact equivalent of the subjects in the other. Apart from the fact that no two individuals are *exactly* alike anyway, not even the members of a pair of identical twins for that matter, the process has a number of very serious disadvantages, to which reference has been made in earlier chapters. Even the less restrictive procedure of matching by groups (on means and standard deviations for measurable characters) does not overcome all these disadvantages. The possibility of matching by regression methods, an example of which we have just considered in the analysis of covariance, holds out the promise of avoiding the disadvantages of matching by individuals and even of the limitations of the matching by groups referred to immediately above. The extension beyond the situation for which the analysis of covariance will suffice is due to Johnson and Neyman.‡‡ However, there are two quite different sets of circumstances considered in the original article by Johnson and Neyman. In the first, the so-called "matching" variables are purely qualitative (i.e. only categories can be set up), whereas, in the second (actually the more important of the two cases), the "matching" variables are measurable, or at least the data have an inherent order so that numerical equivalents can be employed in a regression analysis. Regression techniques do not enter directly into the first type of problems, but do in the second, despite the fact that the problems differ essentially only in the type of data encountered for the matching or control variables.

Categorical Matching Variables

Situations where this method can and should be used, possibly despite the limitation to be mentioned later, arise rather frequently—more frequently, we suspect, than is generally recognized. Consider, for example, the apparently simple and straightforward problem of determining whether girls obtain significantly higher scores than do boys on a reading readiness

‡‡ Readers will find the following references to the method helpful:
1. Palmer O. Johnson and J. Neyman, "Tests of Certain Linear Hypotheses and their Application to some Educational Problems," *Statistical Research Memoirs*, Vol. I, 1936.
2. Palmer O. Johnson and Leo C. Fay, "The Johnson-Neyman Technique, Its Theory and Application," *Psychometrika*, XV, No. 4 (December, 1950).
3. Palmer O. Johnson and Cyril Hoyt, *The Theory of Linear Hypotheses with Applications to Educational Problems* (Minneapolis: Bureau of Educational Research, University of Minnesota, June, 1952).
4. Robert F. Abelson, "A Note on the Neyman-Johnson Technique," *Psychometrika*, XVIII, No. 3 (September, 1953).

test administered at the end of kindergarten.§§ Experience would indicate that the effect of the teacher (or the environment of the class concerned) cannot be ignored, and neither can the effect of the type or form of reading readiness test used. The comparison between boys and girls that we really wish to make, consequently, is for the same form of the test within the same classroom. The data of Table XIII.10 are real data (part of those for a much larger study conducted by the Department of Educational Research, University of Toronto) that illustrate the form of classification and type of preliminary analysis required for the Johnson-Neyman solution of a problem of this nature.

Students will probably observe later (if they have not already done so) that the analysis in the general case is, save for one additional assumption, the usual multiple classification analysis of variance with unequal and disproportionate numbers in the subclasses. In the special case of equal or proportionate numbers (which is rather unlikely to occur in educational, but may in psychological, studies), of course, the usual multiple classification analysis of variance will be applicable. It is important that this similarity be recognized by the reader, because it leads, first, to a simple preliminary test of the results and, second, to a natural extension using analysis of covariance methods to remove the effect of one or more other measurable variables (such as mental age or chronological age in the present example). Moreover, there are implications for the design of the experiment or survey, with the purpose of simplifying the calculations, to secure equal or at least proportionate numbers in the subgroups, perhaps even at the cost of discarding the data for a limited number of cases.

The first step‖‖ in the analysis of the data of Table XIII.10 is the test of homogeneity of variance for the usual analysis of variance for Between and Within the 12 classes concerned. This assumption of homogeneity of variance for Within Classes, basic to the present analysis and also to that of Johnson and Neyman, is satisfied for these data: the value of M for Bartlett's test being approximately 5 for 11 degrees of freedom. Strictly speaking, if this hypothesis of a common variance is not accepted the analysis would be stopped at that point: the groups differ in this regard and probably in others. In practice, however, the researcher may wish, or be forced, to proceed with the analysis even if this hypothesis is re-

§§ As they should if the child psychologists are right. This problem is of considerable practical importance in Ontario, Canada, where kindergartens are provided by local education authorities and the program in Grade 1 to which kindergarten "graduates" are directed is determined in part in some centers by the results of intelligence and reading readiness tests.

‖‖ A test of normality of the Within Classes deviations should be the first step, but see discussion of this point in Chapter VII.

TABLE XIII.10

ORIGINAL DATA FOR JOHNSON–NEYMAN ANALYSIS WITH CATEGORICAL
MATCHING VARIABLES: READING READINESS SCORES OF BOYS AND GIRLS,
CLASSIFIED BY TEACHER AND FORM OF TEST USED

TEACHER	MRS. J. F.				MISS R. P.				MISS M. K.			
Form of Test	A		B		A		B		A		B	
Pupil No.	Boys	Girls	Boys	Girls	Boys	Girls	Boys	Girls	Boys	Girls	Boys	Girls
1	8	8	2	8	6	9	10	6	6	7	4	12
2	6	5	8	11	1	2	5	2	10	11	7	8
3	3	7	2	7	12	5	3	9	7	8	13	6
4	4	13	10		4	3	8	8	6	6	12	16
5	7				6	4	6	10	16	14	7	9
6					3	6		3	12	15	8	11
7									14	8	5	8
8									3	9	8	5
9									3	4	10	13
10									6	9	8	15
11									6	15	10	15
12									7	9	14	
13										6	15	
14										7	11	
15										3	2	
16										13		
Number	5	4	4	3	6	6	5	6	12	16	15	11
Sum(Σ_j)	28	33	22	26	32	29	32	38	96	144	134	118
Mean	5.6	8.25	5.5	8.667	5.333	4.833	6.4	6.333	8.0	9.0	8.933	10.727
Sum of Squares (Σ_j)	174	307	172	234	242	171	234	294	956	1,502	1,390	1,410
n_i	9		7		12		11		28		26	
$\frac{n_{iB}n_{iG}}{n_i}$	2.222		1.714		3.000		2.727		6.857		6.346	
$d_i = X_{iB.} - X_{iG.}$	-2.650		-3.167		+0.500		+0.067		-1.000		-1.794	
$\frac{n_{iB}n_{iG}}{n_i}(d_i)$	-5.888		-5.428		+1.500		+0.183		-6.857		-11.385	
Sum (C_i)	61		48		61		70		240		252	
$\frac{(C_i)^2}{n_i}$	413.44		329.14		310.08		445.45		2,057.14		2,442.46	

jected, but of course he does so at the usual risk (see Chapter VIII for a full discussion of this point) attendant upon such action.##

A transformation may be found which can serve to put the experimental observations on a scale on which the error variance becomes more nearly constant.

The second step in the analysis consists in the preparation of Table XIII.11. Obviously, if the value of F shown in the last column is not significant there would be no point in proceeding with the analysis: having demonstrated that the Class means do not differ significantly, it would be rather absurd to look for significant differences in any combination of them. In this case, however, the observed value of F falls between the 5 per cent and 1 per cent points and we would be inclined to reject the hypothesis of equality of Class means and, therefore, proceed with the analysis.

TABLE XIII.11

PRELIMINARY ANALYSIS OF VARIANCE OF DATA OF TABLE XIII.10

SOURCE OF VARIATION	DEGREES OF FREEDOM	SUM OF SQUARES	MEAN SQUARE	F-RATIO
Between Classes	11	297.03	27.00	2.13
Within Classes	81	1,027.42	12.68	—
Total	92	1,324.45	—	—

Johnson and Neyman require for their solution the assumption that the differences between the means of the subgroups (boys − girls, here) are independent of the classification variables, i.e. constant for them, or in terms of the usual analysis of variance that the interaction of Category (2 for each teacher) and Sex is not significant. The calculations required are shown in the rows at the bottom of Table XIII.10. Denoting the scores for boys and girls by X_{iBj} and X_{iGj}, by $X_{iB.}$ and $X_{iG.}$ the means for boys and girls, respectively, for the ith Category (e.g. one form of the test for one teacher), by n_{iB} and n_{iG} the corresponding number of cases, and defining

$$n_i = n_{iB} + n_{iG} \quad \text{(number of cases in Category)}$$
$$d_i = X_{iB.} - X_{iG.} \quad \text{(difference of means in Category)}$$
$$C_i = n_{iB}X_{iB.} + n_{iG}X_{iG.} \quad \text{(sum of all values in Category)}$$

we must calculate

$$SS_B = \sum_i \sum_j X_{iBj}^2$$

$$SS_G = \sum_i \sum_j X_{iGj}^2$$

and the quantities indicated below. Denoting by k the number of Categories (number of Classes divided by two here), by N the total number of observations, by

$$S_A{}^2 = SS_B + SS_G - \sum_i \frac{C_i^2}{n_i} - S_D{}^2$$

where

$$S_D{}^2 = \frac{\left\{ \sum_i \left(\frac{n_{iB}n_{iG}}{n_i} d_i \right) \right\}^2}{\sum_i \left(\frac{n_{iB}n_{iG}}{n_i} \right)}$$

then the quantity

$$F = \frac{N - k - 1}{1} \cdot \frac{S_D^2}{S_A^2}$$

will be distributed as F with degrees of freedom $n_1 = 1$ (associated with S_D^2) and $n_2 = N - k - 1$ (associated with S_A^2). For our example,

$$N = 93$$
$$k = 6$$
$$S_D^2 = \frac{(-27.875)^2}{22.866} = 33.98$$

and $S_A^2 = 3,168 + 3,918 - 5,997.71 - 33.98 = 1,054.31$

whence $F = \dfrac{86}{1} \cdot \dfrac{33.98}{1,054.31} = \dfrac{33.98}{12.26} = 2.77$

which, for degrees of freedom $n_1 = 1$ and $n_2 = 86$, is quite clearly not significant. We would, therefore, accept the null hypothesis (as set up by Johnson and Neyman) of no difference between boys and girls on the reading readiness tests.***

There is no need, for our present purposes, to press the analysis beyond this point. We may observe, however, that the difference between S_A^2 and the Within Classes sum of squares of Table XIII.11

$$1,054.31 - 1,027.42 = 26.89$$

with $k - 1 = 5$ degrees of freedom, provides upon comparison of its mean square with the Within Classes mean square of Table XIII.11, i.e. 12.68, a valid test of the hypothesis or assumption of no interaction between Sex and Categories (clearly we accept this null hypothesis for our example).†††
Subtracting this Interaction sum of squares, 26.89, and $S_D^2 = 33.98$ from the Between Classes sum of squares, 297.03, with 11 degrees of freedom, leaves the remainder of 236.16 with 5 degrees of freedom for Between Categories. Testing its significance by calculating

$$F = \frac{86}{5} \cdot \frac{236.16}{1,054.31} = \frac{47.23}{12.26} = 3.85$$

for degrees of freedom $n_1 = 5$ and $n_2 = 86$, we find that this particular effect is highly significant. But this block is actually made up of three parts, as follows: Between Forms (A vs. B) with 1 degree of freedom; Between Teachers with 2 degrees of freedom; and an Interaction of Teachers and Forms with 2 degrees of freedom. Casual observation indicates that the only significant factor is the Between Teachers one. Students should, as an exercise, determine the corresponding sums of squares and mean squares and perform the statistical tests indicated. (Clue: rearrange Table XIII.10 by pooling scores for boys and girls for each Form

*** A result that occasioned the researchers some surprise.
††† If this hypothesis is rejected, then the proper procedure to follow will be determined by the particular model selected as appropriate to the situation.

for each Teacher, since no significant Sex effect seems to be present, and work through the analysis for the reduced table step by step as we have just done.)

Quantitative Matching Variables

In this case not only the criterion variable but also the matching variables are measurable, i.e. are quantitative variables. It is worth noting that, as in the ordinary regression analyses, no assumptions need be made concerning the distribution of the matching variables: they must be quantitative, but no other restriction need be applied. This does not apply to the criterion variable (upon which the effect of the experimental factor is primarily determined), as we shall see later. However, it is important that the matching variables be related to the criterion variable, in other words that they may influence the experimental results, and the only restriction specified by Johnson and Neyman was that the function be a linear one. In actual fact, the only case they considered in detail was for two matching variables and for a function that was a first order polynomial:‡‡‡ Abelson§§§ generalized the linear regression case to any number of matching variables but did not consider any other form of function. Possibly his more important contribution|||| was that he showed the relationship of this method to the usual analysis of covariance, and more particularly how the two methods could be used in sequence. In the discussion given below we have adopted Abelson's suggested procedure, and have considered, first, the case of one matching variable (partly because this simple case permits a ready interpretation of the results and facilitates an understanding of the methods) and, second, the case of two matching variables (since this case also illustrates admirably and adequately the situation for more than two matching variables).

As an illustration, we propose to use the data given by Johnson and Fay for which the complete Johnson-Neyman solution has been presented for two matching variables.### This case demonstrates particularly well the relationship between the analysis of covariance method and the Johnson-Neyman method—and a few incidental points also. The problem posed by Johnson and Fay was the comparison of the achievement in social studies of two groups of students (90 in each group, as it happened,

‡‡‡ For the three dimensional case, see, W. L. Deemer and P. J. Rulon, *An Experimental Comparison of Two Shorthand Systems*, Harvard Studies in Education, No. 22 (Cambridge: Harvard University Press, 1943), and P. O. Johnson and C. Hoyt, "On Determining Three Dimensional Regions of Significance," *The Journal of Experimental Education*, XV (1947), 203–12.

§§§ *Psychometrika*, XVIII, No. 3 (September, 1953), 213–18.

|||| Since experience indicates that very little is in fact gained through the use of more than three matching variables.

Psychometrika, XV, No. 4 (December, 1950), 349–67.

although the numbers need not be equal), the first of superior performers and the second of inferior performers in ability to predict the outcome of given events, when the effects of chronological age and of mental age (the two matching variables) are controlled. Denoting social studies achievement by Z, mental age by X and chronological age by Y, using the subscripts 1 and 2 to denote superior and inferior performers, respectively, and N to denote the number of cases, the basic data given by the above-named authors were as follows:

Superior Performers	Inferior Performers
$N_1 = 90$	$N_2 = 90$
$\Sigma Z_1 = 2,858$	$\Sigma Z_2 = 1,522$
$\Sigma Z_1{}^2 = 95,592$	$\Sigma Z_2{}^2 = 30,974$
$\Sigma X_1 = 6,117$	$\Sigma X_2 = 3,752$
$\Sigma X_1{}^2 = 452,017$	$\Sigma X_2{}^2 = 188,944$
$\Sigma Y_1 = 1,564$	$\Sigma Y_2 = 1,834$
$\Sigma Y_1{}^2 = 29,834$	$\Sigma Y_2{}^2 = 42,086$
$\Sigma Z_1 X_1 = 200,788$	$\Sigma Z_2 X_2 = 69,998$
$\Sigma Z_1 Y_1 = 49,288$	$\Sigma Z_2 Y_2 = 31,425$
$\Sigma X_1 Y_1 = 105,578$	$\Sigma X_2 Y_2 = 76,902$

(Note that in these calculations, 100 was subtracted from each mental age, 120 from each chronological age, and 30 from each social studies score.)

Using the · symbol to denote a mean and S to denote sum of squares or sum of products about the means, as in our earlier sections, we may calculate the following set of values, as indicated by the subscripts:

Superior Performers	Inferior Performers
$Z_1. = 31.756$	$Z_2. = 16.911$
$X_1. = 67.967$	$X_2. = 41.689$
$Y_1. = 17.378$	$Y_2. = 20.378$
$S_{ZZ1} = 4,834.622$	$S_{ZZ2} = 5,235.289$
$S_{XX1} = 36,264.900$	$S_{XX2} = 32,527.289$
$S_{YY1} = 2,655.156$	$S_{YY2} = 4,713.156$
$S_{ZX1} = 6,539.267$	$S_{ZX2} = 6,547.511$
$S_{ZY1} = -377.689$	$S_{ZY2} = 410.022$
$S_{XY1} = -721.867$	$S_{XY2} = 444.578$

The first point to note, and this preliminary evaluation should be done *before* any complex statistical method is applied, is that the effect of chronological age, Y, as a matching variable promises to be small indeed. This will be true whether it is used singly or in combination with mental age. To express this observation numerically, we may calculate the correlation coefficients given below (having the meaning indicated by the subscripts):

$$r_{ZY1} = \frac{S_{ZY1}}{\sqrt{S_{ZZ1}S_{YY1}}} = -0.105$$

$$r_{XY1} = \frac{S_{XY1}}{\sqrt{S_{XX1}S_{YY1}}} = -0.074$$

$$r_{ZY2} = \frac{S_{ZY2}}{\sqrt{S_{ZZ2}S_{YY2}}} = 0.083$$

$$r_{XY2} = \frac{S_{XY2}}{\sqrt{S_{XX2}S_{YY2}}} = 0.036$$

None of these being significantly greater than zero, a researcher would ordinarily simply delete this variable from the analysis. Actually, it is important that r_{ZY} be large and r_{XY} be small, but this will become evident only at a later stage. For our purposes, we propose to retain both variables, but we will begin the analysis by using mental age, X, for the single matching variable and then add chronological age, Y, at the next stage.

Case 1: Single Matching Variable

The first basic assumption is that the expected values (or population means) of Z_1 and Z_2, which we may denote by $\hat{Z}_1$ and $\hat{Z}_2$, are polynomials of the first order* (although not necessarily the same) with respect to X, the single matching variable, i.e.

$$\hat{Z}_1 = A_1 + B_1X$$

and
$$\hat{Z}_2 = A_2 + B_2X$$

where the coefficients A and B play the usual roles as in a regression analysis. The second basic assumption is that for any fixed value of X, Z_1 is normally distributed about $\hat{Z}_1$ and Z_2 is normally distributed about $\hat{Z}_2$ with the same, although unknown, standard deviation, σ.

The hypothesis to be tested, H_o, is that the population means are equal, i.e. $\hat{Z}_1 - \hat{Z}_2 = 0$, which may be written as

$$H_o : (A_1 - A_2) + (B_1 - B_2)X = 0$$

Students should observe that if B_1 and B_2 are in fact equal, then the hypothesis H_o reduces to $A_1 - A_2 = 0$ which is equivalent to the hypothesis H_3 that we considered in the section on analysis of covariance. Before testing H_o, we shall test a number of other hypotheses, in fact, since H_o does in most respects constitute a final stage or step in a complete series of tests.

The first step† is the test of the validity of the assumption of a com-

* It is not difficult to extend the analysis to include polynomials of higher order, if such be required.

† As in the previous cases, the residuals should be calculated for each group and a test of normality applied. Most of us "conveniently" omit this step, but we should not do so.

mon standard deviation, σ. If this holds true, then

$$S_{Z\cdot X1}^2 = S_{ZZ1} - \frac{S_{ZX1}^2}{S_{XX1}}$$

will be an estimate of $(N_1 - 2)\ \sigma^2$ and

$$S_{Z\cdot X2}^2 = S_{ZZ2} - \frac{S_{ZX2}^2}{S_{XX2}}$$

will be an estimate of $(N_2 - 2)\ \sigma^2$. Accordingly, the quantity (assuming $S_1^2 \geqslant S_2^2$)

$$F = \frac{N_2 - 2}{N_1 - 2} \cdot \frac{S_{Z\cdot X1}^2}{S_{Z\cdot X2}^2}$$

will be distributed as Snedecor's F with degrees of freedom $n_1 = N_1 - 2$ and $n_2 = N_2 - 2$. For our example,

$$S_{Z\cdot X1}^2 = 3{,}655.465, \qquad N_1 - 2 = 88$$
$$S_{Z\cdot X2}^2 = 3{,}917.322, \qquad N_2 - 2 = 88$$

and, since $S_{Z\cdot X1}^2 < S_{Z\cdot X2}^2$, we calculate

$$F = \frac{N_1 - 2}{N_2 - 2} \cdot \frac{S_{Z\cdot X2}^2}{S_{Z\cdot X1}^2} = \frac{88}{88} \cdot \frac{3{,}917.322}{3{,}655.465} = 1.07$$

and for $n_1 = N_2 - 2 = 88$ and $n_2 = N_1 - 2 = 88$ this value is not significant and we may accept the hypothesis of a common standard deviation, σ. Incidentally, this gives directly the value of Johnson-Neyman's S_a^2, since for the case of one matching variable we will have

$$S_a^2 = S_{Z\cdot X1}^2 + S_{Z\cdot X2}^2$$

with $N_1 + N_2 - 4$ degrees of freedom.

If this hypothesis is accepted, we proceed with the analysis. If it is rejected, the analysis should be stopped at this point since the two groups have different residual deviations, i.e. do differ in this regard at least. However, even if the assumption of a common σ is not satisfied, the researcher may wish to proceed anyway, despite the risk.

The second step, assuming a common σ, is to test the hypothesis that $B_1 = B_2$. This test is quite easy to make. Using the subscript T to indicate totals for the two groups combined, we have

$$N_T = 180$$
$$\Sigma Z_T = 4{,}380$$

$$\Sigma Z_T^2 = 126{,}566$$
$$\Sigma X_T = 9{,}869$$

$$\Sigma X_T^2 = 640{,}961$$
$$\Sigma Z_T X_T = 270{,}786$$

whence

$$S_{ZZT} = 19{,}986.000$$
$$S_{XXT} = 99{,}865.661$$
$$S_{ZXT} = 30{,}640.333$$

Putting these and the former quantities together in the usual fashion we get the breakdown of the sums of squares and products shown in Table XIII.12; this is the usual analysis of variance and covariance table, save that the mean squares and products have not been calculated. In the last column are shown the corresponding regression coefficients (of Z on X here):

TABLE XIII.12

SUMS OF SQUARES AND PRODUCTS FOR JOHNSON–FAY DATA

SOURCE OF VARIATION	DEGREES OF FREEDOM	SUM OF SQUARES		SUM OF PRODUCTS	REGRESSION COEFFICIENT (Z ON X)
		Z	X		
Between Groups	1	9,916.089	31,073.472	17,553.555	0.5649
Within Group 1	89	4,834.622	36,264.900	6,539.267	0.1803
Within Group 2	89	5,235.289	32,527.289	6,547.511	0.2013
Total Within Groups	178	10,069.911	68,792.189	13,086.778	0.1902
Total	179	19,986.000	99,865.661	30,640.333	0.3068

the estimates of B_1 and B_2 being 0.1803 and 0.2013, respectively. (These are obviously not very different from the common value of 0.1902.) Operating on the Within Groups entries, to secure the residual sums of squares of Z, we obtain the values shown in Table XIII.13. Strangely enough, the mean square with 1 degree of freedom for between regression coefficients is smaller than the pooled residual term, of 43.027 with 176 degrees of freedom, but not significantly so, since

$$F = \frac{43.027}{7.543},$$

with $n_1 = 176$ and $n_2 = 1$, is well below the 5 per cent point of the distribution of F. Accordingly, we would accept the hypothesis that $B_1 = B_2$ and proceed with the test of the next hypothesis concerning the A's.‡

Assuming a common σ and that $B_1 = B_2$, which we have just demonstrated can be accepted, we proceed via the usual analysis of variance and covariance to the test of the hypothesis $A_1 = A_2$. Students will observe that H_o has, when $B_1 = B_2$, been reduced to this new hypothesis. For the test of this hypothesis we make the calculations shown in the following table.

‡ The appropriate test of the hypothesis that the common B is zero is given by a comparison of the quantity

$$\frac{(S_{ZX1} + S_{ZX2})^2}{S_{XX1} + S_{XX2}}$$

with the Total Within Groups mean square. For our example, $F = \dfrac{2,489.581}{42.827} = 58.1$ with $n_1 = 1$ and $n_2 = 177$ degrees of freedom (hypothesis will be rejected here, of course).

SOURCE OF VARIATION	DEGREES OF FREEDOM	SUM OF SQUARES	MEAN SQUARE
Total Within Groups Residual	177	7,580.330	42.827
Total Residual	178	10,585.071	—
Difference	1	3,004.741	3,004.741

The quantity $$F = \frac{3,004.741}{42.827} = 70.16,$$

with $n_1 = 1$ and $n_2 = 177$ degrees of freedom, provides the required test, and for our example we would obviously reject the hypothesis $A_1 = A_2$ and conclude that the two groups do differ significantly in achievement in Social Studies, even after allowance is made for the original disparity, on the average, of approximately 26 months $(67.967 - 41.689 = 26.278)$ in mental age between the two groups.

Students should note that if the hypothesis $B_1 = B_2$ is accepted, then the above test completes the analysis. If, on the other hand, the hypothesis $B_1 = B_2$ is rejected, the immediately preceding analysis is not valid and we must test the hypothesis H_o as originally proposed by Johnson and Neyman. Let us assume that $B_1 \neq B_2$ and see what the appropriate test becomes.

Where $B_1 \neq B_2$, the case considered by Johnson and Neyman, the residual mean square to be used in the test is

$$S_a^2 = S_{Z \cdot X1}^2 + S_{Z \cdot X2}^2 ; \qquad \text{d.f.} = N_1 + N_2 - 4$$

as we noted earlier. This is, in terms of the quantities of Table XIII.13, the Subtotal residual sum of squares, 7,572.787, with 176 degrees of freedom. But the difference in achievement that we wish to test, which we may denote by Δ, where

$$\Delta = (A_1 - A_2) + (B_1 - B_2)X$$

is now a function of X, the matching variable, and Δ may be zero for

TABLE XIII.13

RESIDUAL SUMS OF SQUARES FOR Z: WITHIN GROUPS ONLY

RESIDUAL SUM OF SQUARES OF Z	DEGREES OF FREEDOM	SUM OF SQUARES	MEAN SQUARE
Within Group 1	88	3,655.465	—
Within Group 2	88	3,917.322	—
Subtotal	176	7,572.787	43.027
Total Within Groups	177	7,580.330	42.827
Difference Between Regression Coefficients	1	7.543	7.543

certain values of X and not zero for others — Δ may, in fact, be negative for certain values of X and positive for others. The sum of squares corresponding to Δ, with 1 degree of freedom, may be written in the following form for any given value of X,

$$\frac{D^2}{P+Q}$$

where $\quad D = (Z_1. - Z_2.) + \dfrac{S_{ZX1}}{S_{XX1}}(X - X_1.) - \dfrac{S_{ZX2}}{S_{XX2}}(X - X_2.)$

and $\quad P + Q = \dfrac{N_1 + N_2}{N_1 N_2} + \dfrac{(X - X_1.)^2}{S_{XX1}} + \dfrac{(X - X_2.)^2}{S_{XX2}}$

From the point of view of experimental design, we may draw attention to the following facts:

1. It is important, in the sense of reducing the experimental error as represented by the residual sum of squares S_a^2, to select as a matching variable, X, one that is closely related to the criterion variable, Z. Note that in the above example (see tables XIII.12 and XIII.13) the Within Groups mean square is reduced from

$$\frac{10,069.911}{178} = 56.573$$

to

$$\frac{7,572.787}{176} = 43.027$$

which represents a considerable improvement.

2. For a given total number of cases, $N = N_1 + N_2$, it is clearly desirable that $N_1 = N_2$ (so that $P + Q$ will be a minimum). But, if to make $N_1 = N_2$ requires a reduction in N, it is equally clear that it might be better to retain all the cases even if $N_1 \neq N_2$. The guide is that the first factor in $P + Q$ should be as large as possible, and the researcher should plan his design so that for his circumstances (which may even require $N_1 \neq N_2$) the term $\dfrac{N_1 + N_2}{N_1 N_2}$ is as small as possible.

3. In general, it is desirable to make S_{XX1} and S_{XX2} as large as possible because of the effect on the value of $P + Q$, although this is partly offset by the effect on D^2.

One final observation is that if we make $X_1. = X_2. = X..$ or, in other words, equate the two groups on the means of the matching variable, then for the value of the matching variable $X = X..$ (but not for any other) the expression for D becomes $Z_1. - Z_2.$ and for $P + Q$ becomes $\dfrac{N_1 + N_2}{N_1 N_2}$.§ Generally speaking, however, we may not gain greatly through making $X_1. = X_2.$ if this requires any substantial reduction in either N_1 or N_2 (or both).

§ And $\dfrac{D^2}{P+Q}$ reduces to $\dfrac{(Z_1. - Z_2.)^2}{\left\{\dfrac{1}{N_1} + \dfrac{1}{N_2}\right\}}$, which should appear familiar to students.

Let us return, however, to the expression for D, namely,

$$D = (Z_{1.} - Z_{2.}) + \frac{S_{ZX1}}{S_{XX1}}(X - X_{1.}) + \frac{S_{ZX2}}{S_{XX2}}(X - X_{2.})$$

and substitute therein the values earlier secured for our example. Simplifying the result so secured, we have

$$D = 10.981 - 0.021X$$

and for D to be exactly zero the value of X must be approximately $X_0 = 523$, which represents an impossible mental age so that D will be positive over the whole possible range of mental age. This point, X_0, is the one at which the two regression lines

$$\hat{Z}_1 = 19.500 + 0.1803X$$

and
$$\hat{Z}_2 = 8.519 + 0.2013X$$

cross, which, since the two lines are practically parallel must be for a large value of X. This checks with the previous result, of course, since the distance between the two regression lines perpendicular to the X-axis, which is the value of D, is significant when the common slope is used. Students should plot the above two regression lines on the ZX plane to gain a better understanding of the reasoning involved.

The F-ratio we would use to test the significance of D may be written in the form

$$F = \frac{N_1 + N_2 - 4}{1} \cdot \frac{D^2}{(P + Q)(S_a^2)}$$

for degrees of freedom $n_1 = 1$ and $n_2 = N_1 + N_2 - 4$. Now for our example

$$F = \frac{176D^2}{(P + Q)(7,572.787)} = \frac{D^2}{43.027(P + Q)}$$

As students will realize, for D to be significantly greater than zero at the 1 per cent level, for which $F_{.01} = 6.79$ in this case, we must have

$$D^2 \geqslant (F_{.01})(P + Q)\left(\frac{S_a^2}{N_1 + N_2 - 4}\right)$$

which for our example becomes

$$D^2 \geqslant (6.79)(43.027)(P + Q)$$

or, upon simplification,

$$D^2 \geqslant 0.017038X^2 - 1.844X + 59.317$$

Since D is also a function of X (i.e. $D = 10.981 - 0.021X$) we have for the point dividing the X-axis into two parts, for one of which D is significant and for the other it is not, the equation

$$0.016597X^2 - 1.383X - 61.265 = 0$$

to solve for X. Since this is simply a quadratic of the form

$$AX^2 + BX + C = 0$$

the roots will be

$$X = \frac{-B \pm \sqrt{B^2 - 4AC}}{2A}$$

and for our case this yields

$$X = \frac{1.383 \doteq \sqrt{(1.383)^2 + (4)(.016597)(61.265)}}{0.033194}$$

$$= \frac{1.383 \doteq 2.445}{0.033194}$$

or $X_1 = +115$ and $X_2 = -32$ approximately. Since in the original table X was the value secured when 100 was subtracted from the mental age (in months), these two points correspond to mental ages of 215 and 68 months, respectively. The value of D, as we have expressed the quadratic, will be significant between these two points and non-significant beyond them, i.e. not significant for $X > 115$ and $X < -32$, approximately. As a check, when $X = 116$ we have

$$D = 8.545, \qquad D^2 = 73.017$$

and $$(F_{.01})(P + Q)\left(\frac{S_a^2}{N_1 + N_2 - 4}\right) = 74.676$$

whereas for $X = 115$ we have

$$D^2 = 73.376 \text{ and } (F_{.01})(P + Q)\left(\frac{S_a^2}{N_1 + N_2 - 4}\right) = 72.585$$

Similarly, when $X = -32$

$$D^2 = 135.792 \text{ and } (F_{.01})(P + Q)\left(\frac{S_a^2}{N_1 + N_2 - 4}\right) = 135.772$$

Since none of the mental age values in the Johnson-Fay data were below $X = 0$ and only three were above $X = 115$, it is apparent that the hypothesis of $\Delta = 0$ would be rejected over practically the whole range of mental ages. As Abelson has pointed out,‖ there is no real point in performing a Johnson-Neyman analysis if the two regression slopes are equal (as in our case), since the inevitable result will be a significant difference for practically all the possible observable values of X. But even in this case, if the limits of the region of significance are of any interest —the upper bound of 115 is of some importance in the present example, since mental ages of 18 years or more do occur—the Johnson-Neyman technique must be used to locate it exactly.

Case 2: Two Matching Variables

The basic assumption in this case is that the expected values of Z_1 and Z_2 are polynomials of the first order with respect to X and Y, so that we may write

$$\hat{Z}_1 = A_1 + B_1 X + C_1 Y$$
$$\hat{Z}_2 = A_2 + B_2 X + C_2 Y$$

Again the hypothesis to be tested, H_o, is that the population means are equal, i.e. $\hat{Z}_1 = \hat{Z}_2$, which may be expressed in the form

$$H_o: (A_1 - A_2) + (B_1 - B_2) X + (C_1 - C_2)Y = 0$$

Observe that if $C_1 = C_2$, this hypothesis reduces to that of the previous case (although the test of it may not be) whether or not the common value

‖ Robert F. Abelson, *op. cit.*

of C is zero, although it is important to distinguish between the cases $C = 0$ and $C \neq 0$ since the analyses are not equivalent. The implications of the other possibilities we may assume to be obvious, i.e.

when	$C_1 = C_2$	and	$B_1 = B_2$
and	$C_1 \neq C_2$	and	$B_1 = B_2$

and we shall simply state and discuss some of these cases as we come to them in the analysis, beginning with the general case $A_1 \neq A_2$, $B_1 \neq B_2$, and $C_1 \neq C_2$.#

The second basic assumption is again, that for any fixed values of X and Y, Z_1 is normally distributed about $\hat{Z}_1$ and Z_2 is normally distributed about $\hat{Z}_2$ with the same, but unknown, standard deviation σ. The test of the validity of this assumption may be made by noting that the two component parts of S_a^2 give the values required for the comparison. We will return to this point later.

The calculations can be performed most easily, in line with the procedure followed in the multiple regression analysis, if we express the equations in terms of correlation coefficients.** The following values are required

$$r_{ZX1} = .493860; \qquad r_{ZX2} = .501744$$
$$r_{ZY1} = -.105416; \qquad r_{ZY2} = .082543$$
$$r_{XY1} = -.073565; \qquad r_{XY2} = .035906$$

The value of S_a^2 may be written

$$S_a^2 = S_{ZZ1} \left\{ \frac{1 - r_{XY1}^2 - r_{ZX1}^2 - r_{ZY1}^2 + 2r_{XY1}r_{ZX1}r_{ZY1}}{1 - r_{XY1}^2} \right\}$$
$$+ S_{ZZ2} \left\{ \frac{1 - r_{XY2}^2 - r_{ZX2}^2 - r_{ZY2}^2 + 2r_{XY2}r_{ZX2}r_{ZY2}}{1 - r_{XY2}^2} \right\}$$

and the ratio of the two parts, when each is divided by the appropriate number of degrees of freedom ($N_1 - 3$ for the first and $N_2 - 3$ for the second) will provide a test of the assumption of a common standard deviation, σ. For our example

$$S_a^2 = (4,834.622)(0.751303) + (5,235.289)(0.744084) = 3,632.27 +$$
$$3,895.49 = 7,527.76$$

and $N_1 - 3 = N_2 - 3 = 87$, so that the number of degrees of freedom for S_a^2 will be $N_1 + N_2 - 6 = (2)(87) = 174$. To test the assumption of a common σ, we have

$$F = \frac{3,895.49}{3,632.27} = 1.07$$

and for degrees of freedom $n_1 = n_2 = 87$ we would accept the hypothesis. Accordingly, we may proceed with the analysis: unless this assumption is satisfied we should, strictly speaking, stop the analysis at this point.

To return to the formula expressing the difference between $\hat{Z}_1$ and $\hat{Z}_2$,

See the original article (1936) by Johnson and Neyman.
** The equations for more than two matching variables can be most conveniently expressed by matrix algebra (see the article by Abelson, *op. cit.*).

$$\Delta = (A_1 - A_2) + (B_1 - B_2)X + (C_1 - C_2)Y,$$

observe that there are a number of possibilities that should be investigated before the Johnson-Neyman technique is applied. The corresponding hypotheses will be stated and tested below, in the order we deem most appropriate.

1. $H_1 : A_1 = A_2 = A; B_1 = B_2 = B; C_1 = C_2 = C$. If the hypothesis H_1 is true, the two regression planes coincide and Δ must be zero throughout the possible range of values. To test this hypothesis, we combine the results for the two groups into one group and calculate the values as indicated for the total, denoted by the subscript T, in the following formula

$$S_1^2 = S_{ZZT} \left\{ \frac{1 - r_{XYT}^2 - r_{ZXT}^2 - r_{ZYT}^2 + 2r_{XYT}r_{ZXT}r_{ZYT}}{1 - r_{XYT}^2} \right\}$$

For the total group, we have the following values:

$$N_T = 180$$
$$\Sigma Z_T = 4{,}380$$
$$\Sigma Z_T^2 = 126{,}566$$

$\Sigma X_T = 9{,}869$	$S_{ZZT} = 19{,}986.000$
$\Sigma X_T^2 = 640{,}961$	$S_{XXT} = 99{,}865.661$
$\Sigma Y_T = 3{,}398$	$S_{YYT} = 7{,}773.311$
$\Sigma Y_T^2 = 71{,}920$	$S_{ZXT} = 30{,}640.333$
$\Sigma Z_T X_T = 270{,}786$	$S_{ZYT} = -1{,}971.667$
$\Sigma Z_T Y_T = 80{,}713$	$S_{XYT} = -3{,}824.789$
$\Sigma X_T Y_T = 182{,}480$	$r_{ZXT} = .685839$
	$r_{ZYT} = -.158186$
	$r_{XYT} = -.137277$

so that we have

$$S_1^2 = (19{,}986.000)(.515543) = 10{,}303.64$$

with $N_1 + N_2 - 3$ degrees of freedom. To test the hypothesis H_1, we calculate

$$F = \frac{N_1 + N_2 - 6}{3} \cdot \frac{S_1^2 - S_a^2}{S_a^2} = \frac{174}{3} \cdot \frac{2{,}775.88}{7{,}527.76}$$
$$= 21.38$$

with degrees of freedom $n_1 = 3$ and $n_2 = N_1 + N_2 - 6 = 174$. We reject the hypothesis H_1, therefore, and proceed with the analysis. If H_1 had been accepted, the analysis would be stopped at this point.

2. $H_2 : B_1 = B_2 = B; C_1 = C_2 = C$. If hypothesis H_2 is accepted, the regression planes are parallel but do not coincide (since H_1 has been rejected and $\Delta \neq 0$) and the difference Δ, being a constant, will be significant over the whole range of values of both X and Y and no further analysis need be made—unless we wish to determine whether B or C (or both) is equal to zero. If the hypothesis H_2 is rejected, however, this simple explanation will not suffice and we must proceed with the analysis

to determine whether just one, or both, of these differences is significantly different from zero. To test H_2 we require the quantity

$$S_2{}^2 = S_{ZZW} - \frac{S_{ZXW}^2 S_{YYW} + S_{ZYW}^2 S_{XXW} - 2S_{XYW}S_{ZXW}S_{ZYW}}{(S_{XXW})(S_{YYW}) - S_{XYW}^2}$$

where

$$S_{ZZW} = S_{ZZ1} + S_{ZZ2}$$
$$S_{XXW} = S_{XX1} + S_{XX2}$$
$$S_{YYW} = S_{YY1} + S_{YY2}$$
$$S_{ZXW} = S_{ZX1} + S_{ZX2}$$
$$S_{ZYW} = S_{ZY1} + S_{ZY2}$$
$$S_{XYW} = S_{XY1} + S_{XY2}$$

(the W subscript denoting Within Groups Totals). For our example, we have

$$
\begin{array}{ll}
S_{ZZW} = 10{,}069.911 & S_{ZXW} = 13{,}086.778 \\
S_{XXW} = 68{,}792.189 & S_{ZYW} = 32.333 \\
S_{YYW} = 7{,}368.312 & S_{XYW} = -277.289
\end{array}
$$

and

$$S_2{}^2 = [10{,}069.911]\,[.752672] = 7{,}579.34\dagger\dagger$$

with $N_1 + N_2 - 4$ degrees of freedom. To test the hypothesis H_2 we calculate

$$F = \frac{N_1 + N_2 - 6}{2} \cdot \frac{S_2^2 - S_a^2}{S_a^2} = \frac{174}{2} \cdot \frac{51.59}{7{,}527.76}$$

$$= 0.596 \text{ with degrees of freedom } n_1 = 2 \text{ and}$$

$n_2 = N_1 + N_2 - 6 = 174$. Since F is less than unity, though not significantly so, we would accept the hypothesis H_2. The difference, $\Delta = A_1 - A_2$, between the two groups will be significant over practically all values of X and Y. (The test of the hypothesis $H : A_1 = A_2$, assuming $B_1 = B_2$ and $C_1 = C_2$, is given by the quantity

$$F = \frac{N_1 + N_2 - 4}{1} \cdot \frac{S_1{}^2 - S_2{}^2}{S_2{}^2}$$

with degrees of freedom $n_1 = 1$ and $n_2 = N_1 + N_2 - 4$. For our case, $F = 63.3$ and we would reject this hypothesis also.)

3. $H_3 : C_1 = C_2 = C$. If we had rejected the hypothesis H_2, then it still is possible that, for example, $C_1 = C_2$ and that Δ might be significant over all values of Y (to test $H_3{}^1 : B_1 = B_2$, simply interchange X for Y throughout). To test this hypothesis we calculate

$$S_3{}^2 = \left[\frac{\{S_{YY1}(1 - r_{XY1}^2)\}\{S_{YY2}(1 - r_{XY2}^2)\}}{(S_{YY1})(1 - r_{XY1}^2) + (S_{YY2})(1 - r_{XY2}^2)} \right]$$

$$\left[\sqrt{\frac{S_{ZZ1}}{S_{YY1}}} \frac{r_{ZY1} - r_{XY1}r_{ZX1}}{1 - r_{XY1}^2} - \sqrt{\frac{S_{ZZ2}}{S_{YY2}}} \frac{r_{ZY2} - r_{XY2}r_{ZX2}}{1 - r_{XY2}^2} \right]^2$$

and then calculate Snedecor's F-ratio

†† For calculation purposes, we may write

$$S_2^2 = S_{ZZW}\left[\frac{1 - r_{XYW}^2 - r_{ZXW}^2 - r_{ZYW}^2 + 2r_{XYW}r_{ZXW}r_{ZYW}}{1 - r_{XYW}^2} \right]$$

where $r_{ZXW} = 0.497222$; $r_{ZYW} = 0.003753$; and $r_{XYW} = -0.012316$.

$$F = \frac{N_1 + N_2 - 6}{1} \cdot \frac{S_3^2}{S_a^2} \quad \text{with} \quad n_1 = 1 \quad \text{and} \quad n_2 = N_1 + N_2 - 6$$

degrees of freedom. For our example, $S_a^2 = 7{,}527.76$, $n_2 = 174$, and $S_3^2 = 44.301$, so that

$$F = \frac{(174)(44.301)}{7{,}527.76} = 1.02$$

and we would obviously accept $H_3 : C_1 = C_2$.

4. $H_4 : C_1 = C_2 = C = 0$. If we accept H_3 (or its partner $H_3^1 : B_1 = B_2 = B$), there arises the possibility that the common value, C, is not significantly different from zero. To test this hypothesis we use $S_a^2 + S_3^2 = 7{,}572.06$ with $N_1 + N_2 - 5 = 175$ degrees of freedom and the quantity calculated under Case 1: Single Matching Variable, namely

$$S_4^2 = S_{Z.X1}^2 + S_{Z.X2}^2 \quad \text{with} \quad N_1 + N_2 - 4 \text{ degrees of freedom.}$$

For our example, $S_4^2 = 7{,}572.79$ with 176 degrees of freedom, and consequently the appropriate test of H_4 is

$$F = \frac{N_1 + N_2 - 5}{1} \cdot \frac{S_4^2 - (S_a^2 + S_3^2)}{S_a^2 + S_3^2} = \frac{(175)(.73)}{7{,}572.06}$$

$$= \frac{127.75}{7{,}572.06} = 0.017 \quad \text{with degrees of freedom } n_1 = 1 \text{ and}$$

$n_2 = 175$. Since F is less than unity, though not significantly lower, we would in our case accept hypothesis H_4. (We have also the hypothesis H_4^1 : $B_1 = B_2 = B = 0$, and the other possibilities which we will not discuss here since their tests come properly under multiple regression methods.)

5. $H_{JN} : \Delta = (A_1 - A_2) + (B_1 - B_2)X + (C_1 - C_2)Y = 0$. Let us assume that we have through the tests discussed above, and those implied as required if certain possibilities eventuate, satisfied ourselves that the equation for Δ is in fact a function of both X and Y of the form postulated by Johnson and Neyman, namely, that

$$\Delta = (A_1 - A_2) + (B_1 - B_2)X + (C_1 - C_2)Y$$

and cannot be simplified (the constant $A_1 - A_2$ is not of prime importance at this point‡‡). *Then, and only then,* should we proceed with the analysis suggested by Johnson and Neyman. In the Johnson-Fay example we are using, for instance, there is little point in proceeding beyond the tests of H_1 and H_2, immediately above. We have demonstrated that $\Delta > 0$, but we have also demonstrated that it can be adequately represented by the function $\Delta = A_1 - A_2$, and the more complex function is unnecessary. For purposes of illustration of the Johnson-Neyman method, however, we shall proceed to a test of the hypothesis (the subscripts JN denote Johnson-Neyman):

‡‡ We might, for instance, test that $A_1 = A_2 = A$ with no restrictions on the B's and C's, but the more important possibilities to exclude are of a common B, and of $B = 0$, and also of a common C, and of $C = 0$.

$$H_{JN} : (A_1 - A_2) + (B_1 - B_2)X + (C_1 - C_2)Y = \Delta(XY) = 0$$

The test of H_{JN} is given by calculating S_a^2 as at the beginning of this section, where S_a^2 has $N_1 + N_2 - 6$ degrees of freedom, and also the quantity $D^2/(P + Q)$, with 1 degree of freedom, where for any specific values X and Y,

$$
\begin{aligned}
D = (Z_{1.} - Z_{2.}) &+ \left\{ \frac{r_{ZX1} - r_{XY1}r_{ZY1}}{1 - r_{XY1}^2} \sqrt{\frac{S_{ZZ1}}{S_{XX1}}} (X - X_{1.}) \right\} \\
&- \left\{ \frac{r_{ZX2} - r_{XY2}r_{ZY2}}{1 - r_{XY2}^2} \sqrt{\frac{S_{ZZ2}}{S_{XX2}}} (X - X_{2.}) \right\} \\
&+ \left\{ \frac{r_{ZY1} - r_{XY1}r_{ZX1}}{1 - r_{XY1}^2} \sqrt{\frac{S_{ZZ1}}{S_{YY1}}} (Y - Y_{1.}) \right\} \\
&- \left\{ \frac{r_{ZY2} - r_{XY2}r_{ZX2}}{1 - r_{XY2}^2} \sqrt{\frac{S_{ZZ2}}{S_{YY2}}} (Y - Y_{2.}) \right\}
\end{aligned}
$$

and

$$
\begin{aligned}
P + Q = &\left[\frac{1}{N_1} + \frac{1}{1 - r_{XY1}^2} \left\{ \frac{(X - X_{1.})^2}{S_{XX1}} \right.\right. \\
&\left.\left. - 2r_{XY1} \frac{(X - X_{1.})(Y - Y_{1.})}{\sqrt{S_{XX1}S_{YY1}}} + \frac{(Y - Y_{1.})^2}{S_{YY1}} \right\} \right] \\
&+ \left[\frac{1}{N_2} + \frac{1}{1 - r_{XY2}^2} \left\{ \frac{(X - X_{2.})^2}{S_{XX2}} \right.\right. \\
&\left.\left. - 2r_{XY2} \frac{(X - X_{2.})(Y - Y_{2.})}{\sqrt{S_{XX2}S_{YY2}}} + \frac{(Y - Y_{2.})^2}{S_{YY2}} \right\} \right]
\end{aligned}
$$

and the ratio of the two mean squares will be distributed as Snedecor's F with degrees of freedom $n_1 = 1$ and $n_2 = N_1 + N_2 - 6$. Denoting by $F_{.01}$ the 1 per cent point of Snedecor's F-distribution ($F_{.05}$ may be used, or any other desired value), it is clear that Δ will be significant only within the area defined by the inequality

$$D^2 \geqslant \frac{F_{.01} (P + Q)S_a^2}{N_1 + N_2 - 6}$$

As in the case of one matching variable considered in the preceding section, we have what Johnson and Neyman called a "region of significance" within which Δ is significantly greater than zero and outside of which it is not.§§ But now, unlike the previous case where the region consisted of a portion of the X-scale, we have two matching variables and a region of significance, if it exists, in a plane expressed in terms of X and Y (a volume for three matching variables, and so on).

Students will observe that $P + Q$ depends only on the values of the

§§ This concept of a "region of significance" is a unique contribution by Johnson and Neyman to statistical methodology. Not only is it possible to test the hypothesis $\Delta = 0$ for specific values of X and Y (by substituting in the above formulae), but it is possible to define and plot the whole set of values of X and Y (the region) for which we may accept (or reject) this hypothesis.

X's and Y's, whereas D and $S_a{}^2$ depend on the values of Z also. For the special case $X_1. = X_2. = X$ and $Y_1. = Y_2. = Y$ (which may sometimes be arranged by matching the two groups and considering only these specific values of X and Y), the formula for $D^2/(P+Q)$ reduces to the well-known case

$$\frac{D^2}{P+Q} = \frac{(Z_1. - Z_2.)^2}{\left(\dfrac{1}{N_1} + \dfrac{1}{N_2}\right)}$$

Another special case arises when $r_{XY1} = r_{XY2} = 0$, which affects directly all three elements of the statistical test—$S_a{}^2$, D, and $P+Q$.

For our particular example, substituting the values as indicated and simplifying, we have

$$D = 14.09 - 0.0219X - 0.1618Y$$

Setting this equation equal to zero we have for the line of non-significance (actually the line of zero difference) the equation

$$0.0219X + 0.1618Y = 14.09$$

Note that this line is practically parallel to the X (mental age) axis at a value of approximately $Y = 87$ above that axis—actually well above any values that did occur in the samples used by Johnson and Fay. This line of zero difference, by the way, must always be outside the region of significance.

In one sense the problem of testing the hypothesis postulated by Johnson and Neyman is solved, save only that the region of significance has not been drawn on a graph. It is a simple matter to substitute specific values of X and Y in the formulae for D and $P+Q$, solve, and calculate the required value of Snedecor's F-ratio. For the values $X = 80$ and $Y = 30$, for instance, we have $D = 7.48$ and $D^2 = 55.95$. Likewise, $P+Q = 0.151564$ and $D^2/(P+Q) = 369.2$. The comparison with

$$\frac{S_a^2}{N_1 + N_2 - 6} = \frac{7,527.76}{174} = 43.26$$

yields a significant value of Snedecor's F-ratio, for degrees of freedom $n_1 = 1$ and $n_2 = 174$.

To draw the region of significance is not an easy matter, since the expression

$$D^2 - \frac{F_{.01}(P+Q)S_a^2}{N_1 + N_2 - 6} = 0$$

defining the boundary of the region is an equation of the second degree involving X^2, Y^2, XY, X, and Y. It is a problem in analytic geometry, which we need not discuss here. Those requiring to plot the region may find help in any one of a number of references, such as the 1952 Bulletin by Johnson and Hoyt entitled *The Theory of Linear Hypotheses with Applications to Educational Problems* (op. cit.).

THE DISCRIMINANT FUNCTION

Another unique, and perhaps equally useful, application of the methods of multivariate analysis, but for a purpose that is markedly different, may be found in the use of the discriminant function (devised by R. A. Fisher in 1936). In a sense the purpose of the method is closer to description than to tests of hypotheses or drawing inferences, although a number of the latter do, or may, arise in the process. Like the problems we have just been considering, the basic problem is the comparison of two groups. But we are not interested in determining from the data whether or not the two groups differ significantly in some defined respect. What we want now is the linear function of our observations, which Fisher termed the discriminant function, that will distinguish better than any other linear function between the two groups upon which the observations were made.

Mathematically, the problem may be viewed as maximizing the ratio of the between groups to the within groups variances. That the method is equivalent to multiple regression can be more easily seen, however, if we approach the problem in the same fashion as we did multiple correlation and regression. This latter approach has the added advantage that the student can more readily grasp the nature of the process and of the various tests of significance involved. To give point to the matter, let us direct attention to the problem considered by Travers|||| of distinguishing between a group of successful Engineer Apprentices and a group of successful Air Pilots, using six measurements of each individual (the measurements were scores on psychological tests). Any number of measures or scores could, of course, be used and for illustrative purposes we shall use only three of Travers' variables—scores on the Dynamometer, Dotting, and Perseveration tests.

Let the subscripts A and B denote the Engineer and Pilot groups, respectively, and N_A and N_B the number of cases in each. Denote by X_{1i}, X_{2i}, and X_{3i} the scores made by the ith individual on the three tests, and by the function

$$\hat{Y}_i = \alpha + \beta_1 X_{1i} + \beta_2 X_{2i} + \beta_3 X_{3i}$$

any linear function of the X's. Following the usual multiple regression methods, for an ordinary variate Y_i the coefficients of the above function that are used are those that minimize the sum of squares $\chi^2 = \sum_i (Y_i - \hat{Y}_i)^2$, where the Σ is taken over all individuals, $N_A + N_B$. Let us now introduce## a formal variate Y_i (since we haven't one in this problem) which has the peculiar property of being equal to the constant

|||| R. M. W. Travers, "The Use of a Discriminant Function in the Treatment of Psychological Group Differences," *Psychometrika*, IV, No. 1 (March, 1939).

As usual, Fisher suggested the one that yields the simplest solution (although any other similar variate could have been used).

$$\frac{N_B}{N_A + N_B} \text{ for all Engineer Apprentices}$$

and to the constant $-\dfrac{N_A}{N_A + N_B}$ for all Air Pilots.

Now if we can express and minimize the sum of squares $\Sigma(Y - \hat{Y})^2$ to yield the desired coefficients, the problem will be solved in that the usual multiple regression methods and statistical tests may be employed.

Note that the problem will be simplified if we write χ^2 as a sum of the two component parts, as follows:

$$\chi^2 = \sum_{i=1}^{N_A} \left(\frac{N_B}{N_A + N_B} - \alpha - \beta_1 X_{1i} - \beta_2 X_{2i} - \beta_3 X_{3i}\right)^2$$

$$+ \sum_{i=N_A+1}^{N_A+N_B} \left(-\frac{N_A}{N_A + N_B} - \alpha - \beta_1 X_{1i} - \beta_2 X_{2i} - \beta_3 X_{3i}\right)^2$$

Differentiating partially with respect to α, setting the resulting equation equal to zero, and solving, we obtain

$$\alpha = -\beta_1 X_{1.} - \beta_2 X_{2.} - \beta_3 X_{3.}$$

where $\qquad N = N_A + N_B$

and $$X_{j.} = \frac{1}{N} \sum_{i=1}^{N} X_{ji} (j = 1, 2, \text{ and } 3)$$

Defining a new set of X variables, as follows,

$$x_{ji} = X_{ji} - X_{j.}$$

we have

$$\chi^2 = \sum_{i=1}^{N_A} \left(\frac{N_B}{N} - \beta_1 x_{1i} - \beta_2 x_{2i} - \beta_3 x_{3i}\right)^2$$

$$+ \sum_{i=N_A+1}^{N} \left(-\frac{N_A}{N} - \beta_1 x_{1i} - \beta_2 x_{2i} - \beta_3 x_{3i}\right)^2$$

Proceeding as explained in the early part of Chapter XII, by differentiating partially with respect to β_1, β_2, and β_3 in turn, setting the equations equal to zero and simplifying, we obtain the following set of simultaneous equations to solve for β_1, β_2, and β_3.

$$\beta_1 S_{11} + \beta_2 S_{12} + \beta_3 S_{13} = \frac{N_A N_B}{N} d_1$$

$$\beta_1 S_{21} + \beta_2 S_{22} + \beta_3 S_{23} = \frac{N_A N_B}{N} d_2$$

$$\beta_1 S_{31} + \beta_2 S_{32} + \beta_3 S_{33} = \frac{N_A N_B}{N} d_3$$

where

$$S_{uv} = \sum_{i=1}^{N} (x_u x_v) = S_{vu}$$

e.g.
$$S_{12} = \sum_{i=1}^{N_A} (x_{1i})(x_{2i}) + \sum_{i=N_A+1}^{N} (x_{1i})(x_{2i})$$

or, in short, the sums of squares and products are taken over the two groups combined (deviations from a common mean over the N values). The expressions on the right hand side of the equations, where the d's are defined as

$$d_j = \frac{1}{N_A} \sum_{i=1}^{N_A} X_{ji} - \frac{1}{N_B} \sum_{i=N_A+1}^{N} X_{ji}$$

or the difference in the means of the two groups for the jth variable, correspond to the Syx's of the set of equations in Chapter XII, being the sum of products of each variable with the formal variate Y.*** (Surprising as it may seem at first sight, a few minutes' algebra is also sufficient to show that $S_{yy} = \dfrac{N_A N_B}{N}$.) Accordingly, we may write, as in Chapter XII, the set of equations in the form

$$B_1 \quad + B_2 r_{12} + B_3 r_{13} = r_{y1}$$
$$B_1 r_{12} + B_2 \quad + B_3 r_{23} = r_{y2}$$
$$B_1 r_{13} + B_2 r_{23} + B_3 \quad = r_{y3}$$

and from this point on follow the same procedure (using Fisher's set of auxiliary statistics, if we so desire) as in Chapter XII, to solve for the β's and to perform tests of the hypotheses described therein.

Now for Travers' example, using only the three variables, we have

$$N_A = N_B = 20; N = N_A + N_B = 40$$
$$d_1 = -10.90; d_2 = -43.85; d_3 = -29.90$$
$$S_{11} = 5{,}435.90; S_{12} = 5{,}130.35; S_{13} = 1{,}038.50$$
$$S_{22} = 53{,}291.00; S_{23} = 15{,}412.35; S_{33} = 41{,}695.50$$

Solving for the b's, the estimates of the β's, we obtain

$$b_1 = -.01394; b_2 = -.00550; b_3 = -.00479$$

and the value of the multiple correlation coefficient, R, may be secured from the equation

$$R^2 = b_1 d_1 + b_2 d_2 + b_3 d_3$$
$$= 0.5363 \text{ for our example.}$$

Subject to the assumption of a normal distribution of the X's within groups, the test of significance of R (test of the hypothesis $R = 0$) is given by calculating, for k measures,

$$F = \frac{N_A + N_B - k - 1}{k} \cdot \frac{R^2}{1 - R^2}$$

and for our data this becomes

$$F = \frac{36}{3} \cdot \frac{(.5363)}{(.4637)} = 13.9$$

which, for degrees of freedom $n_1 = k = 3$ and $n_2 = N_A + N_B - k - 1 = 36$,

*** See the discussion of the *point biserial correlation coefficient* in Chapter XI.

is seen to be greater than the 1 per cent point of Snedecor's F-table. Consequently we would reject the hypothesis $H_o : R = 0$ and conclude that there is a significant discrimination between the two groups. To show how the regression equation works, observe that one of the Engineer Apprentices had scores of 66, 178, and 209, which gives him a predicted score ($\hat{Y}$) of $+.69$ (as compared with the fixed value of $\dfrac{N_B}{N_A + N_B} = +.50$ for his group); an Air Pilot with scores of 96, 250, and 319, on the other hand, receives a predicted score of $-.65$ (as compared with the fixed value of $-\dfrac{N_A}{N_A + N_B} = -.50$ for his group). Thus a positive predicted score favors the Engineer Apprentices, and a negative predicted score favors the Air Pilots.†††

GENERALIZED DISTANCE FUNCTION

Problems of a classificatory nature are frequently encountered in fields such as general biology, psychology, education, and economics. The problem may be that of allocating an individual as a member of one of a number of groups to which he may possibly belong. Another problem is that of classifying the groups themselves into a significant system on the basis of the configuration of several characters. The groups may be arranged in some hierarchical order that brings into prominence the similarity of some and the distinctness of others. Statements may be made, for example, that two members of a constellation are closer to one another than any two belonging to different constellations.

Solutions of problems of these kinds have been facilitated by the use of the generalized distance function originated by Mahalanobis and developed by him, Rao, and other members of the Calcutta school (see page 450). The generalized distance function called D^2 is a metric unit providing a measure of the amount of overlap or the divergence between groups. Its use, then, makes possible not merely the discrimination but also the classification of different multivariate populations.

In the simplest case of differentiating two groups, D^2 is the square of the difference in mean values of the best linear function of the measurements. For the extension of the linear discriminant function to more than two groups the set of population means must fall on a straight line if a single linear function of the variates is to specify the populations or to

††† Readers interested in further applications of the method may secure some benefit from the cases discussed by R. A. Fisher under the section on the Discriminant Function in his text *Statistical Methods for Research Workers*. The problem of using the coefficients in the classification of an individual has been considered by Abraham Wald (*Annals of Mathematical Statistics*, XV, No. 2 (June, 1944), 145–62). P. O. Johnson extended discriminatory analysis to the case where the primary data are qualitative: "The Quantification of Qualitative Data in Discriminant Analysis," *Journal of the American Statistical Association*, XLV (1950), 65–76.

discriminate adequately between the groups to which individuals belong. The extension of D^2 by Rao is a maximum likelihood discrimination function, which does not force a multi-dimensional set of qualities into a collinear form. In the problem of specifying an individual as a member of one of many groups to which he could possibly belong, Rao's method calculates the likelihood for each individual with respect to each group. The individual's assignment will then be to the group for which he has the maximum likelihood.

The basic form for the generalized distance is given as:

$$D^2 = \Sigma_i \Sigma_j S^{ij} d_i d_j$$

where S^{ij} = elements of the matrix inverse to S_{ij}, the dispersion matrix or within groups variance, covariance matrix.

$$d_i = \bar{X}_i - \bar{X}'_i$$
$$d_j = \bar{X}_j - \bar{X}'_j .$$

where $\bar{X}_i$ = sample mean of the ith variate of one group.

$\bar{X}'_i$ = sample mean of the ith variate of a second group. Likewise for d_j. The formula given for D^2 is not very useful in practice, since the calculation of the inverse matrix and also the computation of the quadratic form in the difference of mean values becomes very heavy whenever the number of characteristics is greater than four or five.

We will limit our presentation here to the calculation of D^2, involving the reduction of a matrix by the method of pivotal condensation. This method does not involve the explicit inversion of a dispersion matrix. It presents no great computational difficulty, and includes checks that insure numerical accuracy. The method is particularly valuable in studying the nature and number of characters useful in discriminating between the groups. Thus it not only provides the value of D^2 between the categories or groups but also the contribution of each characteristic upon which D^2 is based. It thus becomes possible to test the significance of the additional distance contributed by the inclusion of each of the added variables singly or in combination with others.

The calculation of D^2 is by the relationship

$$D^2 = - \left| \begin{array}{c|c} S_{ij} & d_i \\ \hline d_i' & 0 \end{array} \right| \div \left| S_{ij} \right|$$

The matrix in the numerator is reduced following the method of pivotal condensation starting from the first pivotal element. At any stage of this process, the value of the last element of the leading diagonal gives the value of D^2 (with the sign negative) determined on a number of characters equal to the number of columns or rows swept out.

The example which follows has been chosen chiefly to illustrate the method of calculation of D^2 and of studying the various components of D^2.

The assumptions underlying this technique of multivariate analysis are that the variates have a multivariate normal distribution, the same for each, centered about the population means characterizing the groups, with a common dispersion matrix for all groups. Since our emphasis is upon the method, we shall not carry out such tests as are available for validating the assumptions.

In the case of discrimination of many groups with multiple variates, an over-all test of differences in mean values for the several populations should precede the analysis since it must be determined whether the samples come from the same multivariate population. If the null hypothesis is accepted, obviously there is nothing to be gained by trying to effect any discrimination.‡‡‡

Example. R. Mukherjee reported a study of differences in physical development by socio-economic strata.§§§ He took somatometric measurements on fifty-five school children in Calcutta. Each of two free primary schools provided samples of twenty-eight and thirteen children, respectively, and a third sample of fourteen came from a model public school attended by children of well-to-do or middle class parents. All pupils were six-year-old boys. Seven characters were analyzed. The main objective of the study was to differentiate the three groups according to the physical development of the boys.

The D^2 statistic was used to carry out the multivariate analysis. The method of computation of D^2 used by the investigator involved a transformation of the correlated variates to a new orthogonal set. Our analysis will make use of the method of pivotal condensation discussed above, and we have restricted our analysis to three of the seven characters: girth of thorax, length of tibia, and length of humerus.

The variate mean values for the individual groups are given in Table XIII.14.

TABLE XIII.14

	VARIATE MEAN VALUES FOR THE THREE SCHOOLS		
CHARACTER*	SCHOOL		
	Bally-free $G_1(n_1 = 28)$	Bhow-free $G_2(n_2 = 13)$	Bhow-public $G_3(n_3 = 14)$
$\bar{X}_{1j}$: Girth of thorax	548.43	552.54	561.21
$\bar{X}_{2j}$: Length of tibia	253.21	248.38	266.43
$\bar{X}_{3j}$: Length of humerus	210.96	202.15	218.21

* Length is in millimeters

$\bar{X}_{ij}$ signifies the mean of the ith character (variate) for the jth group.

$$i = 1, 2, 3; \qquad j = 1, 2, 3$$

The differences in means by group pairs are given in Table XIII.15.

‡‡‡ For a test of differences in mean values in this case see, C. R. Rao, *Advanced Statistical Methods in Biometric Research*, pp. 262–63.
§§§ *Sankhya*, II, Part 1 (March, 1951), 47–56.

TABLE XIII.15

DIFFERENCES IN MEANS BY GROUP PAIRS

	d_{i1} for G_1 & G_2	d_{i2} for G_3 & G_1	d_{i3} for G_3 & G_2
d_{1j}	−4.11	12.78	8.67
d_{2j}	4.83	13.22	18.05
d_{3j}	8.81	7.25	16.06

$d_{ij} = \bar{X}_{ij} - \bar{X}_{ij}'$, $j \neq j'$, i.e. the difference of means between the jth pair, $j = 1(G_1 - G_2)$, $2(G_3 - G_1)$, $3(G_3 - G_2)$, on the ith variate.

The dispersion matrix (variance-covariance matrix, within groups, or pooled over groups) between the ith and hth variate is presented in Table XIII.16.

TABLE XIII.16

DISPERSION MATRIX

	S_{i1}	S_{i2}	S_{i3}
S_{1h}	891.0225	392.9109	288.2066
S_{2h}		437.2281	268.8093
S_{3h}			324.3601

Since $S_{ij} = S_{ji}$, i.e. $S_{21} = S_{12} = 392.9109$, etc., the lower entries beneath the diagonal are omitted

$$S_{ih} = \sum_{j\alpha}(X_{ij\alpha} - \bar{X}_{ij})(X_{hj\alpha} - \bar{X}_{ij})/\text{d.f.} S_{ih}$$

where $X_{ij\alpha}$ is the measurement of the αth individual of the jth group on the ith variate or character.

$$\text{d.f. } S_{ih} = \Sigma n_j - 3 = 52$$

The reduction of the dispersion matrix by the method of pivotal condensation or sweep-out is shown in Table XIII.17.||||||

|||| Note:

Since $D^2 = - \dfrac{\begin{vmatrix} S_{ih} & d_{ij} \\ \hline d'_{ij} & 0 \end{vmatrix}}{|S_{ih}|}$

$= - \dfrac{[(\prod_i \sqrt{S_{ii}})(\prod_h \sqrt{S_{hh}})]}{[(\prod_i \sqrt{S_{ii}})(\prod_h \sqrt{S_{hh}})]} \cdot \dfrac{\begin{vmatrix} \dfrac{S_{ih}}{\sqrt{S_{ii}}\sqrt{S_{jj}}} & \dfrac{d_{ij}}{\sqrt{S_{ii}}} \\ \hline \dfrac{d_{ij}}{\sqrt{S_{hh}}} & 0 \end{vmatrix}}{\begin{vmatrix} \dfrac{S_{ih}}{\sqrt{S_{ii}}\sqrt{S_{hh}}} \end{vmatrix}}$

$D^2 = - \dfrac{\begin{vmatrix} r_{ih} & \dfrac{d_{ij}}{\sqrt{S_{ii}}} \\ \hline \dfrac{d'_{ij}}{\sqrt{S_{hh}}} & 0 \end{vmatrix}}{|r_{ih}|}$

TABLE XIII.17

Pivotal Condensation Method for Obtaining Successive D^2 Values

ROW NO.	GIRTH OF THORAX X_1	TIBIA X_2	HUMERUS X_3	$G_1 - G_2$ d_{i1}	$G_3 - G_1$ d_{i2}	$G_3 - G_2$ d_{i3}	OPERATION CHECK	SUM CHECK
(1)	891.0225	392.9109	288.2066	−4.11	12.78	8.67	1,589.48000	
(2)		437.2281	268.8093	4.83	13.22	18.05	1,135.04830	
(3)			324.3601	8.81	7.25	16.06	913.49600	
(4)			0	0	0	0		
(5) = (1) ÷ 891.0225	1.000000	.440966	.323456	−.004613	.014343	.009730	1.783883	1.783882
(6) = (2) −392.9109 × (5)		263.967752	141.719912	6.642498	7.584479	14.226977	434.141225	434.141618
(7) = (3) − 288.2066 × (5)			231.137946	10.139497	3.116253	13.255750	399.369146	399.369358
(8) = (4) − {[d_{4i} in (1)] × (5)}*				−.018959	−.183304	−.084359	$= -D_1^2$	
(9) = (6) ÷ 263.967752		1.000000	.536883	.025164	.028733	.053897	1.644675	1.644677
(10) = (7) − 141.719912 × (9)			155.050934	6.573257	−.955786	5.617472	166.285950	166.285877
(11) = (8) − {[d_{4i} in (6)] × (9)}				−.186111	−.401229	−.851150	$= -D_2^2$	
(12) = (10) ÷ 155.050934			1.000000	.042394	−.006164	.036230	1.072460	1.072460
(13) = (11) − {[d_{4i} in (10)] × (12)}				−.464778	−.407120	−1.054671	$= -D_3^2$	

* Thus d_{41} of line (8) is $0 - (-4.11)(-.004613)$ and d_{42} of line (8) is $0 - (12.78)(.014343)$

Hence Table XIII.17 could be changed by resorting to correlation coefficients and mean differences divided by respective standard deviations.

The D^2 values based on the first, first and second, and all three characters for different group pairs are reported in Table XIII.18.

TABLE XIII.18

D^2 VALUES BASED ON THE FIRST, FIRST AND SECOND, AND ALL THREE
CHARACTERS FOR DIFFERENT GROUP PAIRS

CHARACTER (VARIATE α)	BETWEEN		
	G_1 & G_2	G_3 & G_1	G_2 & G_3
X_1	.018959	.183304	.084359
X_2	.186111	.401229	.851150
X_3	.464778	.407120	1.054671

We proceed now to test the significance of the contribution of additional variables or characters. That is, we wish to investigate the nature and number of characters that may be useful in discriminating between the groups. For this, we need a test to judge the significance of the additional distance contributed by including additional characters.

The test criterion is provided by a ratio, F_1'

$$F' = \frac{(f - P - q + 1)}{q} \cdot \left[\frac{n_1 n_2 (D_{P+q}^2 - D_P^2)}{f(n_1 + n_2) + n_1 n_2 D_P^2} \right]$$

where f = degrees of freedom of the dispersion matrix of variances and covariances between the ith and jth characters

P = number of variables in D_P^2

q = number of variables added to form D_{P+q}^2

n_1 = size of sample from first population

n_2 = size of sample from second population

F' may be used as a variance-ratio, and interpreted by means of the F-table with q and $f - P - q + 1$ degrees of freedom.

We calculate the F' values for group pairs: G_1G_2, G_3G_1, G_2G_3, for X_1, $X_1 + X_2$, and for X_1, $X_2 + X_3$.

$$F_1' = \frac{(52 - 0 - 1 + 1)}{1} \left[\frac{(n_1)(n_2)(D_1^2 - 0)}{52(n_1 + n_2) + (n_1)(n_2)0} \right],$$

$$_1F'_{G_1G_2} = 52 \left[\frac{(364)(.018959)}{2,132} \right] = 0.1683$$

$$_1F'_{G_3G_1} = 52 \left[\frac{(392)(.183304)}{2,184} \right] = 1.7108$$

$$_1F'_{G_2G_3} = 52 \left[\frac{(182)(.084359)}{1,404} \right] = 0.5686$$

$$F_2' = \frac{(52 - 1 - 1 + 1)}{1} \left[\frac{n_1 n_2 (D_2^2 - D_1^2)}{52(n_1 + n_2) + n_1 n_2 D_1^2} \right],$$

$$_2F'_{G_1G_2} = 51 \left[\frac{364(.186111 - .018959)}{(2,132) + (364)(.018959)} \right] = 1.4507$$

Similarly,

$$_2F'_{G_3G_1} = 1.9313$$
$$_2F'_{G_2G_3} = 5.0145$$
$$F'_3 = \frac{52 - 2 - 1 + 1}{1} \left[\frac{n_1 n_2 (D_3^2 - D_2^2)}{52(n_1 + n_2) + n_1 n_2 D_2^2} \right],$$
$$_3F'_{G_1G_2} = \frac{50}{1} \left[\frac{364(.464778 - .186111)}{2,132 + 364(.186111)} \right] = 2.3056$$

and

$$_3F'_{G_3G_1} = 0.04931$$
$$_3F'_{G_2G_3} = 1.1880$$

Finally, calculating F'_4 using the total D^2 based on 3 characters:

$$F'_4 = \frac{(52 - 0 - 3 + 1)}{3} \left[\frac{n_1 n_2 (D_3^2 - 0)}{52(n_1 + n_2) + 0} \right],$$
$$_4F'_{G_1G_2} = \frac{50}{3} \left[\frac{364(.464778)}{2,138} \right] = 1.3225$$

and

$$_4F'_{G_3G_1} = 1.2179$$
$$_4F'_{G_2G_3} = 2.2786$$

Upon entering the F-table with q and $f - P - q + 1$ degrees of freedom, it was found that only one of the values of F' was significant at the 5 per cent level: for example, for $_2F'_{G_2G_3} = 5.0145$ with d.f. 1, 51 (i.e. $n_1 = 1$, $n_2 = 51$) $\sim P < 0.05$. This is the only case where the addition of a variable contributed significantly (at the 5 per cent level).

We may conclude that the three characters, girth of thorax, length of tibia, and length of humerus were not effective singly or in combinations to distinguish among the three populations of schools investigated.

EXERCISES

1. Using the data of Table XIII.1, recalculate the values given in the text but using the regression of X on Y. Set up the new hypotheses and formulae and make the corresponding tests (Clue: interchange X for Y throughout, as suggested in the footnote on page 417).
2. Do the tests proposed by Gulliksen and Wilks (*Psychometrika*, XV, 1950) differ from those given in the text? If so, in what respects, *and* why?
3. Rearrange Table XIII.10 as suggested on pages 429 and 430 of the text and work through the Johnson-Neyman categorical matching variables analysis for the reduced table.
4. Use the data given by Johnson (*Journal of Experimental Education*, March, 1949, p. 365) and work through an analysis parallel to that given in the text on pages 430–44.
5. Use the data given by Johnson and Tsao (*Psychometrika*, X, 1945) but calculate the complete analysis of variance and covariance using Initial Score and MA only.

6. Using Beall's data (*Psychometrika*, X, 1945) calculate the exact and approximate discriminant function equations for tests 1 and 3 (see Beall's Table 4, p. 214).

7. Using Christensen's data (*Journal of Experimental Education*, XXI [March, 1953]) test the over-all assumption, and if the null hypothesis is rejected, carry out the multivariate analysis of differences between the preprofessional groups of college students using the method of pivotal condensation described in our text.

CHAPTER XIV

Design and Analysis of Statistical Investigations

In the final chapter of our text, we wish to discuss the most fundamental role of statistics, namely, the part statistical science plays in the design and analysis of statistical investigations. Statistics, as has been emphasized in this volume, is an applied science. Its chief justification rests in the aid it can give in the solution of problems. The tools which the statistician has placed at the disposal of the research worker include methods and procedures for the efficient collection of data, primarily through controlled experiments and sampling surveys, and the techniques for assessing the relevant information of the data collected. This role of statistics is succinctly stated in the function of the statistician as set forth by the National Roster of Scientific and Specialized Personnel: "The statistician uses inductive reasoning, based on the mathematics of probability, to develop and apply the most effective methods for collecting, tabulating, and interpreting quantitative information."

The subject of the design and analysis of statistical investigations is obviously exceedingly broad and an increasing number of books are being written about it (see references at end of chapter). It is not our purpose to deal with the subject exhaustively or in detail, but rather to present the principles of design and show how they are applied in a number of standard forms. We wish to consider especially the theory and use of some of the most important statistical tools that have been developed for the research worker. The modern practitioner or research worker would be quite helpless without a functional understanding of their use.

In carrying out our objective we believe that the statistical concepts and tools which have constituted the content of this volume will attain a new importance and significance as the student observes how they are put to work in making new additions to our scientific knowledge.

The Essential Nature of Experimentation

The term "experiment" generally is used in connection with two kinds of experimental problems: (1) the determination of the magnitude of absolute constants—e.g. the measurement of the velocity of light—and (2) the comparative experiment, which consists of the application and comparison of differential treatments or various technical procedures—e.g. comparison of the individual, group, and lecture-demonstration laboratory methods of teaching high school chemistry. It is the comparative experiment that we shall consider and, more particularly, the role of statistics in the conduct of such experiments.*

The practice of adding to scientific knowledge by experiment in any field beyond the incipient stages as a science usually involves the repetition of the following sequence of events:

1. The critical examination of theories in terms of available evidence.
2. The specification of hypotheses that are testable or appropriate for testing by experimentation.
3. The carrying out or execution of experiments.

An experiment when designed and executed in accordance with certain principles can eventuate in answers of the "yes" or "no" type in terms of the acceptance or non-acceptance of the hypothesis, and in giving estimates of specified unknown population values. It may be stated here that the most fundamental contribution of statistics is to evaluate the uncertainty of the answers based on the experimental results.

The Planning of the Experiment

The word *planning* may be used to refer to the whole procedure of arranging an investigation or an experiment. Some of the aspects are governed more by technical than statistical consideration—aspects that cannot be considered here. But our purpose is served by pointing out the statistical phases which will be treated.

The over-all planning of experiments involves the following:

1. The statement of the purpose of the investigations, which may be presented in the form of the questions whose answers are sought, of the hypotheses under test, or of the effects to be estimated. A specification of the population for which the conclusions apply should be indicated.
2. The description of the experiment, including such salient features as the selection and specification of the treatments, or the number of factors and the range over which they are under investigation, the choice of a scale of measurement and the accuracy of the measurements, the selection of the experimental units, the designation of the general conditions underlying the experimental test, and the specific experimental design to be used.
3. The description of the method proposed for drawing conclusions from the experimental results. This could well include an outline of the analysis of variance, the indication of the tabular forms for presenting the results, an account of the tests of significance with the

---

* Contrast the methodology of the comparative experiment with that reported and discussed by Joseph Berkson, ''Smoking and Lung Cancer,'' *Journal of the American Statistical Association*, LIII (1958), 28–38.

level of significance proposed, and the treatment differences to be estimated, based on the specification of the precision the experimental results should attain. This provides a verification of the treatment comparisons held to be relevant to the specified purposes of the experiment. The possible outcomes of the experiment should be anticipated, and the corresponding conclusions formulated prior to the carrying out of the experiment and the observation of the experimental results. This is required if any inference drawn from the experimental observations is to be supported by a fiducial probability or confidence coefficient statement. Apparently significant but unanticipated inferences can only be applied in suggesting later experiments.

Some Fundamental Ideas and Processes

Population

On nearly all occasions where statistical methods are employed in research, the data that are collected, the sample, are of interest only insofar as they are representative of some larger group of data, called the population. Inductive reasoning is involved in the process of drawing general conclusions from a particular set of conditions. The validity of such inferences is contingent upon the particular set of conditions being a representative sample of the population about which conclusions are drawn. The population studied by the experimenter is formulated by him as representative of an aggregate of future trials and as such is basic in his statistical thinking when he engages in the process of planning the experiment.

The generalizability of experimental evidence depends not only on populational generality but also upon the generality of experimental conditions. The limits of the generalizability with respect to the former depend upon a representative sample of experimental subjects or objects from a specified population, and with respect to the latter upon a sample of experimental conditions that are representative of the populational conditions for which conclusions are drawn. The inferences or conclusions drawn are not certain but probable, and the theory of statistics provides the basis for specifying the degree of uncertainty involved.

The Testing of Hypotheses

A distinguishing property of the scientific method is the formulation of hypotheses that are capable of being tested empirically. Drawing upon knowledge of the theory, subject-matter, and problems of the field of his interest, the research worker conceptualizes that certain results would be obtained if certain factors were operative, or that certain factors may have brought about an observed phenomenon or situation. This formulation represents the scientific hypothesis. As the next step, the investigator studies critically the hypothesis with the view of identifying certain consequences that are amenable to experimental verification. Verification of a hypothesis cannot be made with complete certainty; it can only be shown that the experimental observations are in agreement with the hypothesis within the limits of error which they contain. The experimental hypothesis can never be confirmed but it may be shown to be incompatible with the observational data and thus rejected. This is the basis of the use of the null hypothesis in analyzing the results of experiments. The null hypothesis must be rigorously defined since it must provide the distribution of results basic to the derivation of the test of significance. A specification should also be made by the experimenter of possible alternatives since, without these, it is difficult to establish the appropriateness of the test used. The hypothesis must be formulated before the experimental results are observed and the level of significance specified in advance for the basis of deciding the acceptance or rejection of the hypothesis. Furthermore, the level of significance provides no basis for the calculation of the probability that the hypothesis is true.

The general procedure, then, of the research worker using the experimental method is to formulate hypotheses. Then he proceeds to verify them either directly or by their consequences. For this process of verification, observations must be collected and the design of his experiment is substantially the pattern to be used in their collection. If the experiment is to provide evidence capable of testing the hypothesis, its design must fulfill certain criteria.

During the last thirty years or so, there has been under development a statistical science of experimental design largely conceived by R. A. Fisher. The modern research worker consults these principles before embarking on an experiment. While they have reached their highest state of development in agricultural science, the same general principles have wide applicability and are valid whatever the field of application if its problems are amenable to experimental inquiry. The details will differ according to the circumstances, of course, and it is essential to distinguish general principles from specific details.

Statistics as a Part of Planning and Interpretation

A golden rule of scientific investigations that employ statistical methods is that statistics must be brought into play in the advance planning stage of investigations. This is required because the method of analysis of the data is determined at the time of designing the investigation. Furthermore, as we shall note more fully later, the model of experimentation set up is comprised of assumptions and hypotheses. The statistical test of the appropriate hypothesis involves both hypotheses and assumptions. The test is made of the complete model. Therefore, when the decision is reached relative to the acceptance or rejection of a hypothesis, the conclusions might be wrong, all or in part, due to failure to satisfy the assumptions. The plan for the collection of the data must accordingly take into account the fulfillment of the requirements inherent in the assumptions. When the verdict of the statistical test is "statistically significant," it is highly important for the research worker to know that the result is not attributable to errors in the assumptions before entering upon the scientific interpretation of his experimental results.

This initial role of statistics is not always so evident to the research worker as is the need for statistical assistance in the interpretation of the experimental results. It is quite commonly noted in experimental results that when experiments are repeated, even under the most uniform conditions, there is variation in the effects of the experimental treatments in successive trials. In fact, successive repetitions may give such varying results that the experimenter is in doubt as to which of, say, even two treatments might be more effective in the long run. The critical experimenter recognizes that merely descriptive statements of his experimental results do not take him very far and he realizes the hazards involved in taking things at their face value.

Aware of the limitations in the descriptive statements of his experimental results, the modern experimenter resorts to a different basis for summarizing his results. He contemplates what would happen to his apparent treatment differences if it were practical to repeat the experiment indefinitely under the same experimental conditions. Presumably the average difference in treatments would reach some stable value. It seems reasonable to designate this fixed value, which is not related to the size of the experiment originally carried out, as the true difference between the differential treatments. In summarizing the experimental results, his experimental conclusion is now concerned with what may be said from his experimental results about the true difference between his treatments. This is the problem of inductive inference from the sample to the population, previously indicated.

It is to the problem of inductive inference that the statistician has made his principal contribution. Limits can be established about which it may be said, with a certain probability determined by the experimenter, that they enclose or cover the true difference. This is the problem of statistical estimation.

In testing hypotheses, the experimenter is interested in the supposition that the true difference between the effect of the treatments has some stated value, most frequently zero as specified by the null hypothesis. As observed in the case of estimation, difficulties in testing hypotheses also arise because of the variability of experimental data. Because of this variability the data are not exactly in agreement with the values specified by the hypothesis. Tests of significance are designed to enable the experimenter to determine whether or not the discrepancy between the data and the hypothesis may be attributable to the variability typical of experimental data. The occasions in which the experimenter collects quantitative data solely with the object of testing hypotheses are relatively few. Usually quantitative estimates and confidence limits are needed.

Mention may be made here of the decision function approach. According to this concept, the main purpose of experimentation is to provide a basis for action. The problem is that of selecting one out of a plurality of possible types of action on the basis of the experimental observations. The number of observations may be established in advance or they may be sequentially determined. The choice of a course of action will be affected by the relative importance of the different possible errors the experimenter may commit. A weight function is introduced for the possible errors. The probabilities of the experimental data leading to the various actions are considered. The objective is to minimize the expectation of the risk.

Experimental Error

It is important to consider the meaning of experimental errors and their sources. We have noted that experimental results are affected not only by the treatments under comparison but also by exterior sources of variation that tend to conceal the treatment effects. In the aggregate, these exterior variations are spoken of as *experimental errors*. Two main sources of experimental error may be enumerated. The one source is the important variability in the experimental materials themselves, especially in biological and psychological materials. It is customary to apply the term "experimental unit" to the group of material subjected to a treatment independently of the other groups in a single trial of the experiment, e.g. a class of students subjected to a certain methodology in an experiment comparing different methods of teaching. Such units even when allocated the same treatment give different results. These differences are a constituent of experimental error. The inability or failure to carry out experiments under the same uniform conditions constitutes the second main source of variability that gives rise to experimental error. The primary aim of an experimental design is to minimize experimental error, regardless of its source.

The basic quantity by which experimental errors are measured is the error variance per experimental unit. This quantity is defined as the expected value of the square of the error affecting the observation for a single experimental unit, and its square root is termed the *standard error per unit*. Before discussing the choice of a design and other means for increasing the precision of an experiment, however, we shall present certain principles underlying experimentation, an understanding of which is basic to the problem of reducing experimental error.

The Self-Contained Experiment

A fundamental requirement of an experiment is that it must be so designed that its interpretation is based on its own evidence. Fisher designated this type of experiment as a self-contained experiment, and he specified certain principles that must govern its design and conduct if it is to possess this property.

Controls and Their Function

A primary requirement of a self-contained experiment is that the experiment must provide its own control. This fulfills the need of basing all conclusions with reference to the differential effect of two or more contrasting treatments on the differences in the response or reaction of two or more similar bodies of experimental material. It would be impossible, for example, to draw conclusions in regard to the effect of a single treatment applied to a single group of individuals. Only through the use of control(s) is it possible to calculate the probability of the experimental outcomes being attributable to factors other than the experimental factor(s) under test and evaluation.

It is not to be interpreted that the control is a treatment which has been continually used and against which new treatments are compared. An experiment is often concerned with the relative effectiveness among new treatments themselves. However, a control in the former sense is often needed when a new type of treatment is under evaluation. It should be noted that when a control is needed, it should constitute an integral part of the experiment so that a direct comparison with other treatments becomes possible. In school experimentation, for example, it would not suffice to use prior results from a method of treatment as a basis for comparing a new treatment or treatments. The control and experimental treatments should enter into the same experimental design on an equal basis.

The Valid Estimate of Experimental Error

The second requisite of a self-contained experiment is that it must be able to provide a valid estimate of the experimental errors that actually influence the comparisons made. This is necessary because only under such conditions can tests of significance be applied to the experimental results— tests that are disconnected from all past experience and therefore valid for adding new knowledge. A valid estimate of experimental errors is required as well to make an unbiased estimate of the effects of the contrasted treatments and thence to set up the appropriate confidence limits.

The Principles of Experimental Design

Replication

The principle of replication, the process of repeating the same treatment on more than one experimental unit, is applied in order to obtain an estimate of experimental error to which our comparisons are likely to be subject. Replication is needed not only to estimate the error but also to reduce it. The true variance of any treatment-comparison decreases directly with increase in the number of replicates and information on the comparison increases proportionally.

In planning an experiment it is good practice to estimate the precision that the experiment should attain. In this determination use is made of the standard error of the experimental unit, the number of replications, and the number of degrees of freedom available for estimating the error variance. The precision, or the amount of information the experiment is capable of yielding, may be specified by the size of the true difference which the experiment should detect by a test of significance or by stating the width of the confidence interval for the true difference. Tables are available for use in predicting the number of replicates required for a specified precision (see references 1 and 4). The results, while approximate, are useful for practical purposes.

In applying the principle of replication, provision must be made to insure that no one treatment is likely to be favored in any one replicate than in another. This assurance is based upon the application of the principle of randomization.

Randomization

The experimenter must recognize that equalization of non-experimental conditions is approximate no matter how much care and experimental skill he may have exerted in attempting to equalize them. It is most necessary that this inequality shall not result in biased estimates and invalid tests of significance. The essential safeguard is incorporated into the experimental procedure by the process known as *randomization*. This principle, first introduced by R. A. Fisher, is unique to modern experimentation. The principle serves to make certain that extraneous sources of variation should not introduce biases into the treatment effects. Causes of variation not controlled experimentally must, therefore, be controlled by the device of randomization. It may be used a number of times in the course of an experiment. These occasions of use are left largely to the judgment of the experimenter.

Randomization, along with replication, ensures that the error estimates are valid, and that the estimates of treatment means are unbiased.

Local Control

Introduced into agricultural experimentation, particularly for the control of variation in soil fertility, Fisher used the principle of *local control*. This principle has attained wide utility. It is based on the fact that it is advantageous to have the treatments under comparison as nearly similar as possible with respect to conditions other than the factors on which information is sought. This practice makes it easier for an experimenter to accept treatment differences as attributable to the factor that has been varied among the groups, since other conditions, broadly speaking, have been made equal. The operation of this principle of local control is illustrated in certain experimental designs, such as the randomized block and the Latin square to be discussed later.

Summary

In summary, replication, randomization, and local control are basic principles in modern designs of experiments. Replication furnishes directly an estimate of the experimental error. It provides indirectly by way of randomization the insurance of the validity of the estimate. Moreover, replication serves to reduce experimental error directly, e.g. $\sigma/\sqrt{r}$, and indirectly by means of a system based on the principle of local control. The validity of the chain of inductive reasoning employed eventuating in conclusions based on the experimental results depends upon the application by the experimenter of the full randomization principle.

The Statistical Analysis of the Experimental Results

The development of the science and art of experimentation has been paralleled with that giving rise to tools suitable to analysis of experimental results. The introduction of the powerful methods of the analysis of variance by Fisher opened the way to the whole development of modern techniques of design and analysis of experiments. This technique gives a convenient arithmetical procedure for combining estimates of error from different treatments and at the same time for eliminating variation from other sources made possible by the experimental arrangement.

The Analysis of Variance in Estimating and Testing Mean Effects

In the mathematical model underlying the formal analysis of many experimental results, each experimental observational value may be represented as the sum of four components assignable, respectively, to the general mean, the effect of the treatment, certain environmental effects which the design of the experiment makes it possible to isolate, and the residual effect designated as experimental error. Similarly, the analysis of variance partitions the total sum of squares of the experimental observations into four independent sums of squares corresponding to the four components specified.

Briefly, the analysis of variance provides a shortcut way of getting the error sum of squares. The sum-of-squares for treatments is needed for the F-test of the null hypothesis that there are no differences between the mean effects of the treatments. The analysis may be extended to procure the sums of squares needed in testing the differential effect of a single treatment or the effects of a subgroup of treatments. The component attributable to environmental effects may be utilized to estimate the increase in precision of the experiment resulting from the removal of these effects from the treatment means. The breakdown of the total number of degrees of freedom into subdivisions corresponding to each of the component sum of squares calculated presents the logical structure of the experiment.

Assumptions Underlying Analysis of Variance

We have previously pointed out that a statistical model is comprised of both assumptions and hypotheses. In a broad sense, the assumptions are the things which the experimenter takes for granted. The hypothesis is held in doubt and is that which is under investigation. The mathematical statistician in the development of tests tries to make them as insensitive as possible to errors in the assumptions.† However, the experimenter must always be aware of the possibility that errors in the assumptions may have important effects upon the experimental results. Thus errors in the assumptions can possibly make insignificant one or more differences that would be significant if the assumptions were fulfilled.

The principal assumptions underlying the analysis of variance are that the components of treatment effects and environmental effects are additive and that the experimental errors are normally distributed about zero with the same variance.‡

Failure to fulfill the assumptions will affect both the significance levels and the sensitivity of the tests used, that is, the F-test and the t-test. Generally the effect of non-normality in using the ordinary F- and t-tables is to err in the direction of accepting too many significant results. Use of the one-tailed t-test is likely to lead to more serious error, particularly with a pronounced skew distribution of errors.

One of the more serious consequences results from heterogeneity in experimental errors. In some cases a remedy is provided by dividing the error sum of squares into homogeneous components. Experimental errors

---

† A test is sought which is sensitive to change in the specific factors tested and insensitive to changes in extraneous factors of a size liable to be found in practice. The respective properties have been referred to as powerful and robust.

‡ For a more complete discussion of the effects on the experimental results of failure to satisfy the assumptions and certain remedial courses that may be taken, consult references 1, 4, 7, and 8.

may follow distributions that are markedly skew. A transformation of the data may result in normalizing the data on the new scale as well as in stabilizing the variance. The principal transformations in use include logs, square roots, and inverse sines.

The assumption that the experimental errors from observation to observation are independent may be untenable. This assumption needs to be carefully checked in experiments with human beings or other living organisms, especially when the criterion may be a succession of responses for the same individual. Living organisms are primarily adaptive, and any responses are likely to alter subsequent responses. Proper randomization can often overcome such difficulties by bringing about independence among the experimental errors.

The property of additivity§ is highly important in the interpretation of the experimental results. If the property does not hold the underlying mathematical model is invalidated.

Errors result from the failure to fulfill the assumptions of randomness. There are no statistical tests by which randomness can be confirmed. The experimenter can only look for evidence of special forms of non-randomness. Thus, one form of non-randomness is a trend or pattern within a set of experimental data. Another form is the tendency for the results in each of several series of observations to occur in groups.

A Rationale of Analysis of Variance Tests

The assumption that experimental results conform to some mathematical distribution specified by certain parameter values raises the question of how the experimenter may be certain that the experimental observations will follow the appropriate distribution. Take, for example, the circumstance of sampling by a random process from an infinite population. In a given experimental situation it is difficult to specify any infinite population from which a random sample is to be chosen. Even if it were possible, the experimenter would rarely affirm that his choice of experimental units for particular treatments was made by sampling at random from this infinite population.

The rationale underlying the use of statistical tests in interpreting experimental results is briefly as follows.‖ Take an arrangement, such as a randomized block experiment with 5 treatments in 6 blocks of 5 plots each. If there is no differential effect of the treatments, it may be said that a grouping has been made of the 30 plots into 6 groups of 5 plots, which is a random group of all the possible $(5!)^6$ groupings that could have been made. A characteristic of this grouping might be taken for evaluation, and similarly for all the possible groupings. It may then be said that the particular

§ See Reference 10 for test of non-additivity.
‖ See Reference 8 for a more complete and rigorous discussion of this subject.

grouping is a random sample of 1 from the possible $(5!)^6$ values that could have been secured. The value for the particular grouping chosen has an expectation of the mean value of all the possible groupings under the null hypothesis of no differential treatment effects on each individual plot. If a significance level of 5 per cent were taken, then, if the value of the obtained grouping fell in a set chosen of those values of the highest 5 per cent absolute values, the null hypothesis would be rejected. The very laborious calculation would not have to be made, since some random device could be used to obtain the 5 per cent region.

For the testing method to have value, the power of the test for departures from the null hypothesis would be required. The simplest set of alternatives could be that the treatment effects are unequal. For example, one might test the non-null hypothesis by using the sum of squares between treatment means. Then a procedure could be to examine the distribution of sums of squares between treatment means. The mathematical labor of evaluating the sum of squares for all the possible groups would be impractical. Here the difficulty may be resolved by theory based on the normal distribution. It is known that, if the assumptions of normality and additivity are tenable, the hypothesis that the treatments are equal against the alternative hypothesis of their inequality can be tested by the F-criterion, namely, the ratio of treatment mean square to error mean square. Several empirical and theoretical studies have been made concerning the form of this distribution of F over the possible randomizations. The expectation of the treatment mean squares has been shown to be equal to the expectation of the error mean square, not with respect to some infinite population of repeated experiments, but to the possible randomizations of the treatments.

Analysis of Variance in the Estimation of Components of Variance

The use of the analysis of variance we have considered has been that of testing whether a group or subgroup of treatments have produced the same effects. Another problem to which the technique of the analysis of variance is applied is that of estimating various components of variance that may be suitable to the different factors investigated in an experiment. The value of this type of analysis in experimentation is becoming more greatly appreciated but as yet has not been widely recognized. The information provided by that analysis has been found particularly useful in the interpretation of tests of significance in terms of variance components, and in estimating variance components in connection with the selection of efficient sampling designs. It has had its widest practical application in the study of problems arising in genetics.

The mean squares obtained in the standard analysis of variance may be used for estimating variance components. In general the procedure is to determine the expected values of the mean squares. Each observed mean square is thus set equal to the expected value and the equation solved for the variance component. The estimate of the variance component is thus obtained. No method for constructing exact confidence limits has been found but methods giving good approximations are available (see Reference 4).

Methods of Increasing the Sensitiveness of an Experiment

There are several ways of increasing the sensitiveness of an experiment, that is, of making it possible to detect a quantitatively smaller deviation from the hypothesis under test, e.g. the null hypothesis. The methods are both technical and statistical. The size of the experiment may be enlarged by increasing the number of treatments or the number of replications. In addition to enlargement, or instead of enlarging the experiment, there may be qualitative improvements, such as refinements in experimental technique and changes in the structure of the experiment.

A largely statistical method is that of collecting supplementary measurements, a form of local control, which make it possible to remove or reduce experimental errors originating in factors that may not be capable of being controlled or impractical to control by the experimental plan. The effective use of the plan depends upon the success in selecting a variable or variables that are substantially correlated with the factors under investigation. The technique of the analysis of covariance makes it possible to estimate from the observational data how much the experimental results were affected by variations in the supplementary measures. The aim usually is to select the supplementary or concomitant variables that are unaffected by the treatments. This condition is fully satisfied when the supplementary measures are taken prior to the beginning of the experiment.

The principal means of minimizing experimental error is that of choosing an efficient experimental plan as has previously been stressed. The form of the analysis of variance to be used is laid out in advance and cannot be altered to suit the results as they arise. We may also point out that Tang's tables may be used to obtain an estimate of the power of the analysis of variance test, and this may be useful in the rational planning of experiments. In the case of small experiments, however, there is some evidence to indicate that the sensitiveness of the experiment as indicated by the tables is only approximate.

Specific Experimental Designs

In planning experiments, the research worker proceeds in accordance with the principles of experimental design to select a specific design for a projected experiment. The main considerations in the planning have been previously presented. There are no rules that lead directly to the selection of a specific design. Each experimental situation presents its own problems and the experimenter needs to know the materials and the best techniques and designs available for his use. A practical working principle is to select the simplest design that best serves the experimental purpose. The question of economy arises; economy in time, money, and calculations. These are related again to the precision required in the particular experiment. Numerous procedures have been developed over the past thirty years. Designs are, however, classifiable into a few standard types. The newer developments in the field are mainly specialized devices for specialized purposes, which do not depart in any fundamental way from the general principles of design that have been discussed. Here we can discuss only briefly the main types of designs and give a few examples of their use. There are two basic designs: randomized blocks and Latin squares.

Completely Randomized Design

Completely randomized design is the simplest. Here the treatments are assigned to the experimental units entirely at random. This type of design is used more often in laboratory experiments, where the natural variability of the experimental material is sufficiently under control not to require further refinement. In situations where order of treatment is likely to affect the results, the experimental units should be also treated in random order.

Randomized Complete Block Design

The randomized complete block design is one where the experimental units are arranged into groups (called blocks). Each group has the number of experimental units required for a complete set of treatments, the treatments being assigned at random within each group. Each group of experimental units is called a replicate and enough replicates are required to meet the required precision for the estimates of treatment effects under investigation. Each group of blocks contains experimental units as similar as possible. Only the variation among experimental units within blocks contributes to the error variance. The variance between replicates is removed from the estimated experimental error. This design illustrates the point made earlier that the manner of conducting the experiment establishes the sources of variation to be accounted for by the statistical analysis.

In the randomized blocks design, error may be estimated independently for each effect and interaction under the condition that each treatment combination occurs at least twice in the experiment.

Example: We shall illustrate the randomized block design by analyzing a set of data from the experiment by Hayes.# The set of data was one from a number obtained in an experiment designed to test the relative efficacy

James J. Hayes, ''A Comparison of the Results of Teaching Algebra under Two-Conditions—One Class Period for Two Semesters and Two Class Periods for One Semester,'' (M.A. Thesis, University of Minnesota, 1938), p. 29.

of teaching high school elementary algebra one single class period (50 minute period) for two semesters and two class periods (100 minute period) for one semester. The experimental subjects were 34 pairs of students matched on the basis of I.Q.'s and scores on the Lee Prognostic Test. The methods (treatments) were randomized for each pair. There were thus 34 blocks with two treatments assigned at random to the two matched members of a block. The variable, say X, was the raw score on a Cooperative Algebra Test. The primary data are given in Table XIV.1.

The results of the analysis may be combined in an analysis of variance

TABLE XIV.1

THE SCORES OF 34 PAIRS OF STUDENTS SUBJECTED TO TWO DIFFERENT TREATMENTS IN A RANDOMIZED BLOCK ARRANGEMENT

BLOCKS (REPLICATIONS) Pair No.	TREATMENTS E Exp.	C Cont.	BLOCKS TOTALS E + C
1	73	58	131
2	52	37	89
3	100	53	153
4	60	77	137
5	75	51	126
6	67	62	129
7	61	55	116
8	59	30	89
9	33	39	72
10	19	16	35
11	32	15	47
12	27	37	64
13	68	44	112
14	54	27	81
15	26	43	69
16	30	27	57
17	69	53	122
18	43	29	72
19	23	13	36
20	11	17	28
21	26	20	46
22	30	9	39
23	28	35	63
24	53	21	74
25	23	42	65
26	68	40	108
27	32	25	57
28	25	37	62
29	53	38	91
30	33	28	61
31	25	32	57
32	41	10	51
33	39	27	66
34	26	26	52
Total	1,484	1,173	2,657

table, a form of presentation highly effective in showing both the structure of the experiment by the division of the number of degrees of freedom and the relevant results conveniently arranged for the application of the necessary tests of significance (see Table XIV.2).

TABLE XIV.2

ANALYSIS OF VARIANCE OF ACHIEVEMENT SCORES FOR
THE EXPERIMENT ON TEACHING ALGEBRA

SOURCE OF VARIATION	D.F.	S.S.	M.S.	F
Between Blocks (Pairs)	33	18,235.13235	552.5798	4.29*
Between Treatments	1	1,422.36765	1,422.3677	11.05*
Error (Residual)	33	4,249.13235	128.7616	
Total	67	23,906.63235		

* Significant at 1% level

The treatment value was significant at the 1 per cent level. The superiority was for the experimental method, that is, the teaching of algebra for two periods each day for one semester. There was also found to be a significant difference between blocks (that is, among the means of the pairs of individuals). The separation of this source of variation illustrates the contribution of the experimental design to the precision of the experiment. If this source of variation had not been controlled and isolated, the variation among the pairs would have been included in experimental error, thereby confounding experimental error and greatly reducing the precision of the experiment.

The Latin Square Design

The randomized block type of experimental design is an arrangement such that treatments are randomized under one restriction, namely, that each treatment must occur in each block. The Latin square design carries restriction forward to an additional stage by grouping the treatments into replications in two different ways. In this arrangement each treatment occurs once and once only in each row and once in each column of a rectangular array.

The arrangement of the treatments is chosen at random from all Latin squares of the given size. The procedure is explained by Fisher and Yates.** The variations among the groups of experimental units corresponding to the rows and also those corresponding to the columns are removed from the experimental error. The Latin square design is particularly valuable when the disturbing effects of two factors need to be eliminated from the experimental comparisons.

** R. A. Fisher and F. Yates, *Statistical Tables* (London: Oliver and Boyd, 1948), pp. 15–16.

Example: We shall illustrate the single Latin square design from data reported by Chapanis, Rouse, and Schachter.†† These investigators used a single 5 × 5 Latin square design to test the differential effect of tactile and auditory stimuli upon low contrast sensitivity as measured by the number of correct responses on the Luckiesh-Moss Low Contrast Test Chart. Table XIV.3 exhibits the experimental routine. Subjects were tested on 5 consecutive days and the order of presentation of the various experimental conditions was varied systematically from day to day.

TABLE XIV.3

EXPERIMENTAL LAYOUT

The entries are the days on which experimental conditions were presented

SUBJECTS	EXPERIMENTAL CONDITIONS				CONTROL CONDITIONS
	Loud sound	*Weak sound*	*Heavy pressure*	*Light pressure*	
A	2	3	4	5	1
B	4	1	5	2	3
C	1	5	2	3	4
D	5	4	3	1	2
E	3	2	1	4	5

The primary data are shown in Table XIV.4 which reports the number of correct responses made by each subject in reading the chart under each experimental condition.

TABLE XIV.4

PRIMARY DATA

SUBJECTS	EXPERIMENTAL CONDITIONS				CONTROL CONDITIONS	SUMS	MEANS
	Loud sound	*Weak sound*	*Heavy pressure*	*Light pressure*			
A	21	22	20	22	22	107	21.4
B	22	16	23	19	23	103	20.6
C	14	14	23	24	20	95	19.0
D	29	24	24	24	28	129	25.8
E	16	15	14	15	13	73	14.6
Sums	102	91	104	104	106	507	
Means	20.4	18.2	20.8	20.8	21.2		

Experimental days:	1	2	3	4	5
Sums:	90	106	109	101	101
Means:	18.0	21.2	21.8	20.2	20.2

†† A. Chapanis, R. O. Rouse, and S. Schachter, "The Effect of Inter-Sensory Stimulation on Dark Adaptation and Night Vision," *Journal of Experimental Psychology,* XXXIV (1949), 425–37. Reprinted by permission of the American Psychological Association.

The analysis of variance of the results is shown in Table XIV.5.

TABLE XIV.5

ANALYSIS OF VARIANCE OF THE EXPERIMENTAL OBSERVATIONS

SOURCE OF VARIATION	D.F.	S.S.	M.S.	F
Between Subjects	4	328.64	328.64/4 = 82.16	10.72*
Between Exp. Cond.	4	28.64	7.16	<1
Between Days	4	41.84	10.46	1.36
Residual (Error)	12	91.92	7.66	
Total	24	491.04		

* Significant at the 1% level

From Table XIV.5 it is noted that the only significant source of variation was that between the subjects. There is little doubt that the introduction of experimental stimuli into the environment had no effect on their contrast thresholds.

The two methods—randomized blocks and Latin squares—constitute the principal foundation for the experiment. Other methods are elaborations on this foundation.

Factorial Design

One of the most important designs is the factorial.‡‡ In the randomized block and Latin square designs, a number of treatments, which are not necessarily related to one another, were tested. Often in experimental work, the purpose is to find out how several factors may affect a trait or characteristic of interest and to determine the effects, not only of each factor, but of one factor varying over different levels of the other factors. The traditional procedure would be to estimate the effect of one factor keeping all others constant in one experiment. Thus a set of independent experiments, each devoted to applying one factor at a time would be set up. In contrast the factorial design would include all the factors in a single experiment.

The comprehensive experiment involving all treatment comparisons may be laid out in randomized blocks or in a Latin square. Thus if the error variance were the same in the two situations, the same number of experimental units in a factorial experiment would give the same amount of information on main effects of each factor as would a set of single factor experiments, each one using the same number of experimental units devoted to a single factor. The set of independent single factor experiments could give no information concerning the interactions among the factors, if such exist. The factorial experiment is capable of measuring the effects of inter-

‡‡ Strictly speaking, the factorial experiment is not a unique experimental design, since any of a number of the standard or other designs may be used. The choice of treatments indicates whether or not the experiment is factorial.

actions. The effects of every factor are evaluated for every combination of other factors included in the experiment. Since the aim of much experimentation is to provide recommendations applicable over a wide range of conditions, rather than for only the chosen conditions specified by the single factor experiment, the factorial design is especially advantageous. Often the experimenter is interested in establishing best treatments over a wide range of conditions, and the factorial experiment makes possible the wider generalizability of the experimental evidence.

Example: To illustrate the principles and the analysis of a factorial design we present some results from the comprehensive experiment by Kendall§§ on the conditions under which learning takes place. Learning and relearning sessions were analyzed separately. Four factors were arranged as a $3 \times 2 \times 2 \times 2 \times 2$ factorial design with 48 treatment combinations for both learning and relearning. Each of twenty-four subjects served under two conditions in learning and under two conditions in relearning. Learning was by the method of paired associates. The criterion was the number of trials necessary to reach two successive errorless trials. Japanese *Katakana* were employed as the material to be learned. The *Katakana* were photographed and the film strips mounted under glass for projection on a screen.

For our illustration, we shall use three factors each at two levels. The treatment comparisons were laid out in three blocks comprised of learners of three levels of ability, A: 1. good, 2. average, 3. poor, respectively. The original experiment contained two replications of the design. For our purpose, the first replication has been taken. We have, then, a 2^3 factorial design superimposed on a three blocks' randomized block design.

The three factors and their designations are:

T : the time of exposure of the learning material with levels: $1 = 4$ seconds, $2 = 6$ seconds

L : the length of the learning materials with levels: $1 = 13$ items, $2 = 21$ items

O : the order of presentation of learning materials with levels: $1 =$ serial order, $2 =$ random order.

The primary data are given in Table XIV.6 with sums both over blocks and over-all factors for each block.

We shall now show how to compute the estimates of the effects and interactions of the experimental factors and to carry out the appropriate tests of significance. We need to condense the original data by compiling separate tables which will provide the sums or marginal totals necessary for the calculation of the various sums of squares required.

§§ William E. Kendall, "The Effect of Length of Series, Time of Exposure and Order of Presentation on the Efficiency of Learning of Nonsense Material by Good, Average, and Poor Learners" (Ph.D. Thesis, University of Minnesota, March, 1946).

TABLE XIV.6

The Number of Trials to Read the Criterion of Three Ability Groups (Blocks) Under Three Factors (Time of Exposure, Length of Learning Period, Order of Presentation) at Two Levels Each for First Replication

TIME T		1			2			BLOCK SUMS
LENGTH L	1		2		1		2	
ORDER O	1	2	1	2	1	2	1	2	
ABILITY A 1	5	11	11	7	9	12	9	9	73
2	10	18	17	21	11	16	10	13	116
3	13	22	13	20	11	19	10	17	125
Sums over blocks	28	51	41	48	31	47	29	39	314

For the statistical analysis of the data of this design we need sums of squares for the blocks (A), the factors O, T, and L, the several interactions comprised of three first-order interactions, viz., TXO, LXO, TXL, and one second-order interaction, $TXLXO$, for experimental error, and for the total.

Step 1: We proceed first to compile Tables XIV.7 to XIV.10, inclusive. The two-way tables are formed from Table XIV.6 by adding the values of one of the three variates.

Table XIV.7 gives the sums over blocks for factors T, L, O.

Table XIV.8 provides the sums over blocks for factors O and T;
Table XIV.9 for O and L, and Table XIV.10 for T and L.

Step 2: Now we proceed to find the various sums of squares, SS:
From Table XIV.6, we compute the SS_A due to blocks:

$$SS_A = \frac{129^2 + 116^2 + 125^2}{8} - \frac{314^2}{24}$$
$$= 4,301.2500 - 4,108.1667$$
$$= 193.0833$$

From Table XIV.8, we compute the SS due to T and O:

$$SS_O = \frac{129^2 + 185^2}{12} - \frac{314^2}{24}$$
$$= 4,238.8333 - 4,108.1667$$
$$= 130.6666$$

$$SS_T = \frac{168^2 + 146^2}{12} - \frac{314^2}{24}$$
$$= 4,128.3333 - 4,108.1667$$
$$= 20.1666$$

From Table XIV.9, we compute the SS due to L:

TABLE XIV.7

SUMS OVER BLOCKS FOR T, L, O

T		1		2		SUMS
O $\diagdown$ L	1	2	1	2		
1	28	41	31	29		129
2	51	48	47	39		185
Sums	79	89	78	68		314

TABLE XIV.8

SUMS FOR O AND T

		O		T
		1	2	SUMS
T	1	69	99	168
	2	60	86	146
O Sums		129	185	314

TABLE XIV.9

SUMS FOR O AND L

		O		L
		1	2	SUMS
L	1	59	98	157
	2	70	87	157
O Sums		129	185	314

TABLE XIV.10

SUMS FOR T AND L

		T		L
		1	2	SUMS
L	1	79	78	157
	2	89	68	157
T Sums		168	146	314

Note: The grand total over all factors and blocks is seen to be 314.

$$SS_L = \frac{157^2 + 157^2}{12} - \frac{314^2}{24}$$
$$= 4,108.1667 - 4,108.1667$$
$$= 0$$

From Table XIV.8, we may also compute the SS due to the interaction of T and O factors:
Thus

$$SS_{TO} = \frac{69^2 + 99^2 + 60^2 + 86^2}{6} - \frac{129^2 + 185^2}{12} - \frac{168^2 + 146^2}{12} + \frac{314^2}{24}$$
$$= 4,259.6667 - 4,238.8333 - 4,128.3333 + 4,108.1667$$
$$= 0.6668$$

From Table XIV.9, we compute SS due to interaction of factors O and L:

$$SS_{LO} = \frac{59^2 + 98^2 + 70^2 + 87^2}{6} - \frac{157^2 + 157^2}{12} - \frac{129^2 + 185^2}{12} + \frac{314^2}{24}$$
$$= 4,259.0000 - 4,108.1667 - 4,238.3333 + 4,108.1667$$
$$= 20.6667$$

From Table XIV.10, we compute the SS due to the interaction of factors T and L:

$$SS_{TL} = \frac{79^2 + 78^2 + 89^2 + 68^2}{6} - \frac{157^2 + 157^2}{12} - \frac{168^2 + 146^2}{12} + \frac{314^2}{24}$$
$$= 4,145.0000 - 4,108.1667 - 4,128.3333 + 4,108.1667$$
$$= 16.667$$

From Tables XIV.7, XIV.8, XIV.9, and XIV.10, we compute the SS due to the interaction of T, L, and O:

$$SS_{TLO} = \frac{28^2 + 41^2 + 31^2 + \ldots + 47^2 + 39^2}{3} - \frac{69^2 + 99^2 + 60^2 + 86^2}{6}$$
$$- \frac{59^2 + 98^2 + 70^2 + 87^2}{6} - \frac{79^2 + 78^2 + 89^2 + 68^2}{6}$$
$$+ \frac{157^2 + 157^2}{12} + \frac{168^2 + 146^2}{12} + \frac{129^2 + 185^2}{12} - \frac{314^2}{24}$$
$$= 4,300.6667 - 4,259.6667 - 4,259.0000 - 4,145.0000$$
$$+ 4,108.1667 + 4,128.3333 + 4,238.8333 - 4,108.1667$$
$$= 4.1666$$

Finally from Table XIV.6, we find the total SS to be:

$$SS_{\text{total}} = 5^2 + 11^2 + \ldots + 10^2 + 17^2 - \frac{314^2}{24}$$
$$= 4,596 - 4,108.1667$$
$$= 487.8333$$

SS_{error} is obtained by subtraction:

$$SS_{\text{error}} = SS_{\text{tot.}} - SS_{TLO} - SS_{TL} - SS_{LO} - SS_{TO} - SS_L - SS_T - SS_O$$
$$= 487.8333 - 4.1666 - 16.1667 - 20.6667 - 0.6668 - 0 - 20.1666$$
$$- 130.6666 - 193.0833$$
$$= 101.7500$$

Step 3: We now make up the table of the analysis of variance and calculate the F-ratios involved in the appropriate tests of significance (see Table XIV.11).

We find that none of the interactions is significant and of the main effects only order of presentation of learning materials is significant. There was a significant difference among blocks (ability groups) which has been removed from the experimental comparisons.

Step 4: Since none of the interactions was significant the interaction sums of squares and the corresponding degrees of freedom may be pooled with the error component to form the residual. While not altering the conclusions here, this amalgamation may serve to increase the precision of the experiment since while the residual component now constituting the denominator in the F-ratio becomes larger, the corresponding degrees of freedom also becomes larger. This is illustrated in Table XIV.12.

TABLE XIV.11

ANALYSIS OF VARIANCE TABLE FOR THE DATA OF TABLE XIV.6

SOURCE OF VARIATION	DEGREES OF FREEDOM	SUM OF SQUARES	MEAN SQUARE	F	DECISION
A (Blocks)	2	193.0833	96.5417	13.28	*
O (Order)	1	130.6666	130.6666	17.98	*
T (Time)	1	20.1666	20.1666	2.77	
L (Length)	1	0	0	0	
TXO	1	0.6668	0.6668	0.09	
LXO	1	20.6667	20.6667	2.84	
TXL	1	16.6667	16.6667	2.29	
$TXLXO$	1	4.1666	4.1666	0.57	
Error	14	101.7500	7.2679		
Total	23	487.8333			

* Significant at 1 per cent level; $F(2, 14, .01) = 6.51$
$F(1, 14, .01) = 8.86$

We may use the analysis of variance table XIV.11 to illustrate the sequential F-test for multiple decisions on significance in an analysis of variance table.|||| The need for such a test arises from the following knowledge: given an analysis of variance table in which k mean squares, S_i^2 ($i = 1, 2, \ldots, k$) based on n_i degrees of freedom are all to be tested for significance against an "error mean square" S^2 based on n degrees of freedom, the risk of assessing at least one mean square wrongly as significant is sub-

|||| H. O. Hartley, "Some Recent Developments in Analysis of Variance," *Communications of Principles and Applied Mathematics*, VIII (1955), 47–75.

TABLE XIV.12

ANALYSIS OF VARIANCE TABLE ILLUSTRATING THE POOLING OF
NON-SIGNIFICANT INTERACTION SS AND ERROR SS

SOURCE OF VARIATION	DEGREES OF FREEDOM	SUM OF SQUARES	MEAN SQUARE	F	DECISION
A	2	193.0833	96.5417	12.07	*
O	1	130.6666	130.6666	16.34	*
T	1	20.1666	20.1666	2.52	
L	1	0.0	0.0		
Residual (Error & Interaction SS)	18	143.9168	7.9954		
Total	23	487.8333			

* Significant at 1 per cent level; $F(2, 18, .01) = 6.01$
$$F(1, 18, .01) = 8.28$$

stantially larger than α. Hartley indicates, for example, that with k large
and (say) $\alpha = 0.05$ the risk may be as large as 0.9.

Briefly the test is carried out as follows:

Step 1: Arrange the S_i^2 in ascending order of magnitude. For the data
in Table XIV.11, we get

RANK	EFFECT	F	d.f.	P
1	A	13.28	2,14	P_1: < .001
2	O	17.98	1,14	P_2: < .001
3	LO	2.84	1,14	P_3: .10 < P_3 < .25
4	T	2.77	1,14	P_4: −
5	TL	2.29	1,14	P_5: −
6	TLO	.57	1,14	P_6: > .25
7	TO	.09	1,14	P_7: > .25
8	L	.00	1,14	P_8: > .25

Choose $\alpha = 0.01$: LO, T, TL, TLO, TO, and L are not significant at 0.01.

Step 2: Compare P_1 with α/k; $k = c − r + 1$, c = no. of effects = 8;
r = rank = 1; $\alpha/k = 0.01/8 = 0.0012$, $P_1 < 0.0012$, $\therefore$ A is
significant.

Step 3: Compare P_2 with α/k; $k = 8 − 2 + 1 = 7$; $\alpha/k = 0.01/7 =$
0.0014; $P_2 < 0.001$, $\therefore$ O is significant.

All other effects are non-significant.

It is observed that we proceed sequentially, first testing S_k^2/S^2 against
$F_\alpha(k, n_i, n)$; if this is insignificant no further S_i^2 would be tested. If S_k^2/S^2
is $\geqslant F_\alpha(k, n_i, n)$ the next largest ratio S_{k-1}^2/S^2 would be compared with
$F_\alpha(k − 1; n_i, n)$ and so on until an insignificant result is obtained.

Many of the new developments in experimental design are connected with factorial design.##　The factorial experiment has the disadvantage that, as the number of factors increases, the experiment becomes unwieldy even with each factor at only two levels.　For example, for 6 factors at 2 levels, the factorial experiment needs $2^6 = 64$ runs.　With the increase in the number of factors, then, it becomes increasingly difficult to secure homogeneous replications for a randomized block design.　Likewise, the Latin square also requires usually an impracticable number of replications. As a consequence, the size of the experimental error per experimental unit increases.　One problem is that of reducing the number of runs but still removing the interactions in the analysis; another is that of devising ways for splitting up the factorial experiment into smaller units which can be allotted to homogeneous groupings of materials such that differences between the groups will not affect the estimates of the effects of the various factors and their interactions.

Bases of Some New Designs

The device of confounding*** and the use of split plots for subsidiary treatments were early developments aimed at avoiding the increase in experimental error.　The basic principle common to the new developments is the construction of a "block" smaller than a complete replication.　The designs make it possible to eliminate error from the differences among the smaller blocks.　The reduction of the size of the block is obtained, however, only at the expense of accuracy obtainable in certain treatment comparisons.

An example is an incomplete block design.　This design is adapted for experiments where the number of experimental units of a homogeneous character are few.　The design is arranged in groups smaller in number than a complete replication.　This arrangement makes possible the removal of heterogeneity to a greater extent than do the randomized blocks and Latin squares.　This design may be used in circumstances when a sequence of responses for a number of individuals might be correlated, as is the case in some psychological experiments.　An experiment was carried out involving the use of a "taste panel" for the assessment of the chocolate flavors of liqueurs prepared by a standard procedure.　Preliminary work with randomized blocks and the Latin square designs demonstrated that panel members had to taste several samples per session with consequent deterioration in taste perception.　The method of the incomplete block

---

In this connection read: Otto Dykstra, Jr., "Factorial Experimentation in Scheffé's Analysis of Variance for Paired Comparisons," *Journal of the American Statistical Association*, LIII (June, 1958), 529–42.

*** Generally, factors that vary together so that it becomes impossible to separate their several effects are said to be confounded.　The principle is used in certain experimental designs to sacrifice information on interactions of subordinate interest in order to obtain information on more important comparisons.

design required the tasting of only two samples on any one occasion. The set of samples was arranged in pairs. Each sample was matched against every other sample by each taster. The scoring was done by pair differences on the following basis: each taster was asked to divide ten points between the two samples being tested. Thus, if the taster regarded the samples of equal value, five points were assigned to each, the pair difference in this instance being zero. The order of tasting was at random as was also the distribution of the pairs to each taster.

Basic Ideas in Sampling Surveys

The sweeping theoretical and technical developments leading to modern experimental designs produced a marked advance in the development of sampling designs and techniques.

Both experiments and sampling surveys involve patterns by which observations are collected but in experiments the purpose is to estimate the effects of applied treatments, whereas in survey work the objective is to estimate certain characteristics or parameters for a particular, defined population.

The planning of sampling designs is usually involved in two situations: experimental investigations; and survey studies, descriptive or analytical. In both situations the problem is that of obtaining accurate and representative samples of the population. We have previously considered some aspects of the role of sampling in experimentation. Here we shall present some of the problems of the investigator in carrying out survey studies by means of samples, particularly some of the statistical problems encountered in the sample survey.

Definition of the Population

The object of the survey is to secure certain information about the population. Since it is impossible or impracticable to examine the entire population, the investigator examines a part or sample of it, and on this limited basis makes inferences or draws conclusions about the population.

A major statistical problem in the collection of the survey data is the operation of drawing from the population a sample or samples with certain desirable properties. Likewise, the first step in the interpretation of the data is to consider if the data can be assumed to have been drawn from some specified population.

Once the purpose of the survey has been established, first consideration must be given to the definition of the population from which the sample is to be chosen. It is difficult to see how this obvious principle is so frequently unobserved or violated. There is too often a tendency to select a sample in any convenient manner.

Probability Samples and Judgment Samples

It should be stressed from the beginning that a sample must be a probability or random sample, which is one to which the theory of probability can be applied. Only a probability sample can provide the basis for inductive inference and the measure of the degree of uncertainty attached to it. The word *random* applies to the process by which the sample is selected rather than to the sample itself.

In contrast to a probability sample, there is the judgment sample in which one or more individuals select a "typical," "average," or "representative" sample. The theory of probability is not applicable to a judgment sample, and hence any statement about its biases and sampling errors can only be determined by the judgment of some person. It is the probability sample that we will use and discuss here.

Before proceeding to the problem of sampling survey designs, it is advantageous to consider the nature and source of sampling errors and the requirements of a good sample.

Sampling Error and Bias

The errors in the results introduced by the process of sampling itself are termed the random sampling errors. The average size of the errors will be determined by the size of the sample, by the variability of the population sampled, by the sampling method used, and by the manner in which the survey results are calculated. If the conditions required in taking a probability sample are met, the average magnitude of these random sampling errors and the expected frequency of their occurrence can be calculated from the sample results themselves. Furthermore, statistical methods make possible the use of the sampling results to compare the relative efficiency of different sampling designs that could be used in the particular study. In this way the development of improved designs for future studies results.

It is fundamental for the research worker to remember, however, that another source of sampling error, which is particularly prevalent in sampling surveys, is the error due to the failure of getting responses from all the members of the sample. A probability sample might be designed with meticulous care but still be ruined by these so-called non-response errors. The problem connected with this source of error will be considered more fully later.

Even if all members of the sample respond, there is not always a complete response to all questions, particularly if a questionnaire is used. Likewise, errors in the responses given may occur. Faulty methods may be used in estimation. Population changes may also introduce errors, as the survey results are obtained to predict or estimate values of the population for the future.

The sources of errors enumerated, and others, should serve to point out that the total sampling error may be made up of error due to bias and to the chance differences between the elements of the population included and those not included in the sample. It is only the latter type of error that statistical methods enable us to estimate and to some extent control. The control of the other sources of bias is an important phase of sampling designs if the primary aim of design in relation to reduction of sampling error is to be achieved.

The Choice of Sampling Unit

The choice of the unit of sampling is an important one in situations where the sampling elements may vary in their type and size. With a given proportion of the population to be included in the sample, it may be said that, in general, the smaller the sampling units used, the more accurate and representative the sample results. This principle, however, may be in conflict at times with the principle of economy and may need to be modified in relation to the practical situation.

Substantial reduction in costs may at times be made by using larger aggregates of the units of observation. In sampling human beings, for example, a random sample of individuals selected from the population of the United States, or from a lesser geographical unit, would not be efficient if the information required in a particular study were to be obtained by interview. In sampling in educational investigations the smallest practical sampling unit may be the class.

The structure of the aggregate is also a factor, since it is desired to have a unit in which there is maximum variability within the unit. This procedure leads to a decrease in variability between units, thus reducing the sampling error of the estimate.

Structure of Sample Types and Sampling Designs

Just as the primary aim of the experimental design is to minimize experimental errors, so that of the sampling design is to minimize sampling error. In practice we operate on the principle of economy, that is, we wish to design a method of sampling that will provide the desired degree of accuracy at minimum cost. We shall now describe the more commonly used types of sampling and their use in attaining efficient sampling-survey designs.

Random Sampling without Restriction

The simplest method of increasing the accuracy of the sample, separately from errors resulting from bias, is to increase the size of the sample. Other conditions being the same, the decrease in the error of random sampling is approximately inversely proportional to the square root of the number of sampling units in the sample.

The accuracy reached by the sample, however, is contingent on the portion of the variability of each unit which goes into sampling error. This is the source of error that can be substantially reduced by sampling designs. Certain restrictions are imposed on fully random sampling which result in the reduction of error and still do not introduce bias into the results, since the effects of the restrictions are removed by appropriate statistical analysis.

Stratified Random Sampling

A most elementary process of imposing restrictions on fully random sampling is called stratification. The method is spoken of as stratified random sampling. The population is first subdivided into blocks of units on the basis of some principle that makes the units in each block or stratum as homogeneous as possible. From each stratum a number of observational or sample units are selected at random. If the same proportion of units are taken from each stratum, the method of sampling is called stratification with uniform sampling fractions.

We may also use the method of stratification with a variable sampling fraction. The utilization of a variable sampling fraction involves the use of different proportions of sampling units from different strata based on knowledge of, or the estimation of, certain characteristics of the population. A criterion of "optimum application" is that the number of sample elements in a stratum should be based on the product of the size of the stratum and the standard deviation of the stratum. When the population numbers and the standard deviations are known or useful estimates can be obtained, this criterion is useful particularly when the cost of carrying out the survey is closely proportional to the size of the sample.

Multiple-Stage Sampling†††

Multiple-stage sampling is carried out in two or more stages. The population is first divided into a number of large sampling units which are sampled in the usual random manner. The selected first-stage sample contains a number of smaller sampling units, which are again sampled.

The process can be extended to a number of further stages. For example, if a sample of school children of a state were desired, one might begin by sampling the counties of the state, followed by the sampling of town schools and rural schools of the counties selected. This could be extended to the sampling of classes and of individuals within classes.

Systematic Sampling from Lists

One method of sampling is that of taking every qth entry from a list of individuals. The qth entry is determined by the rate of sampling followed

††† For an experimental comparison of five mathematical models for multistage sampling see Palmer O. Johnson and M. S. Rao, *Modern Sampling Methods: Theory, Experimentation, and Application* (Minneapolis: University of Minnesota Press, 1959).

to obtain a given size. The first entry is determined by selecting a number at random between 1 and q and then taking every qth unit thereafter until the list is exhausted. This systematic method of sampling would be a random sample if the units on the list were arranged wholly random. This is not always the case, however. If there are no periodic features that are associated with the sampling interval, this systematic method of sampling, which is much more convenient than unrestricted random or stratified sampling, is quite satisfactory. While it can give an unbiased estimate of the mean, no generally valid formula for the sampling error of this estimate has been derived. The estimate of error given by the use of available formulas is usually an overestimate.

One fundamental requirement in this method of sampling is the assurance that the list, or frame as it is called, is accurate, complete, and up to date. If it is not, before sampling can begin it is necessary to complete a list with the properties named.‡‡‡

Principles of Design and Statistical Analysis

We note the similarity between sampling surveys and experimental designs in the utilization of at least two common principles: (1) the arrangement of the materials into relatively homogeneous strata using prior knowledge of the population, previous to drawing the sample, and (2) the principle of randomization. It may also be pointed out that local control, including observations on supplementary variables and covariance analysis, is made use of in some sampling designs.

The introduction of the principle of randomization and of the analysis of variance as the statistical technique of analyzing the sample observations makes possible the attainment of unbiased estimates of the quantities under survey and of determining the errors to which the estimates are subject. The analysis of variance, through making it possible to combine estimates of error and to separate components of error that are heterogeneous, has reduced to a relatively few the number of independent sampling units required to be chosen from each quantity of sampled material. Thus it is possible to use relatively complicated sampling designs as illustrated in multiple stage sampling.

Analysis of a Stratified Sample

The role of the analysis of variance is illustrated by the table for the analysis of the results of stratified sampling (Table XIV.13). In estimating the sampling error of a stratified sample, the variability between the different strata must be eliminated from the estimate of the variance of a single sample unit.

‡‡‡ Discussions of other methods of sampling, such as multiple stratification, multiphase sampling, sampling with probabilities proportional to size of unit, from the population and from within strata, point and line samples, and area sampling generally, interpenetrating samples, and sampling on successive occasions are in references 2, 6, and 7.

TABLE XIV.13

ANALYSIS OF VARIANCE OF A STRATIFIED SAMPLE*

SOURCE OF VARIATION	D.F.	SUM OF SQUARES	MEAN SQUARE
Between strata	$t - 1$	A	
Within strata	$n - t$	B	S_i^2
Total	$n - 1$	C	S^2

* t is the number of strata and n the number of observations in the sample.

From Table XIV.13, it is noted that S_i^2, the mean square within strata, is the measure of the sampling error. It may also be pointed out that the standard error of a random sample without restriction is given by the mean square for total, S^2. The ratio S^2/S_i^2 provides the basis for estimating the increase in efficiency attributable to the use of a stratified sample instead of a simple random sample.

Sampling Error of a Cluster Sample

We have previously indicated that cluster sampling may have advantages at times because of certain economics or the necessity of using groups as the unit of sampling. For example, in educational investigations the smallest possible sampling unit may be the class.

In cluster sampling it is usually found that the variance between samples of clusters is larger than the variance between samples of individuals. The usual standard formula for estimating sampling error should not be used in estimating error for cluster samples. Modification in formulae must be made to take care of intraclass correlation, if it exists.

The variance of the estimated mean per element, $\bar{X}$, is given by

$$V(\bar{X}) = \frac{M - m}{M - 1} \frac{\sigma^2}{m\bar{N}} \{1 + (\bar{N} - 1)\rho\}$$

where

M = Number of clusters in the population

m = Number of clusters sampled

$\bar{N}$ = Average number of elements per cluster

σ^2 = Variance of the population

$\bar{X} = \dfrac{X}{m\bar{N}} = \dfrac{X}{N}$, an unbiased estimate of μ

μ = The mean of the population

ρ = The intraclass correlation coefficient

Example: For the purpose of vocational guidance, a speed test was given to high school seniors in the State of Minnesota. A sample of 12 classes was drawn at random from a population of 789 classes by cluster sampling procedure. It was found that the average number of students per class in the sample was 14. The estimated mean, $\bar{\bar{X}}$ was 113.57. The variance of the population was 474.1216, and the coefficient of intraclass correlation was 0.031. The variance of the estimated mean $\bar{\bar{X}}$, as given by the above formula is,

$$V(\bar{\bar{X}}) = \frac{789 - 12}{789 - 1} \cdot \frac{474.1216}{(12)(14)} \{1 + (14 - 1).031\} = 3.9041$$

Determination of Sample Size

In the choice of a sampling design due regard must be given to obtain the desired precision as economically as possible. The investigator must decide first the precision he requires in his survey. This may be defined in terms of a maximum permissible error. In practice it is necessary to specify both a maximum permissible error and the probability of exceeding this maximum that the investigator is willing to accept. Other sources of error, such as response errors, must be considered at least indirectly since there is not much point in obtaining a small sampling error if other types of errors lead to an uncertain estimate. These other sources of error are not taken into account in the following discussion of sample size, since they are incapable of control by merely increasing sample size.

Having decided upon the necessary precision, the next problem is that of estimating for any sampling plan under consideration the size of the sample that will meet the specification of precision set.

The simplest design is unrestricted or simple random sampling, that is, selecting by a random process elements from the population, where each element has an equal and independent chance of being chosen. In the simplest case, one can make use of the formula for the standard error of the mean (if one is estimating the mean of a quantitative variable) in obtaining an estimate of sample size. From sampling theory the standard error of the mean is given by

$$\sigma_{\bar{x}} = \frac{\sigma}{\sqrt{n}} \sqrt{1 - \frac{n}{N}}$$

where σ is the standard deviation of the measurements in the population, and n and N are the sizes of the sample and population, respectively. When the standard deviation of the mean has been specified, this equation can be solved for n.

Taking into account the probability or chance of exceeding the maximum permissible error leads to a more complicated calculation. It is customary to define the accuracy required by specifying a probability level (e.g. .01, .05, .10, etc.) and a margin of error d permissible in the sample mean. This may be stated as follows:

$$\rho\{\,|\bar{Y}_n - \mu| \geqslant d\,\} = \alpha$$

where $\bar{Y}_n$ and μ are the sample mean and population mean, respectively. The equation states that the probability of the sample mean lying within a distance d of the population mean is $(1 - \alpha)$. The confidence interval is $2d$ in width.

Two types of situations are encountered:

In order to predict the size of the sample n, a knowledge of the standard deviation σ in the population is required. Usually σ is unknown so an estimate from previous sampling may be available or, in the absence of this, a guess may be made. If σ were known, the value of d would be

$$d = |\bar{Y}_n - \mu| = t\,(\alpha, \infty)\,\sqrt{\frac{N - n}{N}} \cdot \frac{\sigma}{\sqrt{n}}$$

where $t\,(\alpha, \infty)$ corresponds to the normal deviate read from a normal table with a significance level α. If the population N is very large, so the correction for a finite population may be neglected, solving for n_o gives

$$n_o = \sigma^2 t^2 / d^2$$

If n_o/N is, say, .05 or greater, take $n = \dfrac{n_o}{1 + n_o/N}$

Since the population value σ is usually unknown the estimated or guessed standard deviation is substituted for σ and the confidence interval is calculated by using the t-distribution instead of the normal. This method is chiefly of use in ensuring that the confidence interval will be about the length desired.

Example: Let us consider a case where the population value σ^2 is exactly known.§§§ The Otis Intelligence Test was administered to a population of 505 high school chemistry students. It was found that the mean score on the test was 43.21 and the variance was 94.80, these being the population values. By simple random sampling how many students must be taken to estimate a sample mean within 5 per cent of the population mean with a confidence coefficient of 0.95?

Applying the equation we obtain

$$n_o = \frac{\sigma^2 t^2}{d^2}$$

$$= \frac{(94.80)(4)}{(43.21 \times .05)^2}$$

$$= 81$$

Since
$$\frac{n_o}{N} = .16 > .05, \text{ we take}$$

§§§ In practice, the population value σ^2 is estimated from previous sampling of a similar population. Even with little information from previous experience, an estimate of the true σ of the population may be obtained from the value of the range and shape of the distribution.

$$n = \frac{81}{1 + \frac{81}{505}} = 70$$

A method due to Stein (see Reference 9) provides a more exact confidence interval. Actually in this method the sample is taken in two parts. First, a sample of size n, say, is taken. This is used to give an estimate S_1 of σ as well as an approximation of the mean. The next step determines how many additional observations are needed to satisfy the confidence interval specified.

The steps in the calculation can be indicated by an example. The problem was to determine the teaching experience of the summer session faculty.||||

Step 1: Determine the appropriate sample size for $\alpha = .05$ and $d = 12$ months.

A simple random sample of size $n_1 = 15$ was taken and the variance estimate was calculated: $S_{n_1}^2 = 6{,}035.74$

Step 2: Calculate the statistic d to determine whether its value will fall within the allowable limits.

$$d = \frac{t(\alpha, n_1 - 1)S}{\sqrt{n_1}}$$

$$= \frac{2.145 \sqrt{6{,}035.74}}{\sqrt{15}} > 12 \qquad \text{Note: } [t(.05, 14) = 2.145]$$

Step 3: Calculate the statistic, n_o to determine the proper sample size, n, as based on the sample variance, $S_{n_1}^2$

$$n_o = \frac{S_{n_1}^2 t^2(\alpha, n_1 - 1)}{d^2}$$

$$= \frac{6{,}035.74(2.145)^2}{(12)^2}$$

$$= 192.85$$

Step 4: If n_o is greater than 5 per cent of the finite population, apply the finite population correction

$$n = \frac{n_o}{1 + \frac{n_o}{N}}$$

$$= \frac{192.05}{1 + \frac{192.85}{46}}$$

|||| This example is from an investigation carried out by the laboratory section in Statistical Methods to gain firsthand experience in sampling (data furnished by Dr. William Moonan, Instructor).

$n = 37$, which is the optimum sample size.

Step 5: Take as many additional observations as necessary and calculate the mean from total optimum sample.

Number of additional cases: $37 - 15 = 22$
Sum of original 15 cases (in months) $= 2,103$
Sum of additional 22 cases $= 5,285$
Total sum $= 7,388$

$$\bar{X} = \frac{\Sigma X}{N}$$

$$= \frac{7,388}{37} = 199.68$$

In sampling from a population of binomial type where normal theory can be applied, the estimated size of sample (without the correction for a finite population) is:

$$n = t^2(\alpha)\ p_n q_n / d^2$$

where $t^2(\alpha)$ is taken with ∞ degrees of freedom; d is one-half the width of the confidence interval; p_n is the proportion of the sample having and q_n the proportion not having the trait or attribute.

If $\dfrac{n}{N}$ is negligible, n is a satisfactory approximation. If not, the desired sample size is given by

$$n' = \frac{n_1}{1 + \dfrac{n_1 - 1}{N}}$$

Example: As an example, say that we wish to estimate the number of cigarette smokers in the Minneapolis area. We must first of all specify the precision with which we wish to estimate. Suppose we specify a maximum error of 10 per cent. In other words, we will be satisfied if the percentage of smokers in this area is correct to within $\pm$ 10 per cent. Next we must specify the risk of getting an unlucky sample that we are willing to take. Let the chance of getting an unlucky sample or the probability of exceeding the permissible error be 0.05. The question now is how large a sample is required so as to yield results of desired precision. To determine the sample size required, we must, however, have some knowledge about the smokers in the whole area to be sampled. For instance, if all the residents in the Minneapolis area were smokers, a sample of size one would clearly supply the accurate information desired. On the other hand, if there were only a few smokers in the Minneapolis area a small-sized sample would frequently provide the information with 100 per cent error.

For the estimation required, prior information of the population is highly desirable. In a newspaper readership survey conducted in the Minneapolis area, it was found that 32 per cent of the readers were cigarette smokers on the basis of a cluster sample of 4 adults 18 years and over. This percentage, of course, covers only residents who were regular readers of the newspaper, and may be generally representative of the entire adult population in the area. It would be feasible to select a representative sample of adults who were non-readers of that newspaper and find out how many were cigarette smokers.

Expressing the required sample size for the precision specified above, we estimate the sample size of non-readers as

$$n = \frac{t_\alpha^2 p_{n_1} q_1}{d^2}$$

$$= \frac{4(.32)(.68)}{[(.32)(.10)]^2}$$

$$= 850$$

It should be noted that the basic unit of sampling is assumed to be the individual. In practice, it might be advantageous to use cluster sampling and the sampling procedure would then involve grouping the adults into clusters composed of more than one adult. In this case, the required size for the specified accuracy would need to be increased beyond the sample of 850 individuals estimated.

When normal theory does not apply, one procedure would be to use charts, such as those formed in Simon's *An Engineer's Manual of Statistical Methods*. These charts make possible good approximations to the sample size required.

The situations discussed above are illustrative of some of those encountered in practice. In more complex situations, a number of estimates may be required for each of which a different sample size may be needed. For different designs, the sampling errors will need to be determined, taking the particular design into account.

Survey Costs

We have mentioned the problem of costs.### When the precision required has been specified and the sample size estimated, it becomes possible to make an estimate of the cost of carrying out the survey. The cost of taking the sample will be a function of sample size and its form depends on the type of survey. The selection of the sample design should take into account the relative cost of the various designs.

Some investigations of cost functions have been made and in mathematical form the functions are used in equations of estimation. A con-

The costs would include field costs in the case of collection of data by interview, postal costs in the use of the mailed questionnaire, administrative costs, costs of tabulating, summarizing, interpretation, and writing up the results.

sideration of these processes is beyond our present treatment. A discussion of these issues may be found in Deming's text (see Reference 3) and in other sources.

Method of Dealing with Non-Response

The problem of non-response should constitute one of the principal problems in planning the sampling survey. Every effort must be made to secure complete coverage of the sample units. In spite of such attempts it is usually found that a number of non-respondents remain.

One method of tackling the problem is to take a random subsample of the delinquent cases and exert every effort to collect the data called for in the survey. While technical methods are available for estimating the size of this subsample, it may be said that a sample of at least one of three or better two of three should be aimed for.

REFERENCES

1. Cochran, William G., and Gertrude M. Cox. *Experimental Designs*. Second edition; New York: John Wiley & Sons, Inc., 1957.
2. Cochran, William G. *Sampling Techniques*. New York: John Wiley & Sons, Inc., 1953.
3. Deming, W. E. *Some Theory of Sampling*. New York: John Wiley & Sons, Inc., 1950.
4. Federer, Walter T. *Experimental Design*. New York: The Macmillan Company, 1955.
5. Fisher, R. A. *The Design of Experiments*. Edinburgh: Oliver and Boyd, 1935 (also subsequent editions).
6. Hansen, M. H., W. N. Hurwitz, and W. G. Madow. *Sampling Survey Methods and Theory:* Vol. I, *Methods and Applications*, 1953; Vol. II, *Theory*, 1953. New York: John Wiley & Sons, Inc.
7. Johnson, Palmer O. *Statistical Methods in Research*. New York: Prentice-Hall, Inc., 1949.
8. Kempthorn, Oscar. *The Design and Analysis of Experiments*. New York: John Wiley & Sons, Inc., 1952.
9. Stein, C. "A Two-Sample Test for a Linear Hypothesis Whose Power Is Independent of the Variance." *Annals of Mathematical Statistics*, XVI (1945), 243–58.
10. Tukey, J. W. "One Degree of Freedom for Non-Additivity," *Biometrics*, V (1949), 232–42.

EXERCISES

1. Completely Randomized Design

An experiment in ninth-grade science was designed to compare the effects of two methods of teaching a unit in science. The two methods were:

Method 1, *R*—reading method: The pupil read only the content of the unit in the classroom; no practical applications were given, no equipment was introduced, and there was a minimum of discussion.

Method 2, *D*—demonstration method: Demonstrations were given by the instructor, outcomes were discussed, there was no reading in a formal textbook.

Pupils were randomly assigned to either of two sections and the treatments were randomly assigned. Each teacher taught one section by one method and a second section by the other method. Thus teacher 1 (T_1) taught method 1 (R) to section 1 (S_1); teacher 2 (T_2) taught method 2 (D) to S_1; also T_1 taught D to S_2 and T_2 taught R to S_2.

You are to carry out the following analysis:
(a) Test the underlying assumptions.
(b) Test the null hypothesis that there is no significant difference between method means.
(c) Test the null hypothesis for instructors.
(d) Test the null hypothesis for teacher-method interaction.

The following measures were obtained by T_1 on R to S_1:

SCORES

STUDENT	READING TEST	PRETEST	FINAL WRITTEN	FINAL PERFORMANCE	ATTITUDE
1	23	18	60	23	+13
2	22	22	61	28	+14
3	21	21	55	24	+15
4	18	25	45	17	− 2
5	17	8	53	29	+ 6
6	17	4	28	21	+ 6
7	17	30	63	32	+14
8	16	18	30	21	− 1
9	15	24	20	14	− 5
10	14	15	35	16	− 4
11	11	23	49	22	+11
12	9	18	46	26	+ 6
13	7	16	29	15	− 5

The following measures were obtained by T_1 on D to S_2:

STUDENT	READING TEST	PRETEST	FINAL WRITTEN	FINAL PERFORMANCE	ATTITUDE
1	30	23	57	16	+13
2	22	10	59	31	+17
3	18	24	41	18	+12
4	16	20	52	21	+19
5	15	22	43	22	+10
6	14	17	40	28	+14
7	11	27	26	14	+13
8	9	27	27	18	+15
9	7	32	46	27	+16
10	6	18	61	30	+12
11	3	18	51	27	+15

The following measures were obtained by T_2 on D to S_1:

STUDENT	READING TEST	PRETEST	FINAL WRITTEN	FINAL PERFORMANCE	ATTITUDE
1	25	25	48	18	− 1
2	23	14	51	19	+ 7
3	22	20	57	35	+14
4	20	23	51	23	+15
5	17	25	50	21	+ 1
6	15	12	15	20	+12
7	15	14	37	26	+15
8	15	14	63	29	+18
9	14	24	37	23	+15
10	13	16	24	8	+10
11	9	20	44	22	+12
12	1	17	25	11	+ 9
13	1	2	25	17	0

The following measures were obtained by T_2 on R to S_2:

STUDENT	READING TEST	PRETEST	FINAL WRITTEN	FINAL PERFORMANCE	ATTITUDE
1	24	14	44	13	+ 1
2	23	18	56	26	+ 7
3	17	12	48	19	+ 1
4	17	15	29	16	− 2
5	8	17	16	14	− 8
6	7	6	27	7	− 1
7	6	9	26	13	− 3
8	4	24	19	10	− 3
9	4	21	33	16	− 6
10	1	15	19	8	− 2

2. Randomized Complete Blocks Design

The following set of data was obtained in an experiment designed to test the relative efficiency of teaching high school elementary algebra one single class period (50 minute period) for two semesters and two class periods (100 minute period) for one semester. In this experiment 34 students were paired on the basis of I.Q.'s and scores on the Lee Prognostic Test. The methods (treatments) were randomized for each pair. The variable, say X, is the scaled score on the Cooperative Algebra Test.

(a) Are the assumptions satisfied?

(b) Test the null hypothesis.

(c) If the hypothesis is rejected, obtain the confidence limits (90 per cent) for the mean difference.

(d) Obtain the estimated standard error of the difference between the two treatment means.

(e) Estimate the efficiency of this design relative to a completely randomized design with the same experimental material.

REPLICATE NUMBER (1)	SCALED SCORE ON COOPERATIVE ALGEBRA TEST	
	Single Period (2)	Double Period (3)
1	66	72
2	57	64
3	64	85
4	74	67
5	63	73
6	68	70
7	65	67
8	54	67
9	58	55
10	46	48
11	45	55
12	57	52
13	60	70
14	52	64
15	60	52
16	52	54
17	64	71
18	53	60
19	44	50
20	46	42
21	48	52
22	40	54
23	56	53
24	49	64
25	59	50
26	58	70
27	51	55
28	57	51
29	58	64
30	53	55
31	55	51
32	41	59
33	52	58
34	52	52

3. Replicated Latin-Square Design

The replicated 2×2 Latin-square design was used in a study of sensory conditioning. The diagonals of the square represent the treatment, presence of light with the tone versus no light, the columns of the square represent the ordinal position of treatment, and the rows represent the sequence of treatment. The results (reaction time in seconds) of this study for the experimental group are presented in the following table.

ORDER SEQUENCE	A (LIGHT FIRST) *a*		B (LIGHT SECOND) *b*	
Subject	(*I*) Threshold with light	(*II*) Threshold without light	Subject	(*II*) Threshold without light	(*I*) Threshold with light
1	18.0	20.5	2	25.5	20.5
3	20.5	18.0	4	25.5	25.5
5	8.0	13.0	6	20.5	15.5
7	20.5	23.0	8	15.5	13.0
9	18.0	20.5	10	18.0	15.5
11	13.0	18.0	12	18.0	15.5
13	20.5	23.0	14	15.5	18.0
15	27.5	27.5	16	23.0	20.5
17	−4.5	5.5	18	10.5	10.5
19	15.0	15.0	20	15.5	10.5

Make an analysis of these results.

4. "Kirkman Schoolgirl Problem"—Balanced Incomplete Block Design

A school mistress was accustomed to taking her girls for a daily walk. There were 15 girls, and they were arranged in 5 rows of 3 each, so that each girl might have 2 companions. The problem is to arrange them so that for 7 consecutive days no girl will walk with any of her schoolfellows in any triplet more than once.

5. Factorial Design

See, Palmer O. Johnson, *Statistical Methods in Research*, p. 299.

The experiment consisted in determining the difference-limen (D.L.) of subjects for weights increasing at constant rates.

7 weights, 1, 2, 3, 4, 5, 6, and 7   2 sights:
4 rates, *a*, *b*, *c*, and *d* A = normal
2 subjects, females (1) and (2) B = congenitally blind

Do you agree with the following breakdown of the total degrees of freedom?

SOURCE OF VARIATION	D.F.
Between Weights	6
Between Rates	3
Between Sights	1
Weights × Rates	18
Weights × Sights	6
Rates × Sights	3
Weights × Sights × Rates	18
Error	56
Total	111

The 56 D. F. for error include 2 which represent the variation between replications (or subjects within sights). These 2 D. F. and their associated S. S. should be removed because the experiment was not designed to study individual variation within sight groups, but rather to evaluate the rate and weight effects in the dis-

WT.	RATE	A (1)	(2)	TOTALS	B (1)	(2)	TOTALS	GRAND TOTALS
1	a	18.5	3.1	21.6	9.6	9.0	18.6	40.2
	b	22.3	7.0	29.3	17.9	16.1	34.0	63.3
	c	27.2	12.2	39.4	26.1	19.8	45.9	85.3
	d	33.2	14.5	47.7	35.7	32.5	68.2	115.9
		101.2	36.8	138.0	89.3	77.4	166.7	304.7
2	a	10.2	3.9	14.1	7.3	6.4	13.7	27.8
	b	25.2	5.4	30.6	18.2	15.9	34.1	64.7
	c	41.1	9.6	50.7	21.3	21.2	42.5	93.2
	d	36.0	15.3	51.3	27.9	24.3	52.2	103.5
		112.5	34.2	146.7	74.7	67.8	142.5	289.2
3	a	11.4	3.6	15.0	6.5	6.9	13.4	28.4
	b	19.7	7.3	27.0	15.8	12.9	28.7	55.7
	c	32.2	11.7	43.9	22.1	24.1	46.2	90.1
	d	36.7	15.1	51.8	26.2	24.7	50.9	102.7
		100.0	37.7	137.7	70.6	68.6	139.2	276.9
4	a	11.0	3.3	14.3	5.8	6.6	12.4	26.7
	b	15.4	5.2	20.6	12.5	13.4	25.9	46.5
	c	21.3	12.4	33.7	18.2	19.7	37.9	71.6
	d	31.0	18.9	49.9	27.6	28.8	56.4	106.3
		78.7	39.8	118.5	64.1	68.5	132.6	251.1
5	a	9.6	3.5	13.1	5.3	7.2	12.5	25.6
	b	15.6	5.3	20.9	12.5	12.0	24.5	45.4
	c	33.7	11.9	45.6	16.1	21.5	37.6	83.2
	d	36.0	16.9	52.9	23.9	30.0	53.9	106.8
		94.9	37.6	132.5	57.8	70.7	128.5	261.0
6	a	7.8	3.6	11.4	5.5	6.5	12.0	23.4
	b	16.5	5.5	22.0	11.8	12.9	24.7	46.7
	c	28.2	12.8	41.0	17.7	19.6	37.3	78.3
	d	37.6	16.2	53.8	22.2	28.4	50.6	104.4
		90.1	38.1	128.2	57.2	67.4	124.6	252.8
7	a	10.9	4.2	15.1	6.4	7.3	13.7	28.8
	b	18.4	7.6	26.0	11.1	13.1	24.2	50.2
	c	29.6	10.5	40.1	16.7	21.3	38.0	78.1
	d	32.8	15.9	48.7	19.7	24.0	43.7	92.4
		91.7	38.2	129.9	53.9	65.7	119.6	249.5
		669.1	262.4	931.5	467.6	486.1	953.7	1,885.2

criminatory process. Thus the error should be freed from the effects of the individual differences.

Carry out the analyses with (1) the error term with 56 D. F., and (2) the error term with 54 D. F.

6. Estimating Sample Size

An achievement examination in chemistry was administered to 505 high school students. The mean and variance of the scores on the examination were 49.50 and 207.72, respectively. What size of simple random sample would be required for estimating a sample mean within 10 per cent; take $\alpha = 0.05$.

7. Estimating Sample Size

A simple random sample of size 12 was drawn from a group of high school students and given a pretest in chemistry. From this initial sample, s^2 was found to be 185.2431. We wish to estimate the mean of the population with a confidence interval of half-width (d) equal to 5 score points. How many additional students would be required beyond the preliminary sample; take $\alpha = 0.05$.

8. Cluster Sampling

In a state-wide study, a cluster sample of 16 classes was chosen at random from a population of 789 classes (ninth-grade English classes). A spatial aptitude test of two-dimensional space was administered to each of the 16 classes. The average number of pupils per class was 12. The variance in the population was 42.92. The intraclass correlation coefficient for the clusters was found to be 0.047. What was the variance of the estimated mean per pupil?

level of signif $\begin{cases} .05 \to \text{sign.} \\ .01 \to \text{very sig} \\ .001 \to \text{extremely signif} \end{cases}$

APPENDIX A: TABLE OF AREAS FOR THE STANDARD NORMAL DISTRIBUTION

1) prob. of a deviation greater than Z

$$\left(A = \frac{1}{\sqrt{2\pi}} \int_{-\infty}^{z} e^{\frac{z - z^2}{2}} dz\right)$$

$z = \dfrac{X - \xi}{\sigma}$	.00	.01	.02	.03	.04	.05	.06	.07	.08	.09
.0	.5000	.5040	.5080	.5120	.5160	.5199	.5239	.5279	.5319	.5359
.1	.5398	.5438	.5478	.5517	.5557	.5596	.5636	.5675	.5714	.5753
.2	.5793	.5832	.5871	.5910	.5948	.5987	.6026	.6064	.6103	.6141
.3	.6179	.6217	.6255	.6293	.6331	.6368	.6406	.6443	.6480	.6517
.4	.6554	.6591	.6628	.6664	.6700	.6736	.6772	.6808	.6844	.6879
.5	.6915	.6950	.6985	.7019	.7054	.7088	.7123	.7157	.7190	.7224
.6	.7257	.7291	.7324	.7357	.7389	.7422	.7454	.7486	.7517	.7549
.7	.7580	.7611	.7642	.7673	.7704	.7734	.7764	.7794	.7823	.7852
.8	.7881	.7910	.7939	.7967	.7995	.8023	.8051	.8078	.8106	.8133
.9	.8159	.8186	.8212	.8238	.8264	.8289	.8315	.8340	.8365	.8389
1.0	.8413	.8438	.8461	.8485	.8508	.8531	.8554	.8577	.8599	.8621
1.1	.8643	.8665	.8686	.8708	.8729	.8749	.8770	.8790	.8810	.8830
1.2	.8849	.8869	.8888	.8907	.8925	.8944	.8962	.8980	.8997	.9015
1.3	.9032	.9049	.9066	.9082	.9099	.9115	.9131	.9147	.9162	.9177
1.4	.9192	.9207	.9222	.9236	.9251	.9265	.9279	.9292	.9306	.9319
1.5	.9332	.9345	.9357	.9370	.9382	.9394	.9406	.9418	.9429	.9441
1.6	.9452	.9463	.9474	.9484	.9495	.9505	.9515	.9525	.9535	.9545
1.7	.9554	.9564	.9573	.9582	.9591	.9599	.9608	.9616	.9625	.9633
1.8	.9641	.9649	.9656	.9664	.9671	.9678	.9686	.9693	.9699	.9706
1.9	.9713	.9719	.9726	.9732	.9738	.9744	.9750	.9756	.9761	.9767
2.0	.9772	.9778	.9783	.9788	.9793	.9798	.9803	.9808	.9812	.9817
2.1	.9821	.9826	.9830	.9834	.9838	.9842	.9846	.9850	.9854	.9857
2.2	.9861	.9864	.9868	.9871	.9875	.9878	.9881	.9884	.9887	.9890
2.3	.9893	.9896	.9898	.9901	.9904	.9906	.9909	.9911	.9913	.9916
2.4	.9918	.9920	.9922	.9925	.9927	.9929	.9931	.9932	.9934	.9936
2.5	.9938	.9940	.9941	.9943	.9945	.9946	.9948	.9949	.9951	.9952
2.6	.9953	.9955	.9956	.9957	.9959	.9960	.9961	.9962	.9963	.9964
2.7	.9965	.9966	.9967	.9968	.9969	.9970	.9971	.9972	.9973	.9974
2.8	.9974	.9975	.9976	.9977	.9977	.9978	.9979	.9979	.9980	.9981
2.9	.9981	.9982	.9982	.9983	.9984	.9984	.9985	.9985	.9986	.9986
3.0	.9987	.9987	.9987	.9988	.9988	.9989	.9989	.9989	.9990	.9990
3.1	.9990	.9991	.9991	.9991	.9992	.9992	.9992	.9992	.9993	.9993
3.2	.9993	.9993	.9994	.9994	.9994	.9994	.9994	.9995	.9995	.9995
3.3	.9995	.9995	.9995	.9996	.9996	.9996	.9996	.9996	.9996	.9997
3.4	.9997	.9997	.9997	.9997	.9997	.9997	.9997	.9997	.9997	.9997
3.5	.99977	.99977	.99977	.99977	.99977	.99977	.99977	.99977	.99977	.99977
3.6	.99984	.99984	.99984	.99984	.99984	.99984	.99984	.99984	.99984	.99984
3.7	.99989	.99989	.99989	.99989	.99989	.99989	.99989	.99989	.99989	.99989
3.8	.99993	.99993	.99993	.99993	.99993	.99993	.99993	.99993	.99993	.99993
3.9	.99995	.99995	.99995	.99995	.99995	.99995	.99995	.99995	.99995	.99995

4.0   .000317
4.5   .0000033977
5   .0000002867
6   9.8660×10^{-10}
7   1.2798×10^{-12}
8   6.2210×10^{-16}
9   1.1286×10^{-19}
10   7.6199×10^{-24}

too good a result; suspect or question the data

goodness of fit means comparing the observed distribution and how good it fits or approximates the theoretical dist.

(if goodness of fit) the prob. decreases as the χ² goes up

too poor a result then discard the hypothesis

APPENDIX B: DISTRIBUTION OF χ^2

PROBABILITY

n	.99	.98	.95	.90	.80	.70	.50	.30	.20	.10	.05	.02	.01	.001
1	.0³157	.0³628	.0³393	.0158	.0642	.148	.455	1.074	1.642	2.706	3.841	5.412	6.635	10.827
2	.0201	.0404	.103	.211	.446	.713	1.386	2.408	3.219	4.605	5.991	7.824	9.210	13.815
3	.115	.185	.352	.584	1.005	1.424	2.366	3.665	4.642	6.251	7.815	9.837	11.341	16.268
4	.297	.429	.711	1.064	1.649	2.195	3.357	4.878	5.989	7.779	9.488	11.668	13.277	18.465
5	.554	.752	1.145	1.610	2.343	3.000	4.351	6.064	7.289	9.236	11.070	13.388	15.086	20.517
6	.872	1.134	1.635	2.204	3.070	3.828	5.348	7.231	8.558	10.645	12.592	15.033	16.812	22.457
7	1.239	1.564	2.167	2.833	3.822	4.671	6.346	8.383	9.803	12.017	14.067	16.622	18.475	24.322
8	1.646	2.032	2.733	3.490	4.594	5.527	7.344	9.524	11.030	13.362	15.507	18.168	20.090	26.125
9	2.088	2.532	3.325	4.168	5.380	6.393	8.343	10.656	12.242	14.684	16.919	19.679	21.666	27.877
10	2.558	3.059	3.940	4.865	6.179	7.267	9.342	11.781	13.442	15.987	18.307	21.161	23.209	29.588
11	3.053	3.609	4.575	5.578	6.989	8.148	10.341	12.899	14.631	17.275	19.675	22.618	24.725	31.264
12	3.571	4.178	5.226	6.304	7.807	9.034	11.340	14.011	15.812	18.549	21.026	24.054	26.217	32.909
13	4.107	4.765	5.892	7.042	8.634	9.926	12.340	15.119	16.985	19.812	22.362	25.472	27.688	34.528
14	4.660	5.368	6.571	7.790	9.467	10.821	13.339	16.222	18.151	21.064	23.685	26.873	29.141	36.123
15	5.229	5.985	7.261	8.547	10.307	11.721	14.339	17.322	19.311	22.307	24.996	28.259	30.578	37.697
16	5.812	6.614	7.962	9.312	11.152	12.624	15.338	18.418	20.465	23.542	26.296	29.633	32.000	39.252
17	6.408	7.255	8.672	10.085	12.002	13.531	16.338	19.511	21.615	24.769	27.587	30.995	33.409	40.790
18	7.015	7.906	9.390	10.865	12.857	14.440	17.338	20.601	22.760	25.989	28.869	32.346	34.805	42.312
19	7.633	8.567	10.117	11.651	13.716	15.352	18.338	21.689	23.900	27.204	30.144	33.687	36.191	43.820
20	8.260	9.237	10.851	12.443	14.578	16.266	19.337	22.775	25.038	28.412	31.410	35.020	37.566	45.315
21	8.897	9.915	11.591	13.240	15.445	17.182	20.337	23.858	26.171	29.615	32.671	36.343	38.932	46.797
22	9.542	10.600	12.338	14.041	16.314	18.101	21.337	24.939	27.301	30.813	33.924	37.659	40.289	48.268
23	10.196	11.293	13.091	14.848	17.187	19.021	22.337	26.018	28.429	32.007	35.172	38.968	41.638	49.728
24	10.856	11.992	13.848	15.659	18.062	19.943	23.337	27.096	29.553	33.196	36.415	40.270	42.980	51.179
25	11.524	12.697	14.611	16.473	18.940	20.867	24.337	28.172	30.675	34.382	37.652	41.566	44.314	52.620
26	12.198	13.409	15.379	17.292	19.820	21.792	25.336	29.246	31.795	35.563	38.885	42.856	45.642	54.052
27	12.879	14.125	16.151	18.114	20.703	22.719	26.336	30.319	32.912	36.741	40.113	44.140	46.963	55.476
28	13.565	14.847	16.928	18.939	21.588	23.647	27.336	31.391	34.027	37.916	41.337	45.419	48.278	56.893
29	14.256	15.574	17.708	19.768	22.475	24.577	28.336	32.461	35.139	39.087	42.557	46.693	49.588	58.302
30	14.953	16.306	18.493	20.599	23.364	25.508	29.336	33.530	36.250	40.256	43.773	47.962	50.892	59.703

For larger values of n, the expression $\sqrt{2\chi^2} - \sqrt{2n-1}$ may be used as a normal deviate with unit variance.

Reprinted from Table IV of Fisher and Yates, Statistical Tables for Biological, Agricultural, and Medical Research, published by Oliver and Boyd Ltd., Edinburgh, by permission of the authors and publishers.

APPENDIX C: DISTRIBUTION OF *t*

PROBABILITY

n	.9	.8	.7	.6	.5	.4	.3	.2	.1	.05	.02	.01	.001
1	.158	.325	.510	.727	1.000	1.376	1.963	3.078	6.314	12.706	31.821	63.657	636.619
2	.142	.289	.445	.617	.816	1.061	1.386	1.886	2.920	4.303	6.965	9.925	31.598
3	.137	.277	.424	.584	.765	.978	1.250	1.638	2.353	3.182	4.541	5.841	12.941
4	.134	.271	.414	.569	.741	.941	1.190	1.533	2.132	2.776	3.747	4.604	8.610
5	.132	.267	.408	.559	.727	.920	1.156	1.476	2.015	2.571	3.365	4.032	6.859
6	.131	.265	.404	.553	.718	.906	1.134	1.440	1.943	2.447	3.143	3.707	5.959
7	.130	.263	.402	.549	.711	.896	1.119	1.415	1.895	2.365	2.998	3.499	5.405
8	.130	.262	.399	.546	.706	.889	1.108	1.397	1.860	2.306	2.896	3.355	5.041
9	.129	.261	.398	.543	.703	.883	1.100	1.383	1.833	2.262	2.821	3.250	4.781
10	.129	.260	.397	.542	.700	.879	1.093	1.372	1.812	2.228	2.764	3.169	4.587
11	.129	.260	.396	.540	.697	.876	1.088	1.363	1.796	2.201	2.718	3.106	4.437
12	.128	.259	.395	.539	.695	.873	1.083	1.356	1.782	2.179	2.681	3.055	4.318
13	.128	.259	.394	.538	.694	.870	1.079	1.350	1.771	2.160	2.650	3.012	4.221
14	.128	.258	.393	.537	.692	.868	1.076	1.345	1.761	2.145	2.624	2.977	4.140
15	.128	.258	.393	.536	.691	.866	1.074	1.341	1.753	2.131	2.602	2.947	4.073
16	.128	.258	.392	.535	.690	.865	1.071	1.337	1.746	2.120	2.583	2.921	4.015
17	.128	.257	.392	.534	.689	.863	1.069	1.333	1.740	2.110	2.567	2.898	3.965
18	.127	.257	.392	.534	.688	.862	1.067	1.330	1.734	2.101	2.552	2.878	3.922
19	.127	.257	.391	.533	.688	.861	1.066	1.328	1.729	2.093	2.539	2.861	3.883
20	.127	.257	.391	.533	.687	.860	1.064	1.325	1.725	2.086	2.528	2.845	3.850
21	.127	.257	.391	.532	.686	.859	1.063	1.323	1.721	2.080	2.518	2.831	3.819
22	.127	.256	.390	.532	.686	.858	1.061	1.321	1.717	2.074	2.508	2.819	3.792
23	.127	.256	.390	.532	.685	.858	1.060	1.319	1.714	2.069	2.500	2.807	3.767
24	.127	.256	.390	.531	.685	.857	1.059	1.318	1.711	2.064	2.492	2.797	3.745
25	.127	.256	.390	.531	.684	.856	1.058	1.316	1.708	2.060	2.485	2.787	3.725
26	.127	.256	.390	.531	.684	.856	1.058	1.315	1.706	2.056	2.479	2.779	3.707
27	.127	.256	.389	.531	.684	.855	1.057	1.314	1.703	2.052	2.473	2.771	3.690
28	.127	.256	.389	.530	.683	.855	1.056	1.313	1.701	2.048	2.467	2.763	3.674
29	.127	.256	.389	.530	.683	.854	1.055	1.311	1.699	2.045	2.462	2.756	3.659
30	.127	.256	.389	.530	.683	.854	1.055	1.310	1.697	2.042	2.457	2.750	3.646
40	.126	.255	.388	.529	.681	.851	1.050	1.303	1.684	2.021	2.423	2.704	3.551
60	.126	.254	.387	.527	.679	.848	1.046	1.296	1.671	2.000	2.390	2.660	3.460
120	.126	.254	.386	.526	.677	.845	1.041	1.289	1.658	1.980	2.358	2.617	3.373
∞	.126	.253	.385	.524	674	.842	1.036	1.282	1.645	1.960	2.326	2.576	3.291

APPENDIX D: 5% (ROMAN TYPE) AND 1% (BOLD FACE TYPE) POINTS FOR THE DISTRIBUTION OF F

n_1 degrees of freedom (for greater mean square)

n_2	1	2	3	4	5	6	7	8	9	10	11	12	14	16	20	24	30	40	50	75	100	200	500	∞	n_2
1	161 / **4,052**	200 / **4,999**	216 / **5,403**	225 / **5,625**	230 / **5,764**	234 / **5,859**	237 / **5,928**	239 / **5,981**	241 / **6,022**	242 / **6,056**	243 / **6,082**	244 / **6,106**	245 / **6,142**	246 / **6,169**	248 / **6,208**	249 / **6,234**	250 / **6,258**	251 / **6,286**	252 / **6,302**	253 / **6,323**	253 / **6,334**	254 / **6,352**	254 / **6,361**	254 / **6,366**	1
2	18.51 / **98.49**	19.00 / **99.01**	19.16 / **99.17**	19.25 / **99.25**	19.30 / **99.30**	19.33 / **99.33**	19.36 / **99.34**	19.37 / **99.36**	19.38 / **99.38**	19.39 / **99.40**	19.40 / **99.41**	19.41 / **99.42**	19.42 / **99.43**	19.43 / **99.44**	19.44 / **99.45**	19.45 / **99.46**	19.46 / **99.47**	19.47 / **99.48**	19.47 / **99.48**	19.48 / **99.49**	19.49 / **99.49**	19.49 / **99.49**	19.50 / **99.50**	19.50 / **99.50**	2
3	10.13 / **34.12**	9.55 / **30.81**	9.28 / **29.46**	9.12 / **28.71**	9.01 / **28.24**	8.94 / **27.91**	8.88 / **27.67**	8.84 / **27.49**	8.81 / **27.34**	8.78 / **27.23**	8.76 / **27.13**	8.74 / **27.05**	8.71 / **26.92**	8.69 / **26.83**	8.66 / **26.69**	8.64 / **26.60**	8.62 / **26.50**	8.60 / **26.41**	8.58 / **26.35**	8.57 / **26.27**	8.56 / **26.23**	8.54 / **26.18**	8.54 / **26.14**	8.53 / **26.12**	3
4	7.71 / **21.20**	6.94 / **18.00**	6.59 / **16.69**	6.39 / **15.98**	6.26 / **15.52**	6.16 / **15.21**	6.09 / **14.98**	6.04 / **14.80**	6.00 / **14.66**	5.96 / **14.54**	5.93 / **14.45**	5.91 / **14.37**	5.87 / **14.24**	5.84 / **14.15**	5.80 / **14.02**	5.77 / **13.93**	5.74 / **13.83**	5.71 / **13.74**	5.70 / **13.69**	5.68 / **13.61**	5.66 / **13.57**	5.65 / **13.52**	5.64 / **13.48**	5.63 / **13.46**	4
5	6.61 / **16.26**	5.79 / **13.27**	5.41 / **12.06**	5.19 / **11.39**	5.05 / **10.97**	4.95 / **10.67**	4.88 / **10.45**	4.82 / **10.27**	4.78 / **10.15**	4.74 / **10.05**	4.70 / **9.96**	4.68 / **9.89**	4.64 / **9.77**	4.60 / **9.68**	4.56 / **9.55**	4.53 / **9.47**	4.50 / **9.38**	4.46 / **9.29**	4.44 / **9.24**	4.42 / **9.17**	4.40 / **9.13**	4.38 / **9.07**	4.37 / **9.04**	4.36 / **9.02**	5
6	5.99 / **13.74**	5.14 / **10.92**	4.76 / **9.78**	4.53 / **9.15**	4.39 / **8.75**	4.28 / **8.47**	4.21 / **8.26**	4.15 / **8.10**	4.10 / **7.98**	4.06 / **7.87**	4.03 / **7.79**	4.00 / **7.72**	3.96 / **7.60**	3.92 / **7.52**	3.87 / **7.39**	3.84 / **7.31**	3.81 / **7.23**	3.77 / **7.14**	3.75 / **7.09**	3.72 / **7.02**	3.71 / **6.99**	3.69 / **6.94**	3.68 / **6.90**	3.67 / **6.88**	6
7	5.59 / **12.25**	4.74 / **9.55**	4.35 / **8.45**	4.12 / **7.85**	3.97 / **7.46**	3.87 / **7.19**	3.79 / **7.00**	3.73 / **6.84**	3.68 / **6.71**	3.63 / **6.62**	3.60 / **6.54**	3.57 / **6.47**	3.52 / **6.35**	3.49 / **6.27**	3.44 / **6.15**	3.41 / **6.07**	3.38 / **5.98**	3.34 / **5.90**	3.32 / **5.85**	3.29 / **5.78**	3.28 / **5.75**	3.25 / **5.70**	3.24 / **5.67**	3.23 / **5.65**	7
8	5.32 / **11.26**	4.46 / **8.65**	4.07 / **7.59**	3.84 / **7.01**	3.69 / **6.63**	3.58 / **6.37**	3.50 / **6.19**	3.44 / **6.03**	3.39 / **5.91**	3.34 / **5.82**	3.31 / **5.74**	3.28 / **5.67**	3.23 / **5.56**	3.20 / **5.48**	3.15 / **5.36**	3.12 / **5.28**	3.08 / **5.20**	3.05 / **5.11**	3.03 / **5.06**	3.00 / **5.00**	2.98 / **4.96**	2.96 / **4.91**	2.94 / **4.88**	2.93 / **4.86**	8
9	5.12 / **10.56**	4.26 / **8.02**	3.86 / **6.99**	3.63 / **6.42**	3.48 / **6.06**	3.37 / **5.80**	3.29 / **5.62**	3.23 / **5.47**	3.18 / **5.35**	3.13 / **5.26**	3.10 / **5.18**	3.07 / **5.11**	3.02 / **5.00**	2.98 / **4.92**	2.93 / **4.80**	2.90 / **4.73**	2.86 / **4.64**	2.82 / **4.56**	2.80 / **4.51**	2.77 / **4.45**	2.76 / **4.41**	2.73 / **4.36**	2.72 / **4.33**	2.71 / **4.31**	9
10	4.96 / **10.04**	4.10 / **7.56**	3.71 / **6.55**	3.48 / **5.99**	3.33 / **5.64**	3.22 / **5.39**	3.14 / **5.21**	3.07 / **5.06**	3.02 / **4.95**	2.97 / **4.85**	2.94 / **4.78**	2.91 / **4.71**	2.86 / **4.60**	2.82 / **4.52**	2.77 / **4.41**	2.74 / **4.33**	2.70 / **4.25**	2.67 / **4.17**	2.64 / **4.12**	2.61 / **4.05**	2.59 / **4.01**	2.56 / **3.96**	2.55 / **3.93**	2.54 / **3.91**	10
11	4.84 / **9.65**	3.98 / **7.20**	3.59 / **6.22**	3.36 / **5.67**	3.20 / **5.32**	3.09 / **5.07**	3.01 / **4.88**	2.95 / **4.74**	2.90 / **4.63**	2.86 / **4.54**	2.82 / **4.46**	2.79 / **4.40**	2.74 / **4.29**	2.70 / **4.21**	2.65 / **4.10**	2.61 / **4.02**	2.57 / **3.94**	2.53 / **3.86**	2.50 / **3.80**	2.47 / **3.74**	2.45 / **3.70**	2.42 / **3.66**	2.41 / **3.62**	2.40 / **3.60**	11
12	4.75 / **9.33**	3.88 / **6.93**	3.49 / **5.95**	3.26 / **5.41**	3.11 / **5.06**	3.00 / **4.82**	2.92 / **4.65**	2.85 / **4.50**	2.80 / **4.39**	2.76 / **4.30**	2.72 / **4.22**	2.69 / **4.16**	2.64 / **4.05**	2.60 / **3.98**	2.54 / **3.86**	2.50 / **3.78**	2.46 / **3.70**	2.42 / **3.61**	2.40 / **3.56**	2.36 / **3.49**	2.35 / **3.46**	2.32 / **3.41**	2.31 / **3.38**	2.30 / **3.36**	12
13	4.67 / **9.07**	3.80 / **6.70**	3.41 / **5.74**	3.18 / **5.20**	3.02 / **4.86**	2.92 / **4.62**	2.84 / **4.44**	2.77 / **4.30**	2.72 / **4.19**	2.67 / **4.10**	2.63 / **4.02**	2.60 / **3.96**	2.55 / **3.85**	2.51 / **3.78**	2.46 / **3.67**	2.42 / **3.59**	2.38 / **3.51**	2.34 / **3.42**	2.32 / **3.37**	2.28 / **3.30**	2.26 / **3.27**	2.24 / **3.21**	2.22 / **3.18**	2.21 / **3.16**	13

Reprinted from Table 10.5.3, pp. 346–49, Snedecor, *Statistical Methods*, Fifth Edition, 1956, published by the Iowa State College Press, Ames, by permission of the author and publishers.

APPENDIX D (cont'd): 5% (ROMAN TYPE) AND 1% (BOLD FACE TYPE) POINTS FOR THE DISTRIBUTION OF F

n_1 degrees of freedom (for greater mean square). Each cell gives the 5% point (roman) and the 1% point (bold) as "5% / 1%".

n_2	1	2	3	4	5	6	7	8	9	10	11	12	14	16	20	24	30	40	50	75	100	200	500	∞
14	4.60 / 8.86	3.74 / 6.51	3.34 / 5.56	3.11 / 5.03	2.96 / 4.69	2.85 / 4.46	2.77 / 4.28	2.70 / 4.14	2.65 / 4.03	2.60 / 3.94	2.56 / 3.86	2.53 / 3.80	2.48 / 3.70	2.44 / 3.62	2.39 / 3.51	2.35 / 3.43	2.31 / 3.34	2.27 / 3.26	2.24 / 3.21	2.21 / 3.14	2.19 / 3.11	2.16 / 3.06	2.14 / 3.02	2.13 / 3.00
15	4.54 / 8.68	3.68 / 6.36	3.29 / 5.42	3.06 / 4.89	2.90 / 4.56	2.79 / 4.32	2.70 / 4.14	2.64 / 4.00	2.59 / 3.89	2.55 / 3.80	2.51 / 3.73	2.48 / 3.67	2.43 / 3.56	2.39 / 3.48	2.33 / 3.36	2.29 / 3.29	2.25 / 3.20	2.21 / 3.12	2.18 / 3.07	2.15 / 3.00	2.12 / 2.97	2.10 / 2.92	2.08 / 2.89	2.07 / 2.87
16	4.49 / 8.53	3.63 / 6.23	3.24 / 5.29	3.01 / 4.77	2.85 / 4.44	2.74 / 4.20	2.66 / 4.03	2.59 / 3.89	2.54 / 3.78	2.49 / 3.69	2.45 / 3.61	2.42 / 3.55	2.37 / 3.45	2.33 / 3.37	2.28 / 3.25	2.24 / 3.18	2.20 / 3.10	2.16 / 3.01	2.13 / 2.96	2.09 / 2.89	2.07 / 2.86	2.04 / 2.80	2.02 / 2.77	2.01 / 2.75
17	4.45 / 8.40	3.59 / 6.11	3.20 / 5.18	2.96 / 4.67	2.81 / 4.34	2.70 / 4.10	2.62 / 3.93	2.55 / 3.79	2.50 / 3.68	2.45 / 3.59	2.41 / 3.52	2.38 / 3.45	2.33 / 3.35	2.29 / 3.27	2.23 / 3.16	2.19 / 3.08	2.15 / 3.00	2.11 / 2.92	2.08 / 2.86	2.04 / 2.79	2.02 / 2.76	1.99 / 2.70	1.97 / 2.67	1.96 / 2.65
18	4.41 / 8.28	3.55 / 6.01	3.16 / 5.09	2.93 / 4.58	2.77 / 4.25	2.66 / 4.01	2.58 / 3.85	2.51 / 3.71	2.46 / 3.60	2.41 / 3.51	2.37 / 3.44	2.34 / 3.37	2.29 / 3.27	2.25 / 3.19	2.19 / 3.07	2.15 / 3.00	2.11 / 2.91	2.07 / 2.83	2.04 / 2.78	2.00 / 2.71	1.98 / 2.68	1.95 / 2.62	1.93 / 2.59	1.92 / 2.57
19	4.38 / 8.18	3.52 / 5.93	3.13 / 5.01	2.90 / 4.50	2.74 / 4.17	2.63 / 3.94	2.55 / 3.77	2.48 / 3.63	2.43 / 3.52	2.38 / 3.43	2.34 / 3.36	2.31 / 3.30	2.26 / 3.19	2.21 / 3.12	2.15 / 3.00	2.11 / 2.92	2.07 / 2.84	2.02 / 2.76	2.00 / 2.70	1.96 / 2.63	1.94 / 2.60	1.91 / 2.54	1.90 / 2.51	1.88 / 2.49
20	4.35 / 8.10	3.49 / 5.85	3.10 / 4.94	2.87 / 4.43	2.71 / 4.10	2.60 / 3.87	2.52 / 3.71	2.45 / 3.56	2.40 / 3.45	2.35 / 3.37	2.31 / 3.30	2.28 / 3.23	2.23 / 3.13	2.18 / 3.05	2.12 / 2.94	2.08 / 2.86	2.04 / 2.77	1.99 / 2.69	1.96 / 2.63	1.92 / 2.56	1.90 / 2.53	1.87 / 2.47	1.85 / 2.44	1.84 / 2.42
21	4.32 / 8.02	3.47 / 5.78	3.07 / 4.87	2.84 / 4.37	2.68 / 4.04	2.57 / 3.81	2.49 / 3.65	2.42 / 3.51	2.37 / 3.40	2.32 / 3.31	2.28 / 3.24	2.25 / 3.17	2.20 / 3.07	2.15 / 2.99	2.09 / 2.88	2.05 / 2.80	2.00 / 2.72	1.96 / 2.63	1.93 / 2.58	1.89 / 2.51	1.87 / 2.47	1.84 / 2.42	1.82 / 2.38	1.81 / 2.36
22	4.30 / 7.94	3.44 / 5.72	3.05 / 4.82	2.82 / 4.31	2.66 / 3.99	2.55 / 3.76	2.47 / 3.59	2.40 / 3.45	2.35 / 3.35	2.30 / 3.26	2.26 / 3.18	2.23 / 3.12	2.18 / 3.02	2.13 / 2.94	2.07 / 2.83	2.03 / 2.75	1.98 / 2.67	1.93 / 2.58	1.91 / 2.53	1.87 / 2.46	1.84 / 2.42	1.81 / 2.37	1.80 / 2.33	1.78 / 2.31
23	4.28 / 7.88	3.42 / 5.66	3.03 / 4.76	2.80 / 4.26	2.64 / 3.94	2.53 / 3.71	2.45 / 3.54	2.38 / 3.41	2.32 / 3.30	2.28 / 3.21	2.24 / 3.14	2.20 / 3.07	2.14 / 2.97	2.10 / 2.89	2.04 / 2.78	2.00 / 2.70	1.96 / 2.62	1.91 / 2.53	1.88 / 2.48	1.84 / 2.41	1.82 / 2.37	1.79 / 2.32	1.77 / 2.28	1.76 / 2.26
24	4.26 / 7.82	3.40 / 5.61	3.01 / 4.72	2.78 / 4.22	2.62 / 3.90	2.51 / 3.67	2.43 / 3.50	2.36 / 3.36	2.30 / 3.25	2.26 / 3.17	2.22 / 3.09	2.18 / 3.03	2.13 / 2.93	2.09 / 2.85	2.02 / 2.74	1.98 / 2.66	1.94 / 2.58	1.89 / 2.49	1.86 / 2.44	1.82 / 2.36	1.80 / 2.33	1.76 / 2.27	1.74 / 2.23	1.73 / 2.21
25	4.24 / 7.77	3.38 / 5.57	2.99 / 4.68	2.76 / 4.18	2.60 / 3.86	2.49 / 3.63	2.41 / 3.46	2.34 / 3.32	2.28 / 3.21	2.24 / 3.13	2.20 / 3.05	2.16 / 2.99	2.11 / 2.89	2.06 / 2.81	2.00 / 2.70	1.96 / 2.62	1.92 / 2.54	1.87 / 2.45	1.84 / 2.40	1.80 / 2.32	1.77 / 2.29	1.74 / 2.23	1.72 / 2.19	1.71 / 2.17
26	4.22 / 7.72	3.37 / 5.53	2.98 / 4.64	2.74 / 4.14	2.59 / 3.82	2.47 / 3.59	2.39 / 3.42	2.32 / 3.29	2.27 / 3.17	2.22 / 3.09	2.18 / 3.02	2.15 / 2.96	2.10 / 2.86	2.05 / 2.77	1.99 / 2.66	1.95 / 2.58	1.90 / 2.50	1.85 / 2.41	1.82 / 2.36	1.78 / 2.28	1.76 / 2.25	1.72 / 2.19	1.70 / 2.15	1.69 / 2.13

The function, $F = e$ with exponent $2z$, is computed in part from Fisher's Table VI (7). Additional entries are by interpolation, mostly graphical.

APPENDIX D (cont'd): 5% (ROMAN TYPE) AND 1% (BOLD FACE TYPE) POINTS FOR THE DISTRIBUTION OF F

n_1 degrees of freedom (for greater mean square)

Each cell shows the 5% point (roman type) / 1% point (bold face type).

n_2	1	2	3	4	5	6	7	8	9	10	11	12	14	16	20	24	30	40	50	75	100	200	500	∞	n_2
27	4.21 / **7.68**	3.35 / **5.49**	2.96 / **4.60**	2.73 / **4.11**	2.57 / **3.79**	2.46 / **3.56**	2.37 / **3.39**	2.30 / **3.26**	2.25 / **3.14**	2.20 / **3.06**	2.16 / **2.98**	2.13 / **2.93**	2.08 / **2.83**	2.03 / **2.74**	1.97 / **2.63**	1.93 / **2.55**	1.88 / **2.47**	1.84 / **2.38**	1.80 / **2.33**	1.76 / **2.25**	1.74 / **2.21**	1.71 / **2.16**	1.68 / **2.12**	1.67 / **2.10**	27
28	4.20 / **7.64**	3.34 / **5.45**	2.95 / **4.57**	2.71 / **4.07**	2.56 / **3.76**	2.44 / **3.53**	2.36 / **3.36**	2.29 / **3.23**	2.24 / **3.11**	2.19 / **3.03**	2.15 / **2.95**	2.12 / **2.90**	2.06 / **2.80**	2.02 / **2.71**	1.96 / **2.60**	1.91 / **2.52**	1.87 / **2.44**	1.81 / **2.35**	1.78 / **2.30**	1.75 / **2.22**	1.72 / **2.18**	1.69 / **2.13**	1.67 / **2.09**	1.65 / **2.06**	28
29	4.18 / **7.60**	3.33 / **5.42**	2.93 / **4.54**	2.70 / **4.04**	2.54 / **3.73**	2.43 / **3.50**	2.35 / **3.33**	2.28 / **3.20**	2.22 / **3.08**	2.18 / **3.00**	2.14 / **2.92**	2.10 / **2.87**	2.05 / **2.77**	2.00 / **2.68**	1.94 / **2.57**	1.90 / **2.49**	1.85 / **2.41**	1.80 / **2.32**	1.77 / **2.27**	1.73 / **2.19**	1.71 / **2.15**	1.68 / **2.10**	1.65 / **2.06**	1.64 / **2.03**	29
30	4.17 / **7.56**	3.32 / **5.39**	2.92 / **4.51**	2.69 / **4.02**	2.53 / **3.70**	2.42 / **3.47**	2.34 / **3.30**	2.27 / **3.17**	2.21 / **3.06**	2.16 / **2.98**	2.12 / **2.90**	2.09 / **2.84**	2.04 / **2.74**	1.99 / **2.66**	1.93 / **2.55**	1.89 / **2.47**	1.84 / **2.38**	1.79 / **2.29**	1.76 / **2.24**	1.72 / **2.16**	1.69 / **2.13**	1.66 / **2.07**	1.64 / **2.03**	1.62 / **2.01**	30
32	4.15 / **7.50**	3.30 / **5.34**	2.90 / **4.46**	2.67 / **3.97**	2.51 / **3.66**	2.40 / **3.42**	2.32 / **3.25**	2.25 / **3.12**	2.19 / **3.01**	2.14 / **2.94**	2.10 / **2.86**	2.07 / **2.80**	2.02 / **2.70**	1.97 / **2.62**	1.91 / **2.51**	1.86 / **2.42**	1.82 / **2.34**	1.76 / **2.25**	1.74 / **2.20**	1.69 / **2.12**	1.67 / **2.08**	1.64 / **2.02**	1.61 / **1.98**	1.59 / **1.96**	32
34	4.13 / **7.44**	3.28 / **5.29**	2.88 / **4.42**	2.65 / **3.93**	2.49 / **3.61**	2.38 / **3.38**	2.30 / **3.21**	2.23 / **3.08**	2.17 / **2.97**	2.12 / **2.89**	2.08 / **2.82**	2.05 / **2.76**	2.00 / **2.66**	1.95 / **2.58**	1.89 / **2.47**	1.84 / **2.38**	1.80 / **2.30**	1.74 / **2.21**	1.71 / **2.15**	1.67 / **2.08**	1.64 / **2.04**	1.61 / **1.98**	1.59 / **1.94**	1.57 / **1.91**	34
36	4.11 / **7.39**	3.26 / **5.25**	2.86 / **4.38**	2.63 / **3.89**	2.48 / **3.58**	2.36 / **3.35**	2.28 / **3.18**	2.21 / **3.04**	2.15 / **2.94**	2.10 / **2.86**	2.06 / **2.78**	2.03 / **2.72**	1.98 / **2.62**	1.93 / **2.54**	1.87 / **2.43**	1.82 / **2.35**	1.78 / **2.26**	1.72 / **2.17**	1.69 / **2.12**	1.65 / **2.04**	1.62 / **2.00**	1.59 / **1.94**	1.56 / **1.90**	1.55 / **1.87**	36
38	4.10 / **7.35**	3.25 / **5.21**	2.85 / **4.34**	2.62 / **3.86**	2.46 / **3.54**	2.35 / **3.32**	2.26 / **3.15**	2.19 / **3.02**	2.14 / **2.91**	2.09 / **2.82**	2.05 / **2.75**	2.02 / **2.69**	1.96 / **2.59**	1.92 / **2.51**	1.85 / **2.40**	1.80 / **2.32**	1.76 / **2.22**	1.71 / **2.14**	1.67 / **2.03**	1.63 / **2.00**	1.60 / **1.97**	1.57 / **1.90**	1.54 / **1.86**	1.53 / **1.84**	38
40	4.08 / **7.31**	3.23 / **5.18**	2.84 / **4.31**	2.61 / **3.83**	2.45 / **3.51**	2.34 / **3.29**	2.25 / **3.12**	2.18 / **2.99**	2.12 / **2.88**	2.07 / **2.80**	2.04 / **2.73**	2.00 / **2.66**	1.95 / **2.56**	1.90 / **2.49**	1.84 / **2.37**	1.79 / **2.29**	1.74 / **2.20**	1.69 / **2.11**	1.66 / **2.05**	1.61 / **1.97**	1.59 / **1.94**	1.55 / **1.88**	1.53 / **1.84**	1.51 / **1.81**	40
42	4.07 / **7.27**	3.22 / **5.15**	2.83 / **4.29**	2.59 / **3.80**	2.44 / **3.49**	2.32 / **3.26**	2.24 / **3.10**	2.17 / **2.96**	2.11 / **2.86**	2.06 / **2.77**	2.02 / **2.70**	1.99 / **2.64**	1.94 / **2.54**	1.89 / **2.46**	1.82 / **2.35**	1.78 / **2.26**	1.73 / **2.17**	1.68 / **2.08**	1.64 / **2.02**	1.60 / **1.94**	1.57 / **1.91**	1.54 / **1.85**	1.51 / **1.80**	1.49 / **1.78**	42
44	4.06 / **7.24**	3.21 / **5.12**	2.82 / **4.26**	2.58 / **3.78**	2.43 / **3.46**	2.31 / **3.24**	2.23 / **3.07**	2.16 / **2.94**	2.10 / **2.84**	2.05 / **2.75**	2.01 / **2.68**	1.98 / **2.62**	1.92 / **2.52**	1.88 / **2.44**	1.81 / **2.32**	1.76 / **2.24**	1.72 / **2.15**	1.66 / **2.06**	1.63 / **2.00**	1.58 / **1.92**	1.56 / **1.88**	1.52 / **1.82**	1.50 / **1.78**	1.48 / **1.75**	44
46	4.05 / **7.21**	3.20 / **5.10**	2.81 / **4.24**	2.57 / **3.76**	2.42 / **3.44**	2.30 / **3.22**	2.22 / **3.05**	2.14 / **2.92**	2.09 / **2.82**	2.04 / **2.73**	2.00 / **2.66**	1.97 / **2.60**	1.91 / **2.50**	1.87 / **2.42**	1.80 / **2.30**	1.75 / **2.22**	1.71 / **2.13**	1.65 / **2.04**	1.62 / **1.98**	1.57 / **1.90**	1.54 / **1.86**	1.51 / **1.80**	1.48 / **1.76**	1.46 / **1.72**	46
48	4.04 / **7.19**	3.19 / **5.08**	2.80 / **4.22**	2.56 / **3.74**	2.41 / **3.42**	2.30 / **3.20**	2.21 / **3.04**	2.14 / **2.90**	2.08 / **2.80**	2.03 / **2.71**	1.99 / **2.64**	1.96 / **2.58**	1.90 / **2.48**	1.86 / **2.40**	1.79 / **2.28**	1.74 / **2.20**	1.70 / **2.11**	1.64 / **2.02**	1.61 / **1.96**	1.56 / **1.88**	1.53 / **1.84**	1.50 / **1.78**	1.47 / **1.73**	1.45 / **1.70**	48

APPENDIX D (cont'd): 5% (ROMAN TYPE) AND 1% (BOLD FACE TYPE) POINTS FOR THE DISTRIBUTION OF F

n_1 degrees of freedom (for greater mean square)

n_2	1	2	3	4	5	6	7	8	9	10	11	12	14	16	20	24	30	40	50	75	100	200	500	∞
50	4.03 / 7.17	3.18 / 5.06	2.79 / 4.20	2.56 / 3.72	2.40 / 3.41	2.29 / 3.18	2.20 / 3.02	2.13 / 2.88	2.07 / 2.78	2.02 / 2.70	1.98 / 2.62	1.95 / 2.56	1.90 / 2.46	1.85 / 2.39	1.78 / 2.26	1.74 / 2.18	1.69 / 2.10	1.63 / 2.00	1.60 / 1.94	1.55 / 1.86	1.52 / 1.82	1.48 / 1.76	1.46 / 1.71	1.44 / 1.68
55	4.02 / 7.12	3.17 / 5.01	2.78 / 4.16	2.54 / 3.68	2.38 / 3.37	2.27 / 3.15	2.18 / 2.98	2.11 / 2.85	2.05 / 2.75	2.00 / 2.66	1.97 / 2.59	1.93 / 2.53	1.88 / 2.43	1.83 / 2.35	1.76 / 2.23	1.72 / 2.15	1.67 / 2.06	1.61 / 1.96	1.58 / 1.90	1.52 / 1.82	1.50 / 1.78	1.46 / 1.71	1.43 / 1.66	1.41 / 1.64
60	4.00 / 7.08	3.15 / 4.98	2.76 / 4.13	2.52 / 3.65	2.37 / 3.34	2.25 / 3.12	2.17 / 2.95	2.10 / 2.82	2.04 / 2.72	1.99 / 2.63	1.95 / 2.56	1.92 / 2.50	1.86 / 2.40	1.81 / 2.32	1.75 / 2.20	1.70 / 2.12	1.65 / 2.03	1.59 / 1.93	1.56 / 1.87	1.50 / 1.79	1.48 / 1.74	1.44 / 1.68	1.41 / 1.63	1.39 / 1.60
65	3.99 / 7.04	3.14 / 4.95	2.75 / 4.10	2.51 / 3.62	2.36 / 3.31	2.24 / 3.09	2.15 / 2.93	2.08 / 2.79	2.02 / 2.70	1.98 / 2.61	1.94 / 2.54	1.90 / 2.47	1.85 / 2.37	1.80 / 2.30	1.73 / 2.18	1.68 / 2.09	1.63 / 2.00	1.57 / 1.90	1.54 / 1.84	1.49 / 1.76	1.46 / 1.71	1.42 / 1.64	1.39 / 1.60	1.37 / 1.56
70	3.98 / 7.01	3.13 / 4.92	2.74 / 4.08	2.50 / 3.60	2.35 / 3.29	2.23 / 3.07	2.14 / 2.91	2.07 / 2.77	2.01 / 2.67	1.97 / 2.59	1.93 / 2.51	1.89 / 2.45	1.84 / 2.35	1.79 / 2.28	1.72 / 2.15	1.67 / 2.07	1.62 / 1.98	1.56 / 1.88	1.53 / 1.82	1.47 / 1.74	1.45 / 1.69	1.40 / 1.62	1.37 / 1.56	1.35 / 1.53
80	3.96 / 6.96	3.11 / 4.88	2.72 / 4.04	2.48 / 3.56	2.33 / 3.25	2.21 / 3.04	2.12 / 2.87	2.05 / 2.74	1.99 / 2.64	1.95 / 2.55	1.91 / 2.48	1.88 / 2.41	1.82 / 2.32	1.77 / 2.24	1.70 / 2.11	1.65 / 2.03	1.60 / 1.94	1.54 / 1.84	1.51 / 1.78	1.45 / 1.70	1.42 / 1.65	1.38 / 1.57	1.35 / 1.52	1.32 / 1.49
100	3.94 / 6.90	3.09 / 4.82	2.70 / 3.98	2.46 / 3.51	2.30 / 3.20	2.19 / 2.99	2.10 / 2.82	2.03 / 2.69	1.97 / 2.59	1.92 / 2.51	1.88 / 2.43	1.85 / 2.36	1.79 / 2.26	1.75 / 2.19	1.68 / 2.06	1.63 / 1.98	1.57 / 1.89	1.51 / 1.79	1.48 / 1.73	1.42 / 1.64	1.39 / 1.59	1.34 / 1.51	1.30 / 1.46	1.28 / 1.43
125	3.92 / 6.84	3.07 / 4.78	2.68 / 3.94	2.44 / 3.47	2.29 / 3.17	2.17 / 2.95	2.08 / 2.79	2.01 / 2.65	1.95 / 2.56	1.90 / 2.47	1.86 / 2.40	1.83 / 2.33	1.77 / 2.23	1.72 / 2.15	1.65 / 2.03	1.60 / 1.94	1.55 / 1.85	1.49 / 1.75	1.45 / 1.68	1.39 / 1.59	1.36 / 1.54	1.31 / 1.46	1.27 / 1.40	1.25 / 1.37
150	3.91 / 6.81	3.06 / 4.75	2.67 / 3.91	2.43 / 3.44	2.27 / 3.14	2.16 / 2.92	2.07 / 2.76	2.00 / 2.62	1.94 / 2.53	1.89 / 2.44	1.85 / 2.37	1.82 / 2.30	1.76 / 2.20	1.71 / 2.12	1.64 / 2.00	1.59 / 1.91	1.54 / 1.83	1.47 / 1.72	1.44 / 1.66	1.37 / 1.56	1.34 / 1.51	1.29 / 1.43	1.25 / 1.37	1.22 / 1.33
200	3.89 / 6.76	3.04 / 4.71	2.65 / 3.88	2.41 / 3.41	2.26 / 3.11	2.14 / 2.90	2.05 / 2.73	1.98 / 2.60	1.92 / 2.50	1.87 / 2.41	1.83 / 2.34	1.80 / 2.28	1.74 / 2.17	1.69 / 2.09	1.62 / 1.97	1.57 / 1.88	1.52 / 1.79	1.45 / 1.69	1.42 / 1.62	1.35 / 1.53	1.32 / 1.48	1.26 / 1.39	1.22 / 1.33	1.19 / 1.28
400	3.86 / 6.70	3.02 / 4.66	2.62 / 3.83	2.39 / 3.36	2.23 / 3.06	2.12 / 2.85	2.03 / 2.69	1.96 / 2.55	1.90 / 2.46	1.85 / 2.37	1.81 / 2.29	1.78 / 2.23	1.72 / 2.12	1.67 / 2.04	1.60 / 1.92	1.54 / 1.84	1.49 / 1.74	1.42 / 1.64	1.38 / 1.57	1.32 / 1.47	1.28 / 1.42	1.22 / 1.32	1.16 / 1.24	1.13 / 1.19
1000	3.85 / 6.66	3.00 / 4.62	2.61 / 3.80	2.38 / 3.34	2.22 / 3.04	2.10 / 2.82	2.02 / 2.66	1.95 / 2.53	1.89 / 2.43	1.84 / 2.34	1.80 / 2.26	1.76 / 2.20	1.70 / 2.09	1.65 / 2.01	1.58 / 1.89	1.53 / 1.81	1.47 / 1.71	1.41 / 1.61	1.36 / 1.54	1.30 / 1.44	1.26 / 1.38	1.19 / 1.28	1.13 / 1.19	1.08 / 1.11
∞	3.84 / 6.64	2.99 / 4.60	2.60 / 3.78	2.37 / 3.32	2.21 / 3.02	2.09 / 2.80	2.01 / 2.64	1.94 / 2.51	1.88 / 2.41	1.83 / 2.32	1.79 / 2.24	1.75 / 2.18	1.69 / 2.07	1.64 / 1.99	1.57 / 1.87	1.52 / 1.79	1.46 / 1.69	1.40 / 1.59	1.35 / 1.52	1.28 / 1.41	1.24 / 1.36	1.17 / 1.25	1.11 / 1.15	1.00 / 1.00

Index of Names

Abelson, R. F., 425
Andersen, S. L., 185
Anderson, R. L., 235
Anscombe, F. J., 194

Bancroft, T. A., 235
Bartlett, M. S., 184
Berkson, J., 457
Bernouilli, J., 3
Bessel, F. W., 3
Bishop, D. J., 184
Bowley, A. L., 8
Box, G. E. P., 185
Bregman, E. O., 320
Brownlee, K. A., 9

Chung, J. H., 299
Cochran, W. G., 8, 141, 163, 185, 188, 241, 253, 492
Comstock, R. E., 224
Cox, G. M., 163, 492
Cramer, C. Y., 255
Crump, S. L., 224, 241

David, F. N., 348
De Lury, D. B., 299
Deming, W. E., 8, 492
De Moivre, A., 3
Dixon, W. J., 260, 261
Duncan, D. B., 255
Durbin, J., 276
Dykstra, O., 480

Eisenhart, C., 225, 276
Elderton, W. P., 4
Encke, 3

Fay, L. C., 425
Federer, W. T., 492
Ferguson, G. A., 336

Fermat, 2
Filon, L. N. G., 4
Fisher, R. A., 5, 8, 121, 130, 134, 161, 162, 188, 192, 224, 260, 268, 283, 286, 289, 348, 354, 371, 403, 445, 448, 459, 463

Galton, Sir Francis, 3, 4, 316, 321, 335, 390
Gauss, C. F., 3
Gosset, W. S. (Student), 5, 149, 348
Goulden, C. H., 231, 246
Grant, D. A., 401
Graunt, 3
Grossman, H. A., 300
Gulliksen, H., 424
Gunkle, M. M., 208

Halley, 3
Hamel, L., 161
Hammett, J. E., 205
Hansen, M. H., 8, 492
Hartley, H. O., 185, 478
Hilferty, M. M., 121
Hoeffding, W., 274
Hotelling, H., 257
Hoyt, C., 425
Hsu, P. L., 161, 163
Hurwitz, W. N., 8, 492

Iyer, P. U.K. , 276

Jackson, R. W. B., 167, 302, 304, 336, 390
Johnson, P. O., 216, 246, 273, 281, 302, 304, 306, 424, 425, 429, 430, 442, 448, 484, 492
Jones, H. B., 320

Karpinos, B. D., 300

Subject Index